10 0429156 1
D1577533

Mauritshuis: A Summary Catalogue

ROYAL PICTURE GALLERY
MAURITSHUIS

A Summary Catalogue

Compiled by Quentin Buvelot

with contributions by Carola Vermeeren

Royal Picture Gallery Mauritshuis, The Hague
Waanders Publishers, Zwolle

This publication was sponsored by

The Michael Marks Charitable Trust

Contents

Foreword
7

The history of the Mauritshuis
10

Benefactors of the Mauritshuis
44

Directors of the Mauritshuis
46

Note to the reader
48

Catalogue of paintings and pastels
49

Catalogue of miniatures
362

Catalogue of sculptures
385

Catalogue of prints and drawings
399

Appendices
403

Index by inventory number 404
Paintings and sculptures no longer in the collection 407
Changed attributions 408
List of catalogues and publications of the Mauritshuis 410
List of exhibitions in the Mauritshuis 420
Essential literature on the museum building and its original interior 423
Literature on former directors of the Mauritshuis 424

Key to abbreviated literature and exhibitions
425

Index of names
445

[1] Exterior view of the Mauritshuis, seen from Hofvijver Lake.

Foreword

The Mauritshuis rejoices in a long tradition of scholarly research and of collection catalogues presenting the findings of that research. Many of these books have been compiled by leading art historians such as Victor de Stuers, Abraham Bredius, Cornelis Hofstede de Groot and Wilhelm Martin (see the repertory of Mauritshuis catalogues listed in the appendix). Because of the collection's expansion, and more importantly because of the proliferation of art-historical research in the last decades, there has been no attempt since the Second World War to produce a scholarly catalogue encompassing the entire collection of the Mauritshuis. The last complete catalogue of the collection, *Mauritshuis: Illustrated General Catalogue*, which appeared in July 1993, was in fact a reprint of an appendix to *Art Treasures of Holland: The Royal Picture Gallery Mauritshuis* (1985) with a supplement of new acquisitions. Now, almost twenty years on, we are publishing this fully revised edition, which incorporates many new insights — in addition, of course, to the acquisitions made in the interim. These acquisitions include major purchases, such as Rembrandt's *Portrait of an elderly man* (purchased in 1999), two portraits by Rubens (purchased in 2003) and the monumental *Wooded landscape with cottages* by Meindert Hobbema (purchased in 1994), as well as private donations, such as the very generous gift of five magnificent paintings received from Willem, Baron Van Dedem in 2002. They also include a number of works provided on long-term loan by the Friends of the Mauritshuis Foundation, the Rijksmuseum in Amsterdam, and the Netherlands Institute for Cultural Heritage (ICN) in Amsterdam and Rijswijk (temporary loans from public and private collections are listed in the annual reports). More paintings will hopefully be added to the collection in the years to come, in the form of purchases, donations or bequests, or as long-term loans. After all, any static collection will slowly but surely lose its appeal.

This catalogue contains descriptions and images of all the works that currently belong to the permanent collection of the Mauritshuis: circa 815 paintings and pastels, 46 portrait miniatures, 23 sculptures, as well as 4 prints and drawings. In view of the growing interest in the condition of the catalogued works, all restorations and aesthetic treatments of the paintings and pastels that have been carried out since 1985 are mentioned in the entries.

[2] The Golden Room of the Mauritshuis with paintings by Giovanni Antonio Pellegrini, completed in 1718.

The present catalogue has greatly benefited from two major thematic catalogues published by the Mauritshuis: *Intimacies & Intrigues: History Painting in the Mauritshuis* (1993), discussing 45 history paintings in detail, and *Portraits in the Mauritshuis, 1430–1790*, which was only recently published, focusing on a selection of 60 of the best works but also paying attention to the other portraits in the permanent collection. Equally useful were the countless catalogues that have been published to accompany exhibitions in the Mauritshuis and elsewhere, as well as the diverse monographs and other art-historical studies that have appeared over the past two decades, including, for instance, the catalogue of Italian paintings in Dutch public collections. We were also able to draw on the expertise of many colleagues, in particular the staff of the Netherlands Institute for Art History (RKD) in The Hague and the Rijksmuseum in Amsterdam.

The fact that this publication now lies before you is thanks to the efforts of Quentin Buvelot, curator of the Mauritshuis since May 1998, who compiled the introduction, entries and appendices, and edited their content. Carola Vermeeren, research assistant, contributed to the catalogue entries until October 2000. Rachel Esner assisted in the English language editing of the texts and Dorine Duyster compiled the index. The catalogue entries will serve as the basis for an internal electronic collection registration system that the Mauritshuis will be using in the near future.

The catalogue's layout and design were in the capable hands of Victor de Leeuw, while Waanders Publishers and Printers in Zwolle dealt excellently with the book's production and publication.

A catalogue of this size can only be published with external support. It is highly gratifying that the Michael Marks Charitable Trust was found willing to give the publication its financial backing. We should like to thank Marina, Lady Marks, Chairman of the Michael Marks Charitable Trust, and the Trust's Trustees.

We hope that this catalogue will serve all those interested in the multifarious collection of the Mauritshuis.

Frederik J. Duparc,
Director

[3] Jan van Call, *The 'Plein' with the residence of Constantijn Huygens (left) and the Mauritshuis (middle)*, c.1690. Pen and brush, 17.8 x 27.5 cm. The Hague, Gemeentearchief.

THE HISTORY OF THE MAURITSHUIS

For many art lovers, the Royal Picture Gallery Mauritshuis is their favourite art gallery, for it still has the charm and intimate character of a private house, which in turn has allowed it to remain a museum of human proportions [fig. 1]. The name of the museum reveals the link between the collections and the building. The Mauritshuis itself is a gem of seventeenth-century northern Baroque architecture, compact and orderly in its layout, created for a member of the stadholder's family, and within its walls it houses paintings of exceptionally high quality based on the collections of those same stadholders, all members of the house of Orange. The strictly limited space is a positive advantage rather than an impediment: the intimate displays are a compromise between the traditional princely cabinet or gallery and a small museum employing modern techniques. Its character today thus clearly exploits both the personality of the house and the scope of the collections.

The building

The house was built in large part between 1633 and 1644 by Pieter Post (1608–1669) to the plans of Jacob van Campen (1596–1657) for Count, later Prince Johan Maurits of Nassau-Siegen [see fig. 7]. As Post was only 25 in 1633, he was presumably acting primarily as supervisor rather than as architect. The building was erected close to the centre of The Hague, on the foundations of an earlier circular structure on a piece of land known as the Akerland (arable land) to the east of the old castle of Ten Haghe, part of which dated from the thirteenth century and which had later been extended to become the Binnenhof (inner courtyard). Notwithstanding a number of alterations, the original character of the exterior of the Mauritshuis is relatively well preserved. The former natural stone mouldings have been replaced by wooden mouldings, and the original leaded windows, set in stone mullioned frames, were substituted in the nineteenth century, while the coat of arms carved in stone, which was removed in 1795, was reinstated in zinc in 1880. The front courtyard, which is now surrounded by wrought iron railings brought from the garden of the Royal Library, was originally enclosed by a high, fenestrated brick wall. At the time, the entrance took the form of a monumental *porte cochère*, providing gates with locking doors, similar in style to that of the Lakenhal in Leiden. Opposite this enclosed area and the entrance gate lay the Reygersbosch (heron wood). Johan Maurits enclosed this land to lay out an ornamental garden with a pavilion, elaborate flowerbeds with sculptures, aviaries, grottoes and hillocks. The Mauritshuis was connected to this pleasure garden by an underground passage, which allowed the prince to reach the garden unseen. This passage remained in existence until 1808. The garden in

[4] Pieter Post, *Cross-section of the Mauritshuis*, 1652. Pen and ink, 41.9 x 53.5 cm. The Hague, Royal Library.

[5] Pierre Philippe after Jacob Toorenvliet, *Banquet in the Mauritshuis on the occasion of the visit of Charles II, king of England, 30 May 1660*, 1660. Gift of H.J. Hijmersma, 1987. Inv.no.1087.

turn adjoined the property of the house which Constantijn Huygens [fig. 6], secretary to Stadholder Frederik Hendrik, had built in 1634–1637 on a site at the southeast corner of the Akerland. This fine house, the home of Huygens until 1687, was demolished in 1876 [fig. 3].

Although the exterior of the Mauritshuis still has much of the general character of a seventeenth-century residence, this is unfortunately not true of the interior. If we turn to the series of 39 drawings still preserved in the Royal Library in The Hague [fig. 4], executed in meticulous detail by Post, it is clear that the original staircase was considerably less monumental. Two walls, separating the entrance hall by three arches from the two flights, and a central corridor enclosed the stairs. The various functional spaces were thus initially very clearly differentiated from one another, and the manner in which the courtyard was enclosed by walls reflects the same principles. Such an arrangement was typical of the Dutch classical style: we first come across it in Huis ter Nieuburg, built by Stadholder Frederik Hendrik at Rijswijk, later in Constantijn Huygens's residence, and later still at Het Loo Palace in Apeldoorn. Van Campen laid out apartments — one on each side, following the French convention — to the left and right of the entrance hall, each consisting of three rooms *en suite*: anteroom, bedroom and closet. The largest ground floor room was located in the centre, between the apartments, while on the upper floor the staircase was linked with the landing, as it is now. The print commemorating the banquet given in honour of Charles II of England in 1660 provides valuable additional evidence [fig. 5]. The great upper chamber, now the Potter Room, once possessed a coved ceiling with a balustraded gallery and a cupola over the central *oculus*. This allowed light into the room from above, and also provided a place for musicians. The walls were decorated with garlands, although there is also evidence that Johan Maurits conceived the room for the display of the collection of exotic furniture and paintings he had assembled during his years as governor of the Dutch colony in Brazil. However, Johan Maurits himself lived in the house only from 1644 until 1647, and even during those few years he was often absent on campaigns, serving as an officer in the army of the States General.

In 1647 he was appointed stadholder of Cleves by Friedrich Wilhelm, Elector of Brandenburg, and after his death there in 1679 the house passed, heavily mortgaged, via the prince's cousins into the hands of one Gerrit Maes.

[**6**] Jacob van Campen, *Double portrait of Constantijn Huygens and Suzanna van Baerle*, *c.*1635. Purchased with the support of private individuals, 1992. Inv. no. 1089.

Later history of the building

After 1685 the building was leased to the States General and was used as a temporary residence for ambassadors and distinguished visitors. Thus it was that the Duke of Marlborough stayed in the Mauritshuis in December 1704; on the eve of his departure for England fire broke out, resulting in the complete destruction of the priceless and unique interior. The Maes family, it is true, were able to restore the structure, but the old arrangement of the entrance hall, stairs and landing disappeared, together with the beautiful panelling, ceilings and cupola. The combining of the hall, landing and staircase into a single space dates from this period. The present interior, including the stately open staircase and the ground floor reception room was completed in 1718 in the late Louis XIV style. The Venetian painter Giovanni Antonio Pellegrini, who was passing through the Netherlands at the time, was commissioned to execute the important cycle of early Rococo paintings, at present still in the ground floor reception area [fig. 6]. After this the building was used for a variety of purposes, not all of them entirely in keeping with the intentions of its builder. In 1775 the basement was leased to a wine merchant, while the rooms on the ground and upper floors were used for various committee meetings. The building subsequently served as a prison and as seat of the Military High Court. In 1807 Louis Napoleon established the National Library in the Mauritshuis. In May 1820 the Dutch State purchased the building for 35,000 Dutch guilders, and a royal decree of July 1820 designated it as the premises of the Royal Cabinet of Paintings and the Royal Cabinet of Curiosities, both constituted in 1816. The upper floor was allocated to the Cabinet of Paintings, with the ground floor housing a collection of Oriental curiosities and historical objects. The museum opened its doors to the public on 1 January 1822, with a catalogue listing 274 items. In 1875 the objects of the Royal Cabinet of Curiosities were transferred to other locations and only then was the building given over exclusively to the display of paintings and sculptures. Old prints and drawings reveal that the entire edifice was plastered between 1855 and 1879; around 1885 the sandstone substructure was renewed, and in 1890 parquet floors were laid throughout. By the end of the nineteenth century the interior had thus reached the state in which it is seen today.

[7] Jan de Baen, *Portrait of Johan Maurits (1604–1679), Count of Nassau-Siegen, founder of the Mauritshuis*, c.1668–1670. Purchased by Willem I, 1820. Inv. no. 5.

Johan Maurits

The founder of the Mauritshuis, Johan Maurits of Nassau-Siegen [fig. 7], was born in 1604 in the castle at Dillenburg, the ancestral seat of the Nassau family. He was a grandson of Jan the Elder, the brother of Willem I of Orange (nicknamed 'William the Silent'). Johan Maurits was undoubtedly a man of exceptional qualities and vision in both military terms and in civil administration, as well as in cultural and social affairs. In 1636 he was chosen by the Board of Nineteen Directors — the 'Heeren XIX' — of the Dutch West India Company to serve as captain-governor and admiral-general in Brazil. Due to the shortsightedness of the directors, however, Johan Maurits was unable to exploit the situation fully, as they were more concerned with the short-term profit to be gained from the sugar and tropical wood produced in Brazil than in the colonisation policy advocated by the count. From 1637 until 1644 Johan Maurits resided in Brazil, at the *capitanias* Rio Grande do Norte, Pernambuco, Itamaracà and Parayba. Indians assisted the Dutch troops, who never amounted to more than about 6,000 men, in their fight against the Portuguese. In addition to large building enterprises, Johan Maurits constructed a palace and a country seat, Vrijburg and Boa Vista (now both destroyed), each with pleasure-gardens, and many forts, the remains of some of which can still be seen today. The prince also displayed great interest in the astronomy, cartography, ethnography and natural history of Brazil. He had brought with him the Leiden physician Willem Piso (1611–1678), who undertook studies in medicine, ethnography and natural history, assisted by the German Georg Markgraf (1610–1643). In 1648 Piso published his *Historia Naturalis Brasiliae*. The original drawings for this edition, amounting to more than 800, were executed by Albert Eckhout and others, and some included annotations by Johan Maurits himself. They were presented by the latter to Friedrich Wilhelm, Elector of Brandenburg, in 1652, along with other Brazilian objects. The drawings were compiled in seven volumes by Christian Mentzel under the title *Theatrum Rerum Naturalium Brasiliae* (Jagiellonska Library, Cracow).

Eckhout may have been among the artists who worked on the original interior of the Mauritshuis. Murals next to the double staircase and along the walls leading to the main room on the ground floor included Brazilian motifs, which, even if they were not executed by Eckhout himself, certainly relied heavily on his work. In the literature, these murals are attributed to Leonaert Bramer (1596–1674), who was responsible for several similar decorative projects, and whom contemporary sources name as having worked for Johan Maurits. Many of the murals revolved around images of Brazilian cities and provinces, including Recife and Pernambuco. However, the pictures depicted Africans as well as Brazilians, and showed other remote countries, towns and landscapes. Contemporaries were dismayed by the loss of the frescoes in the fire of 1704. Furthermore, the set of 12 still lifes and the 9 canvases portraying Indians, Afro-Brazilians, Mulattos and Mestizos that may once have graced the Mauritshuis are now in the Nationalmuseet in Copenhagen [figs. 8–9], having been presented by Johan Maurits to the Danish king, Frederik III, in 1654. The two portraits of the prince, both part of the same gift, are unfortunately lost. A series of tapestries woven by Maximiliaan van der Gucht in 1667 after designs by Eckhout were copied until the end of the eighteenth century by the Manufacture Royale des Gobelins.

When, after a period of seven years, Johan Maurits returned from Brazil in 1644 the structure of the Mauritshuis was virtually complete. During his absence the construction had been supervised by Constantijn Huygens, a friend of both the prince and Van Campen. The latter may have become acquainted with Huygens as early as 1632 through Johannes Brosterhuijsen, an engraver and literary figure of the time.

Van Campen and Eckhout may have met before 1637, and it is even possible that Van Campen himself had drawn Johan Maurits's attention to the painter, but it is clear from one of Van Campen's paintings in Huis ten Bosch Palace that he, too, was acquainted with the paintings, objects and studies brought back by Johan Maurits. Eckhout remained in Brazil until 1644 and Mentzel's *Theatrum* contains many of his studies of plants and animals. The interior of the Mauritshuis was in part decorated and panelled with rare specimens of tropical wood and exotic objects, which Johan Maurits had sent to the

[8] Albert Eckhout, *Black woman holding a basket, with her child*, 1641. Canvas, 282 x 189 cm. Copenhagen, Nationalmuseet.

[9] Albert Eckhout, *Black man holding a spear*, 1641. Canvas, 273 x 167 cm. Copenhagen, Nationalmuseet.

Netherlands from Brazil, but by analogy to the living quarters of the stadholders's residence it can be assumed that most of the walls were hung with costly French silk, green damasks and satin or velvet. The other prominent features of the rooms were the carved or sculptured chimney-pieces, decorated in red, green or black and gold, as we see in Post's designs.

Little else is known for certain about the style in which the Mauritshuis was originally decorated, nor is it clear whether the paintings by Eckhout now in Copenhagen were installed in the Mauritshuis or at Vrijburg Palace in Brazil. Portraits of members of the House of Orange were certainly placed in the great rear room around 1647, together with a portrait gallery up the staircase, as is the case now.

The various items offered in 1652 by JohanMaurits to Friedrich Wilhelm, Elector of Brandenburg, including Brazilian paintings, ivory furniture and sketches, served as payment for the Freudenberg estate in Cleves. Furthermore, in 1654 the prince presented Frederik III of Denmark with the paintings by Eckhout mentioned above, and in 1679 Louis XIV received 42 paintings from Johan Maurits, including many works by Frans Post, some of which are now in the Musée du Louvre in Paris, two others in private collections and one in the Mauritshuis (inv. no. 915).

The stadholderly collections

When the Mauritshuis opened its doors as a museum on 1 January 1822, there were on display more than 100 works that had previously belonged to the stadholders. It is thus appropriate to give a brief sketch of the genesis and growth of the collections of the House of Orange. It is known that Willem I of Orange once had in his possession a fine collection of old coins, antique silver, jewels, paintings and tapestries. That part of the collection, which the prince had not been able to transport to safety before his property in Brussels was sequestered by the Spaniards, fell into their hands. One of the paintings, the famous *Garden of delights* by Hieronymus Bosch, is now in the Museo Nacional del Prado in Madrid. The greater part of what was rescued, however, had to be converted into money for the struggle against Spain, and it was left to William the Silent's son Maurits to begin the extension of the Stadholder's Quarter in The Hague once it had been designated as their residence in 1584. Maurits was probably more culturally inclined than has generally been assumed. It is known, for example, that he maintained close contact with the painter Jacques de Gheyn. Between 1611 and 1625 he commissioned Jan van Ravesteyn to paint the series of portraits of his most important army officers which is still part of the collection of the Mauritshuis today.

Maurits began the enlargement of the Stadholder's Quarter only towards the end of his life, and after his death in 1625 his half-brother, Frederik Hendrik, by then a rich man as a result of various legacies, continued the building programme. It was during this period that Johan Maurits came to The Hague. Frederik Hendrik's intention was to transform The Hague from an undistinguished provincial town into an international centre based at his court. Through his French mother, Louise de Coligny, and in consequence of a sojourn in Paris as a youth at the court of Henri IV — one of his godfathers, the other being the Danish monarch — Frederik Hendrik must have been well acquainted with French concepts of art and architecture. Following a period spent in England, he also had close ties with the English court, where the splendour-loving Charles I set the fashion with his famous art collection. Furthermore, Charles I was married to Henrietta Maria, the daughter of Henri IV; Friedrich V of the Palatinate, the so-called Winter King, who settled in The Hague in 1621 after his expulsion from Bohemia, was married to Charles I's sister, Elizabeth. Frederik Hendrik's son, Stadholder Willem II, continued this international tradition by marrying one of Charles I's daughters.

Frederik Hendrik

Following Prince Maurits's death, Frederik Hendrik and his wife Amalia of Solms [fig. 10] established an art gallery in the Stadholder's Quarter. It contained about 50 works by contemporary Dutch painters, mainly Utrecht masters, including Jan van Bijlert, Gerrit van Honthorst, Paulus Moreelse, Cornelis van Poelenburch and Roelant Savery, together with works by older artists such as Hendrik van Balen, Paulus Bril, Jan Brueghel the Elder and Cornelis Cornelisz van Haarlem. The 1632 and 1667 inventories also include works by Jan Lievens and Rembrandt. Both painters were highly praised by Constantijn Huygens, whose visit to their joint studio in Leiden is described in his 1629 diary. It is well known that Huygens acted as intermediary between the stadholder and Rembrandt in commissioning the famous series of representations of the Passion of Christ (now in the Alte Pinakothek, Munich). It speaks well for the stadholder that he allowed himself to be persuaded by his secretary, despite the fact that his personal tastes clearly lay in a different direction. During the 1630s dramatic Baroque forms of expression came into vogue. In the Passion paintings Rembrandt made few concessions to the Italianate and Rubensian style preferred by his patron. More representative of the taste of the Hague court during these and subsequent years were the commissions given to the Flemish painters Jacob Jordaens, Gonzales Coques and Thomas Willeboirts Bosschaert, and the interest taken in such painters of flower still lifes as Jan Brueghel the Elder and Daniel Seghers. Frederik Hendrik owned several works by Sir Peter Paul Rubens but commissioned only one work directly from the artist. Although the Dutch-Spanish wars allowed open contact with the artist only during the truce of 1609–1621, in fact neither side permitted the hostilities to interfere unduly with trade. Indeed, shortly after Rubens's departure from Holland there had been a proposal for an equestrian portrait of Frederik Hendrik, but when Rubens visited the Netherlands in 1627 it was impossible for him to associate himself too closely with the rebel court. Van Dyck, who came to the United Provinces in 1630, executed several commissions, but was not retained any more than Rubens. The stadholder and his wife assembled a collection of works by Dutch painters such as Dirck van Baburen, Abraham Bloemaert, Hendrick Goltzius, Gerrit van Honthorst, Dirck van der Lisse, Paulus Moreelse, Cornelis van Poelenburch, Rembrandt, Herman Saftleven and others. Inventories reveal not only the taste of the court but also the thoughtful and systematic assembly of the stadholder's collection. It is interesting to note that neither they nor their successors were patrons of Jan van Goyen, Frans Hals, Jacob van Ruisdael, Jan Steen or Johannes Vermeer.

From the third decade of the seventeenth century onwards the difference in taste between the court on the one hand, and the middle class and more humanistically inclined intellectuals on the other, became increasingly apparent. Huygens and his friend Van Campen must have been among those instrumental in encouraging the trend towards classicism that eventually resulted in the foundation of 'confrèries' — including the well-known 'confrèrie Pictura', founded in 1656 — and academies of art, which marked a clear departure from the old guild structure.

Willem III

It is a matter of great regret that upon Amalia's death in 1675 — Frederik Hendrik had died already in 1647 — all her possessions were divided among her four daughters: Louise Henriette, Henriette Catharina, Maria and Albertine Agnes, of whom the first three were married to German sovereign princes — Friedrich Wilhelm, Elector of Brandenburg, Johann Georg of Anhalt-Dessau, and the Count Palatine, Ludwig Heinrich of Simmern, respectively. Albertine Agnes was married to Willem Frederik of Nassau-Dietz, stadholder of Friesland. Thus, a large portion of the Orange Collection disappeared from the Netherlands. Willem II, Frederik Hendrik's only son, had died in 1650. Before long, however, the portion inherited by Willem III was considerably enlarged. Like his grandfather Frederik Hendrik before him, King-Stadholder Willem III was keenly interested in architecture: he rebuilt the country house acquired by his father at Soestdijk and began the building of Het Loo hunting lodge near Apeldoorn. Not unlike his grandfather as well, he also showed great interest in and love for painting — he enriched the collection with Dutch and Italian masters. These acquisitions gave a more international flavour to the collection. After the Glorious Revolution of 1688 and his succession, with his wife Mary, to the throne of England, Willem III rebuilt Kensington House (now Kensington Palace) and enlarged the sixteenth-century residence at Hampton Court. He soon began purchasing paintings for these residences, showing great interest in all his acquisitions. An episode following the fire in Kensington House illustrates this well: he himself had established the gallery there and immediately upon hearing of the fire went in person to inspect the extent of the damage to the paintings. Willem III was personally involved in the arrangement and hanging of the paintings at Windsor Castle, transformed by Charles II into one of the most richly decorated Baroque palaces in northern Europe. He brought over 30 paintings from England for his new hunting lodge,

[10] Gerrit van Honthorst, *Double portrait of Frederik Hendrik and Amalia of Solms-Braunfels*, *c.*1637–1638. Transferred from the residence of Constantijn Huygens, 1829. Inv. no. 104.

Het Loo, including two works by Hans Holbein the Younger (inv. nos. 276–277), two splendid portraits by Piero di Cosimo (inv. nos. 287–288), and Gerrit Dou's famous *Young mother* [fig. 11], which had been purchased from the artist by the States General and presented to Charles II in 1660 as part of the Dutch Gift.

When Willem III died without issue in 1702 his nephew, Johan Willem Friso, was named sole heir to the properties of the House of Orange since both his grandmothers were daughters of Frederik Hendrik. Friedrich III, later King Friedrich I of Prussia, however, whose mother, Louise Henriette, was Frederik Hendrik's eldest daughter, contested the will. Friedrich had a very strong claim, as his mother had been named heiress to the Orange possessions by her father in 1644. The future of the stadholder's collection looked even more uncertain when Queen Anne, Willem III's successor to the English throne, laid claim to the paintings that had been taken by him to the Netherlands. To make matters worse, Johan Willem Friso drowned in 1711, just as he was about to settle the dispute on the inheritance.

Some of the paintings thus passed to Johan Willem Friso's widow, Marie Louise of Hessen-Cassel. In 1713 she proceeded to auction this collection of 61 works, including pictures by Rubens and Van Dyck, as well as a few by Titian and other important Italian masters. The kings of Prussia selected works from the remainder of the collection on two occasions, in 1720 and 1742. These were the paintings that had previously constituted the glory of the Oude Hof (Noordeinde Palace), rebuilt by Frederik Hendrik, and other Orange country homes, such as Huis ten Bosch, Honselaarsdijk and Ter Nieuburg. Including brilliant large canvases by Rubens, characteristic of the taste of the court at The Hague, they now take pride of place in many a German museum.

Willem IV

In 1732 Willem IV, who had just turned 21, became stadholder of Gelderland and Friesland. His first purchases must have been made around the time of his marriage, in 1734, to Anne of Hannover, daughter of George II. Willem IV inherited not only parts of the collection of the Frisian stadholder, but at the same time from that of the king-stadholder and, through both grandmothers, from Amalia of Solms, Frederik Hendrik's wife. He could thus begin to reconstruct the battered collection.

In 1733 Willem IV bought Rembrandt's *Simeon's song of praise* (inv. no. 145) at the auction of Adriaan Bout, a work that had probably belonged to Frederik Hendrik. All the works the latter had acquired directly from the master himself had long since disappeared from the Netherlands. It is not without interest to examine how Willem IV and his contemporaries viewed the Dutch seventeenth-century masters. This becomes evident from the choices made at various auctions. On the one hand, Willem IV was influenced by an interest in history, with subject matter being an important factor; on the other, the prince and many others showed a strong preference for such late seventeenth-century *fijnschilders* as Willem van Mieris, Godfried Schalcken and Adriaen van der Werff (inv. nos. 109, 159–162 and 209). Paintings in the same tradition by the greatly admired artists Gerrit Dou, Cornelis van Poelenburch and Philips Wouwerman (inv. nos. 33, 134, 214–222) were also bought. Other acquisitions, such as the architectural piece by Hendrick van Steenwijck the Younger (inv. no. 171) and a large canvas by Gonzales Coques depicting an art gallery (inv. no. 238), reflect Willem IV's interest in paintings with a clearly defined and documentary content. Similar in manner are the paintings by Johannes Lingelbach depicting Charles II leaving Rotterdam and Scheveningen (inv. nos. 88–89) and a panel by Frans Francken the Younger depicting the ball given in 1611 by Ferdinand and Isabella, governors of the Netherlands (inv. no. 244). Potter's *Bull* (inv. no. 136), which has always been popular, perhaps due to its unusually large size as well as its incredible realism, was purchased by Willem IV at an auction in Haarlem in 1749. On Willem IV's premature death in 1751,

[11] Gerrit Dou, *'The young mother'*, 1658. Inv. no. 32.

his wife, Anne of Hannover, acted as princess-regent for her three-year old son. It may have been she who acquired Jan Steen's *'As the old sing, twitter the young'* (inv. no. 169). The 1757 inventory of Het Loo Palace indicates exactly which paintings were purchased by Willem IV since the auction organised by his mother in 1713.

Willem V

Stadholder Willem V, for whose artistic sense the Netherlands have to be thankful, may well have inherited his zest for collecting from his talented mother. His enthusiasm was probably also stimulated by the visits to the court in The Hague of such artists of rank as Jan Baptist Xavery, Jean-Antoine Houdon, Marie-Anne Falconet-Collot, Guillaume de Spinny, Johann Tischbein, Benjamin Bolomey, Hendrik Schweickhardt and others. In addition to accessions to his library, his extensive ethnographic and natural history collections and his collections of engraved gems, coins, medals and curiosities, Willem V also enriched the possessions of the House of Orange with a considerable number of works of art. The quality of the works bought at auctions varied, however. One purchase, made in 1760, when the prince was only twelve years old, was Peter Neeffs's *Interior of the Onze Lieve Vrouwekerk in Antwerp* (inv. no. 248), a work which has little merit for us today, but parallels his father's purchase of Van Steenwijck's 1614 painting (inv. no. 171). The Neeffs may have been purchased at the instigation of Anne of Hannover, whose influence can also be identified in the acquisition of the three works by Jan Steen bought at the Willem Lormier sale in The Hague in 1763, among them *The doctor's visit* (inv. no. 168). Additions to the group of historical pieces were *Cavalry battle* by Philips Wouwerman (inv. no. 219) and a painting by Jan Mijtens depicting the marriage of the Elector of Brandenburg (see below), now in Rennes. In 1763 the collection was transferred from Het Loo Palace to The Hague. In the following year an addition was made to the series of Steen paintings with *The life of man* (inv. no. 170), purchased at the Da Costa sale in The Hague. Houckgeest's beautiful interiors of the Nieuwe Kerk in Delft (inv. nos. 57–58), which were also added during this period, must have especially appealed to the prince and his mother as both works depict the tomb of their ancestor, William the Silent. The well-known Dutch picture dealer Pieter Yver, who, together with his son, attended all the important auctions and often acted as an agent for foreign collectors, broke new ground in 1764 when he delivered two important contemporary French paintings by Claude-Joseph Vernet (inv. nos. 292–293). The king of Poland's sale in 1765 produced the charming *Apelles painting Campaspe* by Willem van Haecht (inv. no. 266) and some less significant Italian works. In the same year, when the possessions of the Amsterdam linen merchant Pieter Leendert de Neufville were auctioned, paintings by Karel du Jardin, Nicolaes Berchem, a naval scene by Willem van de Velde, an animal painting by Adriaen van de Velde, and a portrait of a scholar by Thomas de Keyser were all acquired (inv. nos. 13, 73, 77, 197, 201). Further important purchases, made at the De la Court sale in 1766, were *The garden of Eden with the fall of man* by Peter Paul Rubens and Jan Brueghel the Elder (inv. no. 253), and a hunting still life by Jan Weenix (inv. no. 207). From the sale of the collection of the well-known collector Gerret Braamcamp in Amsterdam in 1771 came Willem V's last acquisitions: amongst others a small portrait sketch by Thomas de Keyser (inv. no. 78) and a painting by Jan van der Heyden (inv. no. 53).

Willem V's activity as a collector had reached its climax in 1768, when at the age of only twenty the prince purchased for 50,000 guilders the group of 41 masterpieces assembled by chief tax collector Govert van Slingelandt. Even before the sale, great interest in this remarkable collection of paintings had already been shown from abroad. The collection of this typical eighteenth-century connoisseur had never consisted of more than around 40 works, and it had always been his avowed intention to possess only a limited number of pieces of the highest quality. Three major portraits by Van Dyck were amongst the gems of this assemblage (inv. nos. 239–240, 242), together with Rembrandt's *Susanna* (inv. no. 147). Gerard ter Borch's *'Unwelcome news'* (inv. no. 176), the *Portrait of Steven van Herwijck* by Anthonis Mor (inv. no. 117), and a series of masterpieces by Gabriel Metsu, Paulus Potter, Adriaen van Ostade, Jan Steen and David Teniers the Younger (inv. nos. 93–94, 128–129, 137–138, 167, 260) all bear witness to the taste and judgement of both Van Slingelandt and Willem V. It is thus particularly disappointing that Willem V purchased virtually nothing more of significance during the remaining quarter of a century before the invasion of the French. The political situation may well have been the main reason for this, as Willem V's personal interest remained undiminished. Nevertheless, the collection, which never amounted to more than around 200 works, must have been very distinguished by 1775, particularly as its scope had been so broadened by the paintings acquired earlier by Willem III. Although we regret the absence of painters who are now regarded as *coryphaei*, such as Frans Hals, Johannes Vermeer, Aelbert Cuyp, Meindert Hobbema, Jacob van Ruisdael and Pieter Saenredam, even these exclusions are nevertheless striking evidence of the prevailing artistic tastes of former generations.

As compared to the collecting activity of Augustus III of Saxony, or George III of England, it is clear that the collection of the House of Orange did not reflect a very progressive taste. The Dutch landscape painters of the mid-seventeenth century, so avidly collected in England and France during the second half of the eighteenth century, were entirely lacking, and of the circa 200 paintings about 130 were Dutch. Of these the majority were genre pieces, history paintings (with historical, mythological or biblical subjects) and the occasional landscape of topographical interest. As in the rest of Europe, however, Dutch paintings of the first quarter of the seventeenth century were almost completely ignored. The collection in The Hague thus had the character of a slightly conservative private cabinet, rather than that of a royal gallery on the lines of those at Dresden and Berlin.

The numerous acquisitions made by Willem IV and Willem V necessitated a search for more suitable accommodation than that provided in the Stadholder's Quarter, and in 1766 the problem was solved with the purchase of the Van Noyelle residence on the corner of Buitenhof. The building, already completely renovated in 1764, was modified in 1766 by the stadholder's architect, David Stolk, in order to house the collections. The court painter Tethart Haag of Kassel (see inv. no. 813), who also gave drawing lessons to Willem V and probably influenced his taste, had been in charge of the art collection since 1752, while the philosopher Frans Hemsterhuis and the physicist Arnout Vosmaer (see inv. no. 1069) supervised the remaining sections of the collections. These included the priceless library, a collection of drawings, prints and historical objects, the cabinet of coins and medals, as well as scientific instruments, coral, shells, stones and fossils, butterflies, all kinds of stuffed animals and other natural curiosities.

Access to the collections in The Hague was given, on application, to art-lovers and scholars three times a week from 11 to 1 o'clock. The catalogue of paintings compiled by Pieter Terwesten in 1770, which lists 101 works, gives a good impression of the collection housed in the Van Noyelle residence. Willem V's collection, like that of Willem III before him, included paintings by contemporary artists as well as Old Masters. The artificial division between the two which so often prevails today was unknown at the time. Before long the need was felt for a separate space to accommodate the paintings, and the architect Philip Schonck was commissioned to build a gallery measuring approximately 25 by 6 metres. This gallery, located next to the Gevangenpoort (Prisoner's gate), was completed in March 1774. It was open to everyone, and as such was the first public collection in the northern Netherlands. Since 1977 it once again serves its original purpose, showing primarily

[12] Interior of the Picture Gallery of Prince Willem V at the Buitenhof, reopened in 1977. Here paintings of the Mauritshuis and loans from the Netherlands Institute for Cultural Heritage and the Rijksmuseum are displayed in an eighteenth-century fashion: frame to frame, covering nearly the entire wall (present situation).

[13] D.L.M. van Valkenburg, *The return of the stadholder's pictures to The Hague, 14 November 1815*, 1839. Pen in brown and brush, 9.6 x 15.7 cm. The Hague, Gemeentearchief.

paintings that used to adorn its walls from floor to ceiling [fig. 12]. With the construction of this gallery Willem V once again took up the old tradition of princely picture galleries, rather than continuing to hang his pictures in small cabinets, as was the tendency among middle-class collectors of the time.

French invasion

On 7 June 1795, just a few months after the French invasion of the Netherlands and the flight of Prince Willem V, the revolutionaries sequestered his most important art treasures for removal to Paris as 'property of the French nation won by force of arms', an event known as 'la conquête artistique'. Within three weeks the selected paintings had been packed and by the autumn of 1795 the bulk of the stadholder's collection had arrived in Paris. The works were displayed as 'biens nationaux' in the Musée Central des Arts (Musée Napoléon) in the Louvre, together with other pictures looted from the finest European collections. Most of the remaining parts of the collections were auctioned, including the contents of the Oude Hof (Noordeinde Palace) and the Stadholder's Quarter, Huis ten Bosch Palace, the country seats at Groningen and Leeuwarden, the castles at Breda and Buren, the houses at Honselaarsdijk and Soestdijk, and the palaces of Oranjewoud and Het Loo.

Under the new government of the Batavian Republic a museum was opened to the public in 1800, the Nationale Konst-Gallery (National Art Gallery), though this was to have a chequered career. Initially set up in Huis ten Bosch Palace, it was transferred three years later to the Buitenhof, and then, in 1808, to Amsterdam as part of the Royal Museum, founded by Louis Napoleon and established in a section of the Dam Palace. Transferred again in 1815, this time to the Trippenhuis in Amsterdam, the collections finally came to rest in the newly built Rijksmuseum in 1885.

Following the Battle of Waterloo it proved extremely difficult to recover the art treasures confiscated by the French, the result of a conflict of interest amongst the allies. In the end, the Prussians took back the collections by force, and thanks to the personal intervention of the Duke of Wellington the bulk of the possessions of the House of Orange was returned to the Netherlands in the autumn of 1815 [fig. 13]. Approximately 125 paintings were recovered and now form the nucleus of the Mauritshuis collection; 68 works remained in France, of which the present whereabouts of about 25 are still unknown. Amongst the group of important works not retrieved and today in the Louvre are Hendrick Pot's portrait of Charles I, two paintings of lute-players and a musical party by Gerrit van Honthorst, and a landscape by Peter Paul Rubens; Jan Mijtens's *Marriage of the Elector of Brandenburg to Louise Henriette* is now in Rennes, while Jan Davidsz de Heem's portrait of Willem III in a garland of flowers is in Lyon. The new king, Willem I of Holland, son of stadholder Willem V, decided to present the collection to the nation, and so this ancient assembly of paintings became a national institution on 1 July 1816. The former gallery next to the Gevangenpoort was brought into use again and opened to the public twice a week. The 1817 catalogue lists 133 works.

The Mauritshuis as museum

The transfer of the collection to the Mauritshuis began in August 1821, and from January 1822 the gallery could be viewed on Wednesdays and Saturdays from 10 in the morning to 1 in the afternoon by anyone 'who was well dressed and not accompanied by children'. As early as 1816 *Jonkheer* Johan Steengracht van Oostkapelle had been appointed honorary director of the Royal Cabinet of Paintings (or Royal Picture Gallery), with the painter Jan Willem Pieneman as deputy director. The latter occupied this position from 1816 to 1820 — in 1843 he was appointed director of the National Museum of

Paintings at the Trippenhuis in Amsterdam, as successor to Cornelis Apostool. Restoration of the paintings was entrusted to him, for which he received a small remuneration. These restorations had been rendered necessary by the damages sustained during transport to and from Paris.

Only the first floor was allocated to the collection of paintings — it was already overcrowded with about 274 works — while the ground floor housed the Cabinet of Curiosities. About 120 paintings had come from the collections of Willem V; the rest were acquired between 1816 and 1822 and supplemented with works by contemporary artists, including Jan Baptist Kobell, Cornelis Kruseman, George Jacobus van Os, Jan Willem Pieneman and Ary Scheffer. These modern masters were transferred to the Welgelegen Pavilion in Haarlem in 1838 and are now in the Rijksmuseum in Amsterdam. Several major Old Master paintings were purchased between 1816 and 1839. Willem I's interest in the museum is evident from the fact that he agreed that Vermeer's *View of Delft*, purchased in 1822, came to the Mauritshuis [fig. 14]. In 1827 he acquired Rogier van der Weyden's *Lamentation of Christ* (inv. no. 264) and in the following year ordered the purchase of Rembrandt's 1632 *Anatomy lesson of Dr Nicolaes Tulp* [fig. 15]. These and similar purchases were financed from special funds under his control. Less fortuitous, however, was the acquisition in 1821 of the De Rainer Collection and of the Reghellini Collection in 1831, together totalling some 122 paintings of mostly indifferent quality by Italian and Spanish artists. These acquisitions were made against the recommendation of Steengracht, and only 30 works were eventually kept, the rest being disposed of in 1828. Fortunately several other valuable acquisitions were made, including Gerard ter Borch's *Self-portrait* (inv. no. 177), and Bartholomeus van der Helst's *Portrait of Paulus Potter* (inv.no. 54). Also acquired in this period were the portrait of the founder of the Mauritshuis by Jan de Baen [fig. 7] and the portrait of Constantijn Huygens with his children by Adriaen Hanneman (inv. no. 241).

The Belgian uprising of 1830 put a sudden end to this phase in the expansion of the collection: the critical financial situation and changed circumstances of the Dutch government resulted in no further purchases being made with official funds for more than 40 years, that is until 1874. With the conspicuous exception of the enthusiastic support of Willem I and the exertions of Willem II on behalf of the Mauritshuis, there was scarcely any interest in cultural policy on the part of the Dutch government. Donations up to 1874 added only four more paintings to the collection, including, however, the fine *portrait historié* by Maerten de Vos, bequeathed by *Jonkheer* Pieter van Panhuys (inv. no. 249). The greatest misfortune was that not a single painting was acquired from the choice personal collection of Willem II when it was auctioned in The Hague in 1850–1851. Thus major paintings by Jan van Eyck, Dirk Bouts, Hans Memling, Jan Gossaert, Rembrandt, Steen, Hobbema, Rubens and Van Dyck, and drawings by Michelangelo and Raphael, which had been exhibited in the Gothic Hall opposite Noordeinde Palace, left the Netherlands forever.

Jean Zacharia Mazel was appointed director in 1841, while also, surprisingly enough, retaining his post as counsellor and permanent undersecretary in the Department of Foreign Affairs (until 1863). All he could do in the few hours available to him was to rearrange the collection, necessitated by the empty spaces left when the contemporary paintings were transferred away from The Hague in 1838. The only paintings he was allowed to purchase, in consultation with his colleague, the director of the National Museum, were by contemporary masters, which were then put on display in Haarlem.

Mazel had known his predecessor Steengracht well. We can assume that he was a highly educated man and a conscientious civil servant. As a young lieutenant in the Engineers he had taken part in the mission of 1815 to bring the Dutch art treasures back from Paris. He was himself an enthusiastic collector of 'curios', with a great interest in drawing and painting, which extended to his activity as an

[14] Johannes Vermeer, *View of Delft*, *c.* 1660–1661. Purchased, 1822. Inv. no. 92.

amateur lithographer. His own collection of prints and original manuscripts was auctioned after his death. Under the directorship of Mazel nearly all the paintings exhibited in the museum were cleaned by the restorer Nicolaas Hopman (1794–1870), using methods we would find questionable today. Every four or five years during the course of the nineteenth century, paintings were 'washed'. The unstable climate in the Mauritshuis will have been the reason why the paintings had to be 'cleaned' so often.

In 1855, on the initiative of Mazel, the museum was closed for six months for urgent restoration work on the interior. Mazel continued as director until the age of 83; then, in 1875, he was succeeded by the 47-year-old *Jonkheer* Jan de Jonge, previously co-director of the collection of modern masters in Haarlem. De Jonge had begun his career as an assistant archivist in the State Archives, later being appointed clerk of Parliament. Almost immediately upon succeeding to the Mauritshuis, disagreements arose with the government in the person of the new, vigorous and often extremely obstinate acting head of the recently established Department of Arts and Science in the Ministry of Home Affairs, *Jonkheer* Victor de Stuers. Appointed to this position in 1875, De Stuers had previously held the post of secretary to the Board of State Advisors for Art Historical Monuments. Controversy raged over the restorations carried out by the director, for which authorisation had not always been sought. De Jonge offered his resignation twice. Still, notwithstanding the difficulties, the annual budget was increased and funds for the purchase of paintings were again put at the director's disposal. The ground floor rooms also became available for exhibiting pictures following the move of the Cabinet of Curiosities in 1875, though it is interesting to learn that even after the transfer of the 'Curiosities' the Mauritshuis was still regarded as but a temporary accommodation for the collection of paintings.

Nevertheless, the *Notice historique et descriptive des tableaux et des sculptures exposés dans le Musée Royal* compiled by De Stuers in 1874 was a landmark, being the first official catalogue of the collection. From 1875 the number of visitors was recorded and annual reports were published. As a result of De Stuers's efforts, the exterior of the Mauritshuis underwent drastic restoration in 1876, involving, among other things, the stripping of the layer of plaster that had been applied in 1855. From 1884 to 1886 the substructure was faced with ashlar and the interior was also modernised when parquet floors were laid in 1890. Contemporary observers felt that at last the period of standstill was over and that the winds of change were beginning to blow — in spite of the conflicts, this was due to the energetic actions of De Stuers.

During the directorship of De Jonge, Vermeer's *View of Delft*, Rembrandt's *Anatomy lesson of Dr Nicolaes Tulp* and other paintings were restored, all in consultation with a committee from the Board of State Advisors, in which De Stuers had a powerful voice if not a decisive vote. In 1880, after having been in charge of the museum for just five years, De Jonge died at the age of 52; he was succeeded by his assistant director, the landscape artist Simon van den Berg (see inv. no. 1104), who was 68 years old at the time. The new director had played a prominent role in the artistic life of The Hague and from 1856 had been a member of the Hague etching society, set up in 1848 as the first organisation in Europe to promote etching as an independent art form.

Van den Berg was able to acquire some fine paintings during his nine-year tenure — in spite of De Stuers's rejection of his proposals on certain occasions and the purchase at auction of totally different works than those for which Van den Berg had petitioned. It is revealing to examine more closely the acquisitions made in this period, as they were by no means always selected by the director but rather by the governmental advisory committee mentioned above. Many of the paintings bought in the 1880s are no longer on display, with the exception of a flower still life by Maria van Oosterwyck (inv.no. 468). However, in 1880 Van den Berg and De Stuers succeeded in acquiring the portraits of Jacob Pietersz Olycan and his wife, Aletta Hanemans, painted by Frans Hals

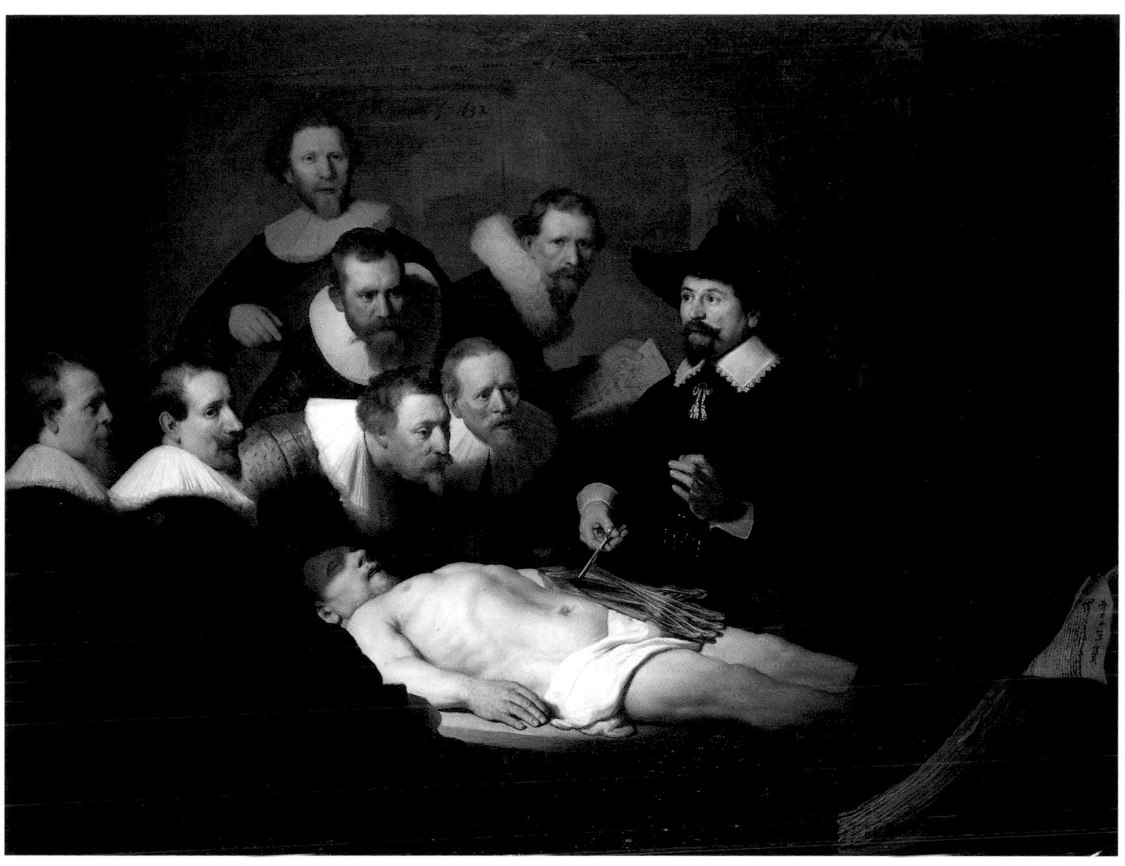

[15] Rembrandt, *The anatomy lesson of Dr Nicolaes Tulp*, 1632. Purchased by the Dutch State and placed in the Mauritshuis at the order of Willem I, 1828. Inv. no. 146.

(inv. nos. 459–460), and in 1883 the large *Interior of an imaginary Catholic church* by Emanuel de Witte (inv. no. 473). Van den Berg was the last professional artist to serve as the museum's director; with him ended a tradition stretching back to the sixteenth century whereby artists were put in charge of the princely collections.

A new epoch

The appointment of Abraham Bredius as director in 1889 heralded the dawn of a new epoch for the Mauritshuis. Whereas up until then painters or 'amateurs' had occupied the post, now a trained art historian with museum experience was given the job. Bredius was born in Amsterdam in 1855, the scion of a rich merchant family. His grandfather possessed some good paintings by Aert van der Neer, David Teniers the Younger and others. Earlier in life he had wanted to study the piano and follow a career in music, but an injury to his hands forced him to abandon this plan and he instead chose the history of art. In the course of a journey through Italy in 1876 he came into contact with the art-lover Dr August Fischer, while it was the great Berlin museum director Wilhelm von Bode who first directed his studies towards seventeenth-century Dutch painting. Through David van der Kellen he made the acquaintance of Victor de Stuers, with whom he was later to quarrel violently. In 1880, at the tender age of 25, Bredius was appointed by the latter as assistant director of the Dutch Museum for Decorative Arts in The Hague, which in 1884 was incorporated into the Rijksmuseum in Amsterdam. Shortly afterwards — he was then 34 — followed his appointment at the Mauritshuis. Bredius combined great diligence and flair with judgement and taste, and as he was personally wealthy he was also able to acquire a large private collection, a part of which he later bequeathed to the city of The Hague (now housed in the Museum Bredius). Although with the appointment of Bredius De Stuers's influence gradually diminished, the two nevertheless engaged in raging controversies, particularly about the quality, desirability or the price of paintings to be bought for the Mauritshuis. For example, Bredius was criticised roundly for buying certain works by Jan van Goyen, Rembrandt, Guillaume du Bois, Simon de Vlieger, Jan van de Cappelle and Adriaen Brouwer. Bredius's interests were concentrated in the seventeenth century, and within his chosen field his formidable talents made him on occasion an outstanding connoisseur. Thanks to his contacts with professional colleagues, art dealers and other collectors, he was able to take advantage of opportunities to find and acquire important works for reasonable prices which others — such as the much richer American collectors of the period — missed.

Bredius's talent as an art historian was soon apparent in the copious new and improved descriptions of the paintings in the Mauritshuis that were published in the annual reports from 1890 onwards. At the same time he undertook the publication of a detailed catalogue, which he produced in French in 1895, in collaboration with Cornelis Hofstede de Groot, his assistant since 1891 (see below). Bredius made many notable discoveries in the archives relating to Dutch painters, which he published in the *Künstler-Inventare* (1915–1922) and in the periodical *Oud Holland*. He held the post of director for twenty years, until 1909, during which period he established the museum's worldwide scholarly reputation, which it still enjoys today. In his time the museum became an international meeting-place for collectors and art-experts, who came to The Hague from all over Europe for information and advice. It was also thanks to Bredius's outstanding knowledge of art and his many connections at home and abroad that he was able to expand the collection considerably. During his years as director, 30 paintings were bought, the most important being the fine *Portrait of a man from the Lespinette family* by Hans Memling (inv. no. 595), Carel Fabritius's *Goldfinch* [fig. 16] and the small *Portrait of a man* by Frans Hals (inv. no. 618), which was stolen in 1905 but fortunately recovered soon afterwards in Antwerp.

[**16**] Carel Fabritius, *The goldfinch*, 1654. Purchased, 1896. Inv. no. 605.

Bredius often loaned major paintings to the Mauritshuis from his own collection: for example, *Saul and David*, which Bredius attributed to Rembrandt, first joined the collection in this way in 1898. In 1899 Bredius managed to purchase Vermeer's *Allegory of Faith*, a late work by the Delft master which was to hang in the Mauritshuis until 1923. In 1928 Bredius sold it and it came to rest in The Metropolitan Museum of Art in New York with the Friedsam Collection. Bredius also arranged for many important loans from other collections. In 1891 a number of Rembrandts belonging to the Duke of Westminster were shown, and in 1899 21 paintings from the collection of Count van Lynden were exhibited on loan, including Hals's splendid late portrait which is thought to be of Willem Croes, now in the Alte Pinakothek in Munich. Following Bredius's resignation, important paintings continued to be lent, including Rembrandt's *Diana and her nymphs* from the collection of the Fürst zu Salm-Salm in 1919, and in 1921 works from the collection of the Earl of Crawford and Balcarres. These included the Hobbema that entered the Toledo Museum of Art through the Ten Cate Collection and two Rembrandts, one of which was the portrait of Titus, now among the most prized possessions of the Museum Boijmans Van Beuningen in Rotterdam. These activities encouraged more people to visit the Mauritshuis: while the attendance figures before 1890 had been below 30,000 per annum, now they rose as high as 45,000. In 1902 they exceeded 50,000 for the first time and in the years immediately after the First World War the numbers increased again to around 80,000.

Bredius certainly succeeded in interesting collectors in the Mauritshuis and one of the most important results was the bequest by Arnoldus des Tombe in 1903 of twelve works, including Vermeer's *Girl with a pearl earring* [fig. 17] and *Vase with flowers in a window* by Ambrosius Bosschaert the Elder (inv.no. 679). Bredius himself loaned seven works by or attributed to Rembrandt, which he left to the museum in 1946 (inv. nos. 556, 565, 584, 621, 626, 685, 707). 1883 saw the foundation of the Rembrandt Society, an institution to which Dutch museums and the Mauritshuis in particular are much indebted — in 1894 the first painting was bought for the museum with its financial assistance (inv. no. 595). It is also worth noting that restorations were carried out under Bredius's directorship, first by Willem A. Hopman, and, after 1900, by the restorer C.F.L. de Wild, including that of Rembrandt's *Anatomy lesson of Dr Nicolaes Tulp*. Hopman was renowned for his wax relinings, a technique which he was the first to employ. Prior to this, Bredius had sent paintings for restoration to Professor Hauser in Berlin.

The collaboration between the artistic but irascible and easily offended Bredius and his dour assistant Hofstede de Groot did not last for long. The similar interests and disparate characters of these two pioneers of Dutch art history gave rise to continual conflict. Hofstede de Groot, who received his doctoral degree in Leipzig and worked briefly in Dresden under Max Lehrs, left The Hague in 1896 to become keeper of the Department of Prints and Drawings of the Rijksmuseum. The year after Hofstede de Groot's departure, Dr Van Houten, Minister for Home Affairs, appointed F.G. Waller assistant director of the Mauritshuis, without Bredius's knowledge. The latter tendered his resignation, but later changed his mind. In 1901, however, Waller was replaced by Wilhelm Martin, who had studied in Leiden and written his doctoral thesis on Gerrit Dou, the first Dutch dissertation in the history of art. Meanwhile, in 1899 Bredius had again threatened to resign his directorate due to 'hurtful interference' on the part of Victor de Stuers. The cause of the trouble was the purchase of a book, as De Stuers thought the acquisition unnecessary in view of the fact that the volume was available in the Royal Library. The affair developed into a fierce controversy, and the Hague artists, headed by Jan Veth, sided with Bredius. Again and again Bredius threatened to resign and bequeath his collection to an institution other than the Mauritshuis. Finally, thanks to the personal intervention of the queen, he consented to remain as director and relinquished plans to

[17] Johannes Vermeer, *Girl with a pearl earring*, c.1665. Bequest of Arnoldus des Tombe, 1903. Inv. no. 670.

publish a pamphlet containing his official correspondence with the Ministry of Home Affairs.

The sedulous Bredius not only paid attention to the extension of the collection and restoration problems, but also to the improvement of the building, replacing the wallpaper in 1890 with a deep red mock-velvet covering. It is hardly surprising, therefore, that after twenty eventful years at the Mauritshuis he should have remained as advisor to Martin, who succeeded him in 1909, despite the occasional heated conflict about purchases, methods of restoration and the resulting press campaigns. Fresh problems arose in 1910 when a member of the Hague Municipal Council put forward a proposal that a new museum be built, to which the Mauritshuis collection would be transferred. The need for a museum of modern art was also recognised and Hofstede de Groot championed the idea of merging the municipal and state collections. He had in fact already offered his own private collection to the Mauritshuis in 1914 on condition that it would not remain in the building but would be housed in another museum. Bredius and Martin, on the other hand, stressed the advantages of having several museums and the row soon developed into 'the Hague museum controversy'. The conflict ended with the building of the Hague Gemeentemuseum (1919–1935), designed by H.P. Berlage, under the stimulating supervision of Dr H.E. van Gelder, head of the Department of Arts and Sciences of the municipality from 1918 and the first director of the new museum.

As a good museum man, and in spite of the continuing conflicts, Martin kept one aim in mind: retention of the Bredius loan, which consisted of 25 paintings, including several Rembrandts. Bredius continued to act in his advisory capacity until 1922, when he moved to Monte Carlo. This by no means implied that he stayed away from the affairs of the Mauritshuis, but for the most part Martin was content to continue Bredius's policies. Martin himself had acquired a considerable reputation even before his designation. At the age of 32 he had been appointed professor of art history at Leiden and at the same time keeper of the Print Room there. He devoted himself to the Mauritshuis with great enthusiasm. A welcome addition to the interior came in 1911 with alterations to the plain ceiling in the Potter Room in order to accommodate the five fine allegorical ceiling paintings by Jacob de Wit (inv. nos. 731–735), which had been executed in 1743 for a residence at 48 Rapenburg in Leiden. Further particularly important acquisitions were the paintings from the Steengracht van Duivenvoorde Collection, auctioned in Paris in 1913, which were secured with the help of the Rembrandt Society, supplemented by contributions from the Dutch royal family and many private individuals. The acquisitions included Gerard ter Borch's *Mother combing the hair of her child* (inv. no. 744), Meindert Hobbema's *Landscape with watermills* (now in Canada, see below) and Jan Steen's *'The way you hear it, is the way you sing it'* (inv. no. 742). Mrs Rose-Molewater presented Jacob Backer's *Portrait of a boy in grey*, also from the Steengracht Collection. 1914 saw the appearance of a revised edition of Bredius's 1895 catalogue. The next and last edition, compiled by Martin in collaboration with the Swiss art historian H. Schneider, who worked in the Mauritshuis as a volunteer assistant from 1915, was published in French in 1935. It was also under Martin's directorship that a separate portion of the budget was first set aside for the purchase of paintings — previously they had been paid for out of the general budget.

Interbellum

Between the world wars the Mauritshuis was especially fortunate in receiving the generous support of Sir Henri Deterding. At the Six sale in Amsterdam in 1928 he purchased *Woman writing a letter* by Gerard ter Borch for the museum [fig. 18]. Later, in 1936, during very difficult years for the Mauritshuis when purchasing funds were virtually reduced to nothing, he donated a further four paintings, including Jan Steen's *Girl eating oysters* (inv. no. 818) and the fine *Ships off the coast* by Jan van de Cappelle (inv. no. 820). In 1939 Martin

[**18**] Gerard ter Borch, *Woman writing a letter*, *c.*1655. Gift of Sir Henri Deterding, 1928. Inv. no. 797.

acquired Jan Gossaert's *Madonna and Child* (inv. no. 830), and even in the dark days of the last year of the Second World War he managed to buy the small portrait of Lysbeth van Duvenvoorde (inv. no. 831), dating from the early fifteenth century, at a public sale in Amsterdam. It was also during the first half of the twentieth century that the first international exhibitions devoted to Dutch art were organised, and the Mauritshuis provided many loans. Before 1940 no major exhibitions were held in the Mauritshuis itself, but Martin was one of the organisers of the Jan Steen exhibition held in Leiden in 1926, and the museum maintained the tradition of scholarship established by Bredius. The years of German occupation, during which the Mauritshuis was renamed the National Picture Gallery Mauritshuis, passed without too much damage, although about nineteen works out on loan elsewhere — by good fortune relatively unimportant paintings — were lost. The most valuable works had already been removed in 1941 and 1942 to bomb-proof shelters in the dunes near Zandvoort and in the St Pietersberg near Maastricht.

After the war

In June 1945, following the liberation, Dr Jan Gerrit van Gelder succeeded Martin as director of the Mauritshuis, combining his duties with the directorship of the nearby Netherlands Institute for Art History (Rijksbureau voor Kunsthistorische Documentatie, known as the RKD), a post which he had already held since December 1940. The 35 years of Martin's directorship thus came to an end and shortly afterwards, in 1946, Bredius died at the age of 90. The 25 paintings already on loan to the museum were bequeathed to it in his will; Martin's efforts over so many years had not been in vain. Included in this princely bequest were Rembrandt's *Andromeda* and *Homer* (inv. nos. 584 and 707), three works by Jan Steen (inv. nos. 553, 664, 736), landscapes by Jan van Goyen and Salomon van Ruysdael (inv. nos. 624, 738), and a small still life by Chardin (inv. no. 656).

Following the liberation, the new director organised a commemorative exhibition of fifteenth- and sixteenth-century Dutch art from private and public collections, and shortly thereafter followed an exhibition under the title *Recovered Art Property*. Indeed, Van Gelder's directorship was, as Martin expressed it, 'as fruitful as it was short': with his appointment as professor of the history of art at the University of Utrecht in 1946, Van Gelder left the Mauritshuis, although not before acquiring the fine *Portrait of a man* by Michel Sittow (inv. no. 832), thanks to its previous owner, A.W. Volz, and the support of the Rembrandt Society.

The 41-year-old Dr Ary Bob de Vries was appointed successor to Van Gelder on 1 August 1946; he had studied at Utrecht under Willem Vogelsang, who trained so many Dutch museum directors. De Vries wrote his doctoral thesis on northern Netherlandish portraits in the second half of the sixteenth century. He had worked in the Department of Paintings at the Rijksmuseum from 1935, but was fired by the Nazis and in 1943 left for Switzerland. In the following year he reached England, where the Allied authorities put him in charge of the preparations for recovering works of art removed by the Germans during the war. His appointment by the commissioner-general as head of the art department for the recuperation of art treasures and his simultaneous appointment as director of the Stichting Nederlands Kunstbezit (Foundation for Dutch Art Possessions) made it impossible for him to take up his duties at the Mauritshuis and the RKD until May 1947. In 1954, De Vries asked to be relieved of the directorship of the latter, while at the same time accepting the directorship of the Rijksmuseum H.W. Mesdag. The collection was considerably enriched during De Vries's tenure at the Mauritshuis, which lasted until 1970: he always felt that additions were necessary if the collection was not to stagnate and the museum was to remain a living institution. As stated in his report for 1969, he never regarded the museum as a static and complete collection. Lack of space was to him a stimulus for improving the overall quality while

[19] Frans Hals, *Laughing boy*, *c.*1625. Purchased with the support of the Rembrandt Society, the Prince Bernhard Culture Fund and the Friends of the Mauritshuis Foundation, 1968. Inv. no. 1032.

revealing new aspects of the work of less well-known artists. About 50 works of art are described in the catalogue of acquisitions for the years 1945–1970, presented to De Vries on his retirement in the latter year. Amongst the most important of these were two oil-sketches by Rubens (inv. nos. 837, 926), a marvellous late *Portrait of a man* by Frans Hals (inv. no. 928), together with his splendid *Laughing boy* [fig. 19], the late self-portrait by Rembrandt (inv. no. 840), which had been on loan to the Rijksmuseum before the war, and a rare landscape by Hercules Seghers (inv. no. 1033). The so-called Italianate landscape painters, previously represented with only one masterpiece by Karel du Jardin, were also reinforced, and the previously neglected group of still lifes acquired greater prominence with the acquisition of two paintings by Pieter Claesz dated 1627 and 1630 (inv. nos. 943 and 947). The collection of architectural paintings was transformed by the addition of two brilliant works by Saenredam (inv. nos. 888, 974). Many of these purchases would have been impossible without the invaluable support of the Rembrandt Society, the Prince Bernhard Culture Fund, and above all the Johan Maurits van Nassau Foundation, which was established in 1957 on the initiative of De Vries for the promotion of the museum's interests. In 1986 the foundation merged with the Friends of the Mauritshuis Foundation, established in 1982, and is now known under that name.

After the Second World War the Mauritshuis collection was augmented with a number of pictures which, after initial confiscation, had been recovered from Germany. At first these paintings were given on loan, but in 1960 this was converted into a gift. In this way several masterpieces from what had formerly been the Mannheimer Collection found their way into the museum: the *View of the Oudezijds Voorburgwal with the Oude Kerk in Amsterdam* by Jan van der Heyden (inv. no. 868) — a picture with an eventful past — and the delicately painted *Brothel scene* by Frans van Mieris the Elder (inv. no. 860), as well as many other paintings from this and other collections.

A deeply felt loss was sustained by the Mauritshuis in 1950 when the Dutch Government decided, without consulting De Vries, to present the Canadian people with *Landscape with watermills* by Meindert Hobbema (inv. no. 743), in grateful recognition of the many sacrifices made by Canada before and after the liberation of the Netherlands. Lack of space and other practical considerations encouraged De Vries to modify the character of the collection through reciprocal exchanges and long-term loans with various museums. Thus, all Italian and Spanish works were given on loan to the Rijksmuseum in Amsterdam in 1950, and in exchange the Mauritshuis received a number of paintings from the fifteenth and sixteenth centuries, Flemish masters of the seventeenth century, as well as 51 miniatures, which had been exhibited in the Mauritshuis until 1875 as part of the Cabinet of Curiosities. The scope of the collection was henceforth restricted to Netherlandish and German paintings of the fifteenth and sixteenth centuries, and seventeenth- and eighteenth-century paintings from the northern and southern Netherlands.

De Vries, with the assistance of the Friends of the Mauritshuis Foundation, devoted much of his energies to the organisation of important exhibitions. In 1948, on the occasion of Queen Wilhelmina's Golden Jubilee, ten Dutch paintings, including three Rembrandts and a Vermeer, and twenty drawings by Hendrick Avercamp, all lent from the English Royal Collection, were exhibited at the Mauritshuis, while in 1953 the exhibition *Maurits de Braziliaan* was organised, followed by the Jan Steen exhibition in 1958. To mark the 150th anniversary of the Mauritshuis's own collection in 1966, the large exhibition *In the light of Vermeer* was arranged for the summer, and in the autumn a small memorial exhibition entitled *150 Jaar* took place, in co-operation with the Royal Library and the Royal Mint Cabinet. These were followed by the Goya exhibition in the summer of 1970, and, under the auspices of the Netherlands-England Society, an exhibition of Dutch and English landscapes was shown in 1970–1971, under the title of *The shock of recognition.*

Notwithstanding all these activities, great attention was also paid to improvements to the Mauritshuis. The old red wall-coverings hung by Bredius in 1890 were replaced by tufted velour in 1950, green on the upper floor and cream on the ground floor. The old coal-burning stoves were removed in 1951, reducing the risk of fire, and both central heating and a new electric lighting system were installed. In addition to these improvements, in 1965 the steps by the entrance and the Golden Room were restored to their original state [see fig. 2]. Educational programmes for schools in The Hague were introduced during the next few years in order to stimulate the interest of young people in the museum, and between 1947 and 1965 the total number of visitors per annum rose from 58,000 to 135,000. It is difficult to believe, but De Vries began his directorship without any qualified staff — in marked contrast to the assistance enjoyed by his predecessors — and his first assistant was appointed only in 1955. A new concise catalogue was produced, while a detailed catalogue of the fifteenth- and sixteenth-century paintings, written by Dr Magdi Tóth-Ubbens, a temporary member of the staff of the Mauritshuis, was published in 1968.

De Vries was succeeded in June 1970 by Dr Sturla Gudlaugsson, chosen partly because of his training, his scholarly achievements, his experience over many years as assistant curator, later director, of the RKD, but above all for his innate sense of quality and his international academic reputation. Born in Skagen in 1913, the son of a Danish poet, he studied in Berlin under Oskar Fischel, Werner Weisbach and Wilhelm Pinder. After this he worked at the Berlin Schlossmuseum under Robert Schmidt, followed by a period in Denmark at Frederiksborg Castle. He settled in the Netherlands in 1943 and published his study on the topic of comedians in the work of Jan Steen and his contemporaries in 1945. His principal work was the large two-volume biography of Gerard ter Borch, published in 1959–1960. In addition to these studies, he published many articles in *Oud Holland*, in the publications of the RKD and in the *Nederlands Kunsthistorisch Jaarboek*. During the nine months of life granted to him from his appointment until his untimely death, Gudlaugsson was scarcely able to begin his duties at the Mauritshuis. However, he did produce the excellent catalogue of the acquisitions made between 1945 and 1970 that was presented to his predecessor on retirement (see p. 38). The only painting he purchased for the Mauritshuis was a landscape by Jan Hackaert (inv. no. 1039), once in the Steengracht Collection. Gudlaugsson's death in March 1971 was a tragic loss to the museum world and to art-historical scholarship in the Netherlands.

In January 1972 Hans R. Hoetink was appointed director, his previous position having been senior curator of the Department of Drawings at the Museum Boijmans Van Beuningen in Rotterdam. Under his directorship, the museum organised monographic exhibitions devoted to Gerard ter Borch (1974, in honour of the late Gudlaugsson), Johan Maurits (1979–1980) and Jacob van Ruisdael (1981), as well as thematic exhibitions such as *Paintings from England* (1988–1989) and *Great Dutch Paintings from America* (1990–1991). Many catalogues and other publications appeared during Hoetink's tenure, including the first illustrated general catalogue (1977), *Rembrandt in the Mauritshuis* (1978), a volume with essays on Johan Maurits (1979), the catalogue of Dutch landscapes (1980), *The Royal Picture Gallery Mauritshuis* (1985) and *Meesterwerken in het Mauritshuis* (Masterpieces in the Mauritshuis; 1987), as well as catalogues accompanying the aforementioned exhibitions.

The acquisition policy of De Vries was continued with the purchase of the only known still life by Pieter van Anraadt (inv. no. 1045) as well as many other paintings, including an attractive still life by Abraham van Beyeren (inv. no. 1056), *Shepherd with flute* by Jacob Backer (inv. no. 1057), the rediscovered *Calling of St Matthew* by Nicolaes Berchem and Jan Baptist Weenix (inv. no. 1058), a small landscape by Hobbema (inv. no. 1061) and the early *Fruit still life with shells and a tulip* by Balthasar van der Ast (inv. no. 1066), while the Friends of the

Mauritshuis Foundation acquired an exceptional allegory by Troost (inv. no. 1034). With the acquisition of *Simeon's song of praise* by Arent de Gelder (inv. no. 1047), this Rembrandt pupil is now represented with a masterpiece. Furthermore, on the occasion of the 70th birthday of De Vries in May 1975, a rare landscape by Pieter Post — who had assisted in the building of the Mauritshuis — dated 1633 (inv. no. 970) was acquired from the collection of the heirs of former director Martin. A history painting by the actual architect of the Mauritshuis, Jacob van Campen, was acquired in 1981 (inv. no. 1062).

On 10 March 1982 the museum closed for a five-year renovation, during which period a major part of the collection was housed in the Johan de Witt House on Kneuterdijk. Some works were exhibited in the Picture Gallery of Prince Willem V at Buitenhof 35, while a selection of top-notch paintings was shown in touring exhibitions in the United States, Canada and Japan (1982–1984). In 1986, a special selection of highlights was shown in the Grand Palais under the title *De Rembrandt à Vermeer*. The restored museum opened its doors on 4 June 1987 with a completely revised climate-control system, while the Picture Gallery of Prince Willem V finally became the official annexe of the Mauritshuis.

The Mauritshuis today

On 1 May 1991, Frederik J. Duparc officially assumed office as director of the Mauritshuis, where he had functioned as curator until 1982. In that capacity he had worked on exhibitions devoted to Ter Borch, Van Ruisdael and Johan Maurits. He also published the first illustrated general catalogue (1977), as well as a catalogue of the seventeenth-century landscapes in the collection (1980). Until 1991, he worked as chief curator of the Museum of Fine Arts in Montreal, where he organised a number of exhibitions on Dutch art. At the Mauritshuis, Duparc continues to pursue an active exhibition policy, with major monographic exhibitions on Paulus Potter (1994–1995), Vermeer (1996), Rembrandt (1999–2000), Hans Holbein the Younger (2003) and Carel Fabritius (2004), in addition to thematic exhibitions devoted to the Dutch flower still life (1992), the stadholderly collections (1997–1998) and the Dutch winter landscape (2000–2001). Many other exhibitions and presentations have been realised since 1991. Next to publications accompanying the exhibitions, a catalogue of the history paintings was published in 1993, as well as publications on the occasion of the restoration of paintings by Vermeer (1994) and Rembrandt (1998). In 2000 the new visitor's guide was published, available in five languages.

A touching show of public support ensued in response to a plea in the press in 1992 for the acquisition of the *Double portrait of Constantijn Huygens and Suzanna van Baerle* by Jacob van Campen [fig. 6]. Thanks to many gifts, and that of one private individual in particular, this portrait could be purchased at a London auction in April 1992. In the same year the *Trompe-l'oeil with a bust of Venus* from 1665 by Caesar van Everdingen (inv. no. 1088) was donated to the museum by Mrs Staring-de Mol van Otterloo. Van Everdingen, who collaborated with Van Campen, is one of the leading exponents of Dutch Classicist painting.

Ever since the purchase of Van Campen's portrait, the first in a long and distinguished series of acquisitions, Duparc has continued the active collecting policy of his predecessors Bredius, Martin, De Vries and Hoetink. Time and again the Friends of the Mauritshuis Foundation, the Sponsor Lottery, the Rembrandt Society, the VSB Fund and other funds, and occasionally the State of the Netherlands, have provided invaluable support to help the museum in the purchase of paintings. In 1999 the museum was able to buy Rembrandt's *Portrait of an elderly man*, executed in 1667 [fig. 20]. The artist's portrayal of the old man is extremely striking. The acquisition of this painting — one of the finest and best preserved portraits from the master's final years — was without question a great day in the history of the Mauritshuis. In 1994 the museum was able to

[20] Rembrandt, *Portrait of an elderly man*, 1667. Purchased with the aid of many sponsors (see p. 262), 1999. Inv. no. 1118.

acquire *The old lacemaker* by Rembrandt's pupil Nicolaes Maes (inv. no. 1101). It is a painting that is undoubtedly seen at its best in the museum's intimate atmosphere. A generous donation by the Onderlinge Levensverzekering-Maatschappij ''s-Gravenhage' in 1995 enabled the Mauritshuis to display for the first time a genre scene by Gerrit van Honthorst (inv. no. 1107). The three genre pieces by this artist that Napoleon seized in 1795 as part of the stadholder's collection were never returned. Van Honthorst's superb *Violin player* of 1626 is a typical example of the work of the Utrecht Caravaggists, very few of whose works can be seen in The Hague.

At the end of 1994 the Mauritshuis acquired Meindert Hobbema's *Wooded landscape with cottages* (inv. no. 1105) at a London auction. The painting, which could only be purchased thanks to the support of many donors, is the first work by Hobbema in a Dutch public collection that displays his qualities to the full. To date, the painting is the only example in the Mauritshuis of a monumental Dutch landscape from the seventeenth century. Gaps in the collection in the area of the Italianate painters — specialising in southern landscapes — have also been filled thanks to the acquisition of paintings by Bartholomeus Breenbergh, Pieter van Laer and Dirck van der Lisse (inv. nos. 1093, 1098, 1102), as well as loans by the Netherlands Institute for Cultural Heritage.

The *Vase with flowers* by Jan Davidsz de Heem, which the Foundation purchased in 1993, is an important addition to the museum's still-life collection [fig. 21]. De Heem, whose flower pieces are rare, is one of the most versatile still-life painters of the Golden Age. In 1995 Mrs Edward Speelman donated the extremely elegant *Still life with wild strawberries* by Adriaen Coorte (inv. no. 1106) in memory of her husband, Mr Edward Joseph Speelman. A year later, the museum acquired *Flowers in a Wan-Li vase, with shells* by Balthasar van der Ast (inv. no. 1108) from the estate of *Jonkheer* John H. Loudon, former president of the Friends of the Mauritshuis Foundation. Together with the acquisition of the De Heem, it has enabled visitors to the museum to gain a far better understanding of the way in which flower still lifes evolved over time.

That private initiative is particularly well-disposed to the Mauritshuis was proved yet again in 2002, when Willem, Baron Van Dedem, donated five major works to the museum. Each of the five masterpieces — painted by Pieter Claesz, Willem Kalf, Frans Post, Salomon van Ruysdael and Roelant Savery (inv. nos. 1125–1129) — is a welcome addition to the collection. With these as well as other recent acquisitions, including two important and very attractive pendant portraits by Rubens that were purchased in 2003 (inv. nos. 1131–1132), the Mauritshuis has been able to improve its collection to no small extent.

Compiled by Quentin Buvelot

[21] Jan Davidsz de Heem, *Vase with flowers*, c. 1670. Purchased with a major contribution from Hans Heinrich, Baron Thyssen-Bornemisza and support from the Rembrandt Society, 1993. Inv. no. 1099.

Benefactors of the Royal Picture Gallery Mauritshuis

Founder

1816 King Willem I

Major benefactors

1894 Rembrandt Society*
1955 *through 1987* Johan Maurits van Nassau Foundation
1987 Friends of the Mauritshuis Foundation*
1994 American Friends of the Mauritshuis*
1994 VSB Fund The Hague and Surroundings
1994 Ministry of Welfare, Public Health and Culture (WVC) / Ministry of Education, Culture and Science (OCW)*
1999 Fund for National Cultural Heritage*
1999 *through 2004* Sponsor Lottery
2003 Mondriaan Foundation

Major private benefactors

1903 A.A. des Tombe
1936 Sir H. Deterding
1946 A. Bredius
1987 Mrs L. Thurkow-van Huffel
1993 *and 1994* Hans Heinrich, Baron Thyssen-Bornemisza
2002 Willem, Baron Van Dedem

Benefactors

1960 Prince Bernhard Culture Fund*
1960 Openbaar Kunstbezit Foundation
1969 Royal Dutch Foundries and Steel Mills Ltd, IJmuiden
1989 Fondation Mauritshuis, Geneva
1994 Procter & Gamble Nederland
1994 Algemene Loterij Nederland
1995 Onderlinge Levensverzekering-Maatschappij ''s-Gravenhage'
1999 ING Groep
1999 Dr Hendrik Muller National Fund
2003 VSB Fund Foundation
2003 Jaffé-Pierson Foundation

* First year of sponsorship

Donors

1825 Queen Frederika Louise Wilhelmina
1836 *Jonkheer* P. van Panhuys
1844 *Jonkheer* J.L. Cremer van den Bergh
1855 *Jonkvrouw* P. de Forestier d'Orges van Waalwijk
1863 H.P. van Ede van de Pals
1873 Mrs A.J.S. Dibbits-Kaas
1874 Hendrik, Count van Limburg Stirum
1876 *Jonkheer* J. de Witte van Citters
1879 Heirs of F.W. de Virieu
1879 W. Hoog
1883 Grand duchess Sophie of Sakse-Weimar-Eisenach
1883 W.N. Lantsheer
1887 *Jonkheer* V. de Stuers
1887 Baroness L.V.S. van Rijckevorsel van Rijsenburg
1888 Count A. van der Straten Ponthoz
1889 H. Willett
1895 T. Humphrey Ward
1895 C.L.M. Lambrechtsen van Ritthem
1895 H.W. Mesdag
1897 Miss G.J.L. van Dijk
1897 A. Stengelin
1900 Dowager C.J. van Lynden van Pallandt
1901 *and 1909, 1926* Dr C. Hofstede de Groot
1903 Lt General P.M. Netscher
1904 Countess C. van Bylandt-van Hogendorp van Hofwegen
1904 Dowager M.J. Grisart-van Hogendorp van Hofwegen
1904 T.H. Blom Coster
1905 *and 1906* L. Nardus
1906 P.J.D. van Dokkum
1906 Miss J.C.H. Roels
1907 Miss M.J. Singendonck
1911 F. Kleinberger
1912 Baron R.W.J. van Pabst van Bingerden
1913 Baron R.T. van Pallandt van Eerde
1914 *and 1923* Mrs C.A. Rose-Molewater
1914 Baron W.F.E. van Aerssen Beyeren van Voshol
1914 *Jonkheren* J.H. Hora Siccama and W. Hora Siccama
1918 D.A.J. Kessler
1919 A.S. van den Bergh
1919 *and 1926* J. Goudstikker
1921 J.G. de Groot Jamin
1922 *and 1923* Mr and Mrs A.F. Philips-de Jong
1923 M.J.F.W. van der Haagen
1926 J.H. van Heek
1929 C.W. Matthes
1929 L. van den Bergh
1930 B. Svenonius
1931 Princess L. de Croy, née d'Espine
1934 W.E. Duits
1935 *and 1939* E.J. Philips

1935 D. Katz
1936 Dr V. Bloch
1938 Mrs S. Larsen
1946 Prof.Dr J.G. van Gelder
1946 A.W. Volz
1947 B. and N. Katz
1947 Mr and Mrs H.E. ten Cate
1947 Mr and Mrs Lugt-Klever
1950 E. Vis
1951 A. Brod
1955 Mr and Mrs H.A. Wetzlar
1956 *Jonkheer* W.A. van den Bosch
1956 *Jonkheer* Dr J. Loudon
1957 Miss M.C. van den Honert
1959 B.H. van der Linden
1960 Mazel Family
1962 S. and H. Nijstad
1963 E. Speelman
1966 Heirs of Mrs A.M. Nienhuys
1974 Mr and Mrs J. Hoogsteder
1979 *Jonkheer* E.V.E. Teixeira de Mattos
1982 *and 2000* R.C. Noortman
1986 Mrs M.J. Vosmaer-Hudig
1987 Mr and Mrs H.J. de Koster
1987 Mrs S.F. Duin-Priester
1987 Mr J. Ortiz-Patino
1987 Miss A.A.W. Schröder
1992 Mrs J.H.M. Staring-de Mol van Otterloo
1992 *and 1996* C.W. van Blijenburgh
1993 *and 2000* Mrs M.A. Stubbé-Butôt
1995 Mrs E. Speelman
1996 *Jonkheer* J.H. Loudon
1997 Mrs M.O. Peters-Wetzlar
1997 H.B. van der Ven
1997 Mrs C.C.M. de Bièvre-Duljndam
1997 Mrs Beatrijs de Rooij
1998 Prof.Dr Drs A.C.R. Dreesmann
1999 Matthijs de Clercq
2000 Mr and Mrs De Koster-van Rijckevorsel
2004 Mr J. Nienhuys

and those who wish to remain anonymous

Sponsors of the building

1982 Oranje-Nassau Groep
1982 Mr P.J.G. van Doorne
1984 Heineken nv
1984 Nihon Philips
1985 Mr and Mrs A. Woudhuysen
1986 Total Marine Exploitatie Maatschappij bv
1986 Banque Paribas Nederland nv
1987 Ministry of Public Health, Environmental Planning and Environment (VROM)
1987 Ministry of Welfare, Public Health and Culture (WVC)
1987 Koninklijke Nederlandsche Petroleum Maatschappij nv
1987 Petroland bv
1987 Philips
1988 Aegon Verzekeringen
1989 Koninklijke Gist Brocades nv
1989 Algemene Bank Nederland
1997 Levi Lassen Foundation
1998 Rabobank
2001 Philips nv

Major corporate sponsors

1974 Grolsch
1987 AEGON*
1990 Koninklijke Nederlandsche Petroleum Maatschappij bv
1991 M.A.O.C. Gravin van Bylandt Stichting
1992 J.P. Morgan
1994 Unilever
1995 VSB Fund The Hague and surroundings
1996 Rabobank
1997 KPN
1998 MeesPierson
1998 Shell Nederland bv
1998 Organon
1998 AKZO Nobel
1999 ING Groep
2000 ABN AMRO
2001 AEGON
2002 Oranje-Nassau Groep
2003 Rabobank
2003 Unilever
2003 NIBCapital*
2004 DSM
2004 Siemens Nederland
2005 TNT
2005 Rabobank

Directors of the Royal Picture Gallery Mauritshuis

1816–1841
Johan Steengracht van Oostkapelle
(1782–1846)

1841–1874
Jean Zacharia Mazel
(1792–1884)

1875–1880
Jan Karel de Jonge
(1828–1880)

1880–1888
Simon van den Berg
(1812–1891)

1889–1909
Abraham Bredius
(1855–1946)

1909–1945
Wilhelm Martin
(1876–1954)

1945–1946
Jan Gerrit van Gelder
(1903–1980)

1946–1970
Ary Bob de Vries
(1905–1983)

1970–1971
Sturla Gudlaugsson
(1913–1971)

1972–1991
Hans Hoetink
(b. 1929)

Note to the reader

ARTIST'S NAME

The name of the artist or artists responsible for the work of art in question is given above the entries. When the name is followed by 'attributed to', the work is probably by the artist, although the compilers are less certain of the authorship. 'Studio of' refers to works that are by an unknown hand in the studio of the artist, possibly executed under the artist's supervision. 'Circle of' refers to works that are by an unidentified but distinct hand, closely associated with the artist, but not necessarily his pupil or someone working in his studio. 'Follower of' refers to works by a follower, sometimes of a later period. 'Manner of' refers to works that are in the style of an artist but of a later date. 'After' refers to copies after known works by the artist. Works by the same artist have been arranged according to their inventory numbers.

NUMBER

The numbers preceding the titles are the inventory numbers used by the museum. They are not subject to changes and are the key to any future research or requests for information.

TITLE

The official title of the work of art, whether the traditional title or a revised one.

DATE

The date on the work of art given by the artist or based on documentary evidence. When a date has been given by the compilers, often based on the existing literature, it is always preceded by '*c.*' for 'circa'.

TECHNIQUE

All paintings have been executed in oil, unless otherwise indicated.

DIMENSIONS

The dimensions of the object have been given in centimeters, with height preceding width.

SIGNATURE

Where possible, the signature from the hand of the artist has always been checked by the compilers. The location is indicated in all entries. When a signature is not autograph, this is indicated by the words 'bears signature'. A slash ('/') indicates that the signature is continued on a next line. For facsimiles of signatures and dates, see Mauritshuis 1935.

INSCRIPTION

Referring to any inscription on the work of art by the artist himself. When an inscription is not autograph, this is indicated by the words 'bears inscription'.

DUTCH TITLE

The English titles are translations of the Dutch titles, which are given here as extra information.

PROVENANCE

Provenances begin with the earliest known owner(s) and have been given as fully as possible in a condensed form. For paintings that entered the collection after 1985, when the previous catalogue was published, provenances have been given as complete as possible. The provenances of the paintings from the collection of Stadholder Willem V have been given until 1795. After that year, all these paintings have the same history:

> [Stadholder Willem V, The Hague; his picture gallery opened its doors on the Buitenhof in The Hague in 1774]; confiscated by the French, transferred to the Musée Napoléon (Musée du Louvre), Paris, 1795–1815; Royal Cabinet of Paintings, housed in the Picture Gallery of Prince Willem V, The Hague, 1816; transferred to the Mauritshuis, 1822

LITERATURE

The most recent or important publications have been selected, including the most recent monographs, exhibition catalogues and/or articles, as well as literature on the stadholderly collections (D/LS [=Drossaers and Lunsingh Scheurleer] 1974–1976).

COMMENT

Key information has been incorporated in this section, i.e. the existence of preparatory drawings, companion pieces to the painting described, biographical data on the sitter(s), etc. Full treatments of paintings have been included from 1985, the year of the previous summary catalogue, which was reprinted in 1993 with an appendix of new acquisitions.

ABBREVIATIONS

ICN | Instituut Collectie Nederland (Netherlands Institute for Cultural Heritage), Amsterdam and Rijswijk

RKD | Rijksbureau voor Kunsthistorische Documentatie (Netherlands Institute for Art History), The Hague

RM | Rijksmuseum, Amsterdam

Paintings and Pastels

A

Willem van Aelst

Delft 1627–after 1683 Amsterdam

2 *Flower still life with a watch*, 1663

Canvas, 62.5 x 49 cm
Signed and dated lower left: *Guill.mo van Aelst. 1663.*
Dutch title: *Bloemstilleven met horloge*

PROVENANCE
Het Loo Palace, Apeldoorn, 1757; Prince Willem V, The Hague

LITERATURE
D/LS 1974–1976, vol. 2, p. 644, no. 110, vol. 3, p. 203, no. 2; Paris 1986, no. 1; Mauritshuis 1987, no. 1; The Hague 1992a, no. 2; London 1996, no. 19; Fransen 1997, p. 84; Meijer 2003, p. 153, note 3

COMMENT
The flowers were identified by Sam Segal (see Mauritshuis 1987, p. 18, fig. 2).

3 *Still life with game*, 1671

Canvas, 58.8 x 47.8 cm
Signed and dated lower left: *Guill.mo. van Aelst. / 1671*
Dutch title: *Jachtstilleven met dode patrijzen*

PROVENANCE
Prince Willem V, The Hague; confiscated by the French, transferred to the Château de Compiègne, 1795–1815; King Willem I, The Hague, 1817; transferred, 1822

LITERATURE
Paris 1986, no. 2; Mauritshuis 1987, p. 398 and fig. 2

Pieter Aertsen (attributed to)

Amsterdam 1509–1575 Amsterdam

836 *The crucifixion*, c.1550?

Panel, 27.6 x 26.7 cm
Dutch title: *De kruisiging*

PROVENANCE
Mertens sale, Cologne, Lempertz, 25–28 May 1909, lot 1100; L. Ruzicka, Zürich, 1940; Frits Lugt, The Hague; gift of Mr and Mrs Lugt-Klever, The Hague, 1947

LITERATURE
Genaille 1954, p. 285, no. 34; Mauritshuis 1968, pp. 5–6; Mauritshuis 1970, no. 6; Genaille 1977, p. 49, no. 35; Buchan 1981, pp. 118, 204, no. 19; Lemmens/Kloek 1990, pp. 135, 255, note 14

Gerrit Alberts

Nijmegen 1663–1757 Nijmegen

723 *Portrait of a man, probably Mathias Lambertus Singendonck (1678–1742), burgomaster of Nijmegen*

Canvas (oval), 78.5 x 62.7 cm
Dutch title: *Portret van een man, waarschijnlijk Mathias Lambertus Singendonck (1678–1742), burgemeester van Nijmegen*

PROVENANCE
Probably by inheritance to Maria Johanna Singendonck, The Hague; bequest of *Jonkvrouw* Maria Johanna Singendonck, 1907

LITERATURE
Moes 1897–1905, vol. 2, p. 379, no. 7209–2 (as anonymous)?

COMMENT
Singendonck was also portrayed by Philip van Dijk, inv. no. 712. For Alberts, see Van Kretschmar 1970.

Alessandro Allori (circle of)

Florence 1535–1607 Florence

303 *Portrait of a woman*, c.1585–1600?

Panel, 95 x 73 cm
Dutch title: *Portret van een vrouw*

PROVENANCE
Victor de Rainer, Brussels, 1821; purchased by King Willem I for the Mauritshuis, 1821

LITERATURE
RM 1976, p. 81 (attributed to Alessandro Allori); Boschloo/Van der Sman 1993, p. 24, no. 1 (with present attribution)

COMMENT
Formerly attributed to the studio of Agnolo Bronzino (1503–1572).

2

3

836

723

303

A

Pieter van Anraadt

Utrecht *c.*1635–1678 Deventer

1045 *Still life with earthenware jug and pipes,* 1658

Canvas, 67 x 58.8 cm
Signed and dated lower left: *Pieter van / Anraadt / An° 1658*
Dutch title: *Stilleven met stenen kruik en pijpen*

PROVENANCE
C. Raven, London, 1938; Vitale Bloch, The Hague; Christopher Norris, Polesden Lacey; Duits Gallery, London, sold to J. Kingston, 1953; Duits Gallery, London, sold to Sidney van den Bergh, Wassenaar, 1955; purchased with the support of the Friends of the Mauritshuis Foundation, the Prince Bernhard Culture Fund and the Rembrandt Society, 1972

LITERATURE
Paris 1986, no. 3; Mauritshuis 1987, no. 2; Amsterdam-Cleveland 1999–2000, no. 46

COMMENT
The rare leather frame dates from the seventeenth century; see *Mauritshuis in focus* 11 (1998) no. 2, p. 25 and fig. 14.

Johannes Anspach (attributed to)

Niederingelheim 1752–1823 Rotterdam

387 *Portrait of a lady*

Pastel on paper (oval), 13.5 x 11.5 cm
Dutch title: *Portret van een dame*

PROVENANCE
Unknown; first catalogued in 1914

Jan Asselijn

Dieppe *c.*1610/14–1652 Amsterdam

950 *Imaginary Italian landscape, c.*1650–1652

Canvas, 52.5 x 45 cm
Signed lower left: *JA.F.* (JA in ligature)
Dutch title: *Gefantaseerd Italiaans landschap*

PROVENANCE
Count Czernin, Vienna, 1844; Alfred Brod Gallery, London; purchased by the Friends of the Mauritshuis Foundation, 1962

LITERATURE
Mauritshuis 1970, no. 42; Steland-Stief 1971, p. 93, no. 206; Steland-Stief 1980, p. 242, fig. 40; Mauritshuis 1980, p. 2

COMMENT
The round building seems to have been inspired by the ancient tomb of Caecilia Metella in Rome.

Balthasar van der Ast

Middelburg 1593–1657 Delft

399 *Shells on a table*

Copper, 7.8 x 12.5 cm
Dutch title: *Schelpen op een tafel*

PROVENANCE
Neville Goldsmid, The Hague; purchased, 1876

LITERATURE
Bol 1960, p. 80, no. 81

1066 *Fruit still life with shells and a tulip,* 1620

Panel, 46 x 64 cm
Signed and dated lower left: *.B. vander. Ast. fe. / .1620.*
Dutch title: *Fruitstilleven met schelpen en een tulp*

PROVENANCE
Sale Amsterdam, Frederik Muller, 26–29 November and 2 December 1946, lot 1147; N. van Bohemen Gallery, The Hague, 1947; Douwes Gallery, Amsterdam, 1963; H. Girardet, Kettwich, 1963; P. de Boer Gallery, Amsterdam, 1983; purchased with the support of the Rembrandt Society, 1983

LITERATURE
Bol 1955, pp. 141, note 21a, 144, 153, no. 23; Bol 1960, p. 77, no. 60; Paris 1986, no. 4; Mauritshuis 1987, no. 3; Amsterdam 1993–1994, no. 280

1073 *Wan-Li vase with flowers, c.*1623

Panel, 41 x 32 cm
Signed lower right: *.B. van der. ast. fé.*
Dutch title: *Bloemen in een Wan-Li-vaas*

PROVENANCE
P. de Boer Gallery, Amsterdam, 1939; C.T.F. Thurkow, The Hague, 1939; his widow, Mrs L. Thurkow-van Huffel; bequest of L. Thurkow-van Huffel, 1987; on loan to The Metropolitan Museum of Art, New York, 2003–2005

LITERATURE
Bol 1960, p. 70, no. 9; Utrecht 1988, pp. 9–10; The Hague-San Francisco 1990–1991, p. 143; Mauritshuis 1991, no. XXVII

1045

1073

399

950

1066

387

1108 *Flowers in a Wan-Li vase, with shells, c.*1640–1650

Panel, 53 x 43 cm
Signed lower right: *·B· vander.Ast*
Dutch title: *Bloemen in een Wan-Li-vaas en schelpen*

PROVENANCE
P.A. Quist, Scheveningen, 1961; M.N. Roegholt, Baarn, 1962 (on loan to the Mauritshuis, 1966–1967, inv. no. 975); *Jonkheer* J.H. Loudon, The Hague, 1967; bequest of J.H. Loudon to the Friends of the Mauritshuis Foundation, 1996

LITERATURE
Bol 1982, pp. 54–55 and fig. 9; Atlanta 1985, no. 2; The Hague 1992a, no. 4; Jonker 1996; San Francisco-Baltimore-London 1997–1998, pp. 362–363 and fig. 2 (as *c.*1630–1635); Foucart 2001, p. 18

COMMENT
To be compared with the still life by Van der Ast in the Musée du Louvre, Paris, which is painted on wood from the same tree (see Foucart 2001).

Jacques-André-Joseph Aved

Douai 1702–1766 Paris

461 *Portrait of Willem IV (1711–1751), painted posthumously,* 1751

Canvas, 113 x 87.5 cm
Signed and dated lower left: *J. Aved f. 1751.*
Dutch title: *Portret van Willem IV (1711–1751), postuum geschilderd*

PROVENANCE
Probably P.C. Huybrechts, The Hague, 1806; probably Nationale Konst-Gallery, The Hague, 1806–1808; transferred, in or before 1841

LITERATURE
Wildenstein 1922, vol. 2, pp. 60–62, nos. 40–42; Paris 1986, no. V

COMMENT
To be compared with the portraits of the sitter by the same artist in the Rijksmuseum, Amsterdam. A copy in Het Loo Palace Nationaal Museum, Apeldoorn. Willem IV, Prince of Nassau-Dietz and Orange, was the son of Johan Willem Friso of Nassau-Dietz, Stadholder of Friesland and Groningen, and Marie Louise of Hessen-Cassel. In 1734 he married Princess Anne of Hannover. He became Stadholder of the Netherlands in 1748. His eldest son was Prince Willem V.

Hendrick Avercamp

Amsterdam 1585–1634 Kampen

785 *On the ice, c.*1610

Panel, 36 x 71 cm
Signed lower left, on the tree: *HA* (in ligature)
Dutch title: *IJsvermaak*

PROVENANCE
P. Opperdoes Alewijn, Hoorn; *Jonkvrouw* M.M. Snouck van Loosen, Enkhuizen; sale Amsterdam, Frederik Muller & Co, 29 April 1886, lot 5; purchased by the Rijksmuseum, Amsterdam (inv. no. SK-A-1320), 1886; on loan from the Rijksmuseum since 1924

LITERATURE
Welcker/Hensbroek-van der Poel 1979, p. 206, no. S 16, p. 208 (in no. S 30), p. 226, no. S 231; Mauritshuis 1980, p. 4; Paris 1986, no. 5; Mauritshuis 1987, no. 4; Amsterdam-Boston-Philadelphia 1987–1988, no. 6; The Hague 2001–2002, no. 5

COMMENT
A copy at the ICN, inv. no. NK 1806.

Jacob Adriaensz Backer

Harlingen 1608–1651 Amsterdam

543 *Portrait of a man,* 1630s

Panel, 71.3 x 60.4 cm
Dutch title: *Portret van een man*

PROVENANCE
M.J. Hollender sale, Brussels, Galerie Saint-Luc, 10–12 April 1888, lot 7 (as a self-portrait by Ferdinand Bol); purchased, 1888

LITERATURE
Bauch 1926, pp. 37 and 92, no. 166; Sumowski 1983–1995, vol. 1, p. 197, no. 34

747 *Portrait of a boy in grey,* 1634

Canvas (oval), 94.2 x 70.8 cm
Signed and dated at right, above centre: *I: De backer / 1634.*
Dutch title: *Portret van een jongen in het grijs*

PROVENANCE
Jonkheer Johan Steengracht van Oostkapelle and heirs, The Hague, before 1846–1913; gift of Mrs Cornelia Adriana Rose-Molewater, The Hague, 1914

785

461

543

1108

747

LITERATURE
Bauch 1926, pp. 92–93, no. 167, p. 97 (in no. 204); Sumowski 1983–1995, vol. 1, p. 200, no. 52; Haarlem-Antwerp 2000–2001, no. 27; *Portraits in the Mauritshuis*, no. 1

COMMENT
Cleaned and restored in 1997.

826 *Portrait of a man, c.*1636

Canvas, 127 x 99.2 cm
Dutch title: *Portret van een man*

PROVENANCE
Gift of Eduard J. Philips, The Hague, 1939

LITERATURE
Von Moltke 1965, p. 132, no. 313 (as by Govert Flinck); Blankert 1982, p. 180, no. R 167; Sumowski 1983–1995, vol. 1, p. 201, no. 58

COMMENT
Possibly a companion piece to Backer's *Portrait of a lady* in Philadelphia, Philadelphia Museum of Art, John G. Johnson Collection, inv. no. 484 (see Blankert 1982). Formerly attributed to Govert Flinck and Ferdinand Bol. A drawing of the head and shoulders in the Staatliches Museum, Schwerin, inv. no. 1218 HE.

1057 *Shepherd with flute (Self-portrait?), c.*1637

Panel, 52.2 x 40.8 cm
Signed lower left: *JAB.* (in ligature)
Dutch title: *Herder met een fluit (Zelfportret?)*

PROVENANCE
Count Otto Thott and heirs, Gavnø Castle, Denmark, 1785–1976; Robert Noortman Gallery, London and Maastricht; purchased, 1977

LITERATURE
Bauch 1926, pp. 37, 84, no. 86; Sumowski 1983–1995, vol. 1, p. 197, no. 36; Paris 1986, no. 6; Mauritshuis 1987, no. 5; *Portraits in the Mauritshuis*, no. 2

Jan de Baen

Haarlem 1633–1702 The Hague

5 *Portrait of Johan Maurits (1604–1679), Count of Nassau-Siegen, founder of the Mauritshuis, c.*1668–1670

Canvas, 151.5 x 114.5 cm
Inscribed on the piece of paper: *Request / Aen S. Fürst Gen*[de]*. / Johan Maurits / Prince van Nassou*
Dutch title: *Portret van Johan Maurits (1604–1679), graaf van Nassau-Siegen, stichter van het Mauritshuis*

PROVENANCE
Purchased by King Willem I for the Mauritshuis, 1820

LITERATURE
Cleves 1979, in no. D 1; Paris 1986, no. III; Den Bosch-Haarlem 1996, no. 140; Amsterdam 1994, p. 66 and fig. 2 (in exhibition); Buijsen *et al.* 1998, pp. 33–34, fig. 5; The Hague 2004, no. 30 and fig. 1a

COMMENT
One of the best versions of this portrait in existence. In the background the garden of Johan Maurits in Cleves, with a sculpture of Athena made in 1660 by Artus Quellinus (now Städtisches Museum Haus Koekkoek, Cleves), presented by the City of Amsterdam and at the time placed in the so-called 'amphitheatre' (see Cleves 1979 and Amsterdam 1994). Johan Maurits, Count and later Prince of Nassau-Siegen, was governor of the Dutch territories in Brazil (1636–1644; see The Hague 1979–1980) and Stadholder of Cleves (1647–1679). His grandfather, Jan the Elder, was the brother of Willem I of Orange.

454 *Allegory of Cornelis de Witt (1623–1672) as prime mover of the victory at Chatham in 1667,* before 1672

Canvas, 66 x 100 cm
Dutch title: *Allegorie op Cornelis de Witt (1623–1672) als aanstichter van de overwinning bij Chatham in 1667*

PROVENANCE
Herman Cornelis Hoog, Noordwijkerhout, 1863–1871; gift of Willem Hoog, Noordwijkerhout, 1879

LITERATURE
Van Luttervelt 1960, pp. 49–52, fig. 15

COMMENT
A copy after a large commemorative painting in the Town Hall of Dordrecht, which was destroyed by rioters in 1672. A model for or a replica of the work in the Rijksmuseum, Amsterdam, inv. no. SK-A-4648. Statesman Cornelis de Witt, brother of Johan de Witt (see Copy after Netscher, inv. no. 716), was a member of the States General. He was the prime mover of the raid of Chatham, when the Dutch fleet, led by Michiel de Ruyter, destroyed the English fleet. In 1672, Cornelis and Johan de Witt were stoned by a mob for opposing the House of Orange.

5

1057

826

454

B

Ludolf Ba(c)khuysen

Emden 1630–1708 Amsterdam

6 *The arrival of King-Stadholder Willem III (1650–1702) in the Oranjepolder on 31 January 1691*, 1692

Canvas, 53.5 x 67.5 cm
Signed and dated lower left, on a barrel: *1692 / L. Bak / huis.*
Dutch title: *De aankomst van koning-stadhouder Willem III (1650–1702) in de Oranjepolder op 31 januari 1691*

PROVENANCE
Ewout van Dishoeck, Middelburg, before 1744; Het Loo Palace, Apeldoorn, 1757; Prince Willem V, The Hague

LITERATURE
HdG 1907–1928, vol. 7, p. 243, no. 23; D/LS 1974–1976, vol. 2, p. 641, no. 40, vol. 3, p. 206, no. 14; Amsterdam-Emden 1985, no. S 29 and p. 102 (in no. T 18); Mauritshuis 1993, no. 1; De Beer 2002, pp. 129–130 and fig. 154; Wardle 2002, fig. 26; Amsterdam 2004, no. 15

COMMENT
A preliminary drawing in the English Royal Collection, attributed to Jan de Bisschop. For the scene depicted, see Mauritshuis 1993. Willem III was the son of Willem II and Mary I Stuart. He became Stadholder of Holland and Zeeland in 1672, of Utrecht in 1674, of Gelderland and Overijssel in 1675, and of Drenthe in 1676. Became supreme commander in the States Army in 1672. In 1677 he married his cousin, Mary II Stuart (see MINIATURES, Gibson [attributed to], inv. no. 994). Willem became King of England, Scotland and Ireland in 1689.

8 *The dock of the Dutch East India Company at Amsterdam*, 1696

Canvas, 126 x 140 cm
Signed on the anchor of the ship at right: *LBAKHUIZ*
Dated lower left, on the mooring post: *1696*
Dutch title: *De werf van de Verenigde Oost-Indische Compagnie te Amsterdam*

PROVENANCE
Probably made for the East India Company, Amsterdam; transferred by the Ministry of Colonial Affairs, The Hague, 1842; on loan to the Amsterdams Historisch Museum, Amsterdam, since 1956

LITERATURE
HdG 1907–1928, vol. 7, pp. 255–256, no. 71; AHM 1975–1979, p. 28, no. 29; De Beer 2002, pp. 143, 145 and fig. 176

Alexander Hugo Bakker Korff

The Hague 1824–1882 Leiden

782 *'La fille du héros'*, 1875

Panel, 56 x 80 cm
Signed and dated lower left: *A.H. Bakker Korff 1875*
Dutch title: *'De dochter van de krijgsheld'*

PROVENANCE
M. Vlierboom, Brussels, before 1896; Bequest of Mrs Cornelia Adriana Rose-Molewater, The Hague, 1923; on loan to the Stedelijk Museum De Lakenhal, Leiden, since 1923

LITERATURE
Lakenhal 1983, p. 62, no. 22

COMMENT
A preliminary drawing in the Stedelijk Museum De Lakenhal, Leiden (Lakenhal 1983, p. 62, no. 988, repr.).

Jacopo de' Barbari (attributed to)

Venice *c.*1460/70–before 1516 Malines or Brussels

898 *Portrait of Heinrich (1479–1552), Duke of Mecklenburg*, 1507

Panel, 59.3 x 37.5 cm
Top right: *HENRICV̄ REFERO DVCĒ MEGAPOLĒSĒ, / MAGNI FILIVM ANNOS NATV̄, / OCTO ET VIGITI / M.D.VII, / ANATALI CRISTIĀO / CALENDIS, / MAIIS*
(I represent Heinrich, Duke of Mecklenburg, son of Magnus, 28 years old, in May of the year A.D. 1507)
Dutch title: *Portret van Heinrich (1479–1552), graaf van Mecklenburg*

PROVENANCE
Lord Cromwell, Misterton Hall, Lutterworth, Leicestershire; M.C. Mège, Paris; B. Houthakker Gallery, Amsterdam, 1929; J.C.H. Heldring, Oosterbeek, 1929–1940; Jacques Goudstikker and other galleries, Amsterdam, 1940; Adolf Hitler, Führermuseum, Linz; Stichting Nederlands Kunstbezit; on loan to the Mauritshuis, 1951–1960; transferred, 1960

LITERATURE
Servolini 1944, pp. 61, 145–146; Mauritshuis 1968, pp. 7–8; Schwarz 2004, no. I/6; *Portraits in the Mauritshuis*, no. 3

COMMENT
A second, smaller version –probably a copy– in the North Carolina Museum of Art, Raleigh. Heinrich (Henry) of Mecklenburg succeeded his father Magnus II as Duke of Mecklenburg in 1503. Having the reputation of being a just and peace-loving ruler, the duke came to be known as Henry the Placid (or Peaceable).

6

8

782

898

B

Bartholomeus van Bassen
The Hague *c.*1590–1652 The Hague

9 *Interior of a Catholic church*, 1626

Canvas, 61 x 83 cm
Signed and dated at right: *B. van Bassen / 1626*
Dutch title: *Interieur van een katholieke kerk*

PROVENANCE
Princess Henriette Catharina; Oranienstein Palace, Diez, 1726; by descent to Prince Willem V, The Hague

LITERATURE
D/LS 1974–1976, vol. 2, p. 371, no. 343, vol. 3, p. 203, no. 3; Jantzen 1979, p. 62, no. 39

COMMENT
Some of the figures may be attributed to Esaias van de Velde.

Bartholomeus van Bassen (attributed to)

26 *Interior of the Great Hall on the Binnenhof in The Hague, during the Great Assembly of the States General in 1651, c.*1651

Panel, 52 x 66 cm, and a copper plate, painted on both sides, 9 x 42 cm
On the table: *CONCORDIA RES PARVÆ CRESCUNT* (Unity makes strength)
For other inscriptions, see Mauritshuis 1935, p. 74
Dutch title: *Interieur van de Grote Zaal op het Binnenhof te Den Haag, tijdens de Grote Vergadering van de Staten-Generaal in 1651*

PROVENANCE
(?) George Bruyn, Amsterdam, 1724; Wouter Valckenier, Amsterdam, until 1784; his widow, Elizabeth Hooft, Amsterdam, until 1796; Diederik, Baron van Leyden, Amsterdam, 1804; Werner Wreesman, Amsterdam, 1816; Jean George Teissier, 1819; purchased, 1819; on loan to the Rijksmuseum, Amsterdam (inv. no. SK-C-1350), since 1948

LITERATURE
Blade 1976, p. 252, no. 105 (as Dirck van Delen); RM 1976, p. 190; Jantzen 1979, p. 223, no. 142; Liedtke 1991, pp. 234, 236; Dumas 1991, pp. 30–31, 55, note 105, 100, note 34 (with present attribution); Scheller 1996, p. 280; RM 2001, p. 47 and fig. 49; Elzenga 2003, p. 122

COMMENT
There is a painted copper plate attached to the panel. When closed, one sees figures in the foreground with a dividing partition behind them, blocking off the view of the rest of the hall. When open, the assembly is revealed in the background, and a table takes the place of the figures (see the colour illustrations in Noordervliet 1999, pp. 86–87). Formerly attributed to Dirck van Delen. The figures can be attributed to Anthonie Palamedesz.

Sybrand van Beest
(?) The Hague *c.*1610–1674 Amsterdam

541 *Hog market*, 1638

Panel, 44 x 68 cm
Signed and dated lower right: *S. VBeest / 1638* (VB in ligature)
Dutch title: *Varkensmarkt*

PROVENANCE
S.B. Bos, Harlingen; purchased, 1888

LITERATURE
Mauritshuis 1980, pp. 5–6; Dumas 1991, pp. 684–685, no. 1; Apeldoorn 2002, p. 110, repr.

Cornelis Pietersz Bega
Haarlem 1631/32–1664 Haarlem

400 *Peasant inn*, 1658
Canvas, 47 x 58 cm
Signed and dated at right, below the cabinet: *1658 c bega*
Dutch title: *Boerenherberg*

PROVENANCE
Neville Goldsmid, The Hague; purchased, 1876; on loan to the ICN

LITERATURE
Philadelphia-Berlin-London 1984, p. 133, note 2

Abraham Begeyn
Leiden 1637/38–1697 Berlin

391 *The quarry*, 1660

Canvas, 67.5 x 81 cm
Signed and dated lower left: *ABegein* / 1660 (AB in ligature)
Dutch title: *De steengroeve*

PROVENANCE
L. Lippmann von Lissingen, Vienna, 1876; purchased, 1876

LITERATURE
Mauritshuis 1980, pp. 6–7

9 

 541

400 

 391

26 

With copper plate closed.

 26

With copper plate opened.

Jacob Adriaensz Bellevois

Rotterdam *c.*1621–1676 Rotterdam

535 *View of a river with ships, c.*1663

Canvas, 106 x 122.5 cm
Signed lower right, on the lee board of the small boat: *Jbellevois*
Dutch title: *Riviergezicht met schepen*

PROVENANCE
Transferred from the Courthouse, The Hague, 1886

LITERATURE
Mauritshuis 1980, pp. 7–8; Basel 1987, p. 68, in no. 7, fig. 7a

COMMENT
To be compared with a painting by Bellevois in the Sammlung der regierenden Fürsten von Liechtenstein, Vaduz, inv. no. 459 (see Basel 1987, no. 7).

Nicolaes Pietersz Berchem

Haarlem 1620–1683 Amsterdam

11 *The infancy of Zeus*, 1648

Canvas, 202 x 262 cm
Signed and dated lower right: *CBerrighem. 1648.* (CB in ligature)
Dutch title: *De opvoeding van Zeus*

PROVENANCE
Gaillard de Gagny Collection, Paris, 1762; Abraham Gevers, Rotterdam, 1827; purchased, 1827

LITERATURE
HdG 1907–1928, vol. 9, p. 62, no. 42; Mauritshuis 1987, no. 6; Mauritshuis 1993, no. 2; Slive 1995, p. 240; Van der Mark 2003, pp. 151–153

COMMENT
Cleaned and restored in 1985.

12 *Wild boar hunt*, 1659

Canvas, 50.3 x 77.8 cm
Signed and dated lower left: *Berchem 1659*
Dutch title: *Wilde zwijnenjacht*

PROVENANCE
Sale Michiel van Hoeken and Theodoor Hartsoeker, The Hague, 1 May 1742, lot 11; Willem Lormier, The Hague, 1742–1754; Govert van Slingelandt, The Hague, 1754; the entire collection sold to Willem V in 1768; Prince Willem V, The Hague, 1768–1795

LITERATURE
HdG 1907–1928, vol. 9, pp. 89–90, no. 138; Schaar 1958, p. 59; D/LS 1974–1976, vol. 3, p. 204, no. 6; Mauritshuis 1980, p. 9; Washington etc. 1982–1984, no. 2; Nagasaki 1992–1993, no. 2; Korthals Altes 2000–2001, pp. 284, 306, no. 38

COMMENT
The companion piece, *The stag hunt*, is in the Musée du Louvre, Paris, inv. no. 2317. A preliminary study, in reverse, in the British Museum, London.

13 *Shepherds beside Roman ruins*, 1661

Canvas, 63.5 x 76.5 cm
Signed and dated lower right: *Berchem 1661*
Dutch title: *Herders bij Romeinse ruïnes*

PROVENANCE
Pieter Leendert de Neufville, Amsterdam, 1765; Prince Willem V, The Hague, 1765–1795

LITERATURE
HdG 1907–1928, vol. 9, p. 157, no. 370; D/LS 1974–1976, vol. 3, p. 204, no. 4; Salerno 1977–1980, vol. 2, p. 718, fig. 33.2; Mauritshuis 1980, pp. 9–10

14 *Travellers attacked by brigands, c.*1670

Canvas, 95.3 x 105 cm
Signed lower right: *Berchem*
Dutch title: *Aanval op een konvooi*

PROVENANCE
Gerard Bicker van Swieten, The Hague, 1741; Hermina Jacoba, Baroness van Leyden, Warmond; purchased, 1816

LITERATURE
HdG 1907–1928, vol. 9, pp. 84–85, no. 122; Mauritshuis 1980, pp. 10–11; Paris 1986, no. 7; Cologne-Utrecht 1991–1992, no. 2.1

COMMENT
Probably based on an engraving by Cornelis Visscher after Pieter van Laer's *'Pistol shot'* (Hollstein, no. 18). A copy with a different background in the Bruckenthal Museum, Sibiu, inv. no. 67. Since this copy has a companion piece, it has been suggested that the Mauritshuis painting also had one.

1091 *Allegory of summer, c.*1680

Canvas, 94 x 88 cm
Signed lower left: *Berchem f.*
Dutch title: *Allegorie op de zomer*

PROVENANCE
Herman van Swoll, Amsterdam, *c.*1680–1698; A.G. Luzern Gallery, Lucerne, 1934; D. Katz Gallery, Dieren; sale The Hague, Van Marle and Bignell, 3 May 1944, lot 10;

535 1091

11 13

12 14

Stichting Nederlands Kunstbezit; on loan from the Netherlands Institute for Cultural Heritage (inv. no. NK 2732), Amsterdam and Rijswijk, since 1992

LITERATURE

HdG 1907–1928, vol. 9, p. 69, no. 68; Montreal 1990, no. 13b; Buijsen/Van der Ploeg 1993, pp. 18–19, no. 1; Den Bosch-Louvain 2002–2003, no. 128

COMMENT

From a series representing the four seasons, the remaining three works presently in private collections. Originally intended as overdoors for a stately residence on the Herengracht, Amsterdam, owned by the wealthy burger Herman van Swoll (1632–1698; see Montreal 1990). Cleaned and restored in 2002.

Nicolaes Berchem with Jan Baptist Weenix

1058 *The calling of St Matthew, c.1657*

Panel, 98.2 x 120.8 cm
Signed on the open book: *Berchem gemaeck[t]/ Weenix [ge]daen*
Dutch title: *De roeping van Mattheus*

PROVENANCE

Lambert van Hairen, Dordrecht, 1718; Van Lill Collection, Dordrecht, 1743; Willem Lormier, The Hague, 1743; Hendrik Muilman, Amsterdam, 1810–1813; Monsieur le Chevalier Francottay; his sale, Paris, 20 February 1816, lot 28, withdrawn (previously unpublished reference); Gérard Tournier, Paris; his sale, Paris, 8 December 1977, lot 18; Robert Noortman Gallery, Maastricht; purchased with the support of the Rembrandt Society, 1979

LITERATURE

HdG 1907–1928, vol. 9, p. 58, no. 24; Duparc 1980; Washington-Detroit-Amsterdam 1980–1981, p. 198; Schloss 1982, p. 12; Mauritshuis 1987, no. 7; Mauritshuis 1993, no. 3; Slive 1995, p. 241

COMMENT

Weenix painted most of the scene, after which Berchem finished it by depicting the group of figures around Christ (see Mauritshuis 1993, no. 3).

Gerrit Adriaensz Berckheyde

Haarlem 1638–1698 Haarlem

690 *A hunting party near the Hofvijver in The Hague, seen from the Buitenhof, c.1685–1690*

Canvas, 53.7 x 63.3 cm
Signed lower left: *Gerrit Berck heyde. Hughtenburgh*
Dutch title: *Een jachtstoet bij de Hofvijver in Den Haag, gezien vanaf het Buitenhof*

PROVENANCE

Johan van der Marck, Leiden, 1773; Jacob Frederiksz van Beek, Amsterdam, until 1828; bequest of Timon Hendrik Blom Coster, The Hague, 1904

LITERATURE

Leeuwarden-Den Bosch-Assen 1979–1980, no. 35; Mauritshuis 1987, pp. 55–56; Dumas 1991, pp. 128–129, 686–687, no. 2

COMMENT

With figures by Jan van Huchtenburgh.

796 *A hunting party near the Hofvijver in The Hague, seen from the Plaats, c.1690*

Canvas, 58 x 68.5 cm
Signed lower right: *gerret: Berck Heijde.*
Dutch title: *Een jachtstoet bij de Hofvijver in Den Haag, gezien vanaf de Plaats*

PROVENANCE

John Hope and heirs, Amsterdam, London and Deepdeene, 1783–1917; *Jonkheer* W.A. van den Bosch, Doorn and Vught, 1925–1956 (on loan to the Mauritshuis since 1928); bequest of W.A. van den Bosch, 1956

LITERATURE

Mauritshuis 1970, no. 48; Paris 1986, no. 8; Mauritshuis 1987, no. 8

Job Adriaensz Berckheyde

Haarlem 1630–1693 Haarlem

746 *View of a Dutch canal, possibly the Oude Gracht in Haarlem, 1666*

Panel, 43.5 x 39.3 cm
Signed and dated at left, on the stairs: *J Berckheyd: 1666* (probably not autograph)
Dutch title: *Gezicht op een Hollandse gracht, mogelijk de Oude Gracht in Haarlem*

PROVENANCE

Jonkheer Johan Steengracht van Oostkapelle and heirs, The Hague, *c.*1824–1913; purchased with the support of the Rembrandt Society, 1913

LITERATURE

Washington etc. 1982–1984, no. 4; Paris 1986, no. 9; Mauritshuis 1987, no. 9

1058

796

746

690

B

Simon van den Berg

Overschie 1812–1891 Arnhem

1104 *Landscape with sandy road*

Canvas, 71.2 x 116.4 cm
Signed lower right: *S. van den Berg*
Dutch title: *Landschap met zandweg*

PROVENANCE
Bequest of E.C. Netten, The Hague, 1997

COMMENT
The painter was Deputy Director of the Mauritshuis from 1875 to 1880 and Director from 1880 until 1889 (see p. 46). Cleaned and restored in 1995.

Christoffel van den Berghe

Middelburg *c.*1590?–after 1628 Middelburg

671 *Winter landscape, c.1615–1620*

Copper, 11.5 x 16.5 cm
Signed lower left, on a barrel: *CVB* (in ligature)
Dutch title: *Winterlandschap*

PROVENANCE
De Witte van Citters Collection, Middelburg; bequest of Arnoldus Andries des Tombe, The Hague, 1903

LITERATURE
Bol 1956, pp. 189–192; Bol 1969, pp. 106–107; Mauritshuis 1980, pp. 12–13; Bol 1982, p. 9, fig. 7; The Hague 2001–2002, no. 11; Den Bosch-Louvain 2002–2003, no. 74

COMMENT
Companion piece to inv. no. 672.

672 *Summer landscape, c.1615–1620*

Copper, 11.5 x 16.5 cm
Signed lower right: *CVB* (in ligature)
Dutch title: *Zomerlandschap*

PROVENANCE
De Witte van Citters Collection, Middelburg; bequest of Arnoldus Andries des Tombe, The Hague, 1903

LITERATURE
Bol 1956, pp. 189–192; Bol 1969, pp. 106–107; Mauritshuis 1980, pp. 12–13; Bol 1982, p. 9, fig. 8; The Hague 2001–2002, p. 94, fig. 1; Den Bosch-Louvain 2002–2003, no. 73

COMMENT
Companion piece to inv. no. 671.

Joachim Beuckelaer

Antwerp *c.*1533–*c.*1574 Antwerp

965 *Kitchen scene with Christ at Emmaus, c.1560–1565*

Panel, 109.5 x 169 cm
Bears inscription lower right: *706*
Dutch title: *Keukenscène met Christus en de Emmaüsgangers*

PROVENANCE
On loan from the P. & N. de Boer Foundation, Amsterdam, since 1960

LITERATURE
Mauritshuis 1968, p. 8; Moxey 1977, p. 100, fig. 58; Amsterdam-Cleveland 1999–2000, no. 2; Vienna-Essen 2002, no. 53

Abraham van Beyeren

The Hague 1620/21–1690 Overschie

401 *Still life with seafood*

Canvas, 75.8 x 68 cm
Signed lower centre, on the edge of the table: *AVB f.* (AVB in ligature)
Dutch title: *Stilleven met zeebanket*

PROVENANCE
Neville Goldsmid, The Hague; purchased, 1876

LITERATURE
Bernt 1969–1970, vol. 1, no. 105

COMMENT
Cleaned and restored in 1999.

548 *Flower still life with a watch, c.1663–1665*

Canvas, 80 x 69 cm
Signed lower centre, on the edge of the table: *AVB f* (AVB in ligature)
Dutch title: *Bloemstilleven met een horloge*

PROVENANCE
Purchased, 1889

LITERATURE
Mauritshuis 1987, p. 16 and fig. 1; The Hague 1992a, no. 5; Taylor 1995, p. 51 and fig. 23

965 

671 

 672

401

548

1104

B

665 *Sumptuous still life, c.*1655

Panel, 98 x 76 cm
Signed lower left, on the edge of the table:
AVB (in ligature)
Dutch title: *Pronkstilleven*

PROVENANCE
Van Leeuwen Collection, Alkmaar; Abraham Bredius, The Hague, 1902–1946 (on loan to the Mauritshuis since 1902); bequest of Abraham Bredius, 1946

LITERATURE
The Hague 1991–1992, no. 1

678 *Fish still life*

Canvas, 68 x 59 cm
Dutch title: *Visstilleven*

PROVENANCE
Bequest of Arnoldus Andries des Tombe, The Hague, 1903

697 *Still life with game and fowl*

Canvas, 79.5 x 68 cm
Dutch title: *Stilleven met wild en gevogelte*

PROVENANCE
Gift of L. Nardus, Arnouville, 1905

LITERATURE
Mauritshuis 1935, p. 22

1056 *Banquet still life,* after 1655

Canvas, 99.5 x 120.5 cm
Signed at right, on the edge of the table:
AVB f (AVB in ligature)
Dutch title: *Pronkstilleven*

PROVENANCE
Private collection, France; Newhouse Gallery, New York; S. Nijstad Gallery, The Hague; purchased with the support of the Rembrandt Society, 1977

LITERATURE
Paris 1986, no. 10; Mauritshuis 1987, no. 10

COMMENT
The artist has depicted himself in the reflection on the silver jug (Mauritshuis 1987, p. 65, fig. 1).

Abraham Bloemaert

Gorinchem 1566–1651 Utrecht

16 *Theagenes receiving the palm of honour from Chariclea*, 1626

Canvas, 157.2 x 157.7 cm
Signed and dated lower left: *A Bloemaert. fe: / 1626*
Bears inscription lower left: *N 43*
Dutch title: *Theagenes ontvangt de erepalm van Chariclea*

PROVENANCE
Stadholder Frederik Hendrik, Honselaarsdijk Palace, Naaldwijk, 1626; thence by descent to Stadholder Willem II; King-Stadholder Willem III; Stadholder Johan Willem Friso, Het Loo Palace, Apeldoorn; Nationale Konst-Gallery, The Hague, 1800; transferred, 1822

LITERATURE
D/LS 1974–1976, vol. 1, p. 649, no. 25, vol. 2, p. 603, no. 24; Paris 1986, no. 11; Mauritshuis 1993, no. 5; Roethlisberger/Bok 1993, vol. 1, no. 425, vol. 2, fig. 595; The Hague 1997–1998a, no. 2

COMMENT
Painted as a commission for Stadholder Frederik Hendrik to commemorate his marriage to Amalia of Solms-Braunfels in 1625. With two other paintings from the set most likely intended for Honselaarsdijk Palace, Naaldwijk. For preliminary drawings, see Mauritshuis 1993, no. 5.

17 *The feast of the gods at the wedding of Peleus and Thetis*, 1638

Canvas, 193.7 x 164.5 cm
Signed and dated lower left: *A. Bloemaert. fe. / 1638*
Dutch title: *Het godenmaal bij de bruiloft van Peleus en Thetis*

PROVENANCE
Johan Balthasar Krauth *et al.* sale, The Hague, 7–8 October 1771, lot 23; Prince Willem V, The Hague, 1771–1795

LITERATURE
D/LS 1974–1976, vol. 3, p. 205, no. 11; Mauritshuis 1987, no. 11; Roethlisberger/Bok 1993, vol. 1, no. 548, vol. 2, fig. 734; Slive 1995, p. 14

1046 *A feast of the gods, possibly the feast at the wedding of Peleus and Thetis*, 1598

Canvas, 31.1 x 41.8 cm
Signed and dated lower right: *A.Blom̄aert.1598*
Dutch title: *Godenmaaltijd, mogelijk de maaltijd bij de bruiloft van Peleus en Thetis*

16

17

1046

1056

665

678

697

PROVENANCE
S. Nijstad Gallery, The Hague, 1963; H. Becker, Dortmund, 1963–1973; H. Cramer Gallery, The Hague; purchased, 1973

LITERATURE
Sluijter 1986, pp. 17–19, 351–352, 412, 488; Roethlisberger/Bok 1993, vol. 1, no. 24, vol. 2, fig. 53 (as dated '159.'); Mauritshuis 1993, no. 4; San Francisco-Baltimore-London 1997–1998, no. 46

COMMENT
Executed in red and white oil paint (rosaille).

Guillaume du Bois

Haarlem *c.*1610–1680 Haarlem

554 *Hilly landscape beside a stream,* 1652 or 1657

Panel, 61 x 84 cm
Signed and dated lower left, on the boat: *GD Bois. 165[.]*
Dutch title: *Heuvelachtig landschap met water*

PROVENANCE
Charles Sedelmeyer Gallery, Paris; purchased, 1890

LITERATURE
Bol 1969, pp. 202–203, fig. 196; Mauritshuis 1980, pp. 13–14

799 *Dune landscape with road and church,* 1649

Panel, 45.7 x 63.5 cm
Signed and dated lower right: *GD Bois 1649*
Dutch title: *Duinlandschap met weg en kerk*

PROVENANCE
Gift of L. van den Bergh, Berlin, 1929

LITERATURE
Bol 1969, p. 202; Mauritshuis 1980, p. 13

Ferdinand Bol

Dordrecht 1616–1680 Amsterdam

With Willem van de Velde the Younger

19 *Portrait of Engel de Ruyter (1649–1683),* 1669

Canvas, 131 x 112 cm
Signed and dated at right, on the balustrade: *fBol. 1669.* (fB in ligature)
Dutch title: *Portret van Engel de Ruyter (1649–1683)*

PROVENANCE
Probably identical with the portrait inventoried in the house of the sitter, Amsterdam, 1683; purchased, presumably in 1817 (first mentioned in 1822)

LITERATURE
Blankert 1982, pp. 64, 128, no. 88; Amsterdam 1984, p. 220; Broos 1995b, pp. 12–13; Prud'homme van Reine 1996, p. 209

COMMENT
The sea and ships in the background were painted by Willem van de Velde the Younger. Inv. no. 19 still has its original, richly decorated frame. A preparatory drawing in the Staatliche Graphische Sammlung, Munich. Engel de Ruyter, the son of Michiel de Ruyter (see inv. no. 585), was appointed Vice-Admiral on 19 October 1678.

With Willem van de Velde the Younger

585 *Portrait of Michiel de Ruyter (1607–1676),* 1667

Canvas, 157 x 135 cm
Signed and dated at right, on the balustrade: *fBol . fecit. A°. 1667* (fB in ligature)
Dutch title: *Portret van Michiel de Ruyter (1607–1676)*

PROVENANCE
Admiralty Chamber, Amsterdam, 1667–1798; 's Lands Zeemagazijn, Amsterdam, 1798–after 1818; Ministry of the Navy, The Hague, after 1818–1894 (until 1889 in the 'marinemodellenkamer', 1889–1894 on loan to the Rijksmuseum, Amsterdam); acquired in exchange with the Rijksmuseum for another portrait of the same sitter attributed to Bol (Mauritshuis inv. no. 18), 1894

LITERATURE
Blankert 1982, pp. 33, 62–64, 124, no. 77; Amsterdam 1984, no. 54; Broos 1995b; Prud'homme van Reine 1996, pp. 188, 197, 216; *Portraits in the Mauritshuis*, no. 5

COMMENT
The sea and ships in the background were painted by Willem van de Velde the Younger. Inv. no. 585 still has its original, richly decorated trophy frame (see Amsterdam 1984, no. 54), with, at the top, the coat of arms of De Ruyter. Cleaned and restored in 1990. Several preparatory drawings are known, for example in the Staatliche Graphische Sammlung, Munich, as are other versions and replicas (see Blankert 1982). Michiel Adriaensz de Ruyter was Commander-in-Chief of the Dutch fleet and won numerous battles against the English. His best-known feat was his victory in the Four Days' Battle (11–14 June 1666) in the Channel.

554 

 799

585 

 19

795 *Portrait of a young man, presumably Louis Trip, Junior (1638–1655)*, 1652

Canvas, 125.7 x 96.2 cm
Signed and dated at left, on the balustrade: *fBol. 1652* (fB in ligature)
Dutch title: *Portret van een jonge man, vermoedelijk Louis Trip junior (1638–1655)*

PROVENANCE
Peter Laurenz Lancelle, Cleves, *c.*1850–1893; purchased with the support of the Rembrandt Society and private individuals, 1927

LITERATURE
Blankert 1982, pp. 33, 34, 62, 135, no. 113; Sumowski 1983–1995, vol. 1, p. 312, no. 168; Paris 1986, no. 12; *Portraits in the Mauritshuis*, no. 4

COMMENT
Louis Trip, Junior was a member of the wealthy Trip family of Amsterdam and made his fortune as a trader.

Ferdinand Bol (manner of)

530 *Portrait of Maerten van Juchen (d. 1672/73), c.*1670

Canvas (oval), 74 x 60.5 cm
Dutch title: *Portret van Maerten van Juchen (overleden 1672/73)*

PROVENANCE
Joseph Monchen Gallery, The Hague; purchased, 1885

LITERATURE
Moes 1897–1905, vol. 1, p. 495, no. 4096–1; Blankert 1982, p. 182, no. R 185 (suggests an attribution to Hendrick Berckman)

COMMENT
Formerly attributed to Bol. Van Juchen was Commander of Wezel.

Hans Bol

Malines 1534–1593 Amsterdam

1043 *Imaginary landscape with John the Evangelist on Patmos*, 1564

Watercolour on canvas, 50.5 x 85.5 cm
Signed and dated lower left, on the rock beneath John: *Hans Bol / 1564*
Dutch title: *Fantasielandschap met Johannes de Evangelist op Patmos*

PROVENANCE
S. Nijstad Gallery, The Hague; purchased with the support of the Rembrandt Society and the Prince Bernhard Culture Fund, 1972

LITERATURE
Bosshard/Van Brüggen 1974, pp. 16–20; Mauritshuis 1991, no. 1; Miedema 1994–1999, vol. 4, p. 210 and fig. 152

Gerard ter Borch

Zwolle 1617–1681 Deventer

176 *The messenger, known as 'The unwelcome news'*, 1653

Panel, 66.7 x 59.5 cm
Signed and dated at left: *GTB 1653* (GTB in ligature)
Dutch title: *De boodschapper, bekend als 'De onwelkome boodschap'*

PROVENANCE
Petronella de la Court, Amsterdam, 1707; Govert van Slingelandt, The Hague, 1752; the entire collection sold to Willem V in 1768; Prince Willem V, The Hague, 1768–1795

LITERATURE
HdG 1907–1928, vol. 5, pp. 15–16, no. 28; Gudlaugsson 1959–1960, vol. 1, pp. 91–92, vol. 2, p. 109, no. 99; The Hague-Münster 1974, no. 27; D/LS 1974–1976, vol. 3, p. 205, no. 12; Mauritshuis 1987, pp. 379–380; Osaka 2000, no. 20; Dublin-Greenwich 2003–2004, p. 18; Washington-Detroit 2004–2005, no. 23

COMMENT
Cleaned and restored in 1998; see *Mauritshuis in focus* 11 (1998), no. 2, p. 7, fig. 2.

177 *Self-portrait, c.*1668

Canvas, 62.7 x 43.7 cm
Dutch title: *Zelfportret*

PROVENANCE
Herman Aarentz, Amsterdam, 1770; Johan van der Marck and heirs, Amsterdam, 1770–1773; sale P.F. Tiberghien, Brussels, 22 May 1827, lot 308; purchased, 1827

LITERATURE
HdG 1907–1928, vol. 5, p. 75, no. 204; Gudlaugsson 1959–1960, vol. 1, pp. 144–146, 363, vol. 2, pp. 210–211, no. 232; The Hague-Münster 1974, no. 54; Zwolle 1997, no. 5; Washington-Detroit 2004–2005, no. 45; *Portraits in the Mauritshuis*, no. 6

COMMENT
Originally accompanied by a portrait of the painter's wife, Geertruid Matthys (1612–before 1672).

795

530

1043

176

177

B

744 *A mother combing the hair of her child, known as 'Hunting for lice', c.1652–1653*

Panel, 33.5 x 29 cm
Signed on the back of the chair: *GTB* (in ligature; barely legible)
Dutch title: *Een moeder die het haar van haar kind kamt, bekend als 'De luizenjacht'*

PROVENANCE
J. van Bergen van der Grijp, Zoeterwoude, 1784; H. Rottermond, Amsterdam, 1786; Baroness De Pagniet, Utrecht, 1836; *Jonkheer* Johan Steengracht van Oostkapelle and heirs, The Hague, before 1836–1913; purchased with the support of the Rembrandt Society, 1913

LITERATURE
HdG 1907–1928, vol. 5, pp. 22–23, no. 46; Gudlaugsson 1959–1960, vol. 1, p. 88, vol. 2, pp. 106–107, no. 95; The Hague-Münster 1974, no. 24; Amsterdam 1976, p. 41, fig. 3a; Paris 1986, no. 13; Mauritshuis 1987, no. 12; Washington-Detroit 2004–2005, no. 19

COMMENT
Companion piece depicting a spinning woman in Rotterdam, Museum Boijmans Van Beuningen, Van der Vorm Collection (Mauritshuis 1987, p. 76, fig. 1).

797 *Woman writing a letter, c.1655*

Panel, 39 x 29.5 cm
Signed on the edge of the table: *GTB* (in ligature)
Dutch title: *De briefschrijfster*

PROVENANCE
Etienne François, Duc de Choiseul, Paris, 1772; Six Collection, Amsterdam; gift of Sir Henri W.A. Deterding, London, 1928

LITERATURE
HdG 1907–1928, vol. 5, pp. 61–62, no. 167; Gudlaugsson 1959–1960, vol. 1, pp. 101–103, vol. 2, pp. 126–127, no. 114; The Hague-Münster 1974, no. 34; Amsterdam 1976, no. 2; The Hague-San Francisco 1990–1991, p. 461; Frankfurt am Main 1993–1994, no. 8; Madrid 2003, no. 3; Dublin-Greenwich 2003–2004, no. 5

COMMENT
Cleaned and restored in 2001.

883 *Portrait of Cornelis de Graeff (1650–1678), 1673*

Canvas, 38.9 x 28.9 cm
Signed below the knob of the cane: *GTB* (in ligature)
Bears inscription upper right: *Cornelis de Graeff. / Out XXIIII Jaer. / M.DC.LXXIIII* (date incorrect) Dutch title: *Portret van Cornelis de Graeff (1650–1678)*

PROVENANCE
Probably by inheritance to dowager Van Lennep-Deutz van Assendelft, The Hague, 1903; dowager A.M.B. van Zuylen van Nijevelt and heirs, Wassenaar, until 1942 (on loan to the Mauritshuis, 1933–1942); E. Plietzsch, The Hague and Berlin, 1942; Staatliche Kunsthalle, Karlsruhe, 1942–1945; Stichting Nederlands Kunstbezit; on loan to the Mauritshuis, 1948–1960; transferred, 1960

LITERATURE
HdG 1907–1928, vol. 5, p. 81, no. 229; Gudlaugsson 1959–1960, vol. 1, p. 157, vol. 2, p. 226, no. 262; The Hague-Münster 1974, no. 57; Amsterdam 2002–2003a, no. 34; *Portraits in the Mauritshuis*, no. 7

COMMENT
Cornelis de Graeff was a scion of one of Amsterdam's most prominent and powerful families. He took a doctorate in law at Leiden and in 1675 married Agneta Deutz. The couple remained childless. In 1677 De Graeff was ennobled by the German emperor Leopold.

1050 *Portrait of Caspar van Kinschot (1622–1649), c.1646–1647*

Copper (oval), 11 x 8 cm
Dutch title: *Portret van Caspar van Kinschot (1622–1649)*

PROVENANCE
Van Kinschot Collection, Leiden; on loan from a private collector since 1975

LITERATURE
HdG 1907–1928, vol. 5, p. 83, no. 240; Gudlaugsson 1959–1960, vol. 1, p. 59, vol. 2, p. 79, no. 51; The Hague-Münster 1974, no. 12; The Hague 1998, no. 11; Münster 1998–1999, no. 618; Washington-Detroit 2004–2005, no. 11

COMMENT
Caspar van Kinschot was a member of the delegation of the province of Holland during the peace negotiations at Münster from 1645 to 1648 (see The Hague 1998).

1133 *Woman sewing near a cradle, c.1655–1656*

Canvas, 46.5 x 38 cm
Dutch title: *Handwerkende vrouw bij een wieg*

PROVENANCE
Bequest of Mr J. Nienhuys, 2004

LITERATURE
HdG 1907–1928, vol. 5, p. 30, no. 72; Gudlaugsson 1959–1960, vol. 1, pp. 108–110, vol. 2, pp. 129–130, no. 115 (with earlier provenance); The Hague-Münster 1974, no. 35; The Hague 1995–1996, no. 6

COMMENT
Cleaned and restored in 2004.

744

1133

883

1050

797

B

Paris Bordone
Treviso 1500–1571 Venice

310 *Christ blessing, c.*1540

Canvas, 73.8 x 64.5 cm
Signed at right, on the wall: *PARIS [.]O*
Dutch title: *Zegenende Christus*

PROVENANCE
Martial Reghellini Schio, Venice and Brussels, until 1826; purchased by King Willem I for the Mauritshuis, 1831

LITERATURE
Canova 1964, p. 79, pl. 65; Boschloo/Van der Sman 1993, pp. 36–37, no. 17

Ambrosius Bosschaert the Elder
Antwerp 1573–1621 The Hague

679 *Vase with flowers in a window, c.*1618

Panel, 64 x 46 cm
Signed lower left: *.AB.* (in ligature)
Dutch title: *Vaas met bloemen in een venster*

PROVENANCE
De Witte van Citters Collection, Middelburg; bequest of Arnoldus Andries des Tombe, The Hague, 1903

LITERATURE
Bol 1960, p. 65, no. 37, fig. 24; Mauritshuis 1987, no. 13; The Hague 1992a, no. 8; Slive 1995, p. 279

COMMENT
The flowers were identified by Sam Segal (see Mauritshuis 1987, p. 82, fig. 4).

Jan Both
Utrecht *c.*1618–1652 Utrecht

20 *Italian landscape, c.*1645

Canvas, 108.2 x 125.8 cm
Signed lower centre: *JBoth* (JB in ligature)
Dutch title: *Italiaans landschap*

PROVENANCE
Hermina Jacoba, Baroness van Leyden, Warmond; purchased, 1816

LITERATURE
HdG 1907–1928, vol. 9, p. 438, no. 56; Burke 1976, pp. 203–204, no. 37; Mauritshuis 1980, pp. 15–16; Washington etc. 1982–1984, no. 10

21 *Italian landscape, c.*1645

Copper on panel, 51 x 70 cm
Signed lower centre: *J. Both*
Dutch title: *Italiaans landschap*

PROVENANCE
Gerrit van der Pot van Groeneveld, Rotterdam, 1785; Hendrik Muilman, Amsterdam; Lapeyrière Collection, Paris, 1817; purchased, 1817

LITERATURE
HdG 1907–1928, vol. 9, p. 470, no. 166; Burke 1976, pp. 204–205, no. 38; Mauritshuis 1980, pp. 16–17

COMMENT
The bridge and tomb have been tentatively identified as the Ponte Lucano with the Sepolcro dei Plautii (tomb of the Plautii), between Rome and Tivoli. Cleaned and restored in 1999.

Dirk Bouts (circle of)
Haarlem *c.*1410–1475 Louvain

762 *The resurrection of Christ, c.*1480

Panel, 28.5 x 23.5 cm
Dutch title: *De opstanding van Christus*

PROVENANCE
Jacques Goudstikker Gallery, Amsterdam; purchased, 1920

LITERATURE
Friedländer 1967–1976, vol. 3, p. 66, no. 56, fig. 69; Mauritshuis 1968, pp. 9–10; Louvain 1975, no. B/35; Louvain 1998, no. 83 (as possibly by Aelbert Bouts)

Richard Brakenburgh
Haarlem 1650–1702 Haarlem

544 *Portrait of a young girl,* 1683

Canvas, 88.5 x 70.5 cm
Signed and dated at right: *R. Brakenburg / 1683.*
Dutch title: *Portret van een jong meisje*

PROVENANCE
M.J. Hollender sale, Brussels, Galerie Saint-Luc, 10–12 April 1888, lot 10; purchased, 1888; on loan to the ICN

LITERATURE
Allgemeines Künstler-Lexikon, vol. 13 (1996), p. 566

Jan de Bray
Haarlem *c.*1627–1697 Haarlem

808 *Portrait of a boy aged six,* 1654

679

808

20

21

544

310

762

Panel, 59.5 x 47 cm
Signed and dated centre right: *1654 / Oud* [traces of a 't'] *6 ja / JDBray* (JDB in ligature)
Dutch title: *Portret van een 6-jarige jongen*

PROVENANCE
F. Rothmann Gallery, Berlin; Anton F. Philips, Eindhoven; purchased, 1932

LITERATURE
Von Moltke 1938–1939, pp. 423–425, 483, no. 168; Haarlem-Antwerp 2000–2001, no. 63; *Portraits in the Mauritshuis*, no. 8

COMMENT
Cleaned and restored in 1986.

1110 *The adoration of the shepherds*, 1665

Panel, 63 x 48 cm
Signed and dated on a foot of the crib: *JDBraij / 1665* (JDB in ligature)
Dutch title: *De aanbidding der herders*

PROVENANCE
G. Winkler, Leipzig, 1768; Julius Alexander Baumgärtner, Leipzig, 1845–1856; The Albright Leasing Corporation, 1973; sale London, Christie's, 30 November 1973, lot 54; Agnew's, London, 1973–1974; Richard Green Gallery, London, 1976; Otto Naumann Ltd, New York; purchased by the Friends of the Mauritshuis Foundation with substantial support of Mr H.B. van der Ven, 1997

LITERATURE
Von Moltke 1938–1939, p. 466, no. 12; Van Suchtelen 1997a

COMMENT
A drawing by the artist after the painting, also signed and dated 1665, is in a private collection, Boston (Van Suchtelen 1997a, fig. 6).

Salomon de Bray

Amsterdam 1597–1664 Haarlem

437 *Putti bearing a cartouche with Stadholder Frederik Hendrik's date of birth*, 1651

Canvas, 103.5 x 255 cm
Signed and dated at right: *SD Bray. / 1651.* (SD in ligature)
Inscribed: *FR.HENR.NASSAVIVS / AVRIACVS / NASC.DELF.IV.CAL.FEB. / CICICXXCIV.* (Frederik Hendrik of Nassau [...], born in Delft on 4 February 1584)
Dutch title: *Putti dragen een cartouche met de geboortedatum van stadhouder Frederik Hendrik*

PROVENANCE
Made for the Oranjezaal, Huis ten Bosch Palace, The Hague, 1651; removed around 1805, when the fireplace was replaced by doors to the Japanese Room; transferred at an unknown date and found in the attic in 1875; on loan to Huis ten Bosch Palace, The Hague

LITERATURE
Von Moltke 1938–1939, p. 384, no. 64; Van Gelder 1948–1949, pp. 121, 149, no. 4; Peter-Raupp 1980, pp. 37–38, fig. 9; Buvelot 1995b, p. 139 and fig. 110; Rotterdam-Frankfurt am Main 1999–2000, p. 88 and fig. 7b

COMMENT
The painting was ordered by Amalia of Solms-Braunfels (1602–1675) for the decoration of the chimneypiece in the Oranjezaal, Huis ten Bosch Palace, The Hague (see Buvelot 1995b, pp. 139–140), commemorating and celebrating the life and deeds of her deceased husband, Stadholder Frederik Hendrik.

Bartholomeus Breenbergh

Deventer 1598–1657 Amsterdam

1098 *Landscape with nymphs (and Diana?)*, 1647

Panel, 37.8 x 50 cm
Signed and dated lower left: *BBreenbergh. f. / 1647* (BB in ligature)
Dutch title: *Landschap met nimfen (en Diana?)*

PROVENANCE
Jan Frans Beschey, Antwerp, 1786; Richard L. Feigen & Co., New York, 1989–1993; purchased with the support of the Rembrandt Society, 1993

LITERATURE
New York 1991, no. 24; Broos 1993a; Broos 1993b; Mauritshuis 1993, no. 6

COMMENT
An old copy was sold in Amsterdam, Sotheby's, 24 November 1986, lot 87, repr.

Bartholomeus Breenbergh (follower of)

932 *Italian landscape with the Aurelian wall*, c. 1650–1660?

Canvas, 52 x 79 cm
Dutch title: *Italiaans landschap met de Aureliaanse muur*

PROVENANCE
Pieter de la Court van der Voort, Leiden, 1772; George Francis Wyndham and heirs, Somerset, 1845–1953; Alfred Brod Gallery, London, 1958; purchased, 1958

437

1110

1098

932

LITERATURE
Utrecht 1965, no. 30 (Dutch school, 1630s); Mauritshuis 1970, no. 41; Mauritshuis 1980, pp. 131–132; Roethlisberger 1981, p. 101, no. 306 (as by a follower of Abraham Begeyn and Willem Romeyn)

COMMENT
Cleaned and restored in 1986.

Quiringh van Brekelenkam

Zwammerdam after 1622?–in or after 1669 Leiden

562 *An old woman cupping a young woman, known as 'Woman cupping', c.1660*

Panel, 48 x 37 cm
Signed on the foot-warmer: *QVB* (in ligature)
Dutch title: *Een oude vrouw die een aderlating uitvoert bij een jonge vrouw, bekend als 'De kopster'*

PROVENANCE
P.F. Clingnet, Leiden, 1776; Hendrik Twent, Leiden, 1789; Menno, Baron Van Coehoorn, Amsterdam, 1801; Pieter de Smeth van Alphen, Amsterdam, 1810; Abraham Bredius, Sr, Oud-Bussem, 1810–1863; Abraham Bredius, Jr, Amsterdam and The Hague, before 1889–1946 (on loan to the Mauritshuis since 1892); bequest of Abraham Bredius, 1946

LITERATURE
De Jongh 1967, pp. 34–38, fig. 22; Leiden 1988, no. 5; The Hague 1991–1992, no. 2; Lasius 1992, pp. 139–140, no. 206, fig. x

COMMENT
Copied in 1776 in a drawing by Abraham Delfos (The Hague 1991–1992, p. 54, fig. 2).

Adriaen Brouwer

Oudenaarde 1605/6–1638 Antwerp

607 *A fat man, c.1634–1637*

Panel, 23 x 16 cm
Dutch title: *Een dikke man*

PROVENANCE
Dowdeswell & Dowdeswell Gallery, London; purchased, 1897

LITERATURE
HdG 1907–1928, vol. 3, pp. 690–691, no. 229; Höhne 1960, p. 50; Knuttel 1962, pp. 159, 182–183; New York-Maastricht 1982, no. 11; Cologne-Antwerp-Vienna 1992– 1993, no. 82; Boston-Toledo 1993–1994, no. 66; De Clippel 2003, pp. 204–209, 212

COMMENT
Wrongly believed to be a self-portrait of Brouwer. A copy was sold in 1902 as part of a series of the seven vices (for more on the iconography, see Boston-Toledo 1993–1994, no. 66 and De Clippel 2003).

847 *Inn with drunken peasants, c.1625–1626*

Panel, 19.5 x 26.5 cm
Formerly signed on the barrel: *AB* (in ligature)
Dutch title: *Herberg met dronken boeren*

PROVENANCE
Adriaan Leonard van Heteren, The Hague, until 1800; Adriaan Leonard van Heteren Gevers, The Hague, 1800–1809; the entire collection bought by King Louis Napoleon for the Royal Museum, Amsterdam, 1809; on loan from the Rijksmuseum, Amsterdam (inv. no. SK-A-64), since 1948

LITERATURE
HdG 1907–1928, vol. 3, p. 628, no. 102; Knuttel 1962, pp. 87–89; RM 1976, p. 152; New York-Maastricht 1982, no. 1; Vlieghe 1998, p. 155

919 *Fighting peasants, c.1625–1626*

Panel, 25.5 x 34 cm
Traces of a signature lower right, on a piece of wood: *AB* (in ligature)
Dutch title: *Vechtende boeren*

PROVENANCE
Count Fraula, Brussels, 1738; Willem Lormier, The Hague, 1738–1763; Adriaan Leonard van Heteren, The Hague, until 1800; Adriaan Leonard van Heteren Gevers, The Hague, 1800–1809; the entire collection bought by King Louis Napoleon for the Royal Museum, Amsterdam, 1809; on loan from the Rijksmuseum, Amsterdam (inv. no. SK-A-65), since 1954

LITERATURE
HdG 1907–1928, vol. 3, pp. 657–658, no. 166; Knuttel 1962, pp. 78–80; RM 1976, p. 152; New York-Maastricht 1982, no. 2; Renger 1987, pp. 254–255; Vlieghe 1998, p. 155; Korthals Altes 2000–2001, p. 262; Haarlem-Hamburg 2003–2004, no. 44; Antwerp 2004, p. 201

Jan Brueghel the Elder

Brussels 1568–1625 Antwerp

1072 *Wan-Li vase with flowers, c.1610–1615*

Panel (cut at the bottom), 42 x 34.5 cm
Dutch title: *Wan-Li-vaas met bloemen*

PROVENANCE
Galerie Internationale, The Hague, 1930; C.T.F. Thurkow, The Hague; his widow, Mrs L. Thurkow-van Huffel; bequest of L. Thurkow-van Huffel, 1987

562 

 1072

607 

 847

919 

LITERATURE
Ertz 1979, no. 208; Utrecht 1988, p. 14; Mauritshuis 1991, no. XXVI; The Hague 1992a, p. 72

COMMENT
Cleaned and restored in 1987.

Jan Brueghel the Elder with Hendrik van Balen
Antwerp *c.*1574/75–1632 Antwerp

233 *Garland of fruit around a depiction of Cybele receiving gifts from personifications of the four seasons, c.*1620–1622

Panel, 106.3 x 69.9 cm
On the verso: 'MV' (in ligature), the mark of the Antwerp panel-maker Michiel Vriendt, and the weapon of the city (see Essen-Vienna-Antwerp 1997–1998, p. 298, fig. 1)
Dutch title: *Krans van vruchten rond een voorstelling met Cybele die geschenken ontvangt van personificaties van de vier jaargetijden*

PROVENANCE
Johan Anthony van Kinschot, Delft, until 1767; Prince Willem V, The Hague, 1770–1795

LITERATURE
D/LS 1974–1976, vol. 3, p. 204, no. 7; Ertz 1979, no. 340; Essen-Vienna-Antwerp 1997–1998, no. 90; Amsterdam-Cleveland 1999–2000, no. 4; Tamis 2002, pp. 118, 128, note 53; Den Bosch-Louvain 2002–2003, no. 78

COMMENT
The letter 'A' on the verso of the panel points to a likely date of execution of *c.*1621–1622 (see Wadum 1998, pp. 192, 198). Another version by the same artists in a corporate collection, Brussels (Ertz 1979, no. 341), is probably depicted in the foreground of the 1618 *Allegory of taste* by Jan Brueghel the Elder and Peter Paul Rubens in the Museo Nacional del Prado, Madrid (Ertz 1979, no. 330). A copy, probably after the Brussels painting, attributed to Jan Brueghel the Younger, is also in the Prado. The scene in the oval by Van Balen is repeated in a drawing in Weimar, Goethehaus (Essen-Vienna-Antwerp 1997–1998, p. 298, fig. 3). Cleaned and restored in 1995.

Jan Brueghel the Elder with an anonymous pupil of Rubens

234 *Nymphs filling the horn of plenty, c.*1615

Panel, 67.5 x 107 cm
On the verso an unidentified panel-maker's mark: a large 'R' with a smaller 'B' between the legs (reproduced in *Mauritshuis in focus* 6 [1993], no. 1, p. 15, fig. 10)
Dutch title: *Nimfen vullen de hoorn des overvloeds*

PROVENANCE
Jan van Beuningen, Amsterdam, until 1716; Het Loo Palace, Apeldoorn, 1757; Prince Willem V, The Hague

LITERATURE
D/LS 1974–1976, vol. 2, p. 644, no. 103, vol. 3, p. 214, no. 54; Ertz 1979, p. 390; Ertz 1984, no. 218; Broos/Wadum 1993; Broos 1995c, pp. 22–23; Härting/Borms 2003, p. 42

COMMENT
Cleaned and restored in 1993. The panel came from the same tree as the painting by Abraham Govaerts, inv. no. 45 (see Broos/Wadum 1993).

Jan Brueghel the Elder with Peter Paul Rubens

253 *The garden of Eden with the fall of man, c.*1615

Panel, 74.3 x 114.7 cm
Signed lower left: *PETRI PAVLI RVBENS FIGR*;
lower right: *IBRUEGHEL FEC* (IB in ligature)
Verso: the mark of panel-maker Guilliam Gabron
Dutch title: *Het aardse paradijs met de zondeval van Adam en Eva*

PROVENANCE
Pieter de la Court van der Voort and heirs, Leiden, in or before 1710–1766; Prince Willem V, The Hague, 1766–1795

LITERATURE
D/LS 1974–1976, vol. 3, p. 226, no. 123; Ertz 1979, no. 308; Mauritshuis 1987, no. 54; Mauritshuis 1993, no. 8; London 1996–1997, pp. 21, 22; Wadum 2001; Wadum 2002; Tamis 2002; Essen-Vienna 2003–2004, no. 106; Antwerp 2004, p. 197

COMMENT
Cleaned and restored in 2001 with the support of art dealer Johnny van Haeften (see Wadum 2001 and 2002). The figures of Adam and Eve as well as the horse and possibly the tree were painted by Rubens, the rest of the landscape and the animals by Brueghel. A drawing for the figures by Rubens in the Museum Boijmans Van Beuningen, Rotterdam (Mauritshuis 1993, p. 90, fig. 1).

Jan Brueghel the Elder with Hans Rottenhammer

283 *Rest on the flight to Egypt, c.*1595

Copper, 22 x 29.1 cm
Marked on the reverse: *BRV[E]GHEL*
Dutch title: *De rust op de vlucht naar Egypte*

PROVENANCE
King-Stadholder Willem III, thence by descent to Prince Willem V, Apeldoorn, The Hague, 1712–1795

233

234

283

253

LITERATURE

Peltzer 1916, pp. 318, 332, 345, no. 31, p. 348, no. 74; Mauritshuis 1968, pp. 10–11; D/LS 1974–1976, vol. 2, p. 645, no. 119, vol. 3, p. 205, no. 9; Ertz 1979, no. 1, p. 540, notes 908–910; The Hague 1988–1989, no. XIV; Phoenix-Kansas City-The Hague 1998–1999, pp. 149, 150, note 8

COMMENT

A comparable painting of the same subject in a German private collection (Ertz 1979, no. 10). A copy in the Kunsthistorisches Museum, Vienna.

Jan Brueghel the Elder with Hans Rottenhammer

285 *Christ descending into limbo*, 1597

Copper, 26.5 x 35.5 cm
Signed and dated lower right: · *BRVEGHEL · 1597*
Dutch title: *Christus in het voorgeborchte*

PROVENANCE

King-Stadholder Willem III, Het Loo Palace, Apeldoorn, before 1697; Stadholder Johan Willem Friso, Apeldoorn, 1712; Prince Willem V, The Hague

LITERATURE

D/LS 1974–1976, vol. 1, p. 677, no. 839, p. 698, no. 69, vol. 2, p. 479, no. 24, vol. 3, p. 206, no. 16 (for the confusion about these inventories, see Mauritshuis 1993, no. 7); Mauritshuis 1968, p. 11; Ertz 1979, no. 2 and p. 540, note 911; Ertz 1984, in no. 128; The Hague 1988–1989, p. 119 (in exhibition); Mauritshuis 1993, no. 7; Costaras 1994; Phoenix-Kansas City-The Hague 1998–1999, no. 8e

COMMENT

Cleaned and restored in 1992 (see Costaras 1994). A smaller version by Jan Brueghel the Younger in Aschaffenburg, Bayerische Staatsgemäldesammlungen in Schloss Johannesburg (Mauritshuis 1993, p. 86, fig. 5).

Jan Brueghel the Younger?

Antwerp 1601–1678 Antwerp

236 *Paradise with the fall of man*, 1630s?

Copper, 12.7 x 19.6 cm
Dutch title: *Het paradijs met de zondeval van Adam en Eva*

PROVENANCE

Unknown; entered the collection in or after 1816

LITERATURE

Speth-Holterhoff 1957, p. 110, fig. 39; Ertz 1979, pp. 248, 526–527, note 299; Ertz 1984, no. 101

COMMENT

Cleaned and restored in 2002.

Hendrick ter Brugghen

The Hague (?) 1588–1629 Utrecht

966 *The liberation of Saint Peter*, 1624

Canvas, 104.5 x 86.5 cm
Signed and dated upper left, by the shoulder of the angel: *HTBrugghe[n] / [16]24* (HTB in ligature)
Dutch title: *De bevrijding van Petrus*

PROVENANCE

Adam Gottlob, Count Moltke, and his heirs, Copenhagen, Amalienborg, before 1756?–1931 (as Guido Reni); Alfred Andersen, Copenhagen, 1931–1954; H. Cramer Gallery, The Hague, 1963; purchased with the support of the Rembrandt Society, 1963

LITERATURE

Nicolson 1958, no. A 19; Mauritshuis 1970, no. 14; Paris 1986, no. 14; Utrecht-Braunschweig 1986–1987, no. 18; Mauritshuis 1987, no. 15; Mauritshuis 1993, no. 9; Buvelot 1996; San Francisco-Baltimore-London 1997–1998, no. 11

COMMENT

Engraved in 1778 by Johann Martin Preisler (Mauritshuis 1993, p. 98, fig. 1). A copy after the engraving by J.W. Lutz (Buvelot 1996, p. 17, fig. 12) was sold in London, Phillips, 21 June 1988, lot 113.

Bartholomäus Bruyn the Elder

Wesel or Cologne 1493–1555 Cologne

739 *Portrait diptych of Johann von Rolinxwerth and his wife Christine von Sternberg*, 1529

Verso of the woman's portrait: *Lucretia*
Panels (arched top), each 68 x 48.5 cm
Dated and inscribed in the arch of the man's portrait: *1529* and *34*; in the arch of the woman's portrait: *1529* and *28*
Dutch title: *Portret-diptiek van Johann von Rolinxwerth en zijn vrouw Christine von Sternberg*

PROVENANCE

Bequest of Rudolph Willem Jacob, Baron van Pabst van Bingerden, The Hague, 1912

LITERATURE

Cologne 1955, nos. 5–6; Westhoff-Krummacher 1965, nos. 13–14; Mauritshuis 1968, pp. 14–15; Van Suchtelen 2000, p. 24 and fig. 13; Löw 2002, pp. 72, 206, fig. 9

COMMENT

Johann von Rolinxwerth, not accidentally holding a glass of wine, was a wine dealer in Wesel (see Löw 2002, p. 72). For the coats of arms, see Mauritshuis 1935, pp. 44–45. >

285

236

966

739 739 739

The coats of arms in the man's portrait are perhaps not entirely autograph. The exact dates of the sitters, born around 1485 and 1501 respectively (see inscriptions), are unknown.

889 *Portrait of Elisabeth Bellinghausen (born c.1520)*, 1538–1539

Reverse: coat of arms (illustrated in Van Suchtelen 2000, fig. 11)
Panel (rounded at the top), 34.5 x 24 cm; painted surface 31.5 x 21.5 cm
Dutch title: *Portret van Elisabeth Bellinghausen (geboren c.1520)*

PROVENANCE
Bequest of Cornelis Hoogendijk to the Rijksmuseum, Amsterdam (inv. no. SK-A-2559), 1912; on loan from the Rijksmuseum since 1951

LITERATURE
Cologne 1955, no. 10; Westhoff-Krummacher 1965, no. 65; Mauritshuis 1968, p. 16; RM 1976, p. 156; Van Suchtelen 2000; *Portraits in the Mauritshuis*, no. 9

COMMENT
In 1538, Elisabeth Bellinghausen married Jacobus Omphalius (1500–1567), advisor and later chancellor in Cologne. Originally, inv. no. 889 formed a diptych with a portrait of Omphalius, the whereabouts of which are now unknown (see Van Suchtelen 2000, fig. 10). The restoration of inv. no. 889 —which is still in a remnant of its original frame, cut from the same piece of wood as the support of the painted surface— was finished in 2000; see P. Noble in *Mauritshuis in focus* 13 (2000), no. 3, pp. 25–26.

François Bunel II (attributed to)

Blois *c.*1550–after 1593 Paris?

875 *The confiscation of the contents of a painter's studio, c.*1590?

Panel, 28 x 46.5 cm
Dutch title: *De inbeslagname van de inhoud van het atelier van een schilder*

PROVENANCE
Jacques Goudstikker Gallery, Amsterdam, 1922–1940; Adolf Hitler, Führermuseum, Linz; Stichting Nederlands Kunstbezit; on loan to the Mauritshuis, 1948–1960; transferred, 1960

LITERATURE
Mauritshuis 1968, pp. 16–17; Hamburg 1984, no. 25; Filipczak 1987, pp. 21, 129, 228, note 18 and fig. 14 (as by Mostaert); Van der Stighelen 1990–1991, pp. 295–296; Schwarz 2004, no. XXIII/50

COMMENT
Attributed to Bunel by S.J. Gudlaugsson; later tentatively attributed to Gillis Mostaert (*c.*1534–1598) by Julius Held.

Friedrich Bury

Hanau 1763–1823 Aachen

272 *Amor triumphant,* before 1810

Canvas, 152 x 121 cm
Dutch title: *Zegevierende amor*

PROVENANCE
Gift of Queen Frederika Louise Wilhelmina, wife of King Willem I, at an unknown date

LITERATURE
Berlin 1996, no. 2/42

COMMENT
First exhibited in 1810 in Berlin. Cleaned and restored in 1996.

Abraham van Calraet

Dordrecht 1642–1722 Dordrecht

754 *Still life with peaches and grapes, c.*1680

Canvas, 89 x 73 cm
Signed lower left, on the edge of the table: *A v Calraet*
Dutch title: *Stilleven met perziken en druiven*

PROVENANCE
Wed. G. Dorens & Zn Gallery, Amsterdam, 1916; Abraham Bredius, The Hague, 1916–1946 (on loan to the Mauritshuis since 1916); bequest of Abraham Bredius, 1946

LITERATURE
The Hague 1991–1992, no. 3; Chong 1992a, p. 521, no. Calr 45; Meijer 2003, pp. 188, 189

Luca Cambiaso

Moneglia (Genoa) 1527–1585 Madrid

313 *Madonna and Child, with John the Baptist, c.*1565

Panel, 84 x 67 cm
Dutch title: *Madonna en kind, met Johannes de Doper*

272

889

754

875

313

PROVENANCE
Victor de Rainer, Brussels, 1821; purchased by King Willem I for the Mauritshuis, 1821

LITERATURE
Boschloo/Van der Sman 1993, p. 42, no. 24; Magnani 1995, pp. 73, 75, 93, note 4

314 *The birth of the Virgin, c.1570*

Canvas, 183 x 168 cm
Dutch title: *De geboorte van Maria*

PROVENANCE
Same as inv. no. 313

LITERATURE
Suida-Manning/Suida 1958, p. 158, fig. 367; Boschloo/Van der Sman 1993, p. 42, no. 25

COMMENT
A preparatory drawing in the Galleria degli Uffizi, Florence, inv. no. 845 F. The portraits at the extreme left are by a different hand and may even have been added later.

Jacob van Campen

Haarlem 1596–1657 Amersfoort

1062 *Argus, Mercury and Io, c.1630–1640?*

Canvas, 204 x 193 cm
Dutch title: *Argus, Mercurius en Io*

PROVENANCE
G.J.T. Bakker, The Hague, 1964; J. Hoogsteder Gallery, The Hague; purchased, 1981

LITERATURE
Paris 1986, no. 15; Mauritshuis 1987, no. 16; Mauritshuis 1993, no. 10; Buvelot 1995a, no. 4; Rotterdam-Frankfurt am Main 1999–2000, no. 4; Apeldoorn 2002, p. 86, repr.

1089 *Double portrait of Constantijn Huygens (1596–1687) and Suzanna van Baerle (1599–1637), c.1635*

Canvas, 95 x 78.5 cm
Dutch title: *Dubbelportret van Constantijn Huygens (1596–1687) en Suzanna van Baerle (1599–1637)*

PROVENANCE
Wittington Hall, Lonsdale, Cumbria, since 1943; sale London, Christie's, 15 April 1992, lot 21; purchased by the Friends of the Mauritshuis Foundation with the support of private individuals, 1992

LITERATURE
Held 1991; Broos 1992; Buijsen/Van der Ploeg 1993, pp. 20–21, no. 3; Wadum/Hermens 1994; Buvelot 1995a, no. 3; *Portraits in the Mauritshuis*, no. 10

COMMENT
Constantijn Huygens was secretary to three successive stadholders. He played a pivotal role in the political and cultural life of The Hague. He was also a musician and poet. In 1627 he married Suzanna van Baerle. This is the only surviving portrait of her, whereas several portraits of Huygens are known (see Hanneman, inv. no. 241). Cleaned and restored in 1993.

Jan van de Cappelle

Amsterdam 1626–1679 Amsterdam

567 *Winter scene,* 1653

Canvas, 51.8 x 61.8 cm
Signed and dated lower centre: *I. v. CAPELLE fe. 1653*
Dutch title: *Winterlandschap*

PROVENANCE
(?) Sir Joshua Reynolds, London; (?) William Hardman, Manchester, 1865; Colnaghi Gallery, London; purchased, 1893

LITERATURE
HdG 1907–1928, vol. 7, pp. 220–221, no. 148; Russell 1975, pp. 30, 34, 84, no. 148; Mauritshuis 1980, p. 18; Paris 1986, no. 16; Mauritshuis 1987, p. 373 and fig. 2; Amsterdam-Boston-Philadelphia 1987–1988, no. 18

COMMENT
A drawing attributed to Van de Cappelle in the Kunsthalle, Hamburg, inv. no. 21790, depicts virtually the same scene, from the same angle.

820 *Ships off the coast,* 1651

Canvas, 72.5 x 87 cm
Signed and dated lower centre: *I V Capelle 1651*
Dutch title: *Schepen voor de kust*

PROVENANCE
R.G. Wilberforce, London, 1887; Charles Crews, London, 1915; Onnes van Nijenrode Collection, Breukelen; Jacques Goudstikker Gallery, Amsterdam, 1920; H.E. ten Cate, Almelo; gift of Sir Henri W.A. Deterding, London, 1936

LITERATURE
HdG 1907–1928, vol. 7, p. 214, no. 133; Russell 1975, pp. 21, 22, 28, 80, no. 133; Mauritshuis 1980, pp. 19–20; Mauritshuis 1987, no. 17; Minneapolis-Toledo-Los Angeles 1990–1991, no. 10; Rotterdam-Berlin 1996–1997, no. 63

COMMENT
Cleaned and restored in 2000.

1062

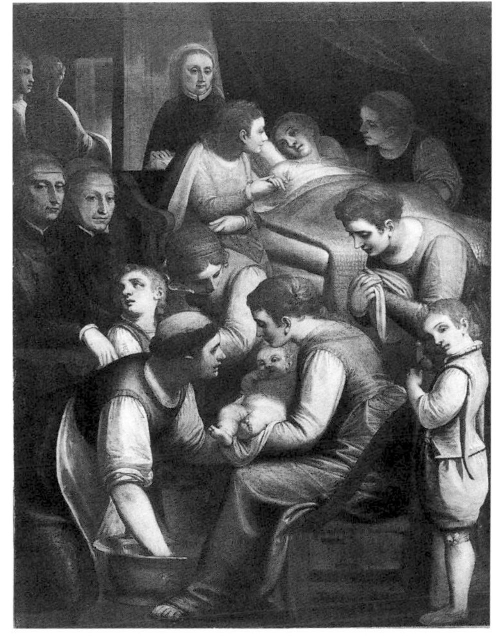

314

1089

567

820

C

Annibale Carracci (after)

Bologna 1560–1609 Rome

315 *The Holy Family with the infant St John the Baptist*, 17th century

Canvas (oval), 51 x 39 cm
Dutch title: *De heilige familie met Johannes de Doper als kind*

PROVENANCE
Martial Reghellini Schio, Venice and Brussels, until 1826; purchased by King Willem I for the Mauritshuis, 1831; on loan to the ICN

LITERATURE
Boschloo/Van der Sman 1993, pp. 42–43, no. 26

COMMENT
This seventeenth-century copy is one of many copies after Carracci's *'Montalto Madonna'* of around 1596–1598, sold at Sotheby's, London, 10 July 2003, lot 35, now in Bologna (copper, 35 x 27.5 cm).

Mateo Cerezo

Burgos 1637–1666 Madrid

300 *The penitent Mary Magdalene*, 1661

Canvas, 103.2 x 83 cm
Signed and dated: *Matheo. zereço ft / añ do / 1661*
Dutch title: *De boetvaardige Maria Magdalena*

PROVENANCE
Count Edmund Bourke, Paris, until 1821; purchased from his widow by King Willem I for the Mauritshuis, 1823; on loan to the Rijksmuseum, Amsterdam (inv. no. SK-C-1347), since 1948

LITERATURE
Van Vliet 1966, pp. 134, 136; RM 1976, p. 166; Buendía/Gutiérrez Pastor 1986, pp. 129–130, no. 29

COMMENT
A different version in the Residenzgalerie, Salzburg. Several copies are known. A miniature version in the Museo Nacional del Prado, Madrid, inv. no. 2950, attributed to Castor Velázquez.

Philippe de Champaigne (circle of)

Brussels 1602–1674 Paris

237 *Portrait of Jacobus Govaerts (b. 1635/36)*, 1665

Canvas, 135 x 108 cm
Inscribed at left: *M. Episcop. Aet Svae: 29: A°: 1665.*
Dutch title: *Portret van Jacobus Govaerts (geb. 1635/36)*

PROVENANCE
Bernard Eugène Rottiers, Antwerp, 1823; purchased by King Willem I for the Mauritshuis, 5 August 1823; on loan to the Rijksmuseum, Amsterdam (inv. no. SK-C-1183), since 1927

LITERATURE
RM 1976, p. 167 (attributed to Philippe de Champaigne); Dorival 1976, p. 320, no. 1748, p. 495, fig. 1748

COMMENT
In 1661, Jacobus Govaerts was appointed master of ceremonies and clerk of the chapter, Antwerp.

Jean-Baptiste-Siméon Chardin

Paris 1699–1799 Paris

656 *Still life with a copper pot, cheese and eggs*, c.1730–1735

Canvas, 33 x 41 cm
Signed lower left: *chardin.*
Dutch title: *Stilleven met koperen ketel, kaas en eieren*

PROVENANCE
Abraham Bredius, The Hague, 1901–1946 (on loan to the Mauritshuis since 1901); bequest of Abraham Bredius, 1946

LITERATURE
Wildenstein 1963, p. 163, no. 143, fig. 62; Rosenberg 1983, no. 143; The Hague 1991–1992, no. 4; Dijon-Paris-Rotterdam 1992–1993, no. 9

Pieter Claesz

Berchem 1597/98–1661 Haarlem

943 *Vanitas still life*, 1630

Panel, 39.5 x 56 cm
Signed and dated right centre, on the book: *PC. A°. 1630* (PC in ligature)

656 

 943

 237

300 

 315

Dutch title: *Vanitas-stilleven*

PROVENANCE
David Hultmark, Saltsjöbaden, Sweden; S. Nijstad Gallery, The Hague; purchased with the support of the Openbaar Kunstbezit Foundation and the Rembrandt Society, 1960

LITERATURE
Vroom 1945, p. 199, no. 32; Mauritshuis 1970, no. 25; Vroom 1980, vol. 1, pp. 95–96, 135, vol. 2, p. 19, no. 58; Bergamo 1981, p. 11, fig. 1; Washington etc. 1982–1984, no. 13; Meijer 2003, pp. 191, 192, note 3; Brenner-Bulst 2004, pp. 232–233, no. 47

947 *Still life with a lighted candle*, 1627

Panel, 26.1 x 37.3 cm
Signed and dated right centre, on the book: *PC A° 1627* (PC in ligature)
Dutch title: *Stilleven met een brandende kaars*

PROVENANCE
Bukowski Gallery, Stockholm, shortly after 1930; Oscar Hedberg, Stockholm; S. Nijstad Gallery, The Hague; purchased, 1961

LITERATURE
Mauritshuis 1970, no. 24; Munster–Baden-Baden 1979–1980, no. 234; Vroom 1980, vol. 1, pp. 23–25, vol. 2, pp. 17–18, no. 49; Brenner-Bulst 2004, p. 222, no. 31

1125 *Still life with tazza*, 1636

Panel, 44 x 61 cm
Signed and dated on the knife blade: *PC 1636* (PC in ligature)
Dutch title: *Stilleven met tazza*

PROVENANCE
Private collection, France; Percy Levy, London, *c.*1959; Anthony Speelman Gallery, London, 1977; gift of Willem, Baron van Dedem to the Friends of the Mauritshuis Foundation, 2002

LITERATURE
Sutton 2002, no. 12; Buvelot 2002a, pp. 16–18, no. 1; Brenner-Bulst 2004, pp. 243–244, no. 70

Joos van Cleve (studio of)

Cleves (?) *c.*1485 – *c.*1540 Antwerp

895 *Portrait of a man*, *c.*1520–1530

Panel, 45.7 x 43.4 cm
Dutch title: *Portret van een man*

PROVENANCE
Presumably English Royal Collection, 1688, as by Hans Holbein the Younger, and subsequently in the collection of the Dutch stadholders in or before 1712 (see The Hague 1988–1989, no. v); Nationale Konst-Gallery, The Hague, 1801–1808; Rijksmuseum, Amsterdam (inv. no. SK-A-165), since 1885; on loan from the Rijksmuseum since 1951

LITERATURE
Friedländer 1967–1976, vol. 9a, p. 68, no. 87; Mauritshuis 1968, pp. 17–18; D/LS 1974–1976, vol. 1, p. 534, no. 283 (?), vol. 2, p. 37, no. 140 (?), p. 506, no. 61 (?), p. 639, no. 15, p. 796, add. p. 639, no. 15; RM 1976, p. 169; Hand 1978, no. 81; Van Thiel 1981, p. 197, no. 110; The Hague 1988–1989, no. v

COMMENT
John Hand, Curator of Northern Renaissance Painting, National Gallery of Art, Washington, attributes the painting to Van Cleve's studio (letter, 19 December 2002). Treated in 1988 (see Mauritshuis Annual Report 1988, pp. 15, 22–23, repr.).

Joos van Cleve (studio of)

348 *Christ and St John the Baptist as children*, *c.*1530

Panel, 39 x 58 cm
Inscribed on the left medallions: *ANTIGONA FI S / OEDIPPVS FILIVS REG.TE*; on the right medallions: *AENEAS TROIAN FILI ANCH / DID.C [...] CARTAG* (quoted after Glück 1928, p. 502)
Dutch title: *Christus en Johannes de Doper als kinderen*

PROVENANCE
Victor de Rainer, Brussels, 1821; purchased by King Willem I for the Mauritshuis, 1821

LITERATURE
Mauritshuis 1968, pp. 18–19; Hecht 1981; The Hague 1988–1989, pp. 87–88 (in exhibition); Traversi/Wadum 1999

COMMENT
May in part be autograph, as was suggested by Hand (see previous entry). There are several other versions painted by Van Cleve and his workshop, amongst others in The Art Institute of Chicago. The composition is derived from Leonardo da Vinci (1452–1519). The two medallions on each column depict Antigone and Oedipus, and Dido and Aeneas.

348

895

947

1125

C

Pieter Codde

Amsterdam 1599–1678 Amsterdam

392 *Merry company with masked dancers,* 1636

Panel, 50 x 76.5 cm
Signed and dated lower right, on a book: *PCodde / A.° 1636* (PC in ligature)
Dutch title: *Vrolijk gezelschap met gemaskerde dansers*

PROVENANCE
Scharff Collection, Paris; purchased, 1876

LITERATURE
Plietzsch 1960, p. 30, fig. 19; Renger 1972, pp. 190–192; Bigler Playter 1972, p. 77; Philadelphia-Berlin-London 1984, p. 77, fig. 1; Kolfin 1998

COMMENT
Cleaned and restored in 1986.

445 *Backgammon players,* 1628

Panel (octagonal), 20.4 x 27 cm
Signed and dated lower right: *PCodde fecit 1628* (PC in ligature)
Dutch title: *Trik-trakspelers*

PROVENANCE
Heemskerck van Beest Collection; transferred from the Nederlands Museum van Geschiedenis en Kunst, 1878

LITERATURE
Delft 1998, no. 120

COMMENT
Originally oval (12.5 x 18.5 cm); enlarged by the painter himself. Cleaned and restored in 1998.

857 *Portrait of a betrothed couple,* 1634

Panel, 43 x 35 cm
Signed and dated upper right, above the door: *16 PC 34* (PC in ligature)
Dutch title: *Portret van een verloofd paar*

PROVENANCE
Willem, Count of Aldenburg Bentinck and Waldeck-Limpurg and heirs, Middachten, before 1882–1944 (on loan to the Mauritshuis, 1901–1903; inv. no. 651); A. Nijstad Gallery, The Hague; D. Katz Gallery, Dieren, 1944; Adolf Hitler, Führermuseum, Linz; Stichting Nederlands Kunstbezit; on loan to the Mauritshuis, 1948–1960; transferred, 1960

LITERATURE
Paris 1986, no. 17; Mauritshuis 1987, no. 18; *Portraits in the Mauritshuis*, no. 11

Edwaert Collier

Breda *c.*1640–1708 London

810 *Vanitas still life,* 1675

Panel, 19.5 x 17 cm
Signed and dated in the middle, on the document: *E. Collier. 1675.*
Inscribed on the book: *Van de Eydelheydt des levens* (On the vanity of life)
Dutch title: *Vanitas-stilleven*

PROVENANCE
Gift of W.E. Duits, London, 1934

LITERATURE
Bol 1969, p. 354

Leendert van der Cooghen

Haarlem 1632–1681 Haarlem

81 *Doubting Thomas,* 1654

Canvas, 111 x 155.2 cm
Signed and dated upper right: *LVCooghen 1654*
Dutch title: *De ongelovige Thomas*

PROVENANCE
G.A. Burn, London; purchased, 1876

LITERATURE
Bolten *et al.* 1981, p. 20, note 11; Defoer *et al.* 2003, pp. 220, 221

Adriaen Coorte

Middelburg active *c.*1683–1707

1106 *Still life with wild strawberries,* 1705

Paper on panel, 16.5 x 14 cm
Signed and dated lower right: *A. C...... / 1705*
Dutch title: *Stilleven met bosaardbeien*

PROVENANCE
Sale London, Sotheby's, 16 March 1966, lot 89; purchased by Edward Speelman, London; gift of Mrs Edward Speelman, in memory of Mr Edward Speelman, 1995

LITERATURE
Bol 1977, p. 58, no. 67; Broos 1995a; Mauritshuis 2000, pp. 60–61; Houston-The Hague 2000–2001, pp. 48–49 and 54, no. 8; Van der Ploeg 2001a, pp. 8, 21; Washington 2003, no. 15; London 2004, p. 54

COMMENT
Strawberries were one of the artist's favourite motifs (see Baltimore 1999, no. 13 and the entry for lot 42 in sale catalogue London, Christie's, 9 July 2003).

1106

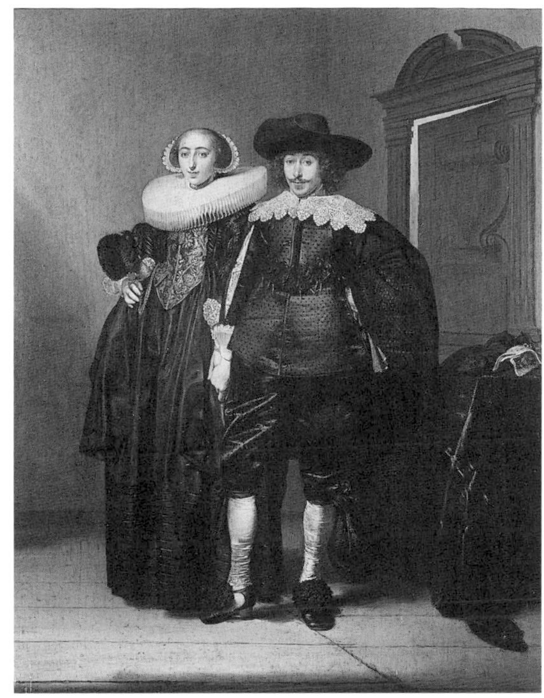
857

392

810

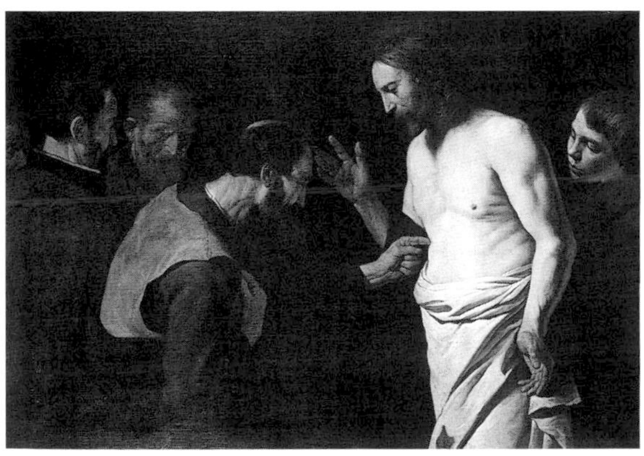
81

445

Gonzales Coques

Antwerp 1614–1684 Antwerp

With many other artists

238 *Interior with figures before a picture collection*, 1667–1672 and 1706

Canvas, 176 x 210.5 cm
Dated on the fire back of the mantlepiece: *1672*
(for other signatures and dates, see below)
Dutch title: *Interieur met figuren te midden van een schilderijenverzameling*

PROVENANCE

Jacob de Wit, Antwerp, 1741; Het Loo Palace, Apeldoorn, 1757; Prince Willem V, The Hague, 1763–1795

LITERATURE

Reznicek 1954; Speth-Holterhoff 1957, pp. 172–181; Delft-Antwerp 1964–1965, no. 26; D/LS 1974–1976, vol. 2, p. 642, no. 60, vol. 3, p. 212, no. 42; Cologne-Antwerp-Vienna 1992–1993, pp. 50–51; Nagasaki 1992–1993, no. 4; Van der Ploeg 1993; De Bruyn 1988, p. 279, no. 248; Vlieghe 1998, p. 206; Lisken Pruss 2002, pp. 147–155, 373–375, no. 48

COMMENT

The figures were painted by Coques, the architecture – attributed in the past to Dirck van Delen or Erasmus II Quellinus – by an anonymous artist. The 42 paintings were executed between *c.*1667 and 1706 by a group of different painters, all from Antwerp; 9 remain anonymous, 8 are copies after famous artists (see the scheme). An anonymous drawing of around 1700, in The Cooper Union Museum, New York, gives attributions for every painting, although these are not always correct. Coques was probably responsible for the realisation of this ambitious work (for a comparable painting dated 1666 coordinated by Wilhelm von Ehrenberg in the Alte Pinakothek, Munich, see Langenstein 1997, no. 1). The figures he painted have in the past been identified as Antoine van Leyen (1628–1686), an Antwerp magistrate and collector, and his wife Marie-Anne van Eywerven and their two daughters. Cleaned and restored in 2001.

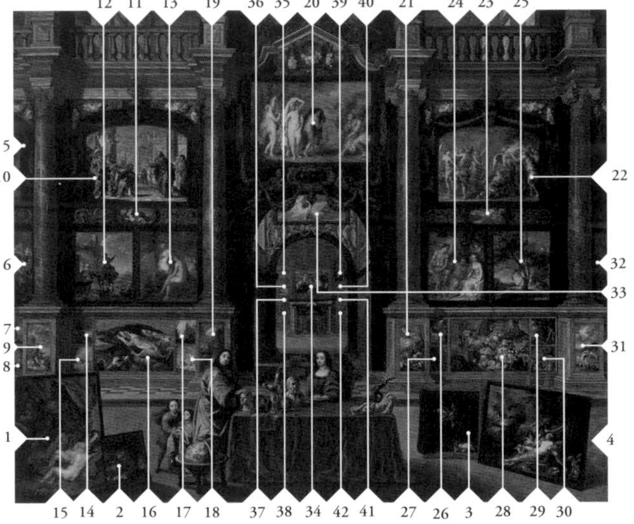

LIST OF COLLABORATORS TO INV. NO. 238

1 Jan de Duits (1629–1676), *Cimon and Iphigenia*, signed and dated: *J. de Duijts f. 1671*
2 Jan Peeters (1624–1676/80), *Sea view*, signed: *IP*
3 Peeter Gijsels (1621–1690), *Still life*, signed: *P[eeter] gijsels*
4 Kaspar van Opstal the Younger (1654–1717), *Venus and Adonis*, signed and dated: *K van opstal / 1706*
5 Unknown, *Sea view*
6 Unknown, *Battle scene*
7 Jan van Hecke (1620–1684), *Landscape*
8 Jan van Hecke (1620–1684), *Landscape*
9 Peeter van Bredael (1629–1719), *Landscape*, signed: *P.V.B. f*
10 Jan [Johannes] Ykens (1613–1679), *The centurion before Christ*, signed and dated: *Ioannes ykens feci[t] A° 1667*
11 Erasmus II Quellinus (1607–1678), *Allegory on the City of Antwerp*, signed: *E.Q.*
12 Anton Goubau (1616–1698), *Italian landscape*, signed: *A Goubau Fc*
13 Charles Emmanuel Biset (1633–1691), *Aesculapius changed into a bird*, formerly indistinctly signed: *C E Biset f*
14 Unknown, *Moonlit landscape*
15 Jan van Kessel the Elder (1626–1679), *Landscape*, signed: *JVK*
16 Attributed to Peeter Boel (1622–1674), *Wild boar hunt*
17 Unknown, *Landscape*
18 Jan van Kessel the Elder (1626–1679), *Butterflies and other insects*
19 Unknown, *Sea view*
20 Theodor Boeijermans (1620–1678), *The judgement of Paris*
21 Jan van Hecke (1620–1684), *Landscape*, signed: *J.V. HECKE.*
22 Jan Cossiers (1600–1671), *The triumph of Bacchus*, formerly indistinctly signed: *Cossiers*
23 Theodor Boeijermans (1620–1678), *A river god* signed: *TB* (in ligature)
24 Theodor Boeijermans (1620–1678), *The four seasons*, signed: *TBoeijermans F.* (TB in ligature)
25 Unknown, *Italian landscape*, formerly indistinctly signed
26 Jan van Hecke (1620–1684), *Pieta*, signed: *IVH*
27 Jan van Hecke (1620–1684), *View of a fortress at night*, signed: *IVH F*
28 Attributed to Peeter Boel (1622–1674), *Fruit still life*
29 Unknown, *Landscape*
30 Pieter Spierinckx (1635–1711), *Village fair*, signed: *PvSpirinckx* ('n' in mirror image)
31 Jan van Hecke (1620–1684), *Bathing men*, signed: *I V HECKE*
32 Unknown, *Landscape with ruins*

33 Theodor Boeijermans (1620–1678), *Leda and the swan*
34 Unknown, *Hero and the Nereids*
35 After Titian (*c.*1488–1567), *Portrait of Emperor Charles V (1500–1558)* (after the portrait of the sitter on horseback in the Museo Nacional del Prado, Madrid; possibly after Rubens's copy in the Courtauld Institute of Art, Princess Gate Collection, London)
36 After Anthony van Dyck (1599–1641), *Double portrait of Thomas Howard, Earl of Arundel, and his wife, Alatheia Talbot* (after the version in the Kunsthistorisches Museum, Vienna, or an English private collection)
37 After Diego Velázquez (1599–1660), *Portrait of Philip IV, King of Spain* (based freely on the full-length portrait dated 1623 in the Museo Nacional del Prado, Madrid)
38 After Van Dyck, *Double portrait of Mountjoy Blunt, Earl of Newport and George, Lord Goring* (after the painting in a private collection)
39 After Van Dyck, *Portrait of Philip II, King of Spain*
40 After Peter Paul Rubens (1577–1640), *Portrait of Charles the Bold* (after the painting in the Kunsthistorisches Museum, Vienna)
41 After Peter Paul Rubens, *Portrait of Ferdinand, Cardinal-Infant of Spain* (after the painting in the Alte Pinakothek, Munich)
42 After Peter Paul Rubens, *Portrait of a man in armour*

SCULPTURES *from left to right:*

A Unidentified bust
B *Christ to the column* (after the original by Willem van Tetrode in the Hearn Family Trust, New York; see Amsterdam-New York 2003, p. 128, no. 38, as kindly communicated by B. van der Mark)
C *The Medici satyr* (after the original in the Palazzo Pitti, Florence)
D Head of Laocoön (after the original in the Vatican Museums, Rome)
E Bust of Homer
F Behind the bust of Homer, a fragment of *Bacchus and panther*, a sculpture by Willem van Tetrode, can be seen (see Amsterdam-New York 2003, p. 32)
G *Cleopatra* (after the original in the Vatican Museums, Rome)
H *The Borghese fighter* (after the original in the Musée du Louvre, Paris)

C

Cornelis Cornelisz van Haarlem

Haarlem 1562–1638 Haarlem

22 *The massacre of the innocents,* 1591

Canvas, 268 x 257 cm
Signed and dated lower right, on a rock: *CC f. / A° 1591*
Dutch title: *De kindermoord te Bethlehem*

PROVENANCE
Commissioned by the Haarlem magistrates for the Prinsenhof, Haarlem, 1591; exchanged with four other paintings for the Haarlem town hall and placed in the Nationale Konst-Gallery, The Hague, 1804; acquired in exchange with the Rijksmuseum, Amsterdam, 1825; on loan to the Frans Hals Museum, Haarlem, since 1917

LITERATURE
Washington-Detroit-Amsterdam 1980–1981, p. 79, fig. 3; Slive 1995, p. 8; Van Thiel 1999, pp. 307–308, no. 42

COMMENT
Before 1604, inv. no. 22 was combined with wings by Maerten van Heemskerck (inv. nos. 51–52) to form a triptych, the former Drapers' Altarpiece.

23 *The wedding of Peleus and Thetis,* *c.*1592–1593

Canvas, 246 x 419 cm
Dutch title: *De bruiloft van Peleus en Thetis*

PROVENANCE
Commissioned by the Haarlem magistrates for the Prinsenhof, Haarlem, 1593; acquired in exchange with four other paintings for the Haarlem town hall and placed in the Nationale Konst-Gallery, The Hague, 1804; Picture Gallery of Prince Willem V, The Hague, until 1821; transferred, 1822 (from 1821–1875 folded up and stored in the attic); on loan to the Frans Hals Museum, Haarlem, since 1913

LITERATURE
Van Thiel 1999, pp. 355–356, no. 159

Cornelis Cornelisz van Haarlem (after)

918 *The depravity of mankind before the flood*

Copper, 23.9 x 27.5 cm
Bears indistinct signature in red: *CH* or *M*
Dutch title: *De verdorvenheid van de mensheid voor de zondvloed*

PROVENANCE
Arcade Gallery, London, 1954; purchased, 1954

LITERATURE
Mauritshuis 1968, p. 19; Mauritshuis 1970, no. 8; Stechow 1972, pp. 166–167, 169, 174, note 15; Van Thiel 1999, p. 320, in no. 72 and fig. 136

COMMENT
Copy after a painting of around 1597, with art dealer Adolphe Stein, Paris, 1989 (Van Thiel 1999, p. 320, no. 72, fig. 135).

Jacob Cornelisz van Oostsanen

Oostzaan (?) *c.*1472–1533 Amsterdam

1 *Salome with the head of John the Baptist,* 1524

Panel, 72 x 53.7 cm
Signed and dated on the banderole: *1524 I A*
(between the 'I' and 'A' is the mark of the painter)
Dutch title: *Salome met het hoofd van Johannes de Doper*

PROVENANCE
Princess Albertine Agnes of Orange-Nassau, Leeuwarden, 1681; Prince Willem V, The Hague; on loan to the Rijksmuseum, Amsterdam (inv. no. SK-C-1349), since 1948

LITERATURE
Friedländer 1967–1976, vol. 12, p. 118, no. 24; D/LS 1974–1976, vol. 2, p. 112, no. 901, vol. 3, p. 241, no. 193; RM 1976, p. 176; Carroll 1987, pp. 245–251, no. 27

Correggio (Antonio Allegri) (after)

Correggio *c.*1489–1534 Correggio

301 *Madonna and Child,* before 1680

Panel, 54 x 41 cm
Dutch title: *Madonna en kind*

PROVENANCE
Victor de Rainer, Brussels, 1821; purchased by King Willem I for the Mauritshuis, 1821; on loan to the ICN

LITERATURE
Boschloo/Van der Sman 1993, p. 45, no. 28

COMMENT
This painting belongs to a series of copies after *La Zingarella* by Correggio in the Museo Nazionale di Capodimonte, Galleria Nazionale, Naples.

23

22

1

918

301

Correggio (after)

302 *Christ on the Mount of Olives*

Panel, 40 x 27 cm
Dutch title: *Christus op de Olijfberg*

PROVENANCE
Victor de Rainer, Brussels, 1821; purchased by King Willem I for the Mauritshuis, 1821; on loan to the ICN

LITERATURE
Boschloo/Van der Sman 1993, pp. 45–46, no. 29

COMMENT
One of many copies after the left part of *The agony in the garden* in Apsley House, London.

Piero di Cosimo

Florence 1462–1521 Florence

287 *Posthumous portrait of Francesco Giamberti (1405–c.1482), father of Giuliano da San Gallo,* after *c.*1482

Panel, 47.5 x 33.7 cm
Dutch title: *Postuum portret van Francesco Giamberti (1405–c.1482), de vader van Giuliano da San Gallo*

PROVENANCE
Francesco da San Gallo, Florence, until 1567; King James II, London, until 1688; King-Stadholder Willem III, London, after 1688; Het Loo Palace, Apeldoorn; Prince Willem V, The Hague; on loan to the Rijksmuseum, Amsterdam (inv. no. SK-C-1367), since 1948

LITERATURE
D/LS 1974–1976, vol. 1, p. 696, no. 14 or 20, vol. 3, p. 219, no. 82; RM 1976, p. 444; Bacci 1976, pp. 91, 93–95, no. 37; The Hague 1988–1989, no. VII; Groningen-Maastricht 1989, no. 34; Forlani Tempesti/Capretti 1996, pp. 123–124, no. 33a; Stockholm 2001–2002, no. 15; Bruges 2002, no. 97

COMMENT
Companion piece to inv. no. 288. Giamberti's likeness also appears in an altarpiece by Filippino Lippi depicting saints Paul and Frediano in Los Angeles, Norton Simon Museum of Art (The Hague 1988–1989, p. 95, fig. b), dated to around 1483. Giamberti, a cabinetmaker and builder from Florence, worked for the Medici family and on special occasions even composed music for them.

288 *Portrait of Giuliano da San Gallo (1445–1516), son of Francesco Giamberti,* after *c.*1482

Panel, 47.2 x 33.5 cm
Dutch title: *Portret van Giuliano da San Gallo (1445–1516), zoon van Francesco Giamberti*

PROVENANCE
Same as inv. no. 287; on loan to the Rijksmuseum, Amsterdam (inv. no. SK-C-1368), since 1948

LITERATURE
D/LS 1974–1976, vol. 1, p. 696, no. 14 or 20, vol. 3, p. 219, no. 81; RM 1976, p. 444; Bacci 1976, pp. 91, 93–95, no. 36; The Hague 1988–1989, no. VIII; Groningen-Maastricht 1989, no. 33; Forlani Tempesti/Capretti 1996, pp. 123–124, no. 33a; Stockholm 2001–2002, no. 16; Bruges 2002, no. 97

COMMENT
Companion piece to inv. no. 287. Reproduced in Giorgio Vasari's *Le vite de' piu eccellenti pittori, scultori e architettori*, second edition, Florence 1568, vol. 2, p. 55 (The Hague 1988–1989, p. 98, fig. b). Giuliano da San Gallo was a successful architect, painter and sculptor, the most important artist of the San Gallo family. He worked mostly in Florence and Rome, amongst others for Pope Julius II.

Lucas Cranach the Elder

Kronach 1472–1553 Weimar

917 *Virgin and Child, c.*1515–1520

Panel, 62.7 x 42 cm
Signed lower left with the painter's mark, the crowned snake with wings and a ring in its mouth (see Mauritshuis 1987, p. 110, fig. 4)
Dutch title: *Maria met kind*

PROVENANCE
Prince Lichnowsky, Kuchelna, Silesia, before 1906; Paul Cassirer Gallery, Berlin and Amsterdam, 1929; Hans Tietje, Amsterdam, 1932; Hermann Göring, Berlin; Stichting Nederlands Kunstbezit; on loan to the Mauritshuis, 1953–1955; transferred, 1955

LITERATURE
Mauritshuis 1968, p. 20; Basel 1974, no. 383; Friedländer/Rosenberg 1978, p. 95, no. 130; Mauritshuis 1987, no. 19

288

287

917

302

C

Lucas Cranach the Elder
(and/or studio?)

891 *Portrait of Philipp Melanchton (1497–1560), c.*1545?

Panel, 36 x 23 cm
Signed centre right: *L*, with the painter's mark, a crowned snake with wings and a ring in its mouth
Dutch title: *Portret van Philipp Melanchton (1497–1560)*

PROVENANCE
Bequest of Cornelis Hoogendijk to the Rijksmuseum, Amsterdam (inv. no. SK-A-2561), 1912; on loan from the Rijksmuseum since 1951

LITERATURE
Mauritshuis 1968, p. 21; RM 1976, p. 180

COMMENT
The portrait of Martin Luther by the workshop of Lucas Cranach the Elder in the Philadelphia Museum of Art, John G. Johnson Collection (cat. 1994, no. 740), has been considered a companion piece to this painting. Restoration completed in 2000. Melanchton — a leading figure of the Reformation (see The Hague 2003, p. 102) — was friends with the painter.

Lucas Cranach the Younger
Wittenberg 1515–1586 Weimar

890 *Portrait of a man with a red beard,* 1548

Panel, 64 x 48 cm
Signed upper left with the painter's mark, a crowned snake with wings and a ring in its mouth, and dated: *1548*
Dutch title: *Portret van een man met een rode baard*

PROVENANCE
Bequest of Cornelis Hoogendijk to the Rijksmuseum, Amsterdam (inv. no. SK-A-2560), 1912; on loan from the Rijksmuseum since 1951

LITERATURE
Mauritshuis 1968, p. 21; Basel 1974, no. 642; RM 1976, p. 180

Pieter Frederik de la Croix
France 1709–1782 The Hague

539 *Portrait of Johan Arnold Zoutman (1724–1793),* 1781

Pastel on paper, 45 x 37.5 cm
Signed and dated upper right: *P.F. de la Croix fecit 1781*
Dutch title: *Portret van Johan Arnold Zoutman (1724–1793)*

PROVENANCE
Gift of Victor Eugène Louis de Stuers, The Hague, 1887; on loan to the Nederlands Scheepvaartmuseum, Amsterdam, since 1931

LITERATURE
Prud'homme van Reine *et al.* 1992, pp. 94–95, in no. 1–28

COMMENT
Vice-Admiral Zoutman is best known for his leadership in the Battle of the 'Doggersbank' against the English in 1781. His victory led to a number of portraits, among them inv. no. 539. Zoutman's blue marine uniform indicates his rank; the medal recalls the famous sea battle. For a portrait of his wife, Adriana van Heusden, see northern Netherlands, inv. no. 540.

Abraham van Cuylenborch
Utrecht *c.*1610–1658 Utrecht

24 *Diana and her companions*

Panel, 32 x 40 cm
Signed centre below: *AVCuylenborch f.* (AVC in ligature)
Dutch title: *Diana en haar nimfen*

PROVENANCE
Entered the collection after 1817

LITERATURE
Bernt 1969–1970, vol. 1, no. 283; Salerno 1977–1980, vol. 1, p. 286; Sluijter 2000a, p. 52 and fig. 166

Aelbert Cuyp
Dordrecht 1620–1691 Dordrecht

25 *Equestrian portrait of Pieter de Roovere (1602–1652), c.*1650

Canvas, 123.5 x 154 cm
Signed lower left: *A. cuijp*
Dutch title: *Ruiterportret van Pieter de Roovere (1602–1652)*

PROVENANCE
Probably Pieter de Roovere and his heirs, Dordrecht; Ocker Repelaer van Driel, Dordrecht, 1804–1820; purchased, 1820 (exhibited in the Picture Gallery of Prince Willem V, The Hague); transferred, 1822

LITERATURE
HdG 1907–1928, vol. 2, p. 20, no. 42; Dordrecht

25

24

890 891 539

1977–1978, no. 25; Mauritshuis 1980, pp. 23–24; Paris 1986, no. 18; Chong 1992a, pp. 372–373, no. 132; *Portraits in the Mauritshuis*, no. 12

COMMENT

Pieter de Roovere, bailiff of South Holland and lord of Hardinxveld, had a monopoly on salmon fishing in Dordrecht and environs. The De Roovere coat of arms is on the horse's harness.

822 *Landscape with the ruins of Rijnsburg Abbey, near Leiden, c.1640–1642*

Panel, 49.7 x 74 cm
Signed lower left: *A. cuyp*
Dutch title: *Landschap met de ruïne van de Abdij Rijnsburg, bij Leiden*

PROVENANCE

Marin Collection, Paris, 1790; D.A. Hoogendijk Gallery, Amsterdam; gift of Sir Henri W.A. Deterding, London, 1936; on loan to the Dordrechts Museum, Dordrecht, since 1995

LITERATURE

Mauritshuis 1980, pp. 21–23; Chong 1992a, p. 294, no. 40

Aelbert Cuyp?

829 *Portrait of a girl with peaches*

Canvas, 63.5 x 48.2 cm
Bears signature upper right: *A: cuyp: f.*
Dutch title: *Portret van een meisje met perziken*

PROVENANCE

Sir Claude Alexander, Ballomyle House, Scotland; L. Koetser Gallery, London, 1938; purchased, 1938

LITERATURE

Dordrecht 1977–1978, no. 22; Chong 1992a, p. 489, no. C 121

COMMENT

Alan Chong rejects the traditional attribution to Cuyp.

Aelbert Cuyp (manner of)

963 *Migrating peasants in a southern landscape*

Panel, 38.1 x 52.2 cm
Signed lower right: *A. cuyp*
Dutch title: *Trekkend landvolk in een zuidelijk landschap*

PROVENANCE

Johan van der Linden van Slingelandt, Dordrecht, 1785; Jean-Baptiste-Pierre Lebrun, Paris; George Hibbert, London, 1818; Richard Foster, London, 1835; Henry Beavan, London, 1842; John Dean Paul, London; Wertheimer Gallery, London; Earl of Crewe, London; Edward Speelman Gallery, London; purchased, 1963

LITERATURE

HdG 1907–1928, vol. 2, pp. 135–136, no. 465; Mauritshuis 1970, no. 47; Reiss 1975, pp. 79, 208; Mauritshuis 1980, pp. 24–26; Chong 1992a, p. 352, no. 111C

COMMENT

Closely related to the painting by Cuyp in The Cleveland Museum of Art, inv. no. 1942–637. According to Chong it is 'an 18th-century pastiche'.

Aelbert Cuyp (manner of)

821 *Cattle near a river*

Panel, 46.2 x 74.2 cm
Bears signature lower right: *A. cuyp*
Dutch title: *Vee bij een rivier*

PROVENANCE

Earl of Howe, London, 1823; Colnaghi Gallery, London, 1933; purchased with the support of the Rembrandt Society, thanks to the Van Weel Bequest, 1936

LITERATURE

HdG 1907–1928, vol. 2, p. 107, no. 372; Mauritshuis 1980, pp. 26–27; Chong 1992a, p. 463, no. C 50

COMMENT

A pastiche, probably from the eighteenth century.

Gerard David

Oudewater *c.*1450–1523 Bruges

843 *Forest scene, c.1510–1515*

Two panels, each 89.9 x 30.7 cm
Dutch title: *Boslandschap*

PROVENANCE

Ramon F. Urrutia, Madrid, 1920; Duveen Brothers Gallery, Paris, 1928; Jules S. Bache Collection, New York, 1928; sometime between 1930 and 1932 the outside wings now in the Mauritshuis were removed from the triptych now in New York and returned to Duveen Brothers; purchased by the Rijksmuseum, Amsterdam (inv. nos. SK-A-3134 and 3135), 1932; on loan from the Rijksmuseum since 1948

LITERATURE

Friedländer 1967–1976, vol. 6b, p. 100, no. 160; RM 1976, p. 189; Van Miegroet 1989, pp. 230–234, 300, no. 30; The

829

963

821

822

843

Hague 1997; New York 1998–1999, no. 80; Essen-Vienna 2003–2004, p. 20; Madrid 2004, pp. 62–63, 122–123

COMMENT
The two panels originally functioned as the outer wings of a triptych; the insides with the donors and saints Jerome and Leonard, as well as the middle panel with the Nativity are in The Metropolitan Museum of Art, New York (see The Hague 1997). Cleaned and restored in 1985–1987.

Gerard David (after)

725 *The lamentation, c.*1540–1545

Panel (rounded at the top), 19.2 x 15.5 cm
Dutch title: *De bewening*

PROVENANCE
Abraham Bredius, The Hague, 1907–1946 (bought in Ronda, Spain; on loan to the Mauritshuis since 1907); bequest of Abraham Bredius, 1946

LITERATURE
Marlier 1957, pp. 92–93, p. 294, no. 46; Mauritshuis 1968, p. 13; Bleyerveld 1991; The Hague 1991–1992, no. 24

COMMENT
This composition, of which there are many other versions, is based on paintings by David. Possibly executed by an artist from the circle of Adriaen Isenbrant or Ambrosius Benson, to whom the painting was formerly attributed. An x-ray revealed that the present scene is painted on top of a portrait of a man with a beard and beret, datable to around 1540 (The Hague 1991–1992, p. 104, fig. 1).

Abraham van Dijck

(?) 1635–1672 Amsterdam

791 *Old man, asleep, c.*1655–1660

Canvas, 50.8 x 47 cm
Signed upper right: *AVDyck f.*
Dutch title: *Slapende oude man*

PROVENANCE
Grossherzogliche Galerie, Oldenburg, before 1805; gift of Jacques Goudstikker, Amsterdam, 1926; on loan to the ICN

LITERATURE
Sumowski 1983–1995, vol. 1, p. 672, no. 378

Abraham van Dijck (attributed to)

798 *The departure of Benjamin, c.*1650

Panel, 74 x 62 cm
Dutch title: *Het afscheid van Benjamin*

PROVENANCE
Asscher and Welcker Gallery, London, *c.*1925; Kleinberger & Co Gallery, Paris and New York, 1929; Abraham Bredius, The Hague (on loan to the Mauritshuis since 1929); bequest of Abraham Bredius, 1946

LITERATURE
Pont 1958, pp. 94, 129, no. 2 (attributed to Constant van Renesse); Sumowski 1983–1995, vol. 5, p. 3091, no. 2046; The Hague 1991–1992, no. 6

COMMENT
Formerly attributed to Barent Fabritius.

Philip van Dijk

Oud-Beijerland 1683–1753 The Hague

27 *Judith with the head of Holofernes,* 1726

Panel, 27.7 x 30.5 cm
Signed and dated upper left: *P. van Dijk / A 1726*
Dutch title: *Judith met het hoofd van Holofernes*

PROVENANCE
Stadholder Willem IV, Leeuwarden, 1731; Prince Willem V, The Hague

LITERATURE
D/LS 1974–1976, vol. 2, p. 405, no. 500, vol. 3, p. 209, no. 31; Mauritshuis 1993, no. 11

COMMENT
The figure of Judith is based on a painting by Adriaen van der Werff in the Niedersächsiches Landesmuseum, Hannover (see Mauritshuis 1993, p. 110 and fig. 1).

28 *Woman playing the lute*

Panel, 15.5 x 12.5 cm
Signed at left: *PVDijk* (PVD in ligature)
Dutch title: *Luitspeelster*

PROVENANCE
Govert van Slingelandt, The Hague, in or before 1752; the entire collection sold to Willem V in 1768; Prince Willem V, The Hague, 1768–1795; on loan to the Rijksmuseum, Amsterdam (inv. no. SK-C-1647), since 1996

LITERATURE
D/LS 1974–1976, vol. 3, p. 208, no. 28

27 

 28

725 

 791

798 

D

29 *Lady attending to her toilet, c.*1720–1730

Panel, 29.5 x 23.5 cm
Signed at right, near the door: *Ph: V Dijk. F:*
Dutch title: *Dame bij haar toilet*

PROVENANCE
Same as inv. no. 27

LITERATURE
D/LS 1974–1976, vol. 2, p. 405, no. 498, vol. 3, p. 208, no. 29; Nagasaki 1992–1993, no. 5; Oxford 1999–2000, p. 24, pl. 19

30 *The bookkeeper*

Canvas, 26.5 x 21.3 cm
Dutch title: *De boekhouder*

PROVENANCE
Same as inv. no. 27

LITERATURE
D/LS 1974–1976, vol. 2, p. 405, no. 502, vol. 3, p. 209, no. 30

712 *Portrait of Mathias Lambertus Singendonck (1678–1742), burgomaster of Nijmegen*

Canvas (oval), 53 x 44.5 cm
Signed centre right: *P. van Dijk*
Dutch title: *Portret van Mathias Lambertus Singendonck (1678–1742), burgemeester van Nijmegen*

PROVENANCE
Probably by inheritance to Maria Johanna Singendonck, The Hague; bequest of *Jonkvrouw* Maria Johanna Singendonck, 1907; on loan to the ICN

LITERATURE
Moes 1897–1905, vol. 2, p. 379, no. 7209–1

COMMENT
Companion piece to inv. no. 713. Singendonck was probably also portrayed by Gerrit Alberts, inv. no. 723.

713 *Portrait of Agneta Catherina Hoeufft (1689–1758)*

Canvas (oval), 53 x 44 cm
Dutch title: *Portret van Agneta Catherina Hoeufft (1689–1758)*

PROVENANCE
Same as inv. no. 712; on loan to the ICN

COMMENT
Agneta Catherina Hoeufft was the second wife of Mathias Lambertus Singendonck — they married in 1723. Companion piece to inv. no. 712.

Heinrich Dittmers

Hamburg (?) *c.*1625–1677 Copenhagen

228 *Portrait of a man,* 1664

Panel (oval), 50 x 37.5 cm
Formerly signed and dated at right: *HDitmars. Fec: / 1664* (HD in ligature; see Mauritshuis 1935, p. 438)
Dutch title: *Portret van een man*

PROVENANCE
Acquired between 1817 and 1822

LITERATURE
Gudlaugsson 1943, p. 147

COMMENT
Formerly regarded as a portrait of Johan de Witt by Jan de Baen.

Simon van der Does

The Hague 1653–after 1718 Antwerp

31 *Shepherdess and shepherd with sheep and goats,* 1711

Canvas, 60 x 70 cm
Signed and dated on the pedestal of the vase: *S: van der Does / MDCCXI*
Dutch title: *Herderin en herder met schapen en geiten*

PROVENANCE
Gerrit van der Pot van Groeneveld, Rotterdam; purchased for the Royal Museum, Amsterdam, 1808; acquired by exchange with the Rijksmuseum, Amsterdam, 1825

LITERATURE
Mauritshuis 1980, pp. 27–28; Dordrecht-Leeuwarden 1988–1989, no. 43; Apeldoorn 2002, p. 47, repr.

COMMENT
The same girl is depicted in other paintings by the artist.

Gerrit Dou

Leiden 1613–1675 Leiden

32 *'The young mother',* 1658

Panel (rounded at the top), 73.5 x 55.5 cm
Signed and dated at left, in the lower part of the coat of arms: *GDOV 1658* (GD in ligature; the last digit superimposed on another)
Bears inscriptions bottom left and right: *N 35* and *501* (see The Hague 1988–1989, p. 79, figs. a–b)
Dutch title: *'De jonge moeder'*

31

<<
29

32 30

712 713 228

D

PROVENANCE
Purchased from the artist by the States of Holland and West Friesland, and given as part of the famous 'Dutch gift' to King Charles II in 1660; King James II, London, 1685–1688; King-Stadholder Willem III; Het Loo Palace, Apeldoorn; Prince Willem IV; Prince Willem V, The Hague

LITERATURE
HdG 1907–1928, vol. 1, p. 376, no. 110; D/LS 1974–1976, vol. 1, p. 695, no. 4, vol. 2, p. 643, no. 86, vol. 3, p. 209, no. 32; Sumowski 1983–1995, vol. 1, p. 533, no. 284; Mauritshuis 1987, no. 20; The Hague 1988–1989, no. IV; Amsterdam 1989–1990, no. 7; Baer 1990, no. 76; Slive 1995, p. 102; Hecht 1997, pp. 89–91; Boersma 2000–2001; Washington-London-The Hague 2000–2001, no. 21; Madrid 2003, no. 7

COMMENT
Cleaned and restored in 1986–1987.

33 *Young woman holding a lamp,* 1660s

Panel, 19 x 14 cm
Dutch title: *Meisje met een lamp*

PROVENANCE
Coenraet, Baron Droste, The Hague, 1734; Count Fraula, Brussels, 1738; Prince Willem IV; Het Loo Palace, Apeldoorn; Prince Willem V, The Hague

LITERATURE
Martin 1901, p. 236, no. 235; HdG 1907–1928, vol. 1, p. 416, no. 230; D/LS 1974–1976, vol. 2, p. 643, no. 83, vol. 3, p. 209, no. 33; Baer 1990, no. C 83 (catalogue of rejected paintings); Nagasaki 1992–1993, no. 6; De Boer *et al.* 1993, pp. 22–23, no. 1; Oxford 1999–2000, pp. 13–14, pl. 12

COMMENT
Cleaned and restored in 2000.

Joost Cornelisz Droochsloot

Utrecht after 1585–1666 Utrecht

34 *Village scene,* 1652

Panel, 44.5 x 80 cm
Signed and dated lower left: *Jc. DS. 1652*
(Jc and DS in ligature)
Dutch title: *Dorpsgezicht*

PROVENANCE
David van der Kellen, Amsterdam; purchased, 1873; on loan to the Centraal Museum, Utrecht, since 1925

LITERATURE
Mauritshuis 1980, pp. 28–29; Amsterdam 1984, no. 31; Helmus 1999, vol. 2, pp. 844–845, no. 188

COMMENT
Companion piece to inv. no. 35. Preserved in its original frame.

35 *River landscape,* 1652

Panel, 44.5 x 80 cm
Signed and dated lower left: *Jc. DS. 1652*
(Js and DS in ligature)
Dutch title: *Rivierlandschap*

PROVENANCE
Same as inv. no. 34; on loan to the Centraal Museum, Utrecht, since 1925

LITERATURE
Mauritshuis 1980, p. 29; Amsterdam 1984, no. 31; Helmus 1999, vol. 2, pp. 846–847, no. 189

COMMENT
Companion piece to inv. no. 34. Preserved in its original frame.

Gaspard Dughet

Rome 1615–1675 Rome

320 *Mountainous landscape*

Canvas, 48.6 x 64 cm
Dutch title: *Berglandschap*

PROVENANCE
Victor de Rainer, Brussels, 1821; purchased by King Willem I for the Mauritshuis, 1821

LITERATURE
RM 1976, p. 203; Boisclair 1986, p. 191, no. 78

Cornelis Dusart

Haarlem 1660–1704 Haarlem

440 *Peasant inn*

Panel, 40.5 x 49.5 cm
Signed at left, near the seated woman: *Corn. dusart.*
(underneath a forged signature of Adriaen van Ostade)
Dutch title: *Boerenherberg*

PROVENANCE
Purchased, 1877

LITERATURE
Mauritshuis 1935, pp. 79–80

33

34

35

320

440

Willem Cornelisz Duyster

Amsterdam 1599–1635 Amsterdam

408 *Standing officer*

Panel, 39.1 x 31 cm
Dutch title: *Een staande officier*

PROVENANCE
B.G. Roelofs, Amsterdam; Neville Goldsmid, The Hague, 1876; purchased, 1876

LITERATURE
Bernt 1969–1970, vol. 1, no. 348; Oxford 1999–2000, pp. 8–9, pl. 5; Rotterdam-Frankfurt am Main 2004–2005, p. 60

COMMENT
Cleaned and restored in 1997–1998.

Anthony van Dyck

Antwerp 1599–1641 London

239 *Portrait of Peeter Stevens (c.1590–1668)*, 1627

Canvas, 112.5 x 99.4 cm
Signed, dated and inscribed at left, on the base of the column: *ÆT. SUÆ 37. 1627 / Ant.° van Dijck. fecit.*
Dutch title: *Portret van Peeter Stevens (c.1590–1668)*

PROVENANCE
Peeter Stevens, Antwerp; Govert van Slingelandt, The Hague, in or before 1752; the entire collection sold to Willem V in 1768; Prince Willem V, The Hague, 1768–1795

LITERATURE
D/LS 1974–1976, vol. 3, p. 208, no. 24; Mauritshuis 1987, in no. 21; Larsen 1988, vol. 1, pp. 244–245, vol. 2, pp. 250–251, no. 617; Washington 1990–1991, no. 44; Antwerp-London 1999, no. 48; *Portraits in the Mauritshuis*, no. 13

COMMENT
Peeter Stevens, one of Antwerp's elite of magistrates, scholars and art-lovers, was a cloth merchant and a benefactor of the poor. In 1628 he married Anna Wake, who was also portrayed by Van Dyck (see inv. no. 240). Part of Stevens's painting collection is depicted in a painting of an art cabinet by Frans Francken the Younger and David Teniers the Younger in London, Courtauld Institute Galleries. Stevens was also portrayed in Van Dyck's *Iconographie* and Willem van Haecht's painting in the Rubenshuis, Antwerp (Mauritshuis 1987, p. 164, fig. 1).

240 *Portrait of Anna Wake (1605–before 1669)*, 1628

Canvas, 112.5 x 99.3 cm
Signed, dated and inscribed centre left: *ÆT. SUÆ 22. AN 1628 / Ant.° van Dyck fecit.*
Dutch title: *Portret van Anna Wake (1605–voor 1669)*

PROVENANCE
Same as inv. no. 239

LITERATURE
D/LS 1974–1976, vol. 3, p. 207, no. 23; Mauritshuis 1987, no. 21; Larsen 1988, vol. 1, pp. 244–245, vol. 2, p. 251, no. 618; Washington 1990–1991, no. 45; Antwerp-London 1999, no. 49; *Portraits in the Mauritshuis*, no. 14

COMMENT
Anna Wake was the daughter of Lionel Wake, a wealthy Englishman, devout Catholic and good friend of Rubens. In 1628 she married Peeter Stevens; this portrait was painted on the occasion as a companion piece to the portrait of her husband executed by Van Dyck the year before.

242 *Portrait of Quintin Symons (b. 1592–after 1646)*, c.1634–1635

Canvas, 95 x 83.7 cm
Dutch title: *Portret van Quintin Symons (geb. 1592–na 1646)*

PROVENANCE
Same as inv. no. 239

LITERATURE
D/LS 1974–1976, vol. 3, p. 208, no. 25; Larsen 1988, vol. 2, pp. 248–249, no. 611; Nagasaki 1992–1993, no. 7; Antwerp-London 1999, no. 82; *Portraits in the Mauritshuis*, no. 15

COMMENT
A preparatory drawing in the British Museum, London; a print by Pieter de Jode the Younger (1606–*c.*1674) is in Van Dyck's *Iconographie* (see Antwerp-London 1999, p. 282, figs. 1–2). Quintin Symons, who came of a long line of apothecaries, was a wealthy amateur painter. Cleaned and restored in 2003.

Anthony van Dyck (after)

243 *Portrait of Andreas Colijns de Nole (1598–1638)*

Panel, 24 x 19 cm
Dutch title: *Portret van Andreas Colijns de Nole (1598–1638)*

PROVENANCE
Adriaan van der Willigen, Haarlem; purchased, 1874; on loan to the ICN

240

239

408

243

242

LITERATURE
Antwerp-Amsterdam 1999–2000, p. 204, note 3

COMMENT
Andreas Colijns de Nole was a sculptor in Antwerp. Inv. no. 243 is a copy after a grisaille by Van Dyck, engraved by Pieter de Jode the Younger (1606–*c.*1674) for Van Dyck's *Iconographie* (both illustrated in Antwerp-Amsterdam 1999–2000, nos. 27a–b).

Anthony van Dyck (after)

472 *Portrait of Jan III (1583–1638), Count of Nassau-Siegen*

Canvas (oval), 73 x 60 cm
Dutch title: *Portret van Jan III (1583–1638), graaf van Nassau-Siegen*

PROVENANCE
Unknown; first catalogued in 1883

LITERATURE
Breda 1952, no. 39

COMMENT
Copy after a lost original. To be compared with the print in mirror image by Lucas Vorsterman the Elder in Van Dyck's *Iconographie.* Count Jan III of Nassau-Siegen, older brother of Johan Maurits of Nassau-Siegen, entered the service of Prince Maurits in 1609 (see his portrait by Van Ravesteyn, inv. no. 418). After converting to Catholicism in 1613, he entered the service of the Archdukes and enjoyed an excellent reputation at the court at Brussels. In 1618 he married Ernestine Yolande, Princess de Ligne (see Van Ravesteyn, inv. no. 120). The sitter is seen wearing the Order of the Golden Fleece.

Anthony van Dyck (after)

823 *Samson and Delilah*

Canvas, 148 x 258 cm
Dutch title: *Samson en Delila*

PROVENANCE
Acquired through government mediation, 1936; on loan to the ICN

COMMENT
Modern copy after the painting in the Kunsthistorisches Museum, Vienna (Larsen 1988, vol. 2, no. 745).

Albert Eckhout (attributed to)

Groningen *c.*1610–1666 Groningen

957 *Two Brazilian tortoises, c.*1640

Tempera and gouache on paper (cut at right), glued on panel, 30.5 x 51 cm
Dutch title: *Twee Braziliaanse schildpadden*

PROVENANCE
Probably Johan Maurits of Nassau-Siegen; Jacques Goudstikker Gallery, Amsterdam, 1936; J.C.H. Heldring, Oosterbeek, 1942–1963; purchased by the Friends of the Mauritshuis Foundation, 1963

LITERATURE
Van Gelder 1960; Mauritshuis 1970, no. 23; The Hague 1979–1980, no. 207; Paris 1986, no. 19; Mauritshuis 1987, no. 22; The Hague 2004, no. 29 and fig. 7

Gerbrand van den Eeckhout

Amsterdam 1621–1674 Amsterdam

1048 *Christ and the woman of Samaria at the well, c.*1640–1645

Oil on paper, 12.7 x 11.4 cm
Signed and dated lower right: *G. Eeckhout 16[4.]*
Dutch title: *Christus en de Samaritaanse vrouw bij de bron*

PROVENANCE
E.G. Spencer-Churchill, Northwick Park; David Koetser Gallery, Zürich; J. Schlichte Bergen Gallery, Amsterdam; gift of Mr and Mrs J. Hoogsteder, The Hague, 1974

LITERATURE
Montreal-Toronto 1969, no. 45; Mauritshuis 1991, no. IV; Sumowski 1983–1995, vol. 2, p. 725, no. 394

1084 *Isaac and Rebecca,* 1665

Canvas, 128.2 x 169.8 cm
Signed and dated lower left: *G. v. Eeckhout. fe / A° 1665*
Dutch title: *Isaak en Rebecca*

PROVENANCE
Pieter van Tol, Leiden and Zoeterwoude, 1779; Jean-Etienne Fizeaux, Amsterdam, 1779–1780; anonymous sale, Nottingham, 30 January 1811 (not in Lugt), lot 77, for 189 pounds to William Palmer-Morewood (as kindly communicated by B. Fredericksen, Los Angeles, 1999); C.R. Palmer Morewood, Alfreton Hall, 1919; J. Hoogsteder Gallery, The Hague, 1986–1989; purchased by the Friends of the Mauritshuis Foundation with a contribution from the Fondation Mauritshuis, Geneva, 1989

957 

1048 

 823

472 

 1084

LITERATURE

Broos 1989a; Mauritshuis 1993, no. 12; Defoer *et al.* 2003, p. 227

Adriaen van Emont (attributed to)

Dordrecht *c.*1626–1662 Dordrecht

741 *Italian landscape with hunting party*

Canvas, 67.3 x 97 cm
Formerly bore false signature: *JBoth* (JB in ligature)
Dutch title: *Italiaans landschap met jachtgezelschap*

PROVENANCE

Bequest of R.T. Baron van Pallandt van Eerde, 1913; on loan to the ICN

LITERATURE

Renckens 1954, p. 123, no. 14; Mauritshuis 1980, pp. 130–131; Harwood 1988, pp. 37–38 (with present attribution)

Juan Antonio de Frias y Escalante

Cordoba 1630–1670 Madrid

295 *A gipsy woman*

Canvas, 97 x 127 cm
Dutch title: *Zigeunerin*

PROVENANCE

Von Schepeler Collection, Aachen; purchased, 1839; on loan to the ICN

Allart van Everdingen

Alkmaar 1621–1675 Amsterdam

953 *View of Montjardin Castle*, 1660s

Canvas, 73 x 95.5 cm
Dutch title: *Gezicht op kasteel Montjardin*

PROVENANCE

Jan Hulswit, Amsterdam, 1822; Malmedé Gallery, Cologne, 1951; Otto Busch, Amsterdam, 1960; P. de Boer Gallery, Amsterdam; Hans Schaeffer Gallery, New York; purchased, 1962

LITERATURE

Mauritshuis 1970, no. 32; Davies 1978, pp. 254–258, 353, no. 155; Mauritshuis 1980, pp. 30–31; Davies 2001, pp. 146–148, 251–252, no. 174

COMMENT

A drawing by the artist with the same subject is in the Albertina, Vienna (Davies 2001, fig. 179). The castle, still standing high on a rock above the Amblève river near the village of Sougné-Remouchamps in the Belgian Ardennes, dates from the Middle Ages. Cleaned and restored *c.*1991.

Caesar van Everdingen

Alkmaar 1617/18–1678 Alkmaar

39 *Diogenes looking for an honest man (Portrait historié of the Steyn family)*, 1652

Canvas, 75.9 x 103.6 cm
Signed and dated at left, above the statue: *ANNO./ 1652 / CVE* (CVE in ligature)
Dutch title: *Diogenes zoekt een mens (Portrait historié van de familie Steyn)*

PROVENANCE

Pieter Steyn, Haarlem and The Hague, until 1772; bequest of Cornelia Steyn-Schellinger, Haarlem and The Hague, to Prince Willem V, The Hague, 1783

LITERATURE

D/LS 1974–1976, vol. 3, p. 210, no. 36; Paris 1986, no. 20; Mauritshuis 1987, no. 23; Schmitt 1993, pp. 222, 231–236, 302, 304, 310; Rotterdam-Frankfurt am Main 1999–2000, no. 30; Huys Janssen 2002, pp. 100–103, no. 41; *Portraits in the Mauritshuis*, no. 16

COMMENT

The ten figures directly around Diogenes with the lamp are members of the Steyn family of Haarlem. Amongst them may be Augustijn Steyn (1636–1669), his mother Maria Deyman (1611–1688) and Pieter Steyn (b. 1651); see Huys Janssen 2002.

1088 *Trompe l'oeil with a bust of Venus*, 1665

Canvas, 74 x 60.8 cm
Signed and dated lower left: *CVE Aº.16.65.* (CVE in ligature)
Dutch title: *Trompe l'oeil met Venusbuste*

PROVENANCE

Estate of the painter, Alkmaar, 1678; sale Amsterdam, De Leth, 26 September 1763, lot 50 or 51; W.S. Traill, Bushmills Antrim, Ireland; Vitale Bloch, London, 1936; Mr A. Staring, Vorden, 1939–1980; gift of Mrs J.H.M. Staring-de Mol van Otterloo, Vorden, 1992

LITERATURE

Van Leeuwen 1992–1993, pp. 94–100; Buijsen/Van der Ploeg 1993, pp. 21–22, no. 4; Fransen 1997, pp. 102–103;

741 

 295

953 

 1088

 39

Rotterdam-Frankfurt am Main 1999–2000, no. 39; Huys Janssen 2002, pp. 85, 103–104, no. 42; Munich-Cologne 2002, no. 100

COMMENT
The companion piece, *Trompe l'oeil with a bust of Adonis*, is in the Michaelis Collection, Capetown (Huys Janssen 2002, pp. 85–86, no. 28). Cleaned and restored in 1992.

Carel Fabritius

Midden-Beemster 1622–1654 Delft

605 *The goldfinch*, 1654

Panel, 33.5 x 22.8 cm
Signed and dated centre below: *C FABRITIVS 1654*
Dutch title: *Het puttertje*

PROVENANCE
Chevalier Joseph-Guillaume-Jean Camberlyn and heirs, Brussels; given to Etienne-Joseph-Théophile Thoré, Paris, 1865; his sale, Paris, Hôtel Drouot, 5 December 1892, lot 10; Martinet Collection, Paris; sold at Paris, Hôtel Drouot, 27 February 1896, lot 16; purchased, 1896

LITERATURE
HdG 1907–1928, vol. 1, p. 581, no. 16; Brown 1981, pp. 47–58, 126–127, no. 7; Sumowski 1983–1995, vol. 2, p. 987, no. 610; Paris 1986, no. 21; Mauritshuis 1987, no. 24; Slive 1995, p. 139; New York–London 2001, no. 21; Washington 2002–2003, no. 48; Wadum 2004; The Hague-Schwerin 2004–2005, no. 11

COMMENT
Cleaned and restored in 2003.

Paolo Farinato

Verona 1524–1606 Verona

311 *The adoration of the magi, c.*1585–1589

Canvas, 115 x 161 cm
Signed lower left with the artist's mark, a snail shell
Dutch title: *De aanbidding van de koningen*

PROVENANCE
Victor de Rainer, Brussels, 1821; purchased by King Willem I for the Mauritshuis, 1821; on loan to the Rijksmuseum, Amsterdam (inv. no. SK-C-1352), since 1948

LITERATURE
RM 1976, p. 225; Rotterdam 1989–1990, no. 9; Boschloo/Van der Sman 1993, pp. 47–48, no. 31

COMMENT
A preliminary drawing is in the Museo Civico, Pavia (Rotterdam 1989–1990, p. 47, fig. 9a). A separate drawing of the figure with the horse, dated 1589, is in London, British Museum.

Domenico Feti (after)

Rome 1589–1624 Venice

398 *Ecce homo*, 18th century

Panel, 68 x 58 cm
Dutch title: *Ecce homo*

PROVENANCE
Martial Reghellini Schio, Venice and Brussels, until 1826; purchased by King Willem I for the Mauritshuis, 1831

LITERATURE
Eidelberg/Rowlands 1994, pp. 257, 258, 285, notes 308, 309; Aikema *et al.* 1997, pp. 65–66, no. 60

COMMENT
One of many copies after a prototype of around 1616–1620 formerly in the Giovanelli Collection, Venice, 1926.

Jan Fijt

Antwerp 1611–1661 Antwerp

867 *Still life with dead birds*

Panel, 52.5 x 67.5 cm
Dutch title: *Stilleven met dode vogels*

PROVENANCE
Count Cavens, Brussels; Jacques Goudstikker Gallery, Amsterdam, 1924–1940; Adolf Hitler, Führermuseum, Linz; Stichting Nederlands Kunstbezit; on loan to the Mauritshuis, 1948–1960; transferred, 1960

LITERATURE
Greindl 1956, p. 165; Greindl 1983, p. 353, no. 230

925 *Still life with game, c.*1640–1650

Canvas, 121.5 x 97.5 cm
Formerly signed and dated: *Johannes Fyt pinx[..] 16[..]*
Dutch title: *Stilleven met jachtbuit*

PROVENANCE
Gift of Mr and Mrs H.A. Wetzlar, Amsterdam, 1955

LITERATURE
Mauritshuis 1970, no. 12; Auckland 1982, no. 21; Greindl 1983, p. 349, no. 66 (as dated '1641')

605

867

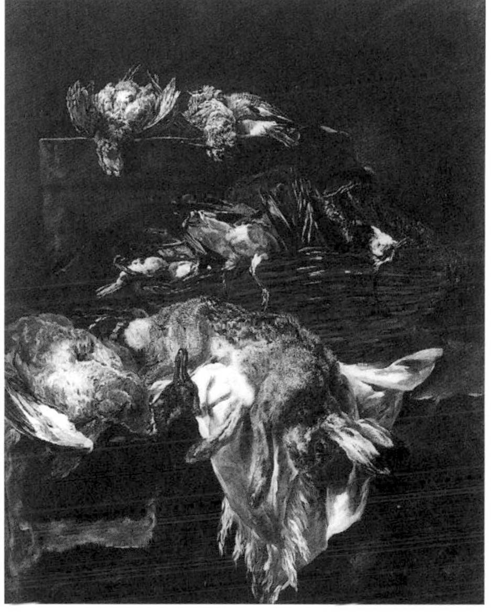
925

311

398

F

Jan Fijt (attributed to)

687 *Still life with dead birds, cage and net, c.*1645–1650

Canvas, 48.4 x 71.5 cm
Dutch title: *Stilleven met dode vogels, een kooi en een net*

PROVENANCE
Purchased, 1904

LITERATURE
Greindl 1956, p. 165; The Hague 1991–1992, pp. 38, 42, fig. 23

Govert Flinck

Cleves 1615–1660 Amsterdam

676 *Girl by a high chair*, 1640

Canvas, 114.3 x 87.1 cm
Signed and dated on the high chair: *G.flinck.f* 1640
Dutch title: *Meisje bij een kinderstoel*

PROVENANCE
Hendrik Willem Cramer, Amsterdam and Cleves, 1853–1867; Arnoldus Andries des Tombe, The Hague, 1867 (on loan to the Mauritshuis since 1890); bequest of Arnoldus Andries des Tombe, The Hague, 1903

LITERATURE
Von Moltke 1965, p. 152, no. 413; Sumowski 1983–1995, vol. 2, p. 1037, no. 691; Paris 1986, no. 22; Mauritshuis 1987, no. 25; Haarlem-Antwerp 2000–2001, no. 35; *Portraits in the Mauritshuis*, no. 18

COMMENT
Cleaned and restored in 1997.

696 *Portrait of a man*, 1630s

Canvas, 72.5 x 58.7 cm
Signed at right, lower centre: *G. flinck 16[3.]*
Dutch title: *Portret van een man*

PROVENANCE
Hendrik Willem Cramer, Amsterdam and Cleves, until 1867; Timon Hendrik Blom Coster, The Hague, 1867–1904; bequest of Timon Hendrik Blom Coster, The Hague, 1904

LITERATURE
Von Moltke 1965, p. 121, no. 264

866 *Portrait of a man aged 44*, 1637

Panel (oval), 74.8 x 60 cm
Signed and dated centre right: *[G. flinc]k. F / 1637*
Inscribed centre left: *Æ 44*
Dutch title: *Portret van een 44-jarige man*

PROVENANCE
Count L. Mniszech, Paris, 1902; F. Kleinberger Gallery, Paris; De Jonge Collection, Paris, 1916; Frits Lugt, The Hague; Van Leeuwen Boomkamp Collection, The Hague; sale Amsterdam, Frederik Muller, 23–30 March 1943, lot 21, to Alois Miedl; Adolf Hitler, Führermuseum, Linz; Stichting Nederlands Kunstbezit; on loan to the Mauritshuis, 1948–1960; transferred, 1960

LITERATURE
Von Moltke 1965, pp. 16, 109–110, no. 213; Sumowski 1983–1995, vol. 2, p. 1036, no. 687; Slive 1995, p. 105; Schwarz 2004, no. XXVII/30; *Portraits in the Mauritshuis*, no. 17

COMMENT
On the basis of a 1636 portrait etched by Rembrandt, the sitter was identified as Menasseh ben Israel (1604–1657). Ben Israel, however, was only 33 in 1637, whereas the age of the sitter is clearly indicated as 44. Cleaned and restored in 1986.

1116 *Allegory on the memory of Stadholder Frederik Hendrik (1584–1647), with a portrait of his widow Amalia of Solms-Braunfels (1602–1675)*, 1654

Canvas, 307 x 189 cm
Signed and dated at right, in the background: *G. Flinck f. 1654*
Dutch title: *Allegorie op de nagedachtenis van stadhouder Frederik Hendrik (1584–1647), met een portret van zijn weduwe Amalia van Solms-Braunfels (1602–1675)*

PROVENANCE
The painting was ordered by Amalia of Solms-Braunfels for the 'large cabinet' of Huis ten Bosch Palace, The Hague, 1654 (see The Hague 1997–1998, p. 130, fig. 2) and was removed in 1816; Picture Gallery of Prince Willem V, The Hague, until 1821; transferred, 1822; transferred to the Nederlands Museum voor Geschiedenis en Kunst, Amsterdam, 1876; Rijksmuseum, Amsterdam (inv. no. SK-A-869), 1885; on loan from the Rijksmuseum for the Picture Gallery of Prince Willem V, since 1998

LITERATURE
Von Moltke 1965, p. 39, 92, no. 118; D/LS 1974–1976, vol. 1, p. 281, no. 1182, p. 540, no. 20; RM 1976, p. 228; Sumowski 1983–1995, vol. 2, p. 1025, no. 636; The Hague 1997–1998a, no. 8; Rotterdam-Frankfurt am Main 1999–2000, no. 27; *Portraits in the Mauritshuis*, no. 19

COMMENT
For biographical data on Frederik Hendrik and Amalia, see Van Honthorst, inv. no. 104.

676

1116

687

696

866

Marcello Fogolino

San Vito al Tagliamento *c.*1470–1550 (?)

347 *Enthroned Madonna and Child with six saints, c.*1516

Canvas, 264.7 x 194 cm
Signed lower centre, at the foot of the throne: *MARCELLVS / VINCENTINVS / P.*
Dutch title: *Tronende madonna met kind en zes heiligen*

PROVENANCE
Probably made for the Chiesa di San Antonio, Camposampiero, serving as an altarpiece; Martial Reghellini Schio, Venice and Brussels, until 1826; purchased by King Willem I for the Mauritshuis, 1831; on loan to the Rijksmuseum, Amsterdam (inv. no. SK-C-1129), since 1924

LITERATURE
Puppi 1966, pp. 7, 12, 18, 20, 21, 26, 58, 74; RM 1976, p. 229; Van Os 1978, pp. 16, 56, 88–91, no. 20, p. 118

COMMENT
The saints, from left to right, are Catherine, Francis, John the Baptist, John the Evangelist, Anthony of Padua and Mary Magdalene.

Marcantonio Franceschini

Bologna 1648–1729 Bologna

316 *Adam and Eve, c.*1680

Canvas, 234 x 158 cm
Dutch title: *Adam en Eva*

PROVENANCE
Augustus III, king of Poland; Prince Willem V, The Hague, 1765–1795

LITERATURE
D/LS 1974–1976, vol. 3, p. 207, no. 21 (as by Carlo Cignani); Aikema *et al.* 1997, pp. 67–68, no. 63

COMMENT
Preliminary drawing in a private collection, Norfolk (see Miller 1971, pl. 5).

Frans Francken the Younger

Antwerp 1581–1642 Antwerp

With Paul Vredeman de Vries
Antwerp 1567–before 1636 Amsterdam

and an unidentified miniaturist
active in the southern Netherlands, *c.*1610

244 *Ballroom scene at a court in Brussels, c.*1610

Panel, 68.6 x 113.3 cm
Signed lower left: *Den J. ffranck.* (The young Francken)
Verso: panel-makers' mark of four criss-crossed lines (Hans van Haecht?)
Dutch title: *Bal aan een Brussels hof*

PROVENANCE
Geertruida Quirina van der Duyn, Countess of Albemarle, 1741; Het Loo Palace, Apeldoorn, 1757; Prince Willem V, The Hague

LITERATURE
D/LS 1974–1976, vol. 2, p. 641, no. 43, vol. 3, p. 211, no. 38; Härting 1983, no. A 336; Härting 1989, no. 431; The Hague 1992–1993; Vlieghe 1998, p. 151; Brussels 1998–1999, no. 173; Lemgo-Antwerp 2002, no. 51

COMMENT
The imaginary architecture is attributed to Paul Vredeman de Vries, who repeated it in another collaboration with Francken (Lemgo-Antwerp 2002, no. 52). An unidentified miniaturist added a number of portraits, some of which can be identified: from left to right Albert of Habsburg (1559–1621), Archduke of Austria and his wife Isabella of Habsburg (1566–1633), Archduchess of Austria, who were the governors of The Netherlands; Princess Charlotte Marguerite of Montmorency (1594–1650); Prince Philip Willem of Orange (1554–1618), son of Willem I of Orange, with his wife Princess Eleonore of Bourbon-Condé (1587–1619). At the far right stands Ambrogio Spinola, Marquis de los Balbases (1569–1630), presumably with his wife (see The Hague 1992–1993, p. 6).

Martinus Josephus Geeraerts

Antwerp 1707–1791 Antwerp

245 *Allegory of autumn*

Canvas, 85 x 100 cm
Dutch title: *Allegorie op de herfst*

PROVENANCE
Gerret Braamcamp, Amsterdam, until 1771; Prince Willem V, The Hague, 1771–1795

244

347

316

245

LITERATURE
D/LS 1974–1976, vol. 3, p. 211, no. 40; Bille 1961, vol. 1, p. 80, fig. 63, vol. 2, p. 96, no. 63; Van Dissel 1980, p. 398, note 12

Martinus Josephus Geeraerts (manner of)

1119 *Playing putti,* mid-18th century

Canvas, 120.7 x 101.6 cm
Dutch title: *Spelende putti*

PROVENANCE
Sale New York, Sotheby's, 14 October 1999, lot 71; gift of Mrs M.A. Stubbé-Butôt to the Friends of the Mauritshuis Foundation, 2000

LITERATURE
Q. Buvelot in *Mauritshuis in focus* 13 (2000), no. 1, pp. 3–4, repr. in colour, and *Mauritshuis in focus* 14 (2001), no. 2, p. 35 and fig. 20

COMMENT
The grisaille, formerly attributed to Jacob de Wit, has been placed as an overdoor in the Van Dyck Room. Cleaned and restored in 2000.

Arent de Gelder

Dordrecht 1645–1727 Dordrecht

40 *Judah and Tamar, c.*1700

Canvas, 80 x 97 cm
Signed lower right, on the paper: *ADe Gelder f* (AD in ligature)
Dutch title: *Juda en Tamar*

PROVENANCE
Gift of Count H. van Limburg-Stirum, 1874; on loan to the National Gallery, London, since 1992

LITERATURE
Sumowski 1983–1995, vol. 2, p. 1168, no. 758; Paris 1986, no. 23; Mauritshuis 1987, no. 26; Von Moltke 1994, pp. 66–67, no. 12; National Gallery 2001, p. 766, no. L 593

737 *The temple entrance,* 1679

Canvas, 70.7 x 91 cm
Signed and dated on the left: *ADe Gelder f. 1679* (AD in ligature)
Dutch title: *De voorhof van een tempel*

PROVENANCE
Gift of F. Kleinberger, Paris, 1911; on loan to the Dordrechts Museum, Dordrecht, since 1999

LITERATURE
Sumowski 1983–1995, vol. 2, p. 1160, no. 724; Von Moltke 1994, pp. 86–87, no. 54; Dordrecht-Cologne 1998–1999, no. 6

COMMENT
A preliminary drawing in the Maida and George Abrams Collection, Boston (Dordrecht-Cologne 1998–1999, no. 58; London-Paris-Cambridge 2002–2003, no. 54).

757 *Portrait of Herman Boerhaave (1688–1738), c.*1722

Canvas (oval), 79.2 x 63.5 cm
Signed upper right: *.deGelder f.*
Bears inscription on the verso: *Degelder Fecit anno 1722 / Herman Boerhave / geb: 31 Dec: 1668 / gest: 23 Sept: 1738*
Dutch title: *Portret van Herman Boerhaave (1688–1738)*

PROVENANCE
Probably heirs of Herman Boerhaave, Leiden, 1738–1918; gift of Dominicus Anthonius Josephus Kessler, The Hague, 1918

LITERATURE
Von Moltke 1994, pp. 100–101, no. 85; Dordrecht-Cologne 1998–1999, no. 56; *Portraits in the Mauritshuis,* no. 20

1047 *Simeon's song of praise, c.*1700

Canvas, 94.5 x 107.5 cm
Dutch title: *Het loflied van Simeon*

PROVENANCE
Sir William Cunliffe Brooks, Aboyne Castle, before 1900; Thomas B. Walker, Minneapolis, before 1912–1927; H.J. de Koster, Wassenaar, 1972–1987 (on loan to the Mauritshuis, 1974–1985; on loan to the Museum Catharijneconvent, Utrecht, 1985–1987); gift of H.J. de Koster to the Friends of the Mauritshuis Foundation, 1987

LITERATURE
Sumowski 1983–1995, vol. 2, p. 1196, no. 761; Mauritshuis 1993, no. 13; Von Moltke 1994, p. 83, no. 47; Dordrecht-Cologne 1998–1999, no. 32; Tokyo 2003, no. 89

Gortzius Geldorp the Elder

Louvain 1553–1618 Cologne

319 *The penitent Mary Magdalene*

Panel, 67 x 52 cm
Dutch title: *De boetvaardige Maria Magdalena*

1047 757

737 1119

40 319

PROVENANCE
Nationale Konst-Gallery, The Hague, 1800; probably transferred to the Picture Gallery of Prince Willem V, The Hague, *c.*1816; transferred, 1822

LITERATURE
Van Thiel 1981, p. 196, no. 106

COMMENT
Another version, possibly a copy (panel, 66 x 50.2 cm), was sold in London, Christie's South Kensington, 7 December 1995, lot 47, repr. A comparable painting with the same subject in sale London, Christie's, 29 October 2003, lot 10.

Jacob de Gheyn the Younger

Antwerp 1565–1629 The Hague

1077 *Glass flask with flowers*, 1612

Copper, 58 x 44 cm
Signed and dated upper centre: *J G 12* (to be read as 1612); lower centre: *JACOBVS DE GHEYN FE:*
Dutch title: *Bloemen in een glazen fles*

PROVENANCE
N. Nieuhoff, Amsterdam, 1777; L. Dimon, Perpignan; Gemeentemuseum, The Hague, acquired in 1934; on permanent loan from the Gemeentemuseum, The Hague (inv. no. 34–1934), since 1987

LITERATURE
Van Regteren Altena 1983, vol. 1, p. 112, vol. 2, p. 21, no. 39; The Hague 1992a, no. 13; Buijsen *et al.* 1998, pp. 136–137; Vienna-Essen 2002, no. 100

Luca Giordano

Naples 1632–1705 Naples

321 *Four women making music, c.*1655–1660

Canvas, 57.2 x 101.6 cm
Dutch title: *Vier musicerende vrouwen*

PROVENANCE
Victor de Rainer, Brussels, 1821; purchased by King Willem I for the Mauritshuis, 1821; on loan to the Rijksmuseum, Amsterdam (inv. no. SK-C-1353), since 1948

LITERATURE
RM 1976, p. 242; Rotterdam 1989–1990, no. 68; Ferrari/Scavizzi 1992, vol. 1, p. 265, no. A 100, vol. 2, p. 520, fig. 176; Aikema *et al.* 1997, pp. 69–70, no. 66

COMMENT
A replica or copy was auctioned in Monaco, Christie's, 22 June 1991, lot 128.

Luca Giordano (follower of)

356 *Samson and Delilah, c.*1660–1670

Canvas, 96 x 125 cm
Dutch title: *Simson en Delila*

PROVENANCE
Martial Reghellini Schio, Venice and Brussels, until 1826; purchased by King Willem I for the Mauritshuis, 1831

LITERATURE
Aikema *et al.* 1997, p. 71, no. 68 (tentatively attributed to a Venetian follower of Giordano)

Luca Giordano (after)

352 *Madonna and Child with Saints Dominic and Anthony of Padua, c.*1700

Canvas (oval), 34.7 x 29.4 cm
Dutch title: *Madonna en Kind met de heiligen Dominicus en Antonius van Padua*

PROVENANCE
Bernard Eugène Rottiers, Antwerp, 1823; purchased by King Willem I for the Mauritshuis, 5 August 1823; on loan to the ICN

LITERATURE
Aikema *et al.* 1997, pp. 182–183, no. 225 ('[possibly] a follower of Luca Giordano from the beginning of the 18th century')

COMMENT
The group of the Virgin and child is a virtually identical —partial— copy of a painting in the church of San Potito, Naples, dated to around 1664.

Fransise de Goltz

Active in The Hague, 1613 or 1618

427 *Portrait of an officer*, 1613 or 1618

Canvas, 115.4 x 96.2 cm
Signed and dated upper right: *aetat. 40. a° 161[3 or 8?]. / fransise de goltz. / fecit.*
Bears inscription lower right: *23.*
Dutch title: *Portret van een officier*

PROVENANCE
The portrait belongs to the set of 24 officer's portraits by Jan van Ravesteyn and was probably also transferred from Honselaarsdijk Palace, Naaldwijk; found in the attic of the Mauritshuis, 1875; on loan to the Paleis Het Loo Nationaal Museum, Apeldoorn, since 1984

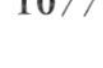

1077

352

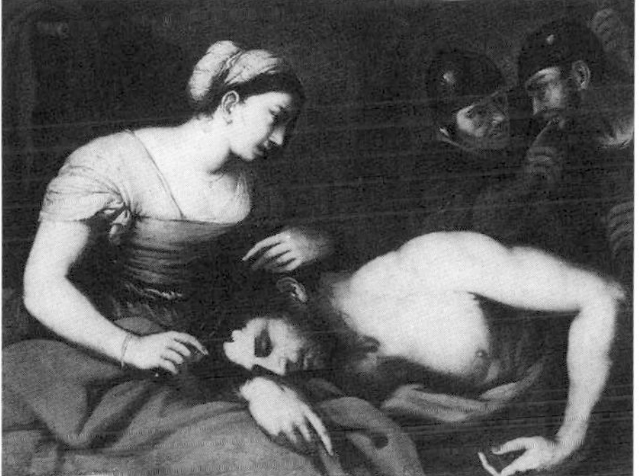

356

427

321

LITERATURE

Portraits in the Mauritshuis, in no. 45

COMMENT

Nothing is known about the life of the painter Fransise (Franciscus?) de Goltz; this portrait is his only known work. He may have worked in Van Ravesteyn's studio, although in that case it is strange that he was allowed to sign with his own name. With its reversed composition, the painting is different from the other portraits in the series, and may be a later addition. Certainly it was already part of the series by 1707, in which year it was marked with the number '23', which curiously also appears on most of the other works.

Hendrick Goltzius

Mühlbracht 1558–1617 Haarlem

42 *Minerva, c.*1611

Canvas, 214 x 120 cm
Dutch title: *Minerva*

PROVENANCE

Executed with the two following paintings for Johan Colterman I, or possibly his son Johan Colterman II, Haarlem; subsequently their heirs in Haarlem and Hoorn, until 1671; François van Bredenhoff and subsequent owners of Huis Oostenhuizen, Hoorn; Léon Gauchez Gallery, Paris, 1875; purchased with inv. nos. 43–44, 1875; on loan to the Frans Hals Museum, Haarlem, since 1917

LITERATURE

Amsterdam 1984, no. 6; Paris 1986, no. 25; Hendriks/Van Grevestein/Groen 1993; Levy-van Halm/Schlüter 1993; Amsterdam 1993–1994, no. 216; De Jongh 1997, pp. 35–39; Munich-Cologne 2002, no. 8; Amsterdam-New York-Toledo 2003–2004, no. 106.2

COMMENT

Minerva is depicted here as a personification of the theory of painting. The combination with inv. nos. 43 and 44 has been interpreted as the defence of art against stupidity, envy and slander (see Amsterdam 1993–1994, no. 216). In its original frame (see Amsterdam 1984, no. 6). Cleaned and restored in 1985.

43 *Hercules and Cacus*, 1613

Canvas, 207 x 142.5 cm
Signed and dated upper left, next to the arm of Hercules: *HG. / A° 1613* (HG in ligature)
Dutch title: *Hercules en Cacus*

PROVENANCE

Same as inv. nos. 42 and 44; on loan to the Frans Hals Museum, Haarlem, since 1917

LITERATURE

Amsterdam 1984, no. 6; Paris 1986, no. 26; Hendriks/Van Grevestein/Groen 1993; Levy-van Halm/Schlüter 1993, pp. 504–505; Amsterdam 1993–1994, no. 216; De Jongh 1997, pp. 35–39; Amsterdam-New York-Toledo 2003–2004, no. 106.3

COMMENT

As a personification of virtue defeating envy (Cacus), Hercules stands for the true artist. It seems likely he is a *portrait historié* of Johan Colterman II (see Paris 1986, p. 220 and fig. 7), son of the man who is supposed to have commissioned the three paintings from Goltzius.
In its original frame. Cleaned and restored in 1985.

44 *Mercury*, 1611

Canvas, 214 x 120 cm
Signed and dated lower right: *HG. / A°. 1611.*
(HG in ligature)
Dutch title: *Mercurius*

PROVENANCE

Same as inv. nos. 42–43; on loan to the Frans Hals Museum, Haarlem, since 1917

LITERATURE

Paris 1986, no. 24; Amsterdam 1984, no. 6; Hendriks/Van Grevestein/Groen 1993; Levy-van Halm/Schlüter 1993; Amsterdam 1993–1994, no. 216; De Jongh 1997, pp. 35–39; Munich-Cologne 2002, no. 8; Amsterdam-New York-Toledo 2003–2004, no. 106.1

COMMENT

Here, Mercury personifies the practice of art. In its original frame. Cleaned and restored in 1985.

Jan Gossaert

Maubeuge (?) *c.*1478–1533/36 Middelburg

830 *Madonna and Child, c.*1520

Panel (rounded at the top), 25.4 x 19.3 cm
Dutch title: *Madonna met kind*

PROVENANCE

Probably William Fuller Maitland, Stansted, Essex, 1868–1876; Carl von Hollitscher, Berlin, after 1912; Camillo Castiglioni, Vienna, 1925; Jacques Goudstikker Gallery, Amsterdam, 1925–1939; purchased, 1939

LITERATURE

Rotterdam-Bruges 1965, no. 29; Herzog 1969, pp. 341–342, no. 68; Mauritshuis 1993, no. 14

COMMENT

Cleaned and restored in 1986.

44

42

43

830

G

841 *Portrait of Floris van Egmond (1469–1539)*, 1519?

Panel, 39.8 x 29.3 cm
Inscribed right of the head: *L*
Dutch title: *Portret van Floris van Egmond (1469–1539)*

PROVENANCE
Anna of Buren, 1548–1558; Buren Castle, 1675, 1712; Nationale Konst-Gallery, The Hague, 1800–1808; Rijksmuseum, Amsterdam (inv. no. SK-A-217), since 1885; on loan from the Rijksmuseum since 1948

LITERATURE
Rotterdam-Bruges 1965, no. 17; Friedländer 1967–1976, vol. 7, p. 98, no. 54; Herzog 1969, pp. 240–241, no. 15; D/LS 1974–1976, vol. 1, p. 528, no. 151, p. 555, no. 13–2; RM 1976, p. 245; Van Thiel 1981, p. 191, no. 49; Mauritshuis 1987, no. 27; *Portraits in the Mauritshuis*, no. 21

COMMENT
Floris van Egmond, Count of Buren and Leerdam, Lord of IJsselstein and Maartensdijk, was a formidable commander and headed a Burgundian force fighting Utrecht and Guelders, and later even the French. He was made Stadholder of Friesland (1515), Holland, Zeeland and West-Friesland (1518) and in 1522 he became captain-general in the army of Charles V. Gossaert depicted him with the Order of the Golden Fleece.

Abraham Govaerts

Antwerp 1589–1626 Antwerp

45 *Forest view with gipsy women*, 1612

Panel, 62.5 x 101 cm
Signed and dated lower centre: *AGOVAERTS / .1.6.12.* (AG and VAE in ligature). On the verso an unidentified panel-maker's mark: a large 'R' with a smaller 'B' between the legs (see *Mauritshuis in focus* 6 [1993], no. 1, p. 15, fig. 10)
Dutch title: *Boslandschap met zigeunerinnen*

PROVENANCE
Princess Albertine Agnes of Orange-Nassau, Leeuwarden, 1681; Oranienstein Palace, Diez, 1726; by descent to Prince Willem V, The Hague

LITERATURE
D/LS 1974–1976, vol. 2, p. 109, no. 814, p. 371, no. 341, vol. 3, p. 211, no. 41; Keyes 1978, pp. 299–300, fig. 8; London 1986, no. 16; Broos/Wadum 1993; London 1996–1997, p. 23, fig. 14; Essen-Vienna 2003–2004, p. 170; Härting/Borms 2003, p. 79, no. 6

COMMENT
Cleaned and restored in 2002–2003. The panel came from the same tree as the painting by Jan Brueghel the Elder and an anonymous pupil of Rubens, inv. no. 234 (see Broos/Wadum 1993).

Jan van Goyen

Leiden 1596–1656 The Hague

551 *View of Dordrecht from Papendrecht*, 1633?

Panel, 46.8 x 73 cm
Signed and dated lower right, on the boat: *v goyen 163[3?]*
Dutch title: *Gezicht op Dordrecht vanuit Papendrecht*

PROVENANCE
Carl Sedelmeyer Gallery, Vienna; L. Lippmann von Lissingen, Vienna, 1872; Comte de Bojano, Paris, 1876–1882; E. Secrétan, Paris; Charles Sedelmeyer Gallery, Paris, 1889; purchased, 1889

LITERATURE
HdG 1907–1928, vol. 8, p. 17, no. 44; Dobrzycka 1966, no. 63; Beck 1972–1973, vol. 2, p. 141, no. 290; Bol 1973, pp. 120–121; Mauritshuis 1980, pp. 33–34

COMMENT
Cleaned and restored in 1991; see *Nieuwsbrief Mauritshuis* 4 (1991), no. 4, pp. 4–5.

624 *Estuary with sailing boats*, 1655

Panel, 41.2 x 55.8 cm
Signed and dated lower left, on the boat: *vG 1655* (vG in ligature)
Dutch title: *Riviermonding met zeilboten*

PROVENANCE
Alexis-Joseph Febure, Paris, 1882; Amédée Gautrey, Paris, 1883; W. Gretor, 1894; Charles Sedelmeyer Gallery, Paris, 1895; Abraham Bredius, The Hague, 1895–1946 (on loan to the Mauritshuis since 1899); bequest of Abraham Bredius, 1946

LITERATURE
HdG 1907–1928, vol. 8, pp. 250–251, no. 1033; Dobrzycka 1966, no. 238; Beck 1972–1973, vol. 2, p. 368, no. 821; Bol 1973, pp. 131–132; Mauritshuis 1980, p. 38; The Hague 1991–1992, no. 7

759 *River view*, c.1644–1648

Panel, 37 x 64 cm
Signed on the sailing boat: *vG* (in ligature)
Dutch title: *Riviergezicht*

PROVENANCE
Charles Sedelmeyer Gallery, Paris; James Simon, Berlin; Karl Haberstock Gallery, Berlin; gift of A.S. van den Bergh, The Hague, 1919

LITERATURE
HdG 1907–1928, vol. 8, p. 132, no. 548; Dobrzycka 1966, no. 90; Beck 1972–1973, vol. 2, p. 275, no. 603; Mauritshuis 1980, pp. 34–35

45

841

551

624

759

G

838 *View of the Rhine near Hoog-Elten*, 1653

Canvas, 81 x 152 cm
Signed and dated on the ferry: *vG 1653* (vG in ligature)
Dutch title: *Gezicht over de Rijn naar de Eltense berg*

PROVENANCE
R.M. Ward Gallery, London, 1932; Ludwig Rössler, Amsterdam, 1935; D. Katz Gallery, Dieren; C. ten Horn, Loon op Zand Castle, before 1947–1975 (on loan to the Mauritshuis, 1947–1962); purchased, 1975

LITERATURE
Dobrzycka 1966, no. 230; Beck 1972–1973, vol. 2, p. 158, no. 321; Mauritshuis 1980, pp. 36–38; Paris 1986, no. 27; Mauritshuis 1987, no. 28

COMMENT
The upper right corner is not original, but probably eighteenth century. Cleaned and restored in 1985.

979 *Fishermen by the lakeshore*, 1651

Paper on linen, 25 x 34 cm
Signed and dated lower centre: *vG 1651*
Dutch title: *Vissers aan de oevers van een plas*

PROVENANCE
A. Kay, Glasgow; F. Schwarz Gallery, Vienna; Marcus Kappel, Berlin; Jacques Goudstikker Gallery, Amsterdam; Hans-Ulrich Beck, Berlin-Munich, 1957; S. Nijstad Gallery, The Hague; purchased, 1967

LITERATURE
HdG 1907–1928, vol. 8, p. 126, no. 516, p. 132, no. 544; Mauritshuis 1970, no. 19; Beck 1972–1973, vol. 2, p. 123, no. 254; Mauritshuis 1980, pp. 35–36

COMMENT
This painting is probably based on a drawing in a private collection from a sketchbook of 1650–1651 (Beck 1972–1973, vol. 1, no. z 847–69), which was used by Van Goyen on his journeys between Leiden and Emmerich.

1081 *Dilapidated farmhouse with peasants*, 1631

Panel, 40 x 54 cm
Signed and dated at right: *vG 1631*
Dutch title: *Landvolk bij een vervallen boerderij*

PROVENANCE
Agnew's, London, 1914; Jacques Goudstikker Gallery, Amsterdam, 1928; G.J. Nieuwenhuizen Segaar Gallery, The Hague, 1934; gift of Mrs S.F. Duin-Priester, Apeldoorn, 1987

LITERATURE
HdG 1907–1928, vol. 8, pp. 189–190, no. 767; Beck 1972–1973, vol. 2, p. 485, no. 1100; Mauritshuis 1991, no. XXVIII

1094 *Winter landscape*, 1626

Panel, 32.5 x 50 cm
Signed and dated lower right: *I.V.GOYEN 1626*
Dutch title: *Winterlandschap*

PROVENANCE
J.T. Irving, Glasgow, 1934; his sale, London, Christie's, 23 March 1934, lot 34; Edward Speelman Gallery, London, 1934; D. Katz Gallery, Dieren, 1934–1935; Hans Ludwig Larsen, Wassenaar, 1937–1943; sale The Hague, Van Marle and Bignell, 14 January 1943, lot 28; E. Göpel, The Hague; Adolf Hitler, Führermuseum, Linz; Stichting Nederlands Kunstbezit; on loan from the Netherlands Institute for Cultural Heritage (inv. no. NK 2463), Amsterdam and Rijswijk, since 1993

LITERATURE
Beck 1972–1973, vol. 2, p. 21, no. 39; Van Straaten 1977, pp. 108–109; Buijsen/Van der Ploeg 1993, pp. 23–24, no. 5; Schwarz 2004, no. XXIV/20

1100 *River view with a church and farm*, 1653

Signed and dated lower right, on the boat: *VG 1653* (VG in ligature)
Dutch title: *Riviergezicht met een kerk en boerderij*

PROVENANCE
Private collection, London, 1985; sale London, Sotheby's, 11 December 1985, lot 58; private collection, New York, 1986–1993; gift of the American Friends of the Mauritshuis, 1994

LITERATURE
Beck 1987, p. 208, no. 565A; Buijsen 1994a; Buijsen 1994b; Leiden 1996–1997, no. 52

Jan van Goyen?

566 *Landscape with bridge, known as 'The small bridge'*, c.1627–1628?

Panel, 36 x 40.5 cm
Formerly bore signature lower right: *S. Ruysda[.]l*
Dutch title: *Landschap met brug, bekend als 'Het bruggetje'*

PROVENANCE
J.E. Goedhart Gallery, Amsterdam; purchased, 1892

LITERATURE
Stechow 1975, p. 143, no. 481; Mauritshuis 1980, pp. 98–99 (circle of Salomon van Ruysdael); The Hague 1991–1992, p. 34, fig. 10; De Kinkelder 2000, p. 21, note 2 ('an attribution to this artist [Jan van Goyen] cannot be excluded')

838

979

1100

1081

1094

566

COMMENT
De Kinkelder has pointed out (oral communication) the stylistic similarities with a signed painting by Van Goyen dated 1627, Xaver Scheidwimmer Gallery, Munich, 1984 (Beck 1972–1973, vol. 2, p. 472, no. 1059, repr.).

Jan van Goyen (manner of)

674 *River landscape*, 1637?

Panel, 35 x 54 cm
Said to bear a signature and date: *vG 1637* (vG in ligature)
Dutch title: *Rivierlandschap*

PROVENANCE
Bequest of Arnoldus Andries des Tombe, The Hague, 1903; on loan to the ICN

LITERATURE
Mauritshuis 1980, p. 131

Tethart Philip Christian Haag

Kassel 1737–1812 The Hague

813 *Orang-utan from the zoo of Stadholder Willem V, picking an apple*, 1777

Canvas, 174 x 110.5 cm
Signed and dated lower right:
TPCHaag Pinx. Ad viv. / 1777 (TPCH in ligature)
Dutch title: *Orang oetang uit de dierentuin van stadhouder Willem V, een appel plukkend*

PROVENANCE
Presumably made for Willem V to decorate a building in his zoo at Voorburg; found in the attic of the Mauritshuis, 1933; on loan to the Paleis Het Loo Nationaal Museum, Apeldoorn

LITERATURE
Mazel 1909, pp. 361–381; Martin 1934; Klessmann 1983, p. 78; Sliggers/Wertheim 1994, pp. 70, 82; Meijer 2004, p. 62, fig. 1

COMMENT
This female orang-utan from Borneo, the first of the species to have reached Europe alive, died on 22 January 1777. The scene with a monkey eating strawberries from a plate with a fork, depicted on the wall, is based on a 1776 painting by Haag in Braunschweig, Herzog Anton Ulrich-Museum, which also owns an earlier version of inv. no. 813 dated 1776 (for more on these paintings by Haag, see Klessmann 1983, pp. 78–79). Haag was keeper of the Cabinet of Willem V.

Joris van der Haagen

Dordrecht or Arnhem *c.*1615–1669 The Hague

46 *Panorama near Arnhem*, 1649

Canvas, 66 x 88.7 cm
Dated left, on the façade of the house: *1649*
Dutch title: *Panorama bij Arnhem*

PROVENANCE
Honselaarsdijk Palace, Naaldwijk, 1758; Prince Willem V, The Hague

LITERATURE
Van der Haagen 1932, pp. 72–73, no. 22; D/LS 1974–1976, vol. 2, p. 511, no. 192, 193, 195 or even 196, vol. 3, p. 235, no. 166 (as by Adriaen van de Velde); Duparc 1978, pp. 282–284; Mauritshuis 1980, pp. 39–40; Tokyo-Kasama-Kumamoto-Leiden 1992–1993, no. 49 B; Dufais 1998

COMMENT
Preparatory drawings in the Teylers Museum, Haarlem (see Tokyo-Kasama-Kumamoto-Leiden 1992–1993, p. 185, fig. 1) and the Rijksmuseum, Rijksprentenkabinet, Amsterdam. Copied in watercolour by Aert Schouman (see PRINTS AND DRAWINGS). Companion piece to inv. no. 47.

47 *Panorama near Arnhem with the Rhine gate*, 1649

Canvas, 66 x 88.7 cm
Dutch title: *Panorama bij Arnhem met de Rijnpoort*

PROVENANCE
Same as inv. no. 46

LITERATURE
Van der Haagen 1932, pp. 72–73, no. 21; D/LS 1974–1976, vol. 2, p. 511, no. 192, 193, or 195, vol. 3, p. 215, no. 61; Mauritshuis 1980, p. 40; Tokyo-Kasama-Kumamoto-Leiden 1992–1993, no. 49 A

COMMENT
The house on the far right is the same as that on the extreme left of inv. no. 46, the companion piece. The two paintings together form a panorama of the environs of Arnhem (see Tokyo-Kasama-Kumamoto-Leiden 1992–1993, pp. 98–99, repr.).

47

46

674

813

H

Jan Hackaert

Amsterdam 1628–in or after 1685 Amsterdam

1039 *Deer hunt in a forest*, after 1660

Canvas, 69 x 54 cm
Dutch title: *Hertenjacht in een bos*

PROVENANCE
A. van Beeftingh, Rotterdam, 1832; *Jonkheer* Johan Steengracht van Oostkapelle and heirs, The Hague, 1832–1913; Frederik Muller Gallery, Amsterdam, 1913; August Janssen, Amsterdam, 1919; Jacques Goudstikker Gallery, Amsterdam, 1919; E. Gutmann, Haarlem; F.B. Gutmann; Karl Haberstock Gallery, Berlin, 1942; Kunstmuseum, Düsseldorf, 1942; Stichting Nederlands Kunstbezit; S. Nijstad Gallery, The Hague; purchased, 1971

LITERATURE
HdG 1907–1928, vol. 9, p. 5, no. 14; Mauritshuis 1980, pp. 41–43

Jan Hackaert (attributed to)

470 *Italian landscape*

Panel, 28 x 34.5 cm
Signed at left: *I.H.*
Dutch title: *Italiaans landschap*

PROVENANCE
J.B. van den Bergh, Amsterdam, 1833; A.W. van Nagell tot Ampsen, The Hague, 1851; Bernard du Bus de Gisignies, Brussels; purchased, 1882

LITERATURE
HdG 1907–1928, vol. 9, p. 10, no. 36; Mauritshuis 1980, p. 41

Willem van Haecht

Antwerp 1593–1637 Antwerp

266 *Apelles painting Campaspe*, *c.*1630

Panel, 104.9 x 148.7 cm
Dutch title: *Apelles schildert Campaspe*

PROVENANCE
Estate of the painter, Antwerp, until 1637; bequeathed to Cornelis van der Geest, Antwerp, 1637–1638; Augustus III, king of Poland; Prince Willem V, The Hague, 1765–1795

LITERATURE
D/LS 1974–1976, vol. 3, p. 211, no. 37 (as by Sebastiaen Vrancx); Speth-Holterhoff 1957, pp. 104–108; Mauritshuis 1987, no. 29; Mauritshuis 1993, no. 15; Schwartz 1996, pp. 47–49; Antwerp 2004, pp. 44, 46–47, 56, 149–151; Braunschweig 2004, pp. 71–72

COMMENT
Some of the works displayed on the walls were part of the collection of Cornelis van der Geest, a prominent collector and benefactor of Rubens. Van Haecht was curator of the Van der Geest Collection, which he depicted in 1628 (Antwerp, Rubenshuis). Most of the paintings shown have been identified; for the most recent overview see Mauritshuis 1993, pp. 142–143, fig. 6. To this list can now be added the painting by Frans Snijders in the upper left corner, which was discovered in 1999 in Charlecote Park, England (see Lang 1999).

Johan van Haensbergen

Gorinchem or Utrecht 1642–1705 The Hague

135 *Nymphs bathing*, *c.*1665

Copper, 17.5 x 22.5 cm
Dutch title: *Badende nimfen*

PROVENANCE
Samuel van Huls, The Hague, 1737; Pieter de Klok, Amsterdam, 1744; Prince Willem V, The Hague

LITERATURE
D/LS 1974–1976, vol. 3, p. 225, no. 118; Enschede 1987–1988, no. 34; Nagasaki 1992–1993, no. 8

COMMENT
Until 1893 attributed to Cornelis van Poelenburch. The standing figure at the left was copied after a signed work with a comparable composition by the latter artist, Colnaghi Gallery, London, 1990.

601 *Still life with a wicker jug*, 1665

Panel, 40 x 30.2 cm
Signed and dated lower centre:
Joh: Haensbergh. Gorco. fec. 1665.
Dutch title: *Stilleven met kantelbeker*

PROVENANCE
Gift of T. Humphrey Ward, London, 1895

720 *Portrait of Pieter Dierquens (1668–1714)*, 1690

Canvas, 57.5 x 46 cm
Signed and dated lower left: *I.V.H. f / 1690*
Dutch title: *Portret van Pieter Dierquens (1668–1714)*

266 

<<
601

470

1039

135

720

PROVENANCE

Probably by inheritance to Maria Johanna Singendonck, The Hague; bequest of *Jonkvrouw* Maria Johanna Singendonck, 1907; on loan to the ICN

LITERATURE

Buijsen *et al.* 1998, p. 151, fig. 2

COMMENT

Pieter Dierquens, son of Elisabeth van Bebber from her first marriage to Johannes Dierquens (see Caspar Netscher, inv. no. 714), was bailiff of The Hague and married Anna Maria Roman in 1704; she is portrayed in the companion piece by Constantijn Netscher, inv. no. 721.

Claes Hals

Haarlem 1628–1686 Haarlem

623 *Girl reading, c.1660*

Panel, 30.8 x 24 cm
Signed left, on the stool: *CH*
Dutch title: *Lezend meisje*

PROVENANCE

Purchased, 1899

LITERATURE

Bredius 1921; Martin 1935–1936, vol. 1, pp. 382–383; The Hague 1991–1992, p. 45, fig. 31

Dirck Hals

Haarlem 1591–1656 Haarlem

771 *The five senses: Sound*, 1636

Panel (round), 12 cm in diameter
Signed and dated at left: *DH / 163[6]* (DH in ligature)
Dutch title: *De vijf zintuigen: Het gehoor*

PROVENANCE

Gift of Mr and Mrs A.F. Philips-de Jong, Eindhoven, 1923; with inv. nos. 772–775 on loan to the ICN

LITERATURE

Bruyn 1987, pp. 49, 51; Haarlem-Hamburg 2003–2004, no. 18; Nehlsen-Marten 2003, pp. 193–194

772 *The five senses: Touch*, 1636

Panel (round), 12 cm in diameter
Signed and dated at left: *DH / 16[3]6* (DH in ligature)
Dutch title: *De vijf zintuigen: Het gevoel*

PROVENANCE

Same as inv. no. 771

LITERATURE

Bruyn 1987, pp. 49, 51; Haarlem-Hamburg 2003–2004, no. 18; Nehlsen-Marten 2003, pp. 193–194

773 *The five senses: Taste*, 1636

Panel (round), 12 cm in diameter
Signed and dated at left: *DH / 1636* (DH in ligature)
Dutch title: *De vijf zintuigen: De smaak*

PROVENANCE

Same as inv. no. 771

LITERATURE

Bruyn 1987, pp. 49, 51; Haarlem-Hamburg 2003–2004, no. 18; Nehlsen-Marten 2003, pp. 193–194

774 *The five senses: Sight*, 1636

Panel (round), 12 cm in diameter
Signed and dated indistinctly at left: *DH / 1636* (DH in ligature)
Dutch title: *De vijf zintuigen: Het gezicht*

PROVENANCE

Same as inv. no. 771

LITERATURE

Bruyn 1987, pp. 49, 51; Haarlem-Hamburg 2003–2004, no. 18; Nehlsen-Marten 2003, pp. 193–194

COMMENT

The girl is styling her hair.

775 *The five senses: Smell*, 1636

Panel (round), 12 cm in diameter
Signed and dated indistinctly at left: *DH / 16[3]6* (DH in ligature)
Dutch title: *De vijf zintuigen: De reuk*

PROVENANCE

Same as inv. no. 771

LITERATURE

Bruyn 1987, pp. 49, 51; Haarlem-Hamburg 2003–2004, no. 18; Nehlsen-Marten 2003, pp. 193–194

COMMENT

The girl is making a bouquet of flowers.

1060 *Merry company*, 1633

Panel, 30 x 51.1 cm
Signed and dated upper right: *DHALS 1633* (DH in ligature)
Dutch title: *Vrolijk gezelschap*

PROVENANCE

Epstein Collection, Vienna; D.F. Teixeira de Mattos, The Hague, 1929; gift of *Jonkheer* E.V.E. Teixeira de Mattos, Monte Carlo, 1979

623

1060

772

774

775

771

773

LITERATURE
Mauritshuis 1991, no. XII; Oxford 1999–2000, p. 5, fig. 3; Nehlsen-Marten 2003, p. 275, no. 78; Seoul 2003, no. 14; Haarlem-Hamburg 2003–2004, p. 182, note 5

Frans Hals

Antwerp 1582/83–1666 Haarlem

459 *Portrait of Jacob Olycan (1596–1638)*, 1625

Canvas, 124.8 x 97.5 cm
Dated and inscribed upper right: *ÆTAT SVÆ. 29 / A° 1625*
Dutch title: *Portret van Jacob Olycan (1596–1638)*

PROVENANCE
Aletta van Loo, widow Olycan, Haarlem, 1638–1653; by inheritance to the Van Sypesteyn family, Haarlem, 1877; Victor de Stuers, The Hague, 1880; sold by him to the Dutch goverment, 1881; placed in the Mauritshuis, 1881

LITERATURE
HdG 1907–1928, vol. 3, p. 62, no. 208; Slive 1970–1974, vol. 1, pp. 50, 123–124, vol. 2, pl. 58, vol. 3, pp. 21–22, no. 32; Paris 1986, no. 29; Mauritshuis 1987, no. 31; Grimm 1989, pp. 178, 272, no. 21; Washington-London-Haarlem 1989–1990, no. 18; *Portraits in the Mauritshuis*, no. 22

COMMENT
At the upper left the sitter's coat of arms, added after 1720: an ostrich holding a horseshoe in its beak and a two-handled jug, referring to the sitter's name. Companion piece to inv. no. 460. Jacob Pietersz Olycan, a Haarlem brewer's eldest son, was not only brewer but also burgomaster, sheriff and delegate to the States General. He held several other public offices, among others governor of St Elizabeth's hospital, and is depicted in Hals's *Civic guard of St George* from 1627, in Haarlem, Frans Hals Museum (Slive 1970–1974, vol. 3, no. 46).

460 *Portrait of Aletta Hanemans (1606–1653)*, 1625

Canvas, 123.8 x 98.3 cm
Dated and inscribed upper left: *ÆTAT SVÆ. 19 / AN° 1625*
Dutch title: *Portret van Aletta Hanemans (1606–1653)*

PROVENANCE
Same as inv. no. 459

LITERATURE
HdG 1907–1928, vol. 3, p. 63, no. 209; Slive 1970–1974, vol. 1, pp. 50, 123–124, vol. 2, pl. 58, vol. 3, p. 22, no. 33; Paris 1986, no. 30; Mauritshuis 1987, in no. 31; Grimm 1989, pp. 272–273, no. 22; Washington-London-Haarlem 1989–1990, no. 19; *Portraits in the Mauritshuis*, no. 23

COMMENT
At the upper right the sitter's coat of arms, a cock. Companion piece to inv. no. 459. Aletta Hanemans of Zwolle married Jacob Olycan in 1624. After his death, she married the brewer Nicolaes Jansz van Loo (1607–1641) in 1641. Following his sudden death she carried on the brewery business on her own.

618 *Portrait of a man, c.1634*

Panel, 24.7 x 19.7 cm
Dutch title: *Portret van een man*

PROVENANCE
Frederik Muller & Co, Amsterdam; purchased, 1898

LITERATURE
HdG 1907–1928, vol. 3, p. 80, no. 279; Slive 1970–1974, vol. 1, pp. 30, 124, 162, vol. 2, fig. 140, vol. 3, p. 54, no. 92; Grimm 1989, pp. 139–140, 275, no. 67

COMMENT
Grimm suggested that this portrait might have been made in preparation for a group portrait that was never carried out.

928 *Portrait of a man, c.1660*

Panel, 31.1 x 25.5 cm
Dutch title: *Portret van een man*

PROVENANCE
Richard Foster, Clewer Manor, London, 1876–1882; Wilhelm Gumprecht, Berlin, 1882–1918; Paul Herman Heilbuth, Copenhagen, 1918–1922/23; William H. Bixby, St Louis, Missouri, 1922/23–1956; Hans Schaeffer Gallery, New York; purchased with the support of the Friends of the Mauritshuis Foundation and the bequest of *Jonkheer* J. Loudon, 1957

LITERATURE
HdG 1907–1928, vol. 3, p. 75, no. 257; Mauritshuis 1970, no. 16; Slive 1970–1974, vol. 1, pp. 198–199, vol. 2, figs. 323–324, vol. 3, pp. 107–108, no. 210; Grimm 1989, pp. 195–196, 283, no. 140; Slive 1995, p. 51; *Portraits in the Mauritshuis*, no. 25

1032 *Laughing boy, c.1625*

Panel, 30.4 cm in diameter (at highest point)
Signed lower left, above the shoulder: *FHF* (in ligature)
Traces of a second signature upper left
Dutch title: *Lachende jongen*

PROVENANCE
Albert, Baron von Oppenheim, Cologne, before 1876–1912; Marie-Anne Friedländer-Fuld, Baroness de Goldschmidt-Rothschild, Berlin and Paris, 1918–1968; purchased with the support of the Rembrandt Society, the Prince Bernhard Culture Fund and the Friends of the Mauritshuis Foundation, 1968

459

460

928

618

1032

LITERATURE
HdG 1907–1928, vol. 3, p. 11, no. 28; Mauritshuis 1970, no. 15; Slive 1970–1974, vol. 1, p. 75, vol. 2, fig. 49, vol. 3, pp. 18–19, no. 29; Paris 1986, no. 28; Mauritshuis 1987, no. 30; Grimm 1989, pp. 178, 209, 223, 224, 272, no. 19; Washington-London-Haarlem 1989–1990, no. 16 (Haarlem only); Stukenbrock 1993, pp. 76–78, 83 and 239, table I, p. 240, table II, no. 1; *Portraits in the Mauritshuis*, no. 24

COMMENT
Many copies are known, the best one in Augsburg, Städtische Kunstsammlungen (see Washington-London-Haarlem 1989–1990, pp. 176–177 and fig. 16f).

Frans Hals (follower of)

692 *The rumble-pot player*

Canvas, 97 x 81 cm
Signed at left: *B.E.*
Dutch title: *De rommelpotspeler*

PROVENANCE
Bequest of Timon Hendrik Blom Coster, The Hague, 1904; on loan to the ICN

COMMENT
The only known work by this artist, whose initials are 'B.E.'.

Harmen Hals

Haarlem 1611–1669 Haarlem

756 *Peasant smoking*

Panel, 63.3 x 48 cm
Dutch title: *Rokende boer*

PROVENANCE
Jacques Goudstikker Gallery, Amsterdam, 1917; purchased, 1918; on loan to the ICN

LITERATURE
Martin 1918, pp. 214–217, fig. 1

Adriaen Hanneman

The Hague *c.*1604–1671 The Hague

241 *Portrait of Constantijn Huygens (1596–1687) with his five children*, 1640

Canvas, 204.2 x 173.9 cm
Dated and inscribed centre below: *ECCE / HÆREDITAS / DOMINI. / Anno. 1640*
Dutch title: *Portret van Constantijn Huygens (1596–1687) en zijn vijf kinderen*

PROVENANCE
Constantijn Huygens and his heirs, Huygens residence, The Hague, 1640–1822; purchased, 1822

LITERATURE
Van Gelder 1957, pp. 24–25, no. 12; Ter Kuile 1976, pp. 25, 59–61, no. 6, p. 62, in no. 6a; Slive 1995, pp. 253–254; Haarlem-Antwerp 2000–2001, p. 54 and fig. 24; *Portraits in the Mauritshuis*, no. 26

COMMENT
Constantijn Huygens, depicted in the centre, was portrayed by a number of Dutch artists. Jacob van Campen painted Huygens with his wife, who died prematurely in 1637 (see Van Campen, inv. no. 1089, with biographical data). Until 1785 at least, inv. no. 241 hung as a chimneypiece in Huygens's residence in The Hague, opposite the Mauritshuis. His children have been identified: at upper left, Constantijn (1628–1697), who —like his father— became secretary of the Prince of Orange; at upper right, Christiaen (1629–1695), who became one of the greatest mathematicians and astronomers of his time and is famous for his invention of the pendulum timepiece; bottom right, Philips (1633–1657), who died while on a diplomatic mission to Sweden and Poland; bottom left, Lodewijk (1631–1699), who later became sheriff and dikegrave of Gorinchem; upper centre, Suzanna (1637–1725), who married her cousin Philips Doublet.

429 *Posthumous portrait of Mary I Stuart (1631–1660) with a servant*, *c.*1664

Canvas, 129.5 x 119.3 cm
Dutch title: *Postuum portret van Maria I Stuart (1631–1660) met een dienstbode*

PROVENANCE
Painted for Prince Willem III, The Hague; Honselaarsdijk Palace, Naaldwijk, 1755; acquired in or before 1875

LITERATURE
D/LS 1974–1976, vol. 1, p. 522, no. 11 (?), vol. 2, p. 510, no. 169; Ter Kuile 1976, pp. 113–114, no. 78a; The Hague 1979–1980, no. 273; The Hague 1997–1998b, pp. 56, 100; Krefeld-Oranienburg-Apeldoorn 1999–2000, no. 10/7; Van der Ploeg *et al.* 2002, p. 73, note 6; Dessau 2003, no. 11–26; The Hague 2004, no. 31 and fig. 46

COMMENT
The sitter is dressed in a South-American, Indian feather cape. Other versions in Hampton Court and Zuylesteyn Castle. Mary I Stuart was a daughter of the English king Charles I and Henrietta Maria (see MINIATURES). In 1641 —at the age of nine— she married Prince Willem II of Orange.

241

429

756

692

H

693 *Portrait of a man, c.1637*

Canvas, 73 x 62 cm
Dutch title: *Portret van een man*

PROVENANCE
Bequest of Timon Hendrik Blom Coster, The Hague, 1904

LITERATURE
Ter Kuile 1976, p. 76, no. 16

Willem Claesz Heda

Haarlem *c.*1596–1680 Haarlem

596 *Still life with a roemer and watch,* 1629

Panel, 46 x 69.2 cm
Signed and dated lower left, on the edge of the table: *.Heda. / 1629*
Remains of a second signature on the blade of the knife (see Mauritshuis 1935, p. 130, repr.)
Dutch title: *Stilleven met een roemer en horloge*

PROVENANCE
H. Gildemeester, Amsterdam, 1894; purchased, 1895

LITERATURE
Vroom 1945, p. 210, no. 175; Bergström 1956, p. 124, fig. 109; Bergström 1977, p. 196; Vroom 1980, vol. 1, p. 66, vol. 2, p. 65, no. 326

Willem Claesz Heda (attributed to)

936 *Still life with nautilus cup,* 1640

Panel, 68.5 x 50 cm
Signed and dated lower centre, on the white cloth: *· HEDA · 1640*
Dutch title: *Stilleven met Nautilusbeker*

PROVENANCE
Galerie Internationale, The Hague; bequest of B.H. van der Linden, New York, in memory of his wife, 1959

LITERATURE
Vroom 1945, pp. 134–135, fig. 116, p. 207, no. 142; Mauritshuis 1970, no. 26; Vroom 1980, vol. 2, p. 58, no. 283; Vroom 1999, p. 193, fig. 142, p. 198; Meijer 2000, pp. 233–234; Van der Willigen/Meijer 2003, p. 103; London 2004, p. 36, note ii

COMMENT
Formerly attributed to Gerrit Willemsz Heda, the son of Willem Heda, to whom the painting is now attributed by Meijer.

Cornelis de Heem

Leiden 1631–1695 Antwerp

50 *Still life with fruit, c.1670*

Canvas, 65 x 50 cm
Signed at left, on a stone: *C. DE HEEM*
Dutch title: *Fruitstilleven*

PROVENANCE
Nationale Konst-Gallery, The Hague, 1800; transferred after 1822

LITERATURE
Van Thiel 1981, p. 203, no. 147; Buijsen *et al.* 1998, pp. 164–165; Seoul 2003, no. 17

Jan Davidsz de Heem

Utrecht 1606–1683/84 Antwerp

48 *Sumptuous fruit still life with jewellery box, c.1650–1655*

Canvas, 94.7 x 120.5 cm
Signed upper left: *J.D. de heem f*
Dutch title: *Pronkstilleven met fruit en een juwelenkist*

PROVENANCE
Prince Willem V, The Hague

LITERATURE
D/LS 1974–1976, vol. 3, p. 214, no. 55; Greindl 1983, pp. 127, 360, no. 61; Utrecht-Braunschweig 1991, no. 10; Nagasaki 1992–1993, no. 9; De Boer *et al.* 1993, pp. 24–25, no. 2; Vlieghe 1998, p. 221

49 *Garland of fruit with some flowers,* probably 1650s

Canvas, 60.2 x 74.7 cm
Signed upper centre: *J.D. de Heem. fecit*
Dutch title: *Guirlande van vruchten met enkele bloemen*

PROVENANCE
Adriaan Bout, The Hague; his sale, 11 August 1733, lot 137; Willem IV, The Hague; Het Loo Palace, Apeldoorn, 1757; Prince Willem V, The Hague

LITERATURE
The Hague 1966, no. 14; D/LS 1974–1976, vol. 2, p. 644, no. 107, vol. 3, p. 215, no. 57; Scrase 1983, pp. 41–42, in no. 57; Greindl 1983, pp. 127, 361, no. 62; Utrecht-Braunschweig 1991, p. 172, fig. 23c; Gemar-Koeltzsch 1995, vol. 2, p. 468, no. 160/34

596

50

936

693

49

48

COMMENT
A copy in watercolour, attributed to Abraham de Lust (active *c.*1650–1659), is in a private collection. Cleaned and restored in 1986.

613 *Still life with books and a violin*, 1628

Panel, 36.1 x 48.5 cm
Signed and dated lower left, on a booklet: *Johannes. de. / Heem. / .i628.*
Inscribed on the books, centre and left: *G.A. BR[E]DEROOS / Treur-spel van RODD'RICK ende ALPHONSVS / [...] / T'AMSTEL[DAM]; .NOTA BENE. [...] .I. WE[...] and .I. WESTERBAENS. / KVSIENS. CLAECHTEN. I. / [...] / II.*
The end of the text of the letter can be deciphered with difficulty as: *[W.?] L. [...] Arns*
Dutch title: *Stilleven met boeken en een viool*

PROVENANCE
Dowager J.K.H. de Jonge-de Kock, The Hague, before 1881; her heir, *Jonkheer* A.H.W. de Jonge (on loan to the Mauritshuis, 1897–1910); purchased by the Rembrandt Society, 1910; transferred, 1912

LITERATURE
Paris 1986, no. 31; Mauritshuis 1987, no. 32; Utrecht-Braunschweig 1991, no. 3; The Hague 2002, pp. 99, 101 and fig. 14a; Van der Ploeg *et al.* 2002, p. 79

1099 *Vase with flowers, c.*1670

Canvas, 74.2 x 52.6 cm
Signed and dated lower right: *J.D. De Heem. R.*
Dutch title: *Vaas met bloemen*

PROVENANCE
Private collection, Switzerland; Robert Noortman Gallery, Maastricht; purchased by the Friends of the Mauritshuis Foundation with a major contribution from Hans Heinrich, Baron Thyssen-Bornemisza and the support of the Rembrandt Society, 1993

LITERATURE
Duparc 1993; Buijsen 1993a; Van Eck 1993; Buvelot *et al.* 1998, p. 226; Mauritshuis 2000, pp. 82–83

Maerten van Heemskerck

Heemskerk 1498–1574 Haarlem

51 *The adoration of the shepherds*, 1546
Verso: *The Virgin*

Panel, 260 x 122.5 cm
Dutch titles: *De aanbidding der herders* and *De maagd*

52 *The adoration of the kings*, 1546
Verso: *Archangel Gabriel*

Panel, 260 x 122.5 cm
Dutch titles: *De aanbidding der koningen* and *De aartsengel Gabriël*

PROVENANCE
Painted for the drapers' guild in Haarlem, 1546; ceded to the Dutch State by the city of Haarlem, 1805; transferred at an unknown date and found in the attic in 1875; on loan to the Frans Hals Museum, Haarlem, since 1917

LITERATURE
Grosshans 1980, no. 55; Biesboer 1983, pp. 23–27; Zevenhuizen/De Boer 1998, pp. 40–43

COMMENT
These wings of a triptych show a continuous representation of the annunciation on the verso. Around 1591 the centre panel was replaced by *The massacre of the innocents* by Cornelis Cornelisz van Haarlem (see inv. no. 22), who also remodelled the wings to a rectangular shape.

Hendrick Heerschop

Haarlem 1620/21–after 1672

801 *Visit to the doctor*, 1668

Panel, 53 x 43.5 cm
Signed and dated lower centre, on a page in a book: *HEERSCHOP: / 1668*
Dutch title: *Het bezoek aan de dokter*

PROVENANCE
Gift of B. Svenonius, Stockholm, 1930

LITERATURE
Sumowski 1983–1995, vol. 1, pp. 83, 87, note 35

Antoon François Heijligers

Batavia 1828–1897 The Hague

1055 *Interior of the Rembrandt Room in the Mauritshuis in 1884*, 1884

Panel, 47 x 59 cm
Signed and dated lower right: *A.F. Heijligers. 1884*
Dutch title: *Interieur van de Rembrandtzaal in het Mauritshuis in 1884*

PROVENANCE
Purchased, 1976

LITERATURE
Mauritshuis 1991, no. VII; Paris 1986, p. 39 and fig. 26; Mauritshuis 2000, p. 23, fig. 13

613

801

>> 51

52

1099

>> 51

52

1055

H

Bartholomeus van der Helst

Haarlem 1613–1670 Amsterdam

54 *Portrait of Paulus Potter (1625–1654)*, 1654

Canvas, 99 x 80 cm
Signed and dated upper left: *B. vander .helst. / 1654*
Dutch title: *Portret van Paulus Potter (1625–1654)*

PROVENANCE
Adriana van Balckeneynde, widow of the sitter, and heirs, The Hague, 1654–1820; purchased, 1821

LITERATURE
De Gelder 1921, pp. 23, 92, 172, nos. 116–117; Paris 1986, no. 32; Mauritshuis 1987, no. 33; Broos 1994; The Hague 1994–1995, p. 174 (in exhibition); *Portraits in the Mauritshuis*, no. 27

COMMENT
Potter became famous as the painter of *The bull* (inv. no. 136), a canvas of monumental proportions. The portrait is based on a drawn self-portrait by the artist in Stockholm, Nationalmuseum (The Hague 1994–1995, no. 40).

545 *Portrait of a young woman*

Canvas, 78 x 67 cm
Dutch title: *Portret van een jonge vrouw*

PROVENANCE
M.J. Hollender sale, Brussels, 10–12 April 1888, lot 42 (as Louis van der Helst); purchased, 1888; on loan to the ICN

LITERATURE
De Gelder 1921, pp. 120–121, 209, no. 548

COMMENT
The female sitter strongly resembles a Venus by Van der Helst in Lille, Musée des Beaux-Arts.

568 *Portrait of a man*, 1660

Panel, 77.2 x 62.5 cm
Signed and dated lower right: *B. vander / helst. 1660*
Dutch title: *Portret van een man*

PROVENANCE
Anonymous gift, 1893

LITERATURE
De Gelder 1921, p. 171, no. 112

COMMENT
Companion piece to inv. no. 569. The sitter is traditionally said to be a member of the Persijn family from The Hague or Amsterdam.

569 *Portrait of a woman*, 1659

Panel, 77 x 62.5 cm
Signed and dated lower left: *B. van der. helst / 16[59]*
Dutch title: *Portret van een vrouw*

PROVENANCE
Same as inv. no. 568

LITERATURE
De Gelder 1921, pp. 171–172, no. 113

COMMENT
Companion piece to inv. no. 568.

Jan Sanders van Hemessen

Hemiksem near Antwerp *c.*1500–1556/57 Antwerp

1067 *Allegorical scene, possibly the personification of poetry with a poet, c.*1550

Panel, 159 x 189 cm
Dutch title: *Allegorische voorstelling, mogelijk de personificatie van de poëzie met een dichter*

PROVENANCE
Alan G. Fenwick, London, 1950 (as by Giorgione); Arcade Gallery, London, 1950; T.A. Heinrich, Toronto, Ontario, 1950–1951; J. Hoogsteder Gallery, The Hague, 1982; purchased with the support of the Rembrandt Society and the Friends of the Mauritshuis Foundation, 1984; on loan to the Rijksmuseum, Amsterdam (inv. no. SK-C-1657), since 1999

LITERATURE
Winternitz 1958, pp. 48–55; Bandmann 1960, pp. 111–118; Winternitz 1967, pp. 47–48, 202–210; Wallen 1983, pp. 24, 25, 114, 314, 315, no. 43; Mauritshuis 1987, no. 34; RM 2000, pp. 152–153, no. 57

Wybrand Hendriks

Amsterdam 1744–1831 Haarlem

827 *Portrait of Jacob Feitama (1726–1797) and his wife Elisabeth de Haan (1735–1800)*, 1790

Canvas, 85.5 x 69.5 cm
Signed and dated lower right, on the tabouret: *Wd Hendriks Pinxit 1790*
Dutch title: *Portret van Jacob Feitama (1726–1797) en zijn echtgenote Elisabeth de Haan (1735–1800)*

54

545

827

1067

568

569

PROVENANCE

Presumably passed to the Smissaert family via Maria Feitama, who married Marinus A.P. Smissaert in 1799; Frans A.E.L. Smissaert, Laren, 1937; purchased, 1937

LITERATURE

Minneapolis-Toledo-Philadelphia 1971–1972, no. 29; Haarlem 1972, no. 14; Haarlem 1989, no. 206; Fock *et al.* 2001, p. 329 and fig. 281; Amsterdam 2002–2003a, no. 91

COMMENT

Cleaned and restored in 1989. Originally, there was a third figure on the left, which was painted out and replaced by the two chairs. Perhaps this figure was one of the couple's four daughters, presumably Maria Feitama, who was the only unmarried child in 1790. Possibly due to their Baptist background, her parents disapproved of her marrying an officer and had her subsequently removed from their portrait. Feitama, an Amsterdam merchant, married Elisabeth de Haan in 1753.

Willem de Heusch

Utrecht *c.*1625–1692 Utrecht

55 *Mountainous landscape in Italy*

Copper, 21.5 x 29 cm
Signed lower centre: *GDHeusch: f* (GDH in ligature)
Inscribed on the verso: *GDHeusch: f:* (GDH in ligature) and *168*
Dutch title: *Bergachtig landschap in Italië*

PROVENANCE

Count Fraula, Brussels, 1738; Hermina Jacoba, Baroness van Leyden, Warmond; purchased, 1816

LITERATURE

Bol 1969, p. 267; Mauritshuis 1980, pp. 43–44

COMMENT

Companion piece to inv. no. 56. Cleaned and restored in 1987.

56 *Mountainous river landscape in Italy*

Copper, 21.5 x 29 cm
Signed lower right: *GDHeusch: f:* (GDH in ligature)
Inscribed on the verso: *GDHeusch: f:* (GDH in ligature) and *174*
Dutch title: *Bergachtig rivierlandschap in Italië*

PROVENANCE

Same as inv. no. 55

LITERATURE

Same as inv. no. 55

COMMENT

Companion piece to inv. no. 55. Cleaned and restored in 1987.

Jan van der Heyden

Gorinchem 1637–1712 Amsterdam

53 *The church of St Andreas in Düsseldorf*, 1667

Panel, 51 x 63.5 cm
Signed and dated lower left:
VHeyde A 1667 (VH in ligature)
Dutch title: *De St Andreaskerk te Düsseldorf*

PROVENANCE

Princess Henriette Catharina; Oranienstein Castle, Diez, 1726; by descent to Prince Willem V, The Hague, 1776

LITERATURE

HdG 1907–1928, vol. 8, p. 375, no. 57; Wagner 1971, pp. 60, 75, no. 37; D/LS 1974–1976, vol. 2, p. 372, no. 346, vol. 3, p. 213, no. 48; Washington etc. 1982–1984, no. 20

COMMENT

A copy of the painting is in the Stadtmuseum, Düsseldorf.

531 *Still life with a bible*, 1664

Panel, 27 x 20.7 cm
Signed and dated upper right: *I.v.d.Heyde 1664*
Dutch title: *Stilleven met bijbel*

PROVENANCE

Purchased, 1885

LITERATURE

HdG 1907–1928, vol. 8, p. 452, no. 334;
Wagner 1971, pp. 51, 113, no. 211

COMMENT

The bible lies open at the Book of Jeremiah.

815 *The church at Veere*

Canvas, 31.5 x 36 cm
Signed lower right: *JVDH*
Dutch title: *De kerk van Veere*

PROVENANCE

L. Cottreau, Paris, 1870; Marcel Cottreau, Paris; his sale, Paris, Georges Petit, 12 June 1919, lot 11; Blumenthal Collection, Paris; Jacques Goudstikker Gallery, Amsterdam; purchased, 1935

LITERATURE

HdG 1907–1928, vol. 8, p. 414, no. 189; Wagner 1971, p. 83, no. 75; Nagasaki 1992–1993, no. 10; De Boer *et al.* 1993, pp. 25–26, no. 3

55 

 56

53 

815

 531

H

868 *View of Oudezijds Voorburgwal with the Oude Kerk in Amsterdam, c.1670?*

Panel, 41.4 x 52.3 cm
Signed lower left, on the boat: *VHeiden* (VH in ligature)
Dutch title: *Gezicht op de Oudezijds Voorburgwal met de Oude Kerk in Amsterdam*

PROVENANCE
Valerius Röver, Delft, 1713; his widow, Cornelia Röver-van der Dussen, 1739–1750; sold with the Röver Collection to Prince Wilhelm VIII of Hessen, Kassel, 1750; Josephine de Beauharnais, Malmaison, 1806–1815; Czar Alexander I, St Petersburg, 1815; Hermitage, St Petersburg, until 1935; Fritz Mannheimer, Amsterdam, 1935; Adolf Hitler; Stichting Nederlands Kunstbezit; on loan to the Mauritshuis, 1948–1960; transferred, 1960

LITERATURE
HdG 1907–1928, vol. 8, p. 366, no.25; Wagner 1971, pp. 18, 31–32, 60, 68, no. 6; Paris 1986, no. 33; Mauritshuis 1987, no. 35

LITERATURE
The staffage was probably painted by Adriaen van de Velde, providing a *terminus ante quem* for the painting, as he died in 1672. The Koninklijk Oudheidkundig Genootschap in Amsterdam possesses a counter-impression in reverse of a preliminary drawing for the painting (Mauritshuis 1987, p. 206, fig. 3).

Pauwels van Hillegaert

Amsterdam 1595–1640 Amsterdam

546 *The princes of Orange and their families on horseback, riding out from The Buitenhof, The Hague, c.1621–1622*

Canvas, 144.6 x 214 cm
Dutch title: *De prinsen van Oranje met familieleden te paard, uitrijdend vanaf het Buitenhof, Den Haag*

PROVENANCE
Sale P.C.G. Guijot, The Hague, 13–14 December 1869, lot 40 (as David Vinckboons); gift of August, Count Van der Straten Ponthoz, The Hague, 1888

LITERATURE
Sluijter-Seijffert 1983–1984; Paris 1986, no. 1; Dumas 1991, pp. 651, 657, note 21; Amberg-The Hague 2003–2004, no. II.11; *Portraits in the Mauritshuis*, no. 28 (with present attribution)

COMMENT
For the persons depicted, see *Portraits in the Mauritshuis*, no. 28. Several of the portraits proved to be posthumous. The painting is an historical impossibility and was probably intended to bolster the legitimacy of the ruling dynasty. A direct precursor of inv. no. 546 is a print of 1621 by Willem Jacobsz Delff after Adriaen van de Venne (Hollstein, vol. 5, p. 231, no. 95). Formerly attributed to the virtually unknown Amsterdam master Hendrick Ambrosius Pacx (1602/3–after 1658?). Cleaned and restored in 1985.

Meindert Hobbema

Amsterdam 1638–1709 Amsterdam

899 *Landscape near Deventer, c.1662–1663*

Panel, 55 x 69.5 cm
Signed lower left: *m. hobbema* (indistinct)
Dutch title: *Landschap bij Deventer*

PROVENANCE
Henry Croese, Amsterdam, 1811; Adriaen Harssevoort, Rotterdam, 1817; Paul Cassirer Gallery, Amsterdam, *c.*1935; gift of E. Vis, Lausanne, 1950

LITERATURE
HdG 1907–1928, vol. 4, p. 377, no. 20a; Broulhiet 1938, no. 132; Mauritshuis 1970, no. 33; Mauritshuis 1980, pp. 45–46; Enschede 1980, no. 13

COMMENT
In the background is the Bergkerk with its two towers (at the left) and the Binnenberg- or Geestpoort (at the right). Cleaned and restored in 1997.

1061 *Cottages in a forest, c.1665*

Panel, 53 x 71 cm
Signed lower left: *m. hobbema*
Dutch title: *Boerenhoeven in een boslandschap*

PROVENANCE
Charles Brind, London, 1849; William Delafield, London, 1870; J. Addington, London, 1886; A.P. Heywood-Lonsdale, Shavington Hall, Shropshire, 1887, and his heirs (on loan to the Walker Art Gallery, Liverpool, from 1959 onwards); Robert Noortman Gallery, Maastricht; purchased with the support of the Rembrandt Society and the Friends of the Mauritshuis Foundation, 1980

LITERATURE
HdG 1907–1928, vol. 4, p. 434, no. 184; Paris 1986, no. 34; Mauritshuis 1987, no. 36; Hamburg-Haarlem 2002, no. 43

1105 *Wooded landscape with cottages, c.1665*

Canvas, 88 x 120.7 cm
Signed lower centre: *M[e]yndert Hobbema*
Dutch title: *Boslandschap met boerenhoeven*

868 

 546

1105 

899 

 1061

PROVENANCE
Jean-Etienne Fizeaux, Amsterdam; his widow, Marie-Anne Massé, Amsterdam, 1780–1794; Henry Welbore Ellis Agar, 2nd Viscount Clifden, London, 1805; Robert, 2nd Earl of Grosvenor, London, 1806; by descent to Hugh, 3rd Marquess of Westminster and Hugh, 2nd Duke of Westminster, Eaton Hall; Lady Mary Grosvenor, Chester; her sale, London, Sotheby's, 6 July 1966, lot 75; Edward Speelman Gallery, London; sale London, Sotheby's, 24 June 1970, lot 20; William Darby; Collection of the British Rail Pension Fund; their sale, London, Sotheby's, 7 December 1994, lot 25; purchased with the support of the Dutch State, Hans Heinrich, Baron Thyssen-Bornemisza, the Friends of the Mauritshuis Foundation, the Prince Bernhard Culture Fund, the Rembrandt Society and the Algemene Loterij Nederland, 1994

LITERATURE
HdG 1907–1928, vol. 4, p. 413, no. 120; Broulhiet 1938, p. 401, no. 188; Van der Ploeg 1995a/b/c; Wadum 1995; Amsterdam 2000a, no. 157

COMMENT
The staffage has been attributed to Johannes Lingelbach (1622–1674). Cleaned and restored in 1995.

Hans Holbein the Younger

Augsburg 1497/98–1543 London

276 *Portrait of Robert Cheseman (1485–1547)*, 1533

Panel, 58.8 x 62.8 cm
Dated and inscribed upper left and right: *ROBERTVS CHESEMAN . ÆTATIS . SVUÆ . XLVIII . / ANNO . DM . M . D . XXXIII .*
Bears inscriptions on the verso: *W. E. P. L. C. / 46*; on a piece of paper: *Hans Holbein* (see The Hague 1988–1989, p. 59, fig. B 5)
Dutch title: *Portret van Robert Cheseman (1485–1547)*

PROVENANCE
King Charles I, London, until 1649; King James II, London, until 1688; King-Stadholder Willem III, London, after 1688; Het Loo Palace, Apeldoorn, 1713; Prince Willem V, The Hague

LITERATURE
D/LS 1974–1976, vol. I, p. 679, no. 887, p. 697, no. 35, pp. 699–700, nos. 1, 4, 9, 15–17, vol. 2, p. 639, no. 9, vol. 3, p. 215, no. 60; Rowlands 1985, pp. 82, 139, no. 46; Mauritshuis 1987, no. 37; Klinger/Höttler 1998, pp. 170–171, no. 49; The Hague 1988–1989, no. III; The Hague 2003, no. 19; *Portraits in the Mauritshuis*, no. 29

COMMENT
Cleaned and restored in 2003.

277 *Portrait of a nobleman with a hawk*, 1542

Panel, 24.6 x 18.8 cm
Dated and inscribed upper left and right: *15 / 42 / . ANNO . ETATIS . / SVÆ. XXVIII*
Bears inscription on the verso, on a piece of paper: *The Man[n]er of Holbein*
Dutch title: *Portret van een edelman met valk*

PROVENANCE
King Charles I, London, until 1649; King Charles II, London; King James II, London, 1666/67–1688; King-Stadholder Willem III, London, after 1688; Het Loo Palace, Apeldoorn, 1713; Prince Willem V, The Hague

LITERATURE
D/LS 1974–1976, vol. I, p. 679, no. 899, p. 697, no. 31, pp. 699–700, nos. 1, 4, 9, 15–17, vol. 2, p. 398, nos. 294–297, p. 645, no. 120, p. 652, no. j, vol. 3, p. 19, no. 18, p. 215, no. 58; Rowlands 1985, p. 120, 147, no. 74; Mauritshuis 1987, p. 216; The Hague 1988–1989, no. X; Klinger/Höttler 1998, p. 222, no. 78; The Hague 2003, no. 36; *Portraits in the Mauritshuis*, no. 30

Hans Holbein the Younger (studio of)

278 *Portrait of Jane Seymour (1509?–1537)*, c.1540

Panel, 26.4 x 18.7 cm
Verso: wax seal of Johan Willem Friso
Dutch title: *Portret van Jane Seymour (1509?–1537)*

PROVENANCE
Probably King-Stadholder Willem III, London, before 1700; thence by descent to Prince Willem V, The Hague

LITERATURE
Mauritshuis 1968, pp. 26–28; D/LS 1974–1976, vol. I, p. 697, vol. 2, p. 269, note 281, p. 645, no. 125, p. 652, no. k, vol. 3, p. 19, no. 19, p. 215, no. 59; Rowlands 1985, p. 114, 144, in no. 62, p. 232, no. R 23 ('English follower of Holbein the Younger'); The Hague 1988–1989, p. 39, fig. 37; The Hague 2003, no. 28 (with present attribution)

COMMENT
Based on a drawing by Holbein of the sitter in the English Royal Collection, Windsor Castle, which was used by the artist for the portrait in Vienna, Kunsthistorisches Museum, dated to around 1536 (The Hague 2003, nos. 26–27). The English king Henry VIII married Jane Seymour in 1536. She died twelve days after giving birth to her son, Edward (1537–1553), Prince of Wales (see MINIATURES, France, inv. no. 982).

ROBERTVS CHESEMAN .
ANNO . DM .
. ETATIS . SVÆ . XLVIII
M . D . XXXIII .

276

1 5 4 2
ANNO · ETATIS ·
SVÆ · XXVIII

277

278

H

Hans Holbein the Younger (formerly attributed to)

275 *Portrait of a woman from southern Germany, c.*1520–1525

Panel, 45 x 34 cm
Verso: a brandmark with the crowned monogram 'CR' of Charles I
Dutch title: *Portret van een Zuid-Duitse vrouw*

PROVENANCE
King Charles I, London, before 1649; very probably Joan de Vries, Amsterdam and his heir, Catharina de Vries; by inheritance to Anna van Aelst, Amsterdam; sale Amsterdam, 13 October 1738, lot 3; (?) sale Gerard Bicker van Swieten, The Hague, 12 April 1741, lot 179; Govert van Slingelandt, The Hague, in or before 1752; the entire collection sold to Willem V in 1768; Prince Willem V, The Hague, 1768–1795

LITERATURE
Mauritshuis 1968, pp. 28–29; D/LS 1974–1976, vol. 3, p. 233, no. 158 (as by Leonardo da Vinci); Rowlands 1985, p. 228, no. R 4 (as by Hans Holbein the Elder); Klinger/Höttler 1998, pp. 142–143, no. 33 (as by Hans Holbein the Younger)

COMMENT
Formerly attributed to Holbein the Younger and thought to be a portrait of Elisabeth Schmid, the painter's wife. Jochen Sander attributes the painting to the so-called Venus Master in his 2003 dissertation, *Hans Holbein als Tafelmaler in Basel 1515–1532.*

Hans Holbein the Younger (after)

279 *Portrait of Desiderius Erasmus (1466/69–1536)*

Panel, 24 x 19 cm
Dutch title: *Portret van Desiderius Erasmus (1466/69–1536)*

PROVENANCE
Victor de Rainer, Brussels, 1821; purchased by King Willem I for the Mauritshuis, 1821

LITERATURE
Brunin 1968, pp. 155–160, no. 25; Rowlands 1985, p. 136, in no. 34d

COMMENT
A rather mediocre copy after Holbein's 1523 portrait of the influential humanist in a private collection, on loan to the National Gallery, London (see The Hague 2003, in no. 1).

Gijsbert Gillisz d'Hondecoeter

Utrecht 1604–1653 Utrecht

405 *Cock and hens in a landscape*

Panel, 52 x 70 cm
Dutch title: *Haan en kippen in een landschap*

PROVENANCE
Dirksen Gallery, The Hague; Neville Goldsmid, The Hague; purchased, 1876

LITERATURE
Mauritshuis 1935, p. 149, no. 405

627 *Cock and hens in a landscape*, 1651?

Panel, 55 x 74 cm
Bears signature and date lower left:
A:cuijp / ANº 1651 (AN in ligature)
Dutch title: *Haan en kippen in een landschap*

PROVENANCE
Christopher Sykes, London, 1899; Abraham Bredius, The Hague, 1899 (on loan to the Mauritshuis since 1899); bequest of Abraham Bredius, 1946

LITERATURE
HdG 1907–1928, vol. 2, p. 221, no. 800; Reiss 1975, p. 211; The Hague 1991–1992, no. 5; Chong 1992a, p. 498, no. C 157

Melchior d'Hondecoeter

Utrecht 1636–1695 Amsterdam

59 *The raven robbed of the feathers he wore to adorn himself*, 1671

Canvas, 176 x 189 cm
Signed and dated on the tomb: *M d hondecoeter / Aº 1671*
Dutch title: *De raaf wordt beroofd van de veren waarmee hij zich had getooid*

PROVENANCE
Het Loo Palace, Apeldoorn, 1757; Prince Willem V, The Hague; on loan to the Fondation Custodia, Paris

LITERATURE
Martin 1935–1936, vol. 2, p. 440, fig. 232; D/LS 1974–1976, vol. 2, p. 640, no. 26, vol. 3, p. 214, no. 52

59

275

627

405

279

H

60 *Landscape with exotic animals, c.*1690–1692

Canvas, 169 x 156.8 cm
Signed lower right: *M d'Hondecoeter*
Dutch title: *Landschap met uitheemse dieren*

PROVENANCE
Probably painted for King-Stadholder Willem III, Het Loo Palace, Apeldoorn, recorded there in 1713; Prince Willem V, The Hague, 1795; on loan to the Paleis Het Loo Nationaal Museum, Apeldoorn, since 1984

LITERATURE
Evers 1912, pp. 533–534; Evers 1914, pp. 201–213; D/LS 1974–1976, vol. 1, p. 667, no. 536, vol. 2, p. 607, no. 143, vol. 3, p. 214, no. 53; New York 1979, no. 61; Sliggers/ Wertheim 1994, pp. 74–75; Apeldoorn 2002, p. 104, repr.

COMMENT
Formerly thought to represent the zoological garden of King-Stadholder Willem III at Het Loo Palace, Apeldoorn. Now shown as a chimneypiece in the reconstructed 'Private Cabinet' of Willem III in Het Loo Palace.

61 *Geese and ducks*

Canvas, 115 x 136 cm
Signed on the fence: *M d'Hondecoeter*
Dutch title: *Ganzen en eenden*

PROVENANCE
Princess Henriette Catharina; Oranienstein Palace, Diez, 1726; by descent to Prince Willem V, The Hague, 1776

LITERATURE
D/LS 1974–1976, vol. 2, p. 371, no. 340, vol. 3, p. 213, no. 50 or 51; Apeldoorn 2002, p. 104, repr.

COMMENT
Probably the companion piece of inv. no. 62. Cleaned and restored in 1989.

62 *Hens and ducks*

Canvas, 115 x 136 cm
Signed lower centre: *M D'Hondecoeter*
Dutch title: *Kippen en eenden*

PROVENANCE
Same as inv. no. 61

LITERATURE
D/LS 1974–1976, vol. 2, p. 371, no. 340, vol. 3, p. 213, no. 50 or 51; Apeldoorn 2002, p. 100, repr.

COMMENT
Probably the companion piece of inv. no. 61. Cleaned and restored in 1989.

Melchior d'Hondecoeter?

968 *Dead rooster hanging from a nail*

Canvas, 76 x 62.5 cm
Bears signature upper left: *M: d'Hondekoeter*
Dutch title: *Dode haan, hangend aan een spijker*

PROVENANCE
S. Nijstad Gallery, The Hague; purchased, 1964

LITERATURE
Mauritshuis 1970, no. 46; Buijsen *et al.* 1998, p. 172, note 3 (doubtful attribution)

COMMENT
To be compared with the painting by D'Hondecoeter in Aachen, Suermondt-Ludwig-Museum (Copenhagen 1999, no. 47, repr.). The attribution was doubted by F.G. Meijer in Buijsen *et al.* 1998. Cleaned and restored in 1999.

Gerrit van Honthorst

Utrecht 1592–1656 Utrecht

64 *Double portrait of Prince Willem III (1650–1702) and his aunt Maria, Princess of Orange (1642–1688), as children*, 1653

Canvas, 130.7 x 108.4 cm
Signed and dated lower left: *GHonthorst / 1653*
(GH in ligature)
Dutch title: *Dubbelportret van prins Willem III (1650–1702) en zijn tante Maria, prinses van Oranje (1642–1688), als kinderen, 1653*

PROVENANCE
Amalia of Solms-Braunfels, Huis ten Bosch Palace, The Hague; probably by descent to Prince Willem V, The Hague; transferred, in or before 1841

LITERATURE
Braun 1966, no. 123; D/LS 1974–1976, vol. 1, p. 281, no. 1177, p. 539, no. 8; Judson/Ekkart 1999, no. 305

COMMENT
For biographical data on Willem III, see Bakhuysen, inv. no. 6. Maria, Princess of Orange, was the youngest daughter of Frederik Hendrik and Amalia of Solms-Braunfels. In 1666 she married Ludwig Heinrich of Simmern, Count Palatine. For another portrait of Maria, see Mijtens, inv. no. 114.

60

61

62

968

64

H

65 *A child picking fruit, c.*1632

Canvas, 108.5 x 83.5 cm
Dutch title: *Fruitplukkend kind*

PROVENANCE
Honselaarsdijk Palace, Naaldwijk, 1707; Nationale Konst-Gallery, The Hague, 1801; transferred, 1822; on loan to Paleis Het Loo Nationaal Museum, Apeldoorn, since 2004

LITERATURE
Braun 1966, no. w 15 (as Willem van Honthorst); D/LS 1974–1976, vol. 1, p. 521, no. 2, vol. 2, p. 510, no. 176; The Hague 1997–1998b, pp. 169, 180, 188; Judson/Ekkart 1999, no. 320

COMMENT
Possibly a portrait of Isabella Charlotte (1632–1642), the fourth daughter of Stadholder Frederik Hendrik and Amalia of Solms-Braunfels.

104 *Double portrait of Frederik Hendrik (1584–1647) and Amalia of Solms-Braunfels (1602–1675), c.*1637–1638

Canvas, 213.2 x 201.7 cm
Dutch title: *Dubbelportret van Frederik Hendrik (1584–1647) en Amalia van Solms-Braunfels (1602–1675)*

PROVENANCE
Constantijn Huygens and heirs, *c.*1637/38–1800; transferred from the Huygens residence, 1829

LITERATURE
Braun 1966, no. 103; Paris 1986, no. 11; Slive 1995, p. 27; Buijsen *et al.* 1998, p. 177; Judson/Ekkart 1999, no. 295; Krefeld-Oranienburg-Apeldoorn 1999–2000, no. 5/8a; *Portraits in the Mauritshuis*, no. 31

COMMENT
Commissioned by Constantijn Huygens, the stadholder's secretary, for his residence in The Hague. The chimneypiece, which remained in its original setting until 1829, is a replica of the chimneypiece at the Huis ter Nieuburg, one of Frederik Hendrik and Amalia's country residences (see Buvelot 1995b, p. 130, fig. 94). Cleaned and restored in 1990. Frederik Hendrik, Prince of Orange, was the youngest son of Willem I and Louise de Coligny. He became stadholder after the death of his half-brother Maurits in 1625. In the same year he married Amalia of Solms-Braunfels, a daughter of Johann Albrecht of Solms and Agnes of Sayn-Wittgenstein.

1107 *The violin player,* 1626

Canvas, 84.5 x 66 cm
Signed and dated upper right: *GHonthorst. fe. i626*
Dutch title: *De vioolspeelster*

PROVENANCE
L. Hauser, Paris, 1937; W. van Gelder, Uccle, 1963; Bob Haboldt Gallery, Paris and New York, 1993–1994; gift of the Onderlinge Levensverzekering-Maatschappij ''s-Gravenhage', The Hague, 1995

LITERATURE
Braun 1966, no. 67; Buvelot 1995c; Amsterdam 1997a, pp. 199–200, fig. 1; Judson/Ekkart 1999, no. 225

Gerrit van Honthorst (and studio)

428 *Double portrait of Friedrich Wilhelm I (1620–1688) and Louise Henriette (1627–1667), c.*1647

Canvas, 220 x 181 cm
Dutch title: *Dubbelportret van Friedrich Wilhelm I (1620–1688) en Louise Henriette (1627–1667)*

PROVENANCE
Probably one of the palaces of the stadholders; transferred, before 1875

LITERATURE
Braun 1966, no. 119; Judson/Ekkart 1999, no. 303–1 (replica); Krefeld-Oranienburg-Apeldoorn 1999–2000, no. 5–8a; Dessau 2003, no. 11–42

COMMENT
Replica of the portrait in the Rijksmuseum, Amsterdam, dated 1647 (Judson/Ekkart 1999, no. 303). Around 1660, this painting or another replica was on display in the Mauritshuis: it is depicted in an engraving after Jacob Toorenvliet (see PRINTS AND DRAWINGS, Pierre Philippe). Cleaned and restored in 1990. Friedrich Wilhelm of Hohenzollern was the son of Georg Wilhelm of Hohenzollern, Elector of Brandenburg, and Elisabeth Charlotte Wittelsbach. In 1646 he married Louise Henriette, the eldest daughter of Frederik Hendrik. He became Grand Elector of Brandenburg in 1640.

Gerrit van Honthorst (studio of)

63 *Portrait of Prince Willem II (1626–1650),* after 1647

Canvas, 116.4 x 92.3 cm
Dutch title: *Portret van prins Willem II (1626–1650)*

PROVENANCE
Possibly Nationale Konst-Gallery, The Hague, 1800–1808; transferred, 1822

1107 

 428

63 

65 

 104

LITERATURE

Braun 1966, no. 118e; Judson/Ekkart 1999, no. 301–8; Dessau 2003, no. 11–25

COMMENT

Partial replica of the double portrait in the Rijksmuseum, Amsterdam, dated 1647 (Judson/Ekkart 1999, no. 301). Willem II, Prince of Orange, was the son of Frederik Hendrik and Amalia of Solms-Braunfels. In 1641 he married Mary I Stuart, daughter of the English king Charles I and Henrietta Maria. He became stadholder after his father's death in 1647. The sitter is depicted wearing the Order of the Garter.

Gerrit van Honthorst (after)

430 *Portrait of Frederik Hendrik (1584–1647),* after 1647

Panel, 74.4 x 59.7 cm
Dutch title: *Portret van Frederik Hendrik (1584–1647)*

PROVENANCE

Transferred, in or before 1841

LITERATURE

Braun 1966, no. 103b; Judson/Ekkart 1999, no. 296–8

COMMENT

Partial copy after the portrait of Frederik Hendrik with his wife and their three youngest daughters in the Rijksmuseum, Amsterdam, probably painted in 1647 (Judson/Ekkart 1999, no. 296). For biographical data, see Van Honthorst, inv. no. 104.

Pieter de Hooch

Rotterdam 1629–1684 Amsterdam

835 *A man smoking and a woman drinking in a courtyard, c.*1658–1660

Canvas, 78 x 65 cm
Dutch title: *Een binnenplaats met een rokende man en een drinkende vrouw*

PROVENANCE

John Smith, 1822; William Wells of Redleaf, 1828–1848; Lord Overstone, London, 1871; Lord and Lady Wantage, London, 1888; Earl of Crawford and Balcarres, London, 1921; D. Katz Gallery, Dieren, 1935; gift of Mr and Mrs Ten Cate-van Wulfften Palthe, Almelo, 1947

LITERATURE

HdG 1907–1928, vol. 1, p. 558, no. 297; Mauritshuis 1970, no. 35; Sutton 1980, no. 35B; Edinburgh 1992, no. 25

COMMENT

Another autograph version, with an extra figure sitting at the table, is in the National Gallery of Art, Washington (Sutton 1980, no. 35A).

Samuel van Hoogstraten

Dordrecht 1627–1678 Dordrecht

66 *Perspective with a woman reading a letter, c.*1662–1667

Canvas, 214 x 179 cm
Signed upper left, on the feigned stone archway: *SvH*
Dutch title: *Perspectief met een brieflezende vrouw*

PROVENANCE

According to Johan van Gool, the painting was bought at the Confrerie Pictura, The Hague, by a Mr Kruyselbergen; Gerard van Oostrum, The Hague; his sale, The Hague, 23 September 1765, lot 1; sale The Hague, Pictura, 31 March 1770, lot 2; Prince Willem V, The Hague, 1770

LITERATURE

Van Gool 1750–1751, vol. 2, pp. 489–490; D/LS 1974–1976, vol. 3, p. 213, no. 49; Sumowski 1983–1995, vol. 2, p. 1304, no. 897; Roscam Abbing 1993, p. 132, no. 33; Brusati 1995, pp. 126, 297, notes 140–141, p. 365, no. 92

COMMENT

The Van Hoogstraten coat of arms is visible above the door, centre right. Brusati supposed that the painting was made for (or offered by the painter to) the Confrerie Pictura (Painter's Confraternity), The Hague. It should be noted, however, that Pictura was the location for public sales in The Hague. In the past, the woman was wrongly identified as Anne Conway.

Gerard Houckgeest

The Hague (?) 1600–1661 Bergen op Zoom

57 *Ambulatory of the Nieuwe Kerk in Delft, with the tomb of Willem I,* 1651

Panel, 65.5 x 77.5 cm
Signed and dated below, on the front column: *GH. 1651* (GH in ligature)
Dutch title: *Kooromgang van de Nieuwe Kerk in Delft, met de graftombe van Willem I*

PROVENANCE

Johan Anthony van Kinschot, Delft, until 1767; Prince Willem V, The Hague, 1767

LITERATURE

Jantzen 1979, no. 170; Liedtke 1982, pp. 43, 46–49; Mauritshuis 1987, p. 218; Rotterdam 1991, no. 31; Hamburg 1995–1996,

66

835

430

57

no. 11; Delft 1996, pp. 55–56, 223; Krefeld-Oranienburg-Apeldoorn 1999–2000, no. 2/13a; New York-London 2001, no. 39

COMMENT

The painter repeated parts of this view in other works (see Liedtke 1982). For the tomb, see inv. no. 58 and Ex/Scholten 2001. Cleaned and restored in 2002.

58 *The tomb of Willem I in the Nieuwe Kerk in Delft*, 1651

Panel (rounded at the top), 56 x 38 cm
Signed and dated centre below, on the base of the column: *GH 1651* (GH in ligature)
Dutch title: *De graftombe van Willem de Zwijger in de Nieuwe Kerk in Delft*

PROVENANCE

P.H. Gelijs, Antwerp; Willem Lormier, The Hague, 1757–1763; Pieter Leendert de Neufville, Amsterdam, 1764; Prince Willem V, The Hague, 1764

LITERATURE

De Vries 1975, no. 14; D/LS 1974–1976, vol. 3, p. 28, no. 190, p. 212, no. 43; Jantzen 1979, no. 169; Liedtke 1982, no. 6; Paris 1986, no. 35; Mauritshuis 1987, no. 38; Rotterdam 1991, pp. 170–171

COMMENT

A similar composition, dated 1650, is in the Hamburger Kunsthalle. For the tomb, see Ex/Scholten 2001.

Jan van Huchtenburgh

Haarlem 1647–1733 Amsterdam

67 *Equestrian portrait of Hendrik Casimir II (1657–1696)*, 1692

Canvas, 121 x 165 cm
Signed and dated centre below: *Hugtenburgh.f. 1692*
Dutch title: *Ruiterportret van Hendrik Casimir II (1657–1696)*

PROVENANCE

Prince Willem V, Het Loo Palace, Apeldoorn, 1757; Nationale Konst-Gallery, The Hague, 1800; transferred, 1822; on loan to the Rijksmuseum, Amsterdam (inv. no. SK-C-1226), since 1933

LITERATURE

D/LS 1974–1976, vol. 2, p. 642, no. 65; RM 1976, p. 292; Leeuwarden-Den Bosch-Assen 1979–1980, no. 24; Van Thiel 1981, p. 205, no. 153

COMMENT

Hendrik Casimir II, Prince of Nassau-Dietz and Stadholder of Friesland, Groningen and Drenthe, was the son of Stadholder Willem Frederik and Albertine Agnes, daughter of Stadholder Frederik Hendrik. He is here depicted as a commanding officer at a battle. Until 1893, this portrait was wrongly identified as that of Eugenius of Savoy.

68 *Cavalry engagement*

Canvas (cut at the bottom and the right side), 53.2 x 62.5 cm
Signed lower right: *HB* (in ligature)
Dutch title: *Rencontre van de cavalerie*

PROVENANCE

Commissioned by Pieter de la Court van der Voort, Leiden; his heirs, until 1766; purchased by Prince Willem V, The Hague, 1766

LITERATURE

D/LS 1974–1976, vol. 3, p. 213, no. 46; Mauritshuis 1980, pp. 48–49; De Boer *et al.* 1993, p. 28

COMMENT

Cut down between 1766 and 1795 to make it a pendant to inv. no. 69, which was also bought at the 1766 De la Court sale.

69 *Attack on a convoy*

Canvas, 53.2 x 62.5 cm
Signed lower right: *HB* (in ligature)
Dutch title: *Aanval op een konvooi*

PROVENANCE

Same as inv. no. 68

LITERATURE

D/LS 1974–1976, vol. 3, p. 212, no. 45; Mauritshuis 1980, p. 49; Nagasaki 1992–1993, no. 12; De Boer *et al.* 1993, pp. 26–28, no. 4

Ozias Humphry (attributed to)

Honiton 1742–1810 London

792 *Portrait of a man*

Panel (oval), 11.6 x 9.3 cm
Dutch title: *Portret van een man*

PROVENANCE

Gift of Cornelis Hofstede de Groot, The Hague, 1926, in honour of the 25th anniversary of Wilhelm Martin's directorship of the Mauritshuis

COMMENT

Companion piece to inv. no. 793.

793 *Portrait of a woman*

Panel (oval), 11.6 x 9.4 cm
Dutch title: *Portret van een vrouw*

68

69

67

58

792

793

PROVENANCE
Same as inv. no. 792

COMMENT
Companion piece to inv. no. 792.

Jan van Huysum

Amsterdam 1682–1749 Amsterdam

70 *Fruit still life*

Copper, 21 x 27 cm
Signed lower left, on the edge of the marble ledge: *Jan Van Huijsum fecit*
Dutch title: *Fruitstilleven*

PROVENANCE
Robert de Neufville, Leiden, 1736; Hermina Jacoba, Baroness van Leyden, Warmond; purchased, 1816

LITERATURE
HdG 1907–1928, vol. 10, p. 378, no. 204; Grant 1954, p. 28, no. 163; Amsterdam-Braunschweig 1983, no. 68

COMMENT
Companion piece to inv. no. 71.

71 *Flower still life*

Copper, 21 x 27 cm
Signed lower left, on the edge of the marble ledge: *Jan Van / Huijsum fecit*
Dutch title: *Bloemstilleven*

PROVENANCE
Same as inv. no. 70

LITERATURE
HdG 1907–1928, vol. 10, p. 368, no. 149; Grant 1954, p. 24, no. 110

COMMENT
Companion piece to inv. no. 70.

72 *Italian landscape*

Canvas, 59 x 70 cm
Signed left of the middle, on a stone: *Jan Van Huijsum*
Dutch title: *Italiaans landschap*

PROVENANCE
Nationale Konst-Gallery, The Hague, 1800–1809; City of The Hague, 1809; transferred to the Picture Gallery of Prince Willem V, The Hague, *c.* 1815/17–1821; transferred, 1822; on loan to the ICN

LITERATURE
HdG 1907–1928, vol. 10, p. 339, no. 9; Moes/Van Biema 1909; p. 222; Buvelot 1998, p. 24

1113 *Arcadian landscape with a bust of Flora*, 1724–1725

Canvas, 52 x 71 cm
Signed and dated lower left: *Jan Van Huysum f / Amsterdam 1724 en / 1725*
Dutch title: *Arcadisch landschap met borstbeeld van Flora*

PROVENANCE
Gift of Mrs C.C.M. de Bièvre-Duijndam to the Friends of the Mauritshuis Foundation, 1997

LITERATURE
Tokyo-Kasama-Kumamoto-Leiden 1992–1993, no. 79 B; Buvelot 1998

COMMENT
Companion piece to inv. no. 1114.

1114 *Arcadian landscape with the healing of the crippled man by Saints Peter and John*, 1724–1725

Canvas, 52 x 71 cm
Signed and dated lower right: *Jan Van Huysum / fecit Amsterdam / 1724 en 1725*
Dutch title: *Arcadisch landschap met de genezing van een verlamde door Petrus en Johannes*

PROVENANCE
Same as inv. no. 1113

LITERATURE
Tokyo-Kasama-Kumamoto-Leiden 1992–1993, no. 79 A; Buvelot 1998

COMMENT
Companion piece to inv. no. 1113.

Ignacio de Iriarte

Azcoitia 1621–1685 Seville

299 *Landscape with hunters*

Canvas, 104 x 82 cm
Dutch title: *Landschap met jagers*

PROVENANCE
Count Edmund Bourke, Paris, until 1821; purchased from his widow by King Willem I for the Mauritshuis, 1823; on loan to the Rijksmuseum, Amsterdam (inv. no. SK-C-1371), since 1948

LITERATURE
Van Vliet 1966, pp. 134, 136, 138, fig. 5; RM 1976, p. 295

70

71

1113

72

1114

299

J

Karel du Jardin

Amsterdam 1627–1678 Venice

73 *The waterfalls near Tivoli*, 1673

Canvas, 64.2 x 69.5 cm
Signed and dated lower right: *K. dv Iardin / fe / 1673*
Dutch title: *De watervallen bij Tivoli*

PROVENANCE
Pieter Leendert de Neufville, Amsterdam, 1765; Govert van Slingelandt and heirs, The Hague, 1765–1768; the entire collection sold to Willem V in 1768; Prince Willem V, The Hague, 1768–1795

LITERATURE
HdG 1907–1928, vol. 9, p. 342, no. 184; Brochhagen 1958, pp. 120–122; D/LS 1974–1976, vol. 3, p. 217, no. 70; Blankert 1978, pp. 209–210; Mauritshuis 1980, pp. 52–53; Tokyo-Kasama-Kumamoto-Leiden 1992–1993, no. 75

COMMENT
Cleaned and restored in 1995.

74 *Landscape with a shepherdess*

Panel, 32 x 40 cm
Dutch title: *Landschap met herderin*

PROVENANCE
Coenraet, Baron Droste, The Hague, 1717–1734; J.P. Wierman, Leiden, 1762; Govert van Slingelandt and heirs, The Hague, 1768; the entire collection sold to Willem V in 1768; Prince Willem V, The Hague, 1768–1795

LITERATURE
D/LS 1974–1976, vol. 3, p. 217, no. 71; HdG 1907–1928, vol. 9, pp. 309–310, no. 57; Brochhagen 1958, p. 89; Mauritshuis 1980, pp. 51–52

760 *Italian landscape with a young shepherd playing with his dog*, c.1660–1665

Panel, 31.2 x 37.6 cm
Bears signature lower left: *K: dv Iardin f.*
Dutch title: *Italiaans landschap met een jonge herder, spelend met zijn hond*

PROVENANCE
Comte de Vence Collection, Paris; Etienne François, Duc de Choiseul, Paris, 1772; Comte de Conti, Paris, 1777; Solirène Collection, Paris, 1812; Lapeyrière Collection, Paris, 1817; William Buchanan, London; Edward Gray, London; C.J. Nieuwenhuys Gallery, London; Hendrik Adolf Steengracht van Duivenvoorde, The Hague, before 1893–1913; August Janssen, Amsterdam, 1913; gift of Jacques Goudstikker, 1919

LITERATURE
HdG 1907–1928, vol. 9, p. 310, no. 58; Brochhagen 1958, pp. 88–89, notes 312–315; Blankert 1978, no. 128; Mauritshuis 1980, pp. 50–51; Montreal 1990, no. 36; Madrid 1994–1995, no. 33; Slive 1995, p. 243; London 2002, no. 34

1095 *Italianate landscape with cattle*, 1660s

Panel, 41 x 37 cm
Signed lower centre: *K. DU. JARDIN fec*
Dutch title: *Italianiserend landschap met vee*

PROVENANCE
Aert Schouman, Rotterdam, 1753; Jan and Pieter Bisschop, Rotterdam, 1753–1771; Jan Hope, Amsterdam, 1771, Hope Collection, London, until 1898; Wertheimer Gallery, London; Peter A.B. Widener, Philadelphia; J.E. Widener, Philadelphia; Knoedler Gallery, New York, 1923; G.L.M. van Es, Dordrecht; his sale, Dordrecht, A. Mak, 22 September 1942, lot 122, to Bloch; Vitale Bloch, The Hague, 1942; Adolf Hitler; Stichting Nederlands Kunstbezit; on loan from the ICN (inv. no. NK 2933), since 1993

LITERATURE
HdG 1907–1928, vol. 9, p. 318, no. 88; Brochhagen 1958, p. 96; Dordrecht-Leeuwarden 1988–1989, no. 29; Montreal 1990, no. 37; Buijsen/Van der Ploeg 1993, pp. 24–25, no. 6; Apeldoorn 2002, p. 23, repr.; Schwarz 2004, no. XXII/21

Karel du Jardin (after)

75 *Young shepherd milking a goat*

Panel, 31 x 26 cm
Dutch title: *Jonge herder die een geit melkt*

PROVENANCE
Martial Reghellini Schio, Venice and Brussels, until 1826; purchased by King Willem I for the Mauritshuis, 1831

COMMENT
After the painting in the Alte Pinakothek, Munich.

Cornelis Jonson van Ceulen

London 1593–1661 Utrecht

688 *Portrait of Jan Beck (1611–1676) and his five children*, 1650

Canvas, 181.5 x 151.5 cm
Signed and dated lower right: *Cornelis Janson: van Ceulen / fecit 1650*
Inscribed upper centre: *Dulcia vallantur duris* (The soft is surrounded by the hard)
Dutch title: *Portret van Jan Beck (1611–1676) en zijn vijf kinderen*

73

74

688

75

1095

760

PROVENANCE
Probably Jan Beck and his heirs, The Hague, 1650–1904; bequest of Catharina Frederica Augustina Alexandrina, Countess van Bylandt, née van Hogendorp van Hofwegen, The Hague, 1904

LITERATURE
Collins Baker 1912, vol. 1, pp. 85–86; Schaffers-Bodenhausen/Tiethoff-Spliethoff 1993, p. 42, note 39

COMMENT
The sitters, identified by L.J. van der Klooster, are Jan Beck, who was born in London and was probably related to the artist, and his children Margaretha, Catharina, Sara, Jan and Nicolaas. In the 1630s Beck moved to Middelburg, where he became an elector and married Catherina Nicolaesdr de Wael Rogiers in 1636.

Jacob Jordaens

Antwerp 1593–1678 Antwerp

849 *Nymphs cutting off Pan's beard, c.*1640

Canvas, 77.2 x 120.6 cm
Dutch title: *Nimfen knippen de baard van Pan af*

PROVENANCE
Willem Six, Amsterdam, before 1733; Gerard Bicker van Swieten, The Hague, 1734–1741; Adriaan Leonard van Heteren, The Hague, until 1800; Adriaan Leonard van Heteren Gevers, The Hague, 1800–1809; the entire collection bought by King Louis Napoleon for the Royal Museum, Amsterdam, 1809; on loan from the Rijksmuseum, Amsterdam (inv. no. SK-A-601), since 1948

LITERATURE
RM 1976, p. 309; Antwerp 1993, no. A 59; Mauritshuis 1993, no. 18

937 *The adoration of the shepherds, c.*1617

Panel, 125 x 95.7 cm
Signed and dated lower left, on the handle of the jug: *I.IOR*
Dutch title: *De aanbidding der herders*

PROVENANCE
Prince Lichnowsky, Kuchelna, Silesia, before 1905; Paul Cassirer Gallery, Berlin and Amsterdam, 1927–1928; A.N.F. Rhodius, Bennebroek; F.R.H. Rhodius, Heemstede, 1953; purchased with the support of the Friends of the Mauritshuis Foundation, 1959

LITERATURE
Mauritshuis 1970, no. 11; Mauritshuis 1987, no. 39; Mauritshuis 1993, no. 17

COMMENT
An autograph version of the painting in the Nationalmuseum in Stockholm, dated 1618 and signed in full. Another comparable version in the Herzog Anton Ulrich-Museum in Braunschweig.

Willem Kalf

Rotterdam 1619–1693 Amsterdam

927 *Still life with a roemer*, 1659

Canvas, 49.9 x 42.4 cm
Signed and dated lower right: *W. KALF 1659*
Dutch title: *Stilleven met roemer*

PROVENANCE
Private collection, France; C. Benedict Gallery, Paris; S. Nijstad Gallery, The Hague; purchased with the support of the Rembrandt Society and the Friends of the Mauritshuis Foundation, 1957

LITERATURE
Mauritshuis 1970, no. 38; Grisebach 1974, p. 255, no. 97; Auckland 1982, no. 10

971 *Still life with shells, c.*1690?

Panel, 25 x 33 cm
Signed lower left: *W KALF*
Dutch title: *Stilleven met schelpen*

PROVENANCE
Adolf Goldschmidt, Berlin; S. Nijstad Gallery, The Hague; purchased, 1965

LITERATURE
Mauritshuis 1970, no. 39; Grisebach 1974, p. 281, no. 144

COMMENT
Companion piece to inv. no. 972.

972 *Still life with shells and coral, c.*1690

Panel, 25 x 33 cm
Signed lower right: *W KALF*
Dutch title: *Stilleven met schelpen en koraal*

PROVENANCE
Same as inv. no. 971

LITERATURE
Mauritshuis 1970, no. 40; Grisebach 1974, p. 281, no. 145

COMMENT
Companion piece to inv. no. 971.

849

927

937

971

972

K

1126 *Still life with fruit and glasses on a silver plate, c.*1659–1660

Canvas, 49.3 x 42.9 cm
Signed upper left: *kalf*
Dutch title: *Stilleven met fruit en glazen op een zilveren schaal*

PROVENANCE
5th Earl Spencer, by 1892; 8th Earl Spencer, Althorp, Northamptonshire; Robert Noortman Gallery, Maastricht; Diethelm Doll, Bad Godesberg; sale London, Christie's, 8 December 1995, lot 42, unsold; acquired after the sale by Willem, Baron van Dedem; gift of Willem, Baron van Dedem to the Friends of the Mauritshuis Foundation, 2002

LITERATURE
Grisebach 1974, p. 284, no. A 5; Sutton 2002, no. 29; Buvelot 2002a, pp. 19–21, no. 11

Bernhard Keil (attributed to)

Helsingör 1624–1687 Rome

825 *Girl teasing a boy*, 1650s

Canvas, 59 x 72 cm
Dutch title: *Een meisje dat een jongen plaagt*

PROVENANCE
Gift of Vitale Bloch, The Hague, 1936

LITERATURE
Bloch 1946; Heimbürger 1988, p. 210, no. 112; Aikema *et al.* 1997, p. 83, no. 85

Alexander Keirincx

Antwerp 1600–1652 Amsterdam

With Cornelis van Poelenburch

79 *Wooded landscape with figures, c.*1630?

Panel, 64 x 92 cm
Signed left of centre: *A. Keirincx*
Dutch title: *Boslandschap met figuren*

PROVENANCE
Stadholder Frederik Hendrik, The Hague, 1632/1634; Honselaarsdijk Palace, Naaldwijk, 1755; Nationale Konst-Gallery, The Hague, 1800

LITERATURE
Thiéry 1953, pp. 180, 183; D/LS 1974–1976, vol. 1, p. 235, no. 1246, vol. 2, p. 511, no. 194; Van Thiel 1981, p. 208, no. 170; The Hague 1988–1989, p. 68; *Mauritshuis in focus* 13 (2000), no. 2, pp. 5–6, fig. 2

COMMENT
A restoration in 1999–2000 revealed an extensive underdrawing. The figures can be attributed to Van Poelenburch.

Adriaen Thomasz Key

Antwerp *c.*1544–after 1589 Antwerp

225 *Portrait of Willem I (1533–1584), Prince of Orange, c.*1579

Panel, 48 x 34 cm
Dutch title: *Portret van Willem I (1533–1584), prins van Oranje*

PROVENANCE
Acquired in or before 1874

LITERATURE
Van Berensteyn 1933, p. 13, no. 62; Mauritshuis 1968, pp. 29–30; Krefeld-Oranienburg-Apeldoorn 1999–2000, no. 2/4; Dessau 2003, no. II–9

COMMENT
One of a number of portraits which were probably based on a possibly full-length likeness no longer in existence. Other autograph replicas are in the Rijksmuseum, Amsterdam (inv. no. SK-A-3148), and Museo Thyssen-Bornemisza, Madrid, dated 1579. Willem I of Orange, Count of Nassau — also known as William the Silent — was Prince of Orange since 1544. He was Stadholder for the Spanish king Philip II of Burgundy, Holland, Zeeland and Utrecht. Later he would become the leader of the Dutch revolt against Spain.

Jan Keynooghe

(?) *c.*1507–after 1570 Malines

923 *Perseus and Andromeda,* 1561

Panel (round), 22.4 cm in diameter
Signed and dated at right: *1561 / IKvM* (in ligature)
Inscribed on the sword of Perseus: *HARPE*
Dutch title: *Perseus en Andromeda*

PROVENANCE
S. Nijstad Gallery, The Hague; purchased, 1955

LITERATURE
Mauritshuis 1968, pp. 30–31; Mauritshuis 1970, no. 5; Pijl 2002 (with reproduction of the decorated verso); Den Bosch 2003–2004, p. 67 and fig. 9

1126

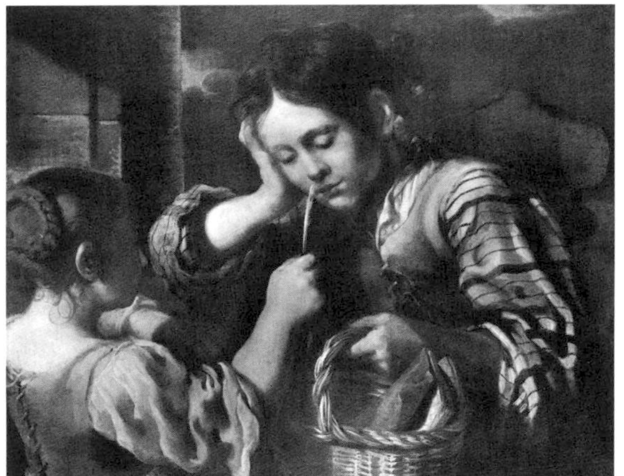
825

79

225

923

COMMENT

Attributed to Keynooghe by E. Haverkamp Begemann on the basis of the monogram, read by him as 'Jan Keynooghe van [= of] Mechelen'. The pendant, *Perseus turning Atlas to stone*, was sold in London, Christie's, 10 July 2002, lot 6 (see Pijl 2002). Both panels depict scenes from Ovid's *Metamorphoses*, where the rescue of Andromeda is described immediately after the story of Perseus and Atlas.

Thomas de Keyser

Amsterdam 1596/97–1667 Amsterdam

77 *Portrait of a scholar*, 1631

Panel, 82.5 x 61 cm
Signed and dated at left, on the closet: *TDK ANº. 1631* (TDK in ligature; only traces of the date visible)
Dutch title: *Portret van een geleerde*

PROVENANCE

Pieter Leendert de Neufville, Amsterdam, 1759; Leendert Pieter de Neufville, Amsterdam, 1759–1765; Prince Willem V, The Hague, 1765–1795

LITERATURE

Oldenbourg 1911, p. 79, no. 64; D/LS 1974–1976, vol. 3, p. 218, no. 77; Adams 1985, pp. 68–70, no. 36; London 2004, p. 16

COMMENT

Several copies and engravings are known.

78 *The four burgomasters of Amsterdam learning of the arrival of Maria de' Medici on 1 September 1638*, 1638

Panel, 28.5 x 38 cm
Dutch title: *De vier burgemeesters van Amsterdam vernemen de aankomst van Maria de' Medici op 1 september 1638*

PROVENANCE

Steven de Leeuw, Amsterdam, 1692; Gerret Braamcamp, Amsterdam, until 1771; Prince Willem V, The Hague, 1771–1795; on loan to the Amsterdams Historisch Museum, Amsterdam (inv. no. SB 5755), since 1980

LITERATURE

D/LS 1974–1976, vol. 3, p. 218, no. 76; Oldenbourg 1911, p. 79, no. 63; Bille 1961, vol. 1, p. 85, vol. 2, pp. 24, 101, no. 102; Adams 1985, pp. VI, 136–139, no. 77, vol. 2, pp. 378–384, 387; Amsterdam 2002–2003a, no. 47

COMMENT

Sitters from left to right: Anthonie Oetgens van Waveren (1585–1658), Pieter Hasselaar (1583–1651), Albert Coenraedsz Burgh (1593–1647), and Abraham Pietersz Boom (1575–1642). The man entering at the right, city lawyer Cornelis van Davelaer, is announcing the arrival of Maria de' Medici, the French queen mother, who visited Amsterdam in 1638. Ann Jensen Adams suggests that Van Davelaer commissioned the painting as a *modello* for the print by Jonas Suyderhoeff (1613–1686), dated 1638 (Hollstein, vol. 28, p. 208, no. 14); for the painting and the print, and the partly revised identification of the sitters, see Amsterdam 2002–2003a, no. 47.

689 *Portrait of a man, probably Hans van Hogendorp*, 1636

Panel, 73.5 x 68.5 cm
Signed, dated and inscribed at right: *TDKEYSER ANº.1636 / ÆTATIS SVÆ 66* (TDK in ligature)
Upper left: *1636*, above a family coat of arms (both not autograph)
Dutch title: *Portret van een man, waarschijnlijk Hans van Hogendorp*

PROVENANCE

Probably Hans van Hogendorp and heirs, Amsterdam, 1636–1904; bequest of dowager Margaretha Johanna Grisart-van Hogendorp van Hofwegen, The Hague, 1904

LITERATURE

Oldenbourg 1911, p. 79, no. 65; Van der Klooster 1959; Adams 1985, p. 120, no. 64

COMMENT

Hans van Hogendorp (1569–1652) was a goldsmith from Antwerp. He moved to Amsterdam in 1595, where he became assayer and 'waardijn' of the exchange bank.

806 *Portrait of Loef Vredericx (1590–1668) as an ensign*, 1626

Panel, 92.5 x 69 cm
Signed and dated above the door: *ANNO TDK 1626* (TDK in ligature)
The words on the standard can be deciphered as: *'PR[O] [P]A[TRIA]* (for the fatherland)
Bears inscription on the verso: *LOEF, VREDERICX, SOON, VAN V, I. / IST GEWORDEN ANº 1626. .15. AVGVSTI* (Loef, son of V[rerijk] J[anssen], became ensign of the city of Amsterdam in 1626)
Dutch title: *Portret van Loef Vredericx (1590–1668) als vaandeldrager*

PROVENANCE

Loef Vredericx, Amsterdam and Utrecht, 1626–1668; Tsar Paul I, Gatschina Palace, near St Petersburg, before 1924; Hirschmann Gallery, Berlin, before 1930; Van Diemen Gallery, Amsterdam, 1930–1931; purchased with the support of the Rembrandt Society and private individuals, 1931

LITERATURE

Adams 1985, vol. 1, pp. 96–97, 290, vol. 2, p. 24, no. 8, p. 42, fig. 8, pp. 110–111; Amsterdam 2002–2003a, no. 4; *Portraits in the Mauritshuis*, no. 32

689 

 78

77 

 806

COMMENT
Loef Vredericx (1590–1668), goldsmith and silversmith, came of a long line of goldsmiths in Amsterdam and was a member of the civic guard. Vredericx was depicted by De Keyser on two other occasions, both in 1627: in a group portrait of the Amsterdam goldsmiths' guild (Toledo, Ohio, Toledo Museum of Art) and in a portrait with his brother Andries and Andries's son Simon Valckenier, which was altered ten years later (lost during World War II). Cordial relationships existed between Vredericx and De Keyser, who had married Vredericx's niece, Machtelt Vredericx.

Isaac van Kipshaven

Amsterdam (?) *c.*1635–after 1672

814 *Sumptuous still life*, 1661

Canvas, 84 x 73 cm
Signed and dated lower left: *IV Kipshaven 1661*
Dutch title: *Pronkstilleven*

PROVENANCE
Gift of D. Katz, Dieren, 1935

LITERATURE
Auckland 1982, no. 12

Barend Cornelis Koekkoek

Middelburg 1803–1862 Cleves

781 *Brook by the edge of the forest*, 1849

Panel, 79 x 105.5 cm
Signed and dated lower centre: *B.C. Koekoek fec. / 1849*
Dutch title: *Beek aan een bosrand*

PROVENANCE
Bequest of Mrs Cornelia Adriana Rose-Molewater, The Hague, 1923; on loan to the Gemeentemuseum, The Hague, since 1923

LITERATURE
Gorissen 1962, no. 49/80

Philips Koninck (after)

Amsterdam 1619–1688 Amsterdam

80 *Panoramic landscape with a hawking party*, 19th century

Canvas, 65 x 78 cm
Dutch title: *Weids landschap met een valkenjacht*

PROVENANCE
Héris Gallery, Brussels; purchased, 1830; on loan to the ICN

LITERATURE
MacLaren 1960, p. 211, in no. 836; Gerson 1980, p. 40, note 81, p. 106, no. 31, fig. 16; Duparc 1996, p. 19 and fig. 12

COMMENT
Copy, presumably dating from the beginning of the nineteenth century, of the painting by Koninck in the National Gallery, London, inv. no. NG 836, on loan to the Mauritshuis since 1996 (see Duparc 1996).

Salomon Koninck

Amsterdam 1609–1656 Amsterdam

36 *The adoration of the kings, c.*1650

Canvas (rounded at the upper corners), 81 x 66 cm
Dutch title: *De aanbidding der koningen*

PROVENANCE
Joan de Vries and heirs, Amsterdam, 1708–1738; Dirk Kindt, The Hague, 1762; Prince Willem V, The Hague, 1762–1795 (as by Gerbrand van den Eeckhout)

LITERATURE
D/LS 1974–1976, vol. 3, p. 19, no. 24, p. 209, no. 35; Sumowski 1983–1995, vol. 3, p. 1659, no. 1085; The Hague 1992b, no. 26; Mauritshuis 1993, no. 19

Hans Suess von Kulmbach

Kulmbach *c.*1480–1522 Nuremberg

904 *Mary Cleophas and her family, c.*1513

Panel, 55 x 28 cm
Dutch title: *Maria Cleophas en haar familie*

PROVENANCE
Count von Cauda, Berlin, 1925; J. Böhler Gallery, Lucerne; H. Perls, Berlin; Jacques Goudstikker Gallery, Amsterdam, 1928; W.A. Hofer, Berlin; Hermann Göring, Berlin; Stichting Nederlands Kunstbezit; on loan to the Mauritshuis, 1951–1960; transferred, 1960

814

781

36

80

904

LITERATURE
Winkler 1959a, p. 69; The Hague 1997, no. 10b; Te Marvelde 1997

COMMENT
Depicted are Mary Cleophas — daughter of St Anne and her second husband Cleophas — with her husband Alphaus and their children, St Jude (with club), St James the Lesser (in the middle), St Simon (with saw), and, in the background, Joseph the Righteous. Belonged to an altarpiece that was dedicated to St Anne, Mary's mother, and her descendants (see inv. no. 905). The panels have been sawn through, separating the painted front and back sides. The verso, depicting St Anne and Joachim at the Golden Gate, is now in the Barnes Foundation Museum, Merion, Pennsylvania (The Hague 1997, p. 85, fig. 2). Cleaned and restored in 1997.

905 *Mary Salome and her family*, 1513

Panel, 55 x 28 cm
Dated centre right: *1513*
Dutch title: *Maria Salomas en haar familie*

PROVENANCE
Same as inv. no. 904

LITERATURE
Winkler 1960a, p. 69; The Hague 1997, no. 10a; Te Marvelde 1997

COMMENT
Depicted are Mary Salome, daughter of St Anne and her third husband Salomas; her husband Zebedee and their children, St James the Greater (with sack) and John the Evangelist (with chalice). Inv. no. 905 belonged to an altarpiece dedicated to St Anne (see inv. no. 904); the original verso, depicting the annuncation to Joachim, is now known only from an old photograph (The Hague 1997, p. 85, fig. 1). Cleaned and restored in 1997.

Pieter van Laer

Haarlem 1599–after 1642

1102 *Landscape with hunters, c.*1640

Panel, 30.6 x 43.4 cm
Signed lower right: *P. v. Laer*
Dutch title: *Landschap met jagers*

PROVENANCE
Isaac Walraven, Amsterdam, 1765; Johan van der Marck, Leiden, 1765–1770; sale London, Greenwood, 10 May 1785, lot 76; sale London, Christie's, 15 November 1946, lot 42; Hallsborough Gallery, London; private collection, London; Salomon Lilian Gallery, Amsterdam; gift of Procter & Gamble Nederland, 1994

LITERATURE
Janeck 1968, pp. 84–85, nos. A IV 1a–b; The Hague 1994–1995, p. 88 and fig. 2; Duparc 1995a/b; London 2002, no. 15

COMMENT
Engraved by Cornelis Visscher (Hollstein, vol. 40, p. 79, no. 63).

Louis-Jean-François Lagrenée

Paris 1725–1805 Paris

776 *Woman bathing, c.*1778

Copper, 38.5 x 30 cm
Dutch title: *Badende vrouw*

PROVENANCE
Gift of M.J.F.W. van der Haagen, The Hague, 1923

LITERATURE
Dijon-Paris-Rotterdam 1992–1993, no. 19

Gerard de Lairesse

Liège 1641–1711 Amsterdam

82 *Achilles discovered among the daughters of Lycomedes, c.*1680

Canvas (with additions along the top and bottom), 138 x 190 cm
Signed lower left, on the base: *G. Lairesse*
Dutch title: *Achilles wordt ontdekt tussen de dochters van Lycomedes*

PROVENANCE
Possibly Petronella de la Court, Amsterdam, 1707; Het Loo Palace, Apeldoorn, 1757; Prince Willem V, 1774–1795

LITERATURE
D/LS 1974–1976, vol. 2, p. 639, no. 10, vol. 3, p. 219, no. 83; Roy 1992, pp. 335–336, no. P. 186; Mauritshuis 1993, no. 20; De Vries 1998, pp. 65–67; Rotterdam-Frankfurt am Main 1999–2000, no. 66

COMMENT
Engraved by Pieter van den Bergen (Mauritshuis 1993, p. 176, fig. 3).

82

905

904

776

1102

L

83 *Bacchus and Ariadne, c.*1676–1678

Canvas, 175.2 x 92.5 cm
Dutch title: *Bacchus en Ariadne*

PROVENANCE
Soestdijk Palace, after 1674–1799; Nationale Konst-Gallery, The Hague, 1800–1805; transferred, 1822

LITERATURE
D/LS 1974–1976, vol. 1, p. 622, nos. 24, 28; Roy 1992, p. 290, no. P. 126; Mauritshuis 1993, no. 21

COMMENT
Another version in reduced format is in the Philadelphia Museum of Art.

446 *Glorification of King-Stadholder Willem III (1650–1702)*

Canvas, 64.2 x 78 cm
Signed lower left: *G. de Lairesse*
Dutch title: *De verheerlijking van koning-stadhouder Willem III (1650–1702)*

PROVENANCE
Binnenhof, The Hague, 1754; Nationale Konst-Gallery, The Hague; transferred at an unknown date; on loan to the Paleis Het Loo Nationaal Museum, Apeldoorn

LITERATURE
D/LS 1974–1976, vol. 2, p. 479, no. 20, vol. 3, p. 22, no. 59, pp. 209–210, no. 177; Van Thiel 1981, pp. 209–210, no. 177; Roy 1992, pp. 358–360, no. P. 212; Muller 1998

COMMENT
Willem III is depicted as war victor and peacemaker: at the centre a bust of the King-Stadholder, wearing the insignia of English royalty and set on a globe on top of other trophies of war. Female figures, bearing the attributes of Glory, Truth, Eternity (on the left) and Minerva (on the right), pay homage to him.

Giovanni Battista Langetti

Genoa 1635–1676 Venice

334 *Tityus, c.*1660–1665

Canvas, 109.5 x 119.5 cm
Dutch title: *Titius*

PROVENANCE
Dukes of Mantua; Martial Reghellini Schio, Venice and Brussels, 1826; purchased by King Willem I for the Mauritshuis, 1831

LITERATURE
Rotterdam 1989–1990, no. 16; Aikema *et al.* 1997, pp. 85–86, no. 87

COMMENT
Companion piece to *Sisyphus* by Antonio Zanchi (inv. no. 335). Restoration completed in 1989.

Jan Willemsz Lapp

The Hague 1605/10 (?)–after 1663 Amsterdam

84 *Italianate landscape with shepherds*

Canvas, 58.9 x 68.2 cm
Signed lower left, on a stone: *J Lapp*
Dutch title: *Italianiserend landschap met herders*

PROVENANCE
Nationale Konst-Gallery, The Hague, 1800; transferred, 1822; found in the attic in 1875

LITERATURE
Moes/Van Biema 1909, p. 32; Mauritshuis 1980, p. 54; Salerno 1977–1980, vol. 2, p. 770, fig. 130.1; Buijsen *et al.* 1998, p. 323; Kolfin/Pottasch 2003, p. 41

Jan Willemsz Lapp

273 *Italianate landscape with buildings,* 1660s?

Copper, 16 x 12 cm
Bears inscription on verso: *Gio Lapp*
Dutch title: *Italianiserend landschap met gebouwen*

PROVENANCE
Victor de Rainer, Brussels, 1821; purchased by King Willem I for the Mauritshuis, 1821

LITERATURE
Mauritshuis 1980, p. 54; Amsterdam 2001, p. 184; Kolfin/Pottasch 2003; Pottasch 2003b

COMMENT
Formerly attributed to Adam Elsheimer. The companion piece, a landscape painted on a copperplate of the same size, was attributed to Lapp but proved to be of a later date (inv. no. 274; see Kolfin/Pottasch). Cleaned and restored in 2000.

Jan Willemsz Lapp (manner of)

274 *Italianate landscape, c.*1680?

Copper, 16 x 12 cm
Dutch title: *Italianiserend landschap*

83

446

334

84

273

274

PROVENANCE
Victor de Rainer, Brussels, 1821; purchased by King Willem I for the Mauritshuis, 1821

LITERATURE
Mauritshuis 1980, p. 54; Kolfin/Pottasch 2003; Pottasch 2003b

COMMENT
Formerly attributed to Lapp (see inv. no. 273) and Adam Elsheimer. Cleaned and restored in 2000.

Nicolas de Largillière

Paris 1656–1746 Paris

294 *Portrait of Willem Hyacinth (1666–1743)*

Canvas, 129.7 x 105.5 cm
Dutch title: *Portret van Willem Hyacinth (1666–1743)*

PROVENANCE
Probably Prince Willem IV, thence by descent to Prince Willem V, The Hague; transferred, in or before 1875

LITERATURE
D/LS 1974–1976, vol. 2, p. 478, no. 6, vol. 3, p. 22, no. 54

COMMENT
Willem Hyacinth, Prince of Nassau-Siegen, called himself Prince of Orange after the death of King-Stadholder Willem III.

Pieter Lastman

Amsterdam 1583–1633 Amsterdam

393 *The raising of Lazarus*, 1622

Panel, 64 x 97.5 cm
Signed and dated lower left, on the tomb stone: *PLastman fecit 1622* (PL in ligature) and *FECIT A 1622*
Dutch title: *De opwekking van Lazarus*

PROVENANCE
Christiaan Kramm, Utrecht, 1875; purchased, 1875; on loan to the Stedelijk Museum De Lakenhal, Leiden, since 1957

LITERATURE
Freise 1911, p. 60, no. 67; *Corpus*, vol. 1 (1982), p. 305; Lakenhal 1983, p. 192, no. 1752; Amsterdam 1991–1992, pp. 28–29, fig. 15

1074 *David handing over a letter to Uriah*, 1619

Panel, 42.5 x 63 cm
Signed and dated lower right: *PLastman fecit 1619* (PL in ligature)
Dutch title: *David geeft de brief aan Uria*

PROVENANCE
Jacques Clemens, Ghent, 1779; Wilhelm Schmidt, Munich, 1911; [Friedrich ?] Lippmann, Berlin; Jacques Goudstikker Gallery, Amsterdam, before 1919–1940; Adolf Hitler, Führermuseum, Linz; Stichting Nederlands Kunstbezit; on loan from the ICN (inv. no. NK 2834), since 1987

LITERATURE
Washington-Detroit-Amsterdam 1980–1981, no. 22; Amsterdam 1991–1992, no. 12; Mauritshuis 1993, no. 22; Münster 1994, no. 45; Montias 2002, p. 228, fig. 11

Ger Lataster

Schaesberg 1920–

1078 *Designs for 'Icarus Atlanticus'*, 1987
1079 Canvas, each 100 x 100.5 cm
Dutch title: *Ontwerpen voor 'Icarus Atlanticus'*

PROVENANCE
Gift of the artist to Hans R. Hoetink, then director of the Mauritshuis, 1988

LITERATURE
Mauritshuis 1991, no. XXXI

COMMENT
Preparatory studies for the ceiling painting in the Mauritshuis (see below).

1082 *Icarus Atlanticus: Allegory of human*
1083 *vanity and allegory of the working man*, 1987

Cotton, each *c.*500 x 500 cm
Signed and dated lower left, near Atlanticus: *G. Lataster 87*
Dutch title: *Icarus Atlanticus: Allegorie op de ijdelheid van de mens en allegorie op de werkende mens*

PROVENANCE
Painted for the ceiling of the main landing of the Mauritshuis, as a commission from the Dutch State, 1987

LITERATURE
Rempt 1988, pp. 20–21; Berkhof 1988, pp. 12–14; Wolf 1989, pp. 34–37; Mauritshuis 1991, no. XXX; Van Grevestein *et al.* 1998, pp. 322–323, 350

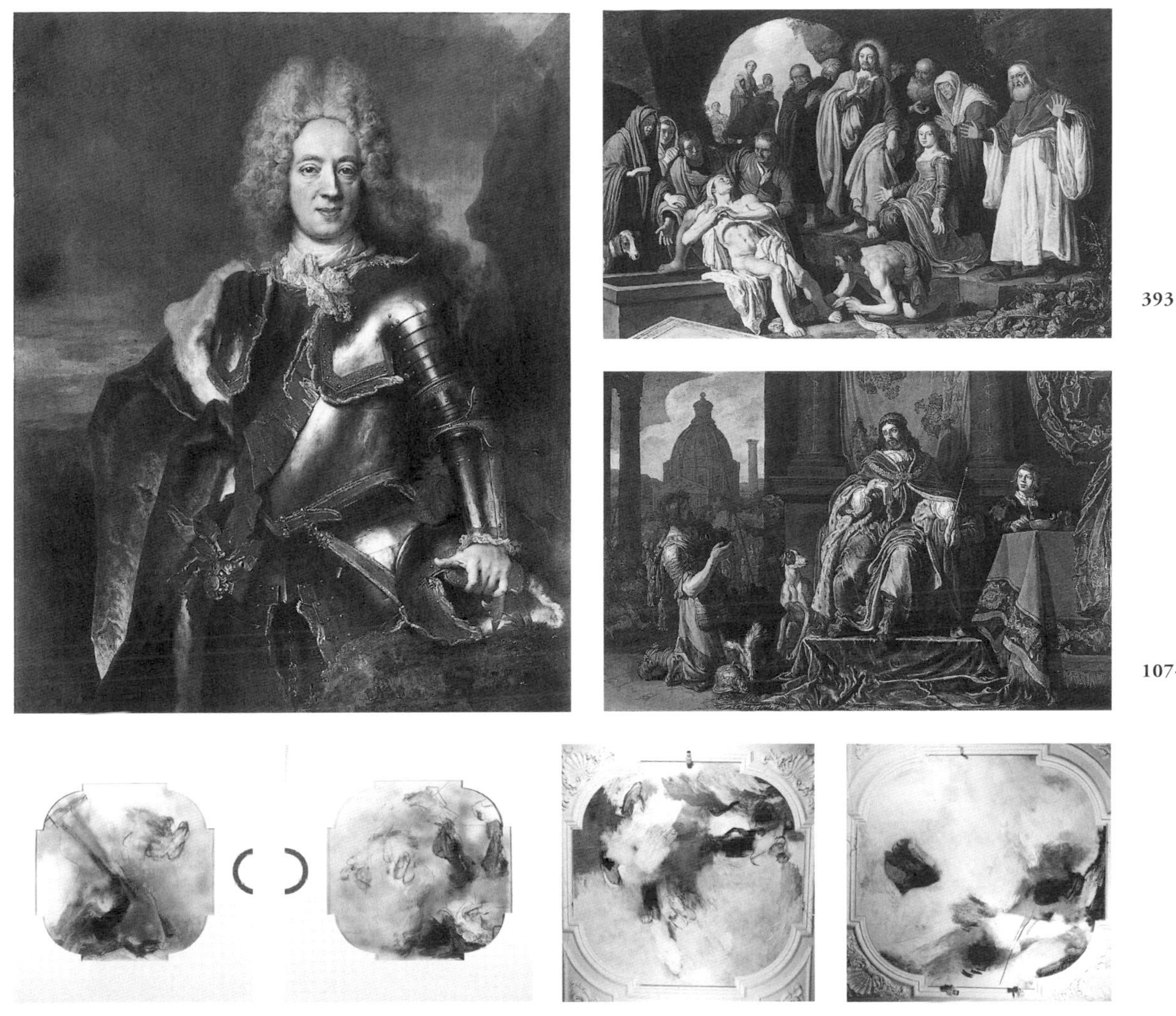

294

393

1074

1078 1079 1082 1083

L

Filippo Lauri

Rome 1623–1694 Rome

322 *Landscape with Mercury, Argus and Io, c.1660–1670*

Canvas, 69 x 56 cm
Dutch title: *Landschap met Mercurius, Argus en Io*

PROVENANCE
Martial Reghellini Schio, Venice and Brussels, until 1826; purchased by King Willem I for the Mauritshuis, 1831; on loan to the ICN

LITERATURE
Aikema *et al.* 1997, pp. 89–90, no. 95

Nicolas-Bernard Lépicié

Paris 1735–1784 Paris

870 *Portrait of a boy with a drawing book, possibly a pupil of the artist, c.1772*

Canvas, 41.5 x 32.3 cm
Dutch title: *Portret van een jongen met tekenboek, mogelijk een leerling van de kunstenaar*

PROVENANCE
J.B. Delestre, Paris, 1850; David Weill, Paris; Fritz Mannheimer, Amsterdam; Adolf Hitler, Führermuseum, Linz; Stichting Nederlands Kunstbezit; on loan to the Mauritshuis, 1948–1960; transferred, 1960; on loan to the Rijksmuseum, Amsterdam (inv. no. SK-C-1685), since 2002

LITERATURE
Gaston-Dreyfus/Ingersoll-Smouse 1923, pp. 50–51, no. 79; Dijon-Paris-Rotterdam 1992–1993, no. 29; Karlsruhe 1999, no. 110

COMMENT
In the original eighteenth-century French carved and gilt oak frame.

Judith Leyster

Haarlem 1609–1660 Heemstede

564 *Man offering money to a young woman,* 1631

Panel, 30.9 x 24.2 cm
Signed and dated left, below the table:
ILS / 1631* (ILS in ligature)
Dutch title: *Man die een vrouw geld aanbiedt*

PROVENANCE
Münzenberger Collection, Frankfurt am Main; Werner Dahl, Düsseldorf; purchased, 1892

LITERATURE
Hofrichter 1975/1982; Hofrichter 1989, pp. 47–48, no. 16; Haarlem-Worcester 1993, no. 8; Slive 1995, pp. 128–129; Antwerp-Arnhem 1999–2000, no. 36; Neumeister 2003, pp. 219, 221, 222

COMMENT
The star in the signature stands for the last part of the artist's name: Leyster (the Dutch 'ster' means star). Cleaned and restored in 2002.

Jan Lievens (after?)

Leiden 1607–1674 Amsterdam

85 *'Tronie' of an old man*

Panel, 65.5 x 51.4 cm
Dutch title: *Tronie van een oude man*

PROVENANCE
Prince Willem V, The Hague, 1774–1795

LITERATURE
Schneider/Ekkart 1973, pp. 132, 329, no. 159; D/LS 1974–1976, vol. 3, p. 228, no. 133; Braunschweig 1979, no. 21

COMMENT
Presumably a copy after the painting in the Herzog Anton Ulrich-Museum, Braunschweig (Braunschweig 1979, no. 20).

Johannes Lingelbach

Frankfurt am Main 1622–1674 Amsterdam

86 *Harbour on the Mediterranean*, 1670

Canvas, 154 x 194 cm
Signed and dated lower left, on the base of the column:
I Lingelbach / 1670
Dutch title: *Haven aan de Middellandse Zee*

PROVENANCE
Elector of Saxony, Hubertusburg Castle; acquired at his sale in Amsterdam for Prince Willem V, The Hague, 1765

LITERATURE
D/LS 1974–1976, vol. 3, p. 219, no. 78; Burger-Wegener 1976, pp. 269–270, no. 90; Mauritshuis 1980, p. 56; Schloss 1982, pp. 23, 39, 40; Nagasaki 1992–1993, no. 14; De Boer *et al.* 1993, p. 29, no. 5

86

870

564

322

85

L

87 *Harvesting the hay*

Panel, 41 x 52.5 cm
Signed lower left: *I. Lingelbach*
Dutch title: *De hooioogst*

PROVENANCE
Justus Oosterdijk, Amsterdam; his widow, Catharina Bullens, Amsterdam, 1777; Pieter Calkoen, Amsterdam, 1781; Gerrit van der Pot van Groeneveld, Rotterdam, 1781–1808; purchased at his sale by the Rijksmuseum, Amsterdam; acquired through exchange with the Rijksmuseum, 1825; on loan to the ICN

LITERATURE
Burger-Wegener 1976, p. 304, no. 159; Mauritshuis 1980, pp. 55–56

88 *Charles II (1630–1685) halting at the estate of Wema on the Rotte during his journey from Rotterdam to The Hague, 25 May 1660*

Canvas, 57.3 x 98.5 cm
Signed lower right: *I. Lingelbach*
Dutch title: *Het halthouden van Karel II (1630–1685) bij de buitenplaats Wema aan de Rotte tijdens zijn tocht van Rotterdam naar Den Haag, 25 mei 1660*

PROVENANCE
Jonas Witsen, Amsterdam, until 1717; Prince Willem V, Apeldoorn and The Hague, 1763–1795; on loan to the Rijksmuseum, Amsterdam (inv. no. SK-C-1223), since 1933

LITERATURE
D/LS 1974–1976, vol. 2, p. 640, no. 23, vol. 3, p. 219, no. 80; Burger–Wegener 1976, pp. 141–142, 328–329, no. 205; RM 1976, pp. 348–349

COMMENT
A less probable identification of the subject matter is: The troops of Prince Willem II halting at the estate of Wema on the Amstel during their march on Amsterdam, 31 May–4 August 1650. Companion piece to inv. no. 89. For biographical data on Charles II, see MINIATURES, Cooper, inv. no. 993.

89 *The departure of Charles II (1630–1685) from Scheveningen, 2 June 1660*

Canvas, 58.5 x 99.2 cm
Signed lower left: *I. Lingelbach*
Dutch title: *Het vertrek van Karel II (1630–1685) uit Scheveningen, 2 juni 1660*

PROVENANCE
Same as inv. no. 88; on loan to the Rijksmuseum, Amsterdam (inv. no. SK-C-1224), since 1933

LITERATURE
D/LS 1974–1976, vol. 2, p. 640, no. 22, vol. 3, p. 219, no. 79; Burger-Wegener 1976, pp. 142, 329–330, no. 206; RM 1976, p. 349

COMMENT
Companion piece to inv. no. 88.

951 *Italian landscape with resting peasants, c.1655–1660*

Canvas on panel, 57.4 x 47.5 cm
Signed lower right: *J. Lingelbach f.*
Dutch title: *Italiaans landschap met rustend landvolk*

PROVENANCE
Willem Lormier, The Hague, before 1754–1763; Adam Gottlob, Count Moltke, and his heirs, Copenhagen, until 1931; Holger Drucker, Copenhagen, 1961; H. Cramer Gallery, The Hague; purchased, 1962

LITERATURE
Mauritshuis 1970, no. 43; Burger-Wegener 1976, pp. 122, 290, no. 131; Mauritshuis 1980, p. 55

Andrea de Lione (attributed to)

Naples 1610–1685 Naples

289 *The peddlers, c.*1640–1650

Canvas, 98 x 132 cm
Dutch title: *De marskramers*

PROVENANCE
Martial Reghellini Schio, Venice and Brussels, until 1826; purchased by King Willem I for the Mauritshuis, 1831; on loan to the Rijksmuseum, Amsterdam (inv. no. SK-C-1346), since 1948

LITERATURE
RM 1976, p. 344; Chiarini 1977, p. 95; Brejon de Lavergnée 1984, p. 667, fig. 651; Aikema *et al.* 1997, pp. 90–91, no. 97

COMMENT
In the past attributed to Sébastien Bourdon (1616–1671).

Dirck van der Lisse

The Hague 1607–1657 The Hague

1093 *A sleeping nymph of the hunt, c.*1640–1650?

Panel, 44 x 51.8 cm
Signed on a quiver at right: *·DVL·* (in ligature)
Dutch title: *Een slapende jachtnimf*

951

88

89

87

289

1093

PROVENANCE
Possibly the estate of the painter; Schwarzenraben Collection, Westphalia, 1939; F.C. Butôt and heirs, Sankt Gilgen, 1969–1993; gift of Mrs M.A. Stubbé-Butôt from the estate of F.C. Butôt, 1993

LITERATURE
Salerno 1977–1980, vol. 1, p. 268, no. 46; Butôt/Bol/Keyes 1981, pp. 196–197, no. 81; Buijsen/Van der Ploeg 1993, pp. 26–27, no. 7; Mauritshuis 1993, no. 23; San Francisco-Baltimore-London 1997–1998, no. 55

Jacob van Loo

Sluis 1615–1670 Paris

599 *Portrait of a lady, c.1647?*

Canvas, 88.5 x 75.5 cm
Formerly signed lower left: *J:v Loo fecit*
Dutch title: *Portret van een dame*

PROVENANCE
Gift of Hendrik Willem Mesdag, The Hague, 1895

LITERATURE
Von Schneider 1925–1926, pp. 77–78

COMMENT
The *Portrait of a man* in the museum of Riga, dated 1647 and with the same size and composition, may be regarded as the companion piece.

885 *'Wooing', c.1650*

Canvas, 73.3 x 66.8 cm
Dutch title: *'Het paartje'*

PROVENANCE
Alfons Jaffé, Berlin, 1911; Stichting Nederlands Kunstbezit; Mrs. H. Jaffé, London, 1950; purchased, 1950

LITERATURE
Von Schneider 1925–1926, pp. 72, 74–76; Mauritshuis 1970, no. 34; Oxford 1999–2000, pl. 20; Schwarz 2004, no. XXII/40

Isaac Luttichuys

London 1616–1673 Amsterdam

722 *Portrait of a young lady*, after 1660

Canvas, 126 x 101 cm
Dutch title: *Portret van een jonge vrouw*

PROVENANCE
Bequest of *Jonkvrouw* Maria Johanna Singendonck, The Hague, 1907; on loan to the ICN

COMMENT
In 1938, a portrait of a young lady in the same posture but with different clothing, appeared on the art market in New York.

Nicolaes Maes

Dordrecht 1634–1693 Amsterdam

90 *Portrait of Jacob Trip (c.1576–1661)*, 1665?

Canvas, 121.8 x 100.5 cm
Signed, dated and inscribed lower left: *AEt 84. / .N.MAES / 1[...]*
Dutch title: *Portret van Jacob Trip (c.1576–1661)*

PROVENANCE
Ministry of the Navy, The Hague; transferred, 1822

LITERATURE
HdG 1907–1928, vol. 6, p. 561, no. 322; Sumowski 1983–1995, vol. 3, p. 2028, no. 1396, vol. 6, p. 3629, no. 1396; Berlin-Amsterdam-London 1991–1992, no. 79; Németh 1996; Krempel 2000, p. 296, no. A70a; *Portraits in the Mauritshuis*, no. 33

COMMENT
Jacob Trip was a wealthy merchant who moved to Dordrecht some time before 1600. In 1603 he married Margaretha de Geer (1583–1672), sister of a wealthy arms dealer. Trip had his portrait painted by Maes at least four times. The portrait of Margaretha de Geer by Maes, formerly in Nederhemert Castle, signed and dated 1665, was presumably the companion piece to inv. no. 90.

717 *Portrait of Cornelis ten Hove (1658–1694), c.1682*

Canvas, 58.2 x 46.2 cm
Signed lower right: *MAES*
Dutch title: *Portret van Cornelis ten Hove (1658–1694)*

PROVENANCE
Probably Cornelis ten Hove, Catharina Dierquens and their heirs, The Hague, until 1907; bequest of *Jonkvrouw* Maria Johanna Singendonck, The Hague, 1907

LITERATURE
HdG 1907–1928, vol. 6, p. 534, no. 193

COMMENT
Cornelis ten Hove was secretary to the treasury and commander of the West India Company. In 1682 he married Catharina Dierquens, who is portrayed on the companion

90

722

599

885

717

718

piece (inv. no. 718). Both portraits were presumably made on the occasion of their marriage. Ten Hove's brother Michiel was portrayed by a studio-assistant of Caspar Netscher (inv. no. 715).

< 718 *Portrait of Catharina Dierquens (1664–1715), c.*1682

Canvas, 57.4 x 45.5 cm
Signed bottom left: *MAES*
Dutch title: *Portret van Catharina Dierquens (1664–1715)*

PROVENANCE
Same as inv. no. 717

LITERATURE
HdG 1907–1928, vol. 6, p. 534, no. 194; Sumowski 1983–1995, vol. 3, p. 2034, in no.1429; Fransen 1997, p. 121; Krempel 2000, pp. 106, 132, note 219

COMMENT
Catharina Dierquens was the daughter of Elisabeth van Bebber and her first husband, Johannes Dierquens (see Caspar Netscher, inv. no. 714). In 1682 she married Cornelis ten Hove, portrayed in the companion piece (inv. no. 717).

1101 *The old lacemaker, c.*1655

Panel, 37.5 x 35 cm
Signed lower right, on the foot-warmer: *N. MAES* (MAE in ligature)
Dutch title: *De oude kantwerkster*

PROVENANCE
Edward Vernon Utterson, London; his sale, London, Christie's, 26 May 1832, lot 49, as by Dirck Maes (kindly communicated by B. Fredericksen); to Richard Artis, London; his sale, London, Christie's, 23 April 1836, lot 60; presumably sale Lord Northwick, London, Christie's, 24 May 1838, lot 9; H.A. Clowes, Norbury, Derbyshire; his sale, London, Christie's, 17 February 1950, lot 40; Brod Gallery, London, 1950; Stanley S. Wulc, Rydal, Pennsylvania; his sale, London, Christie's, 29 June 1973, lot 57; sale London, Christie's, 18 April 1985, lot 14; Reggie Graham; Diethelm Doll, Bad Godesberg; sale London, Sotheby's, 6 July 1994, lot 18; purchased with the support of the Friends of the Mauritshuis Foundation, the VSB Foundation The Hague and the Rembrandt Society, 1994

LITERATURE
HdG 1907–1928, vol. 6, pp. 501–502, no. 71; Sumowski 1983–1995, vol. 3, p. 2013, no. 1337, vol. 6, p. 3628, no. 1337; Dordrecht 1992–1993, no. 61; Duparc 1994; Van der Ploeg 1994; Robinson 1996, p. 250, no. A-34; Krempel 2000, p. 357, no. D 18; Blankert 2004, pp. 271, 273

Alessandro Magnasco

Genoa 1667–1749 Genoa

332 *Three Camaldolese monks in ecstatic prayer, c.*1710–1735

Canvas, 54.2 x 38.5 cm
Dutch title: *Drie Camaldolenser monniken in extatisch gebed*

PROVENANCE
Purchased by King Willem I for the Mauritshuis, 1822; on loan to the Rijksmuseum, Amsterdam (inv. no. SK-C-1358), since 1948

LITERATURE
Geiger 1949, p. 67; RM 1976, p. 359; Muti/De Sarno Prignano 1994, pp. 81, 200, no. 6; Milan 1996, no. 36; Aikema *et al.* 1997, pp. 101–103, no. 111

COMMENT
Companion piece to inv. no. 333.

333 *Three Capuchin monks in meditative prayer, c.*1710–1735

Canvas, 54.5 x 38.9 cm
Dutch title: *Drie Capucijner monniken in mediterend gebed*

PROVENANCE
Same as inv. no. 332; on loan to the Rijksmuseum, Amsterdam (inv. no. SK-C-1359), since 1948

LITERATURE
Geiger 1949, p. 67; RM 1976, p. 359; Muti/De Sarno Prignano 1994, p. 200, no. 7; Milan 1996, no. 37; Aikema *et al.* 1997, p. 103, no. 112

COMMENT
Companion piece to inv. no. 332. A virtually identical version is in the Galleria Nazionale d'Arte Antica (Palazzo Corsini), Rome.

816 *The massacre of the innocents,* after *c.*1710

Canvas, 65.5 x 83.5 cm
Dutch title: *De kindermoord te Bethlehem*

PROVENANCE
Gift of Eduard J. Philips, The Hague, 1935; on loan to the Rijksmuseum, Amsterdam (inv. no. SK-C-1360), since 1948

LITERATURE
Geiger 1949, p. 67, fig. 230; Genoa 1949, no. 34; RM 1976, p. 360; Rotterdam 1989–1990, no. 40; Muti/De Sarno Prignano 1994, p. 200, no. 8; Aikema *et al.* 1997, pp. 99–100, no. 109

332

333

1101

816

817

COMMENT
Companion piece to inv. no. 817. A different version formerly in the Modiano Collection, Bologna (Rotterdam 1989–1990, p. 89, fig. 40a).

817 *The raising of Lazarus*, after *c.*1710?

Canvas, 65.5 x 83.5 cm
Dutch title: *De opwekking van Lazarus*

PROVENANCE
Same as inv. no. 816; on loan to the Rijksmuseum, Amsterdam (inv. no. SK-C-1361), since 1948

LITERATURE
Geiger 1949, p. 67, fig. 244; Genoa 1949, no. 33; RM 1976, p. 360; Muti/De Sarno Prignano 1994, p. 200, no. 9; Aikema *et al.* 1997, p. 101, no. 110

COMMENT
Companion piece to inv. no. 816.

Cornelis de Man

Delft 1621–1706 Delft

91 *'La main chaude'*, *c.*1660

Canvas, 69 x 84 cm
Signed lower left: *k de man*
Dutch title: *'La main chaude'*

PROVENANCE
Purchased, 1875

LITERATURE
Amsterdam 1976, no. 37; W. Liedtke in New York-London 2001, p. 308

856 *Interior of the Laurenskerk in Rotterdam, c.*1665–1667

Canvas, 39.5 x 46.5 cm
Dutch title: *Interieur van de Laurenskerk in Rotterdam*

PROVENANCE
John Charles Robinson, London, 1869 (as by Gerrit Berckheyde); Sir Francis Cook, Doughty House, Richmond; by inheritance to Herbert Cook, Richmond, 1934; D. Katz Gallery, Dieren, 1939; Adolf Hitler, Führermuseum, Linz; Stichting Nederlands Kunstbezit; on loan to the Mauritshuis, 1948–1960; transferred, 1960

LITERATURE
Liedtke 1982, pp. 118, 122, 123, no. 291; De Boer *et al.* 1993, pp. 30–31, no. 6; New York-London 2001, no. 41; Schwarz 2004, no. IV/35

COMMENT
The figure in the centre is probably a portrait of the woman who commissioned the painting.

Jacob Sibrandi Mancadan

Minnertsga 1602–1680 Leeuwarden

770 *Landscape with a shepherd and a shepherdess*

Panel, 34.8 x 27.7 cm
Dutch title: *Landschap met een herder en een herderin*

PROVENANCE
Jacques Goudstikker Gallery, Amsterdam, 1919–1922; gift of H.E. ten Cate, 1923

LITERATURE
Mauritshuis 1980, p. 57

887 *Italian landscape with ruins*

Panel, 30.5 x 50 cm
Dutch title: *Italiaans landschap met ruïnes*

PROVENANCE
Vitale Bloch, The Hague, *c.*1949–1951; purchased, 1951

LITERATURE
Mauritshuis 1970, no. 27; Mauritshuis 1980, pp. 57–58; Leeuwarden 2001

COMMENT
A painting of the same format in the Wallraf-Richartz-Museum, Cologne, may be the companion piece.

Otto Marseus van Schrieck

Nijmegen 1619/20–1678 Amsterdam

532 *Plants and insects*, 1665

Canvas, 102.3 x 75.8 cm
Signed and dated lower right: *OTTO / Marseus.D. Schrick / 1665. / 9:5*
Dutch title: *Planten en insecten*

PROVENANCE
D.M. Alewijn sale, 16 December 1885, lot 82; M.F. van Gelder, Amsterdam; purchased, 1886

LITERATURE
Bol 1982, p. 102–103; Gemar-Koeltzsch 1995, vol. 3, p. 929, no. 362/7; Buvelot *et al.* 1998, pp. 112, 114; Steensma 1999, p. 135, no. B I.52

817

91

770

887

532

856

M

Quinten Massys (and/or studio)

Louvain 1465/66–1530 Antwerp

842 *Madonna and Child*

Panel, 75 x 63 cm
Dutch title: *Madonna en kind*

PROVENANCE
Het Loo Palace, Apeldoorn; Nationale Konstgallery, The Hague; Rijksmuseum, Amsterdam (inv. no. SK-A-247), since 1885; on loan from the Rijksmuseum since 1948

LITERATURE
Mauritshuis 1968, pp. 39–40; D/LS 1974–1976, vol. 2, p. 112, no. 899, p. 520, no. 289; De Bosque 1975, pp. 222–224; Van Thiel 1981, p. 196, no. 108; Silver 1984, pp. 230–231, in no. 50

COMMENT
There are several replicas in existence, and this one may not be autograph either. The composition is comparable to the painting by Massys depicted by Willem van Haecht in 1628 (see Mauritshuis 1993, p. 136, fig. 1), and now presumed lost.

Juan Bautista Martínez del Mazo (studio of?)

Cuenca 1612–1667 Madrid

298 *Portrait of Infante Balthasar Carlos (1629–1646)*

Canvas, 149.5 x 112.5 cm
Dutch title: *Portret van Infante Balthasar Carlos (1629–1646)*

PROVENANCE
Victor de Rainer, Brussels, 1821; purchased by King Willem I for the Mauritshuis, 1821 (as by Velázquez); on loan to the Rijksmuseum, Amsterdam (inv. no. SK-C-1362), since 1948

LITERATURE
Gaya Nuño 1958, p. 230, no. 1720 (as by Del Mazo); Van Vliet 1966, pp. 140–141, 143; RM 1976, p. 373 (as attributed to Del Mazo); Hillebrand 1996, pp. 24–26, no. 15

COMMENT
Possibly after a lost original by the master. There is a larger version in the Royal Collection, London. Balthasar Carlos was a son of the Spanish king Philip IV and Princess Elizabeth of France.

Lodovico Mazzolino

Ferrara *c.*1480–1528 Ferrara

323 *Massacre of the innocents*, 1528?

Panel, 31 x 38 cm
Dated lower right, on the wall: *1548 FE*
(the '4' is not autograph)
Dutch title: *De kindermoord te Bethlehem*

PROVENANCE
Victor de Rainer, Brussels, 1821; purchased by King Willem I for the Mauritshuis, 1821; on loan to the Rijksmuseum, Amsterdam (inv. no. SK-C-1363), since 1948

LITERATURE
Zamboni 1968, pp. 35–36, no. 2, fig. 61a; RM 1976, p. 374; Rotterdam 1989–1990, no. 43; Boschloo/Van der Sman 1993, pp. 60–61, no. 45

COMMENT
Other paintings by Mazzolino of the same subject in the Galleria degli Uffizi, Florence, and in the Galleria Doria Pamphilj, Rome.

Hans Memling

Seligenstadt *c.*1440–1494 Bruges

595 *Portrait of a man from the Lespinette family*, *c.*1485–1490

Verso: coat of arms of the Lespinette family
Panel, 30.1 x 22.3 cm
Dutch title: *Portret van een man uit de familie Lespinette*

PROVENANCE
Sir Andrew Fontaine, Harford Hall, Norfolk, before 1850–1894; purchased by the Rembrandt Society, 1894; transferred to the Dutch State in 1895 to be placed in the Mauritshuis, 1895

LITERATURE
Mauritshuis 1968, pp. 37–38; Friedländer 1967–1976, vol. VI a, p. 55, no. 79; Mauritshuis 1987, no. 40; De Vos 1994, pp. 184–185, no. 40; Bruges 1994, no. 18; The Hague 1997, no. 2; *Portraits in the Mauritshuis*, no. 35

COMMENT
This panel must have been the right wing of a devotional diptych, with a depiction of the Virgin and Child on the left.

595

842

298

323

Gabriel Metsu

Leiden 1629–1667 Amsterdam

93 *A huntsman*, 1661

Panel, 28 x 22.8 cm
Signed and dated lower centre, below the bird:
G. Metsu. 1661
Dutch title: *De jager*

PROVENANCE
Govert van Slingelandt, The Hague; the entire collection sold to Willem V in 1768; Prince Willem V, The Hague, 1768–1795

LITERATURE
HdG 1907–1928, vol. 1, p. 318, no. 207; Robinson 1974, pp. 28–29, 115, fig. 29; D/LS 1974–1976, vol. 3, p. 221, no. 94; Nagasaki 1992–1993, no. 16; De Boer *et al.* 1993, pp. 31–32, no. 7

COMMENT
Cleaned and restored in 1988.

94 *A young woman composing music*, c.1662–1663

Panel, 57.8 x 43.5 cm
Signed at right, on the door: *G. Metsu*
Dutch title: *Een jonge vrouw die muziek schrijft*

PROVENANCE
Same as inv. no. 93

LITERATURE
HdG 1907–1928, vol. 1, p. 299, no. 162; Robinson 1974, pp. 39, 64, 200, fig. 158; D/LS 1974–1976, vol. 3, p. 221, no. 93; Paris 1986, no. 36; Mauritshuis 1987, no. 41; Amsterdam 1997b, no. 21; Rotterdam-Frankfurt am Main 2004–2005, no. 61

COMMENT
The design of the mantle is based on a chimneypiece in Amsterdam City Hall, now Royal Palace.

95 *The triumph of Justice*, c.1655–1660

Canvas, 152.5 x 120 cm
Signed lower centre, on the step:
GMetsu (GM in ligature)
Dutch title: *De triomf der Gerechtigheid*

PROVENANCE
Sara de Witte, widow of Michiel van Peene, Leiden, 1667; her heirs; purchased for the Nationaal Kabinet (Royal Museum), Picture Gallery of Prince Willem V, The Hague, in or after 1804; transferred, 1822

LITERATURE
HdG 1907–1928, vol.1, p. 261, no. 20; Robinson 1974, pp. 25–26, 60, 74, note 33, p. 75, note 39; Van Thiel 1981, p. 206, in no. 158; Mauritshuis 1993, no. 25; Stone-Ferrier 2000

Martin Meytens the Younger (studio of)

Stockholm 1695–1770 Vienna

37 *Portrait of Francis I (1708–1765)*, after 1745

Canvas, 162.2 x 132.5 cm
Dutch title: *Portret van Frans I (1708–1765)*

PROVENANCE
Probably Prince Willem IV, thence by descent to Prince Willem V, The Hague, before 1751–1795; Nationale Konst-Gallery, The Hague, 1801–1808; Picture Gallery of Prince Willem V, The Hague, 1808–1821; transferred, 1822

LITERATURE
Moes/Van Biema 1909, pp. 11, 41, no. 129, p. 50, no. 128, p. 127, no. 364, p. 137, no. 57; D/LS 1974–1976, vol. 2, p. 691, no. 27; Van Thiel 1981, p. 203, no. 144; Te Marvelde/Van den Berg 1998

COMMENT
Francis I of Austria married Maria Theresa, who is depicted in the companion piece (inv. no. 38), in 1736. This portrait, of which there are many repetitions, was probably executed shortly after the coronation of Francis as emperor in 1745, possibly by Meytens's assistant Peter Kobler. Cleaned and restored in 1997.

38 *Portrait of Maria Theresa (1717–1780)*, after 1745

Canvas, 162.5 x 132.3 cm
Dutch title: *Portret van Maria Theresa (1717–1780)*

PROVENANCE
Same as inv. no. 37

LITERATURE
Moes/Van Biema 1909, p. 127, no. 364, p. 137, no. 57; D/LS 1974–1976, vol. 2, p. 691, no. 27; Te Marvelde/Van den Berg 1998

COMMENT
Companion piece to inv. no. 37. Maria Theresa was German Empress, but also Queen of Hungary and Bohemia. This portrait was probably made shortly after the coronation of her husband in 1745.

93

94

95

37

38

M

Michiel Jansz van Mierevelt
Delft 1567–1641 Delft

749 *Portrait of Cornelis van Aerssen (1545–1627)*, 1597?

Panel, 72 x 59.8 cm
Formerly bore signature and date at right:
M. Mierevelt / Fec. A°. 1597
Formerly bore inscription upper left:
Cornelis van Aerssen / Hr. van Somerdijk en Spijk / Gestorven A° 1627 Aet: 83
Dutch title: *Portret van Cornelis van Aerssen (1545–1627)*

PROVENANCE
Van Aerssen family and heirs, The Hague and Zwolle, until 1914; bequest of Willem Frederik Ernst, Baron van Aerssen Beyeren van Voshol, Zwolle, 1914

LITERATURE
Hoogewerff 1936–1947, vol. 4, p. 580; The Hague 1948, no. 954

COMMENT
Companion piece to the portrait of Cornelis's son, François van Aerssen, also painted by Van Mierevelt (inv. no. 750). Engraved by Jacob Houbraken (1698–1780) in 1753, on the basis of a drawing by Aert Schouman. Cornelis van Aerssen was clerk to the States General.

750 *Portrait of François van Aerssen (1572–1641)*, 1636?

Panel, 72.2 x 59.1 cm
Formerly bore signature and date at bottom right:
M Miereveld / A° 1636 (see Mauritshuis 1935, p. 204)
Formerly inscribed upper left: *A° 1636 / Æts 64*
Dutch title: *Portret van François van Aerssen (1572–1641)*

PROVENANCE
Same as inv. no. 749; on loan to the Dutch Embassy, London, since 2002

LITERATURE
Moes 1897–1905, vol. 2, p. 9, no. 70–1

COMMENT
Companion piece to the portrait of François's father, Cornelis van Aerssen, also painted by Van Mierevelt (inv. no. 749). A comparable composition is in the Rijksmuseum, Amsterdam, inv. no. SK-A-3833. Engraved by Jacob Houbraken (1698–1780) in 1753. François van Aerssen was member of the States of Holland and a prominent diplomat. He was a delegate of the States General in France.

Michiel Jansz van Mierevelt (studio of)

96 *Portrait of Willem I (1533–1584), Prince of Orange*

Copper (oval), 28 x 23 cm
Dutch title: *Portret van Willem I (1533–1584), prins van Oranje*

PROVENANCE
Johannes Goldberg, The Hague, 1828; purchased, 1828; on loan to the ICN

LITERATURE
Moes 1897–1905, vol. 2, p. 602, no. 9094–14

COMMENT
Belongs to a series of six portraits, all from the studio of Van Mierevelt (inv. nos. 97–101). Probably a copy after a lost original of 1577 by Cornelis de Visscher (*c.*1520–1586). A version of higher quality is in Delft, Stedelijk Museum Het Prinsenhof. Many other painted and engraved versions in existence. For biographical data, see Key, inv. no. 225.

Michiel Jansz van Mierevelt (studio of)

97 *Portrait of Louise de Coligny (1555–1620)*

Copper (oval), 28.1 x 23.1 cm
Signed and dated centre right: *Miere[. . . .]*
Bears signature left of centre: *Mierevelt*
Dutch title: *Portret van Louise de Coligny (1555–1620)*

PROVENANCE
Same as inv. no. 96

LITERATURE
Brussels 1984, no. 7.3; The Hague 1997–1998b, pp. 21, 77, fig. 59

COMMENT
Belongs to a series of six portraits, all from the studio of Van Mierevelt (inv. nos. 96–101). Another version in the Six Collection, Amsterdam. Engraved by Willem Delff (1580–1638) in 1627, Claes Visscher II (1586–1652) and others. Louise de Coligny was the fourth wife of Willem of Orange (see inv. no. 96) and the mother of Frederik Hendrik (see inv. no. 100). She is here depicted with a widow's cap.

749

750

96

97

M

Michiel Jansz van Mierevelt (studio of)

98 *Portrait of Philip Willem (1554–1618), Prince of Orange*

Copper (oval), 28 x 23.3 cm
Signed left centre: *V Mierevelt*
Dutch title: *Portret van Philip Willem (1554–1618), prins van Oranje*

PROVENANCE
Same as inv. no. 96

COMMENT
Belongs to a series of six portraits, all from the studio of Van Mierevelt (inv. nos. 96–101). Philip Willem was the eldest son of Willem I of Orange and Anna of Egmond and Buren, and became Prince of Orange after his father's death in 1584.

Michiel Jansz van Mierevelt (studio of)

99 *Portrait of Stadholder Maurits (1567–1625), Prince of Orange*, 1617

Copper (oval), 28 x 23 cm
Signed and dated left: *Mierevelt. / Ætatis 49 / A° 1617*
Dutch title: *Portret van stadhouder Maurits (1567–1625), prins van Oranje*

PROVENANCE
Same as inv. no. 96; on loan to the Musée Municipal, Orange, France, since 1952

LITERATURE
Siegen 1930, p. 16; Martin 1935–1936, vol. 1, p. 93, fig. 51, p. 99; Breda 1952, no. 38; Amsterdam 1993–1994, p. 593, in no. 265

COMMENT
Belongs to a series of six portraits, all from the studio of Van Mierevelt (inv. nos. 96–101). Based on the official portrait of Maurits by Van Mierevelt, painted in 1607 (Delft, Stedelijk Museum Het Prinsenhof). Maurits was the eldest son of Willem I of Orange and Anna of Saxony. He became stadholder of Holland and Zeeland after the death of his father in 1584, stadholder of Gelderland, Utrecht and Overijssel in 1585, and stadholder of Groningen and Drenthe in 1620.

Michiel Jansz van Mierevelt (studio of)

100 *Portrait of Frederik Hendrik (1584–1647), Prince of Orange*

Copper (oval), 28 x 23 cm
Formerly signed at left: *Mierevelt*
Dutch title: *Portret van Frederik Hendrik (1584–1647), prins van Oranje*

PROVENANCE
Same as inv. no. 96; on loan to the Musée Municipal, Orange, France, since 1952

LITERATURE
Siegen 1930, p. 16; Paris 1937, no. 79

COMMENT
Belongs to a series of six portraits, all from the studio of Van Mierevelt (inv. nos. 96–101). Based on a (lost) full-length portrait by Van Mierevelt of which there is a good autograph repetition in Delft, Stedelijk Museum Het Prinsenhof. For biographical data, see Van Honthorst, inv. no. 104.

Michiel Jansz van Mierevelt (studio of)

101 *Portrait of Friedrich V (1596–1632)*, 1613

Copper (oval), 27.9 x 23 cm
Dated and inscribed left middle:
Ætatis 16 / A°. 1613 (in part not original)
Bears signature lower right: *MJ v. Mierevelt*
(not autograph; MJ in ligature)
Dutch title: *Portret van Friedrich V (1596–1632)*

PROVENANCE
Same as inv. no. 96

LITERATURE
Siegen 1930, p. 16; Paris 1937, no. 274; Amberg-The Hague 2003–2004, no. 2.2

COMMENT
Belongs to a series of six portraits, all from the studio of Van Mierevelt (inv. nos. 96–100). Cleaned and restored in 1989. Friedrich V, a grandson of Willem I of Orange known as the Winter King, was Elector Palatine and in 1619–1620 King of Bohemia. After a military defeat he escaped to The Hague, where he and his wife soon played an important role in court life. He is shown wearing the Order of the Garter.

98

99

100

101

M

Michiel Jansz van Mierevelt (after)

226 *Portrait of Stadholder Maurits (1567–1625), Prince of Orange*

Canvas, 118.8 x 94.3 cm
Dutch title: *Portret van stadhouder Maurits (1567–1625), prins van Oranje*

PROVENANCE
Anonymous gift, 1819

LITERATURE
Veere-Vlissingen 1955, no. 5

COMMENT
Copy after a lost original by Van Mierevelt, dated 1607. Engraved by Jan Muller (1571–1628). For biographical data, see Van Mierevelt (studio of), inv. no. 99.

507 *Portrait of Johannes Uyttenboogaert (1557–1644)*

Panel, 48.3 x 40 cm
Dutch title: *Portret van Johannes Uyttenboogaert (1557–1644)*

PROVENANCE
Purchased for the Nationale Konst-Gallery, The Hague, 1803; Picture Gallery of Prince Willem V, The Hague, until 1821; transferred, 1822

LITERATURE
Moes/Van Biema 1909, pp. 62, 99, no. 24

COMMENT
This painting is one of the many repetitions of Van Mierevelt's portrait dated 1631 (Rotterdam, Remonstrantse Gemeente). Uyttenboogaert was chaplain to Prince Maurits and councillor to Johan van Oldenbarneveldt. He was the founder of the Brotherhood of Remonstrants.

Frans van Mieris the Elder

Leiden 1635–1681 Leiden

106 *A boy blowing bubbles*, 1663

Panel (rounded at the top), 25.5 x 19 cm
Signed, dated and inscribed lower centre: *M.DC.LXIII. / F. van Mieris. fect. Lugd. Bat.*
Dutch title: *Bellenblazende jongen*

PROVENANCE
Count Fraula, Brussels, 1738; Willem Lormier, The Hague, 1738–1763; Govert van Slingelandt, The Hague, 1763; the entire collection sold to Willem V in 1768; Prince Willem V, The Hague, 1768–1795

LITERATURE
HdG 1907–1928, vol. 10, p. 60, no. 229; D/LS 1974–1976, vol. 3, p. 220, no. 90; Naumann 1981, vol. 1, p. 74, vol. 2, pp. 70–76, no. 58; Sumowski 1983–1995, vol. 1, pp. 502–503, note 36; Korthals Altes 2000–2001, pp. 251, 262; Rotterdam-Frankfurt am Main 2004–2005, no. 82

COMMENT
Cleaned and restored in 2004.

107 *Portrait of Florentius Schuyl (1619–1669)*, 1666

Copper, 21.3 x 16.5 cm
Signed and dated lower left, on the balustrade: *F. van Mieris. fe. A° 1666*
Dutch title: *Portret van Florentius Schuyl (1619–1669)*

PROVENANCE
Govert van Slingelandt, The Hague, in or before 1752; the entire collection sold to Willem V in 1768; Prince Willem V, The Hague, 1768–1795

LITERATURE
HdG 1907–1928, vol. 10, p. 74, no. 275; D/LS 1974–1976, vol. 3, p. 220, no. 89; Naumann 1981, pp. 79–80, no. 63; *Portraits in the Mauritshuis*, no. 36

COMMENT
Florentius Schuyl was professor of philosophy at the 'Illustre School' in Den Bosch. He was later appointed professor of medicine (1664) and botany (1667) at Leiden University, where he became *rector magnificus* in 1666. Cleaned and restored in 2001.

108 *A man and a woman with two dogs, known as 'Teasing the pet'*, 1660

Panel (rounded at the top), 27.5 x 20 cm
Signed and dated upper right, on the door: *Fv Mieris A° 1660* (indistinct)
Dutch title: *Een man en een vrouw met twee honden, bekend als 'Hondje plagen'*

PROVENANCE
Coenraet, Baron Droste, The Hague, 1717; Gerard Bicker van Swieten, The Hague, 1741; Govert van Slingelandt, The Hague, 1752; the entire collection sold to Willem V in 1768; Prince Willem V, The Hague, 1768–1795

LITERATURE
HdG 1907–1928, vol. 10, pp. 53–54, no. 208; D/LS 1974–1976, vol. 3, p. 220, no. 88; Naumann 1981, vol. 2, no. 35 (with list of versions and copies); Philadelphia-Berlin-London 1984, no. 75; Leiden 1988, no. 23; Madrid 2003, no. 27

106

108

226

507

107

COMMENT

The painter and his wife probably served as models. The presumed companion piece to *The oyster dinner* (inv. no. 819).

819 *The oyster dinner*, 1661

Panel (rounded at the top), 27 x 20 cm
Signed, dated and inscribed lower right: *F. van Mieris fescit / Leyd. Bat / A° 1661* (not fully authentic)
Dutch title: *Het oestermaal*

PROVENANCE

Elector Johann Wilhelm of Pfalz-Neuburg, Düsseldorf and Mannheim, until 1716; by descent to King Ludwig I of Bavaria, Munich, 1868; Alte Pinakothek, Munich, 1925–1931; D.A. Hoogendijk Gallery, Amsterdam, 1931; gift of Sir Henri W.A. Deterding, London, 1936

LITERATURE

HdG 1907–1928, vol. 10, p. 29, no. 102a; Naumann 1981, vol. 2, no. 36 (with list of versions and copies); Nagasaki 1992–1993, no. 17; Slive 1995, p. 168

COMMENT

The painter and his wife probably served as models. The presumed companion piece to *'Teasing the pet'* (inv. no. 108).

860 *Brothel scene*, *c.* 1658

Panel, 42.8 x 33.3 cm
Signed and dated at right, above the door:
F. van [M]ieris 165[8?]
Dutch title: *Bordeelscène*

PROVENANCE

Chaplin Collection, England, 1838; Charles Bredel, 1839; A. Levy, London, 1876; Earl of Dudley, London, 1876–1892; Edward Steinkopf, London, 1894; Duits Gallery, London, 1935; Fritz Mannheimer, Amsterdam; Adolf Hitler, Führermuseum, Linz; Stichting Nederlands Kunstbezit; on loan to the Mauritshuis, 1948–1960; transferred, 1960

LITERATURE

HdG 1907–1928, vol. 10, p. 29, no. 102; Kuretsky 1979, pp. 15–16, 30, 61–62; Naumann 1981, vol. 1, pp. 104–108, vol. 2, pp. 26–27, no. 23; Paris 1986, no. 37; Mauritshuis 1987, no. 42; Broos 1989b (about the date); Amsterdam 1989–1990, no. 13; Slive 1995, p. 168; Hecht 1997, pp. 94–95; Amsterdam 2000a, no. 123; Schwarz 2004, no. III/36

COMMENT

A restoration in 1985 revealed the signature and date.

Willem van Mieris

Leiden 1662–1747 Leiden

109 *A grocer's shop*, 1717

Panel, 49.5 x 41 cm
Signed and dated upper left: *W. van Mieris. Fe. 1717*
Dutch title: *Kruidenierswinkel*

PROVENANCE

Purchased from the artist by Johan Hendrik, Count van Wassenaer Obdam, The Hague, 1718; his sale, The Hague, 19 August 1750, lot 56; Prince Willem V, Het Loo Palace, Apeldoorn, 1757

LITERATURE

HdG 1907–1928, vol. 10, p. 154, no. 193; D/LS 1974–1976, vol. 2, p. 640, no. 30, vol. 3, p. 221, no. 91; Leiden 1988, no. 40; Nagasaki 1992–1993, no. 18; De Boer *et al.* 1993, pp. 33–34, no. 8; Korthals Altes 2003, pp. 36, 40, 47, note 13 and fig. 13

COMMENT

The relief – a compilation of motifs by the Flemish sculptor François Duquesnoy – is similar to the ones depicted in the work of Gerrit Dou. *The poultry shop* by Van Mieris in the Musée du Louvre, Paris, is traditionally considered to be the companion piece to inv. no. 109.

1071 *Armida binding the sleeping Rinaldo*, 1709

Panel, 66.8 x 85.7 cm
Signed and dated lower right, on the stone:
W. van Mieris / Fe. Anno. 1709
Dutch title: *Armida bindt de slapende Rinaldo*

PROVENANCE

Pieter de la Court van der Voort and heirs, Leiden, 1709–1748; Hendrick van Kretschmar, The Hague, 1757; Sir Henry Ibbetson, Denton Park, Yorkshire, 1758–1761; Constable Burton, Yorkshire; Alexander Davison, London, 1817; Brod Gallery, London, 1982–1987; purchased, 1987

LITERATURE

HdG 1907–1928, vol. 10, p. 139, nos. 140–141; Fock 1983, p. 268, pp. 270–274, 281, notes 36–37; Leiden 1988, pp. 24, 43, p. 54, note 252, p. 166; Mauritshuis 1993, no. 26; Scholten 1999, p. 39 and fig. 18

COMMENT

Van Mieris depicted the same subject in a number of paintings and drawings (see Mauritshuis 1993, in no. 26).

819 

 860

109 

 1071

M

Abraham Mignon

Frankfurt am Main 1640–1679 Utrecht

110 *Flowers and fruit*

Canvas, 75 x 63 cm
Signed lower left, on a stone: *AB. Mignon: fec*
Dutch title: *Bloemen en vruchten*

PROVENANCE
Princess Henriette Catharina; Oranienstein Palace, Diez, 1726; by descent to Prince Willem V, The Hague, until 1795

LITERATURE
Kraemer-Noble 1973, p. 24, no. A 36; D/LS 1974–1976, vol. 2, p. 371, no. 339, vol. 3, p. 222

COMMENT
The companion piece — now in the Musée du Louvre, Paris — was not returned by the French in 1815.

111 *Flowers in a metal vase, c.1670*

Canvas, 90 x 72.5 cm
Signed lower left, under the edge of the surface: *AB. Mignon: fec.*
Dutch title: *Bloemen in een metalen vaas*

PROVENANCE
Same as inv. no. 110

LITERATURE
Kraemer-Noble 1973, p. 23, no. A 34; D/LS 1974–1976, vol. 2, p. 371, no. 338, vol. 3, p. 222; Meijer 2003, pp. 255–256

COMMENT
Companion piece to inv. no. 112.

112 *Flowers in a glass vase, c.1670*

Canvas, 90 x 72.5 cm
Signed at left, under the edge of the niche: *AB Mignon. fec.*
Dutch title: *Bloemen in een glazen vaas*

PROVENANCE
Same as inv. no. 110

LITERATURE
Kraemer-Noble 1973, p. 23–24, no. A 35; D/LS 1974–1976, vol. 2 p. 371, no. 338, vol. 3, p. 222; The Hague 1992a, no. 19; Nagasaki 1992–1993, no. 19; Meijer 2003, pp. 255–256

COMMENT
Companion piece to inv. no. 111.

George van der Mijn

London 1726/27–Amsterdam 1763

729 *Portrait of Cornelis Ploos van Amstel (1726–1798)*, 1758?

Canvas, 54.8 x 45.5 cm
Formerly bore signature and date lower left: *G van der Mijn 1748*
Dutch title: *Portret van Cornelis Ploos van Amstel (1726–1798)*

PROVENANCE
Cornelis Ploos van Amstel, Amsterdam, until 1798; Margaretha Sonmans, Moordrecht, 1798–1822; (?) Meinouda Engelberts, The Hague, 1822–1832; sale London, Christie's, 9 May 1910, lot 115; purchased with the support of private individuals, 1910

LITERATURE
Niemeijer 1962, pp. 184, 188, 198–199, 204–205, no. 4; Laurentius/Niemeijer/Ploos van Amstel 1980, pp. 60, 105–107, 153, 169–172, 249; Ploos van Amstel 1980, pp. 15, 24, 194–195; Slive 1995, p. 315; Amsterdam 2002–2003a, no. 99a; Pottasch 2003a; *Portraits in the Mauritshuis*, no. 37

COMMENT
Companion piece to inv. no. 730. Both paintings are depicted in Jacob Maurer's 1764 painting of Ploos van Amstel showing his collections to guests (London, private collection; see Haarlem-Paris 2001–2002, no. 111; Fock *et al.* 2001, pp. 294–295, fig. 243). Ploos van Amstel made an etching after his own portrait. Cleaned and restored in 2002. Cornelis Ploos van Amstel, who came from a prominent family of public servants and merchants, bought and sold timber and acted as an art dealer. He played a central role in the cultural life of Amsterdam, was a fair draughtsman and engraver, and assembled a substantial collection of paintings, prints, sculptures, coins, medals and books. In 1758 he married Elisabeth Troost, and in 1791 Margaretha Sonmans. He was befriended with Van der Mijn.

730 *Portrait of Elisabeth Troost (1730–1790)*, 1758?

Canvas, 54.7 x 45.7 cm
Signed and dated lower left: *G. van der Mijn. 1748* (4 and 8 not autograph)
Dutch title: *Portret van Elisabeth Troost (1730–1790)*

PROVENANCE
Same as inv. no. 729

LITERATURE
Niemeijer 1962, pp. 184, 188, 198–199, 204–205, no. 4; Laurentius/Niemeijer/Ploos van Amstel 1980, pp. 60, 105–107, 169–172; Ploos van Amstel 1980, pp. 15, 24, 194–195; Slive 1995, p. 315; Amsterdam 2002–2003a, no. 99b; Pottasch 2003a; *Portraits in the Mauritshuis*, no. 38

729

730

110

111

112

COMMENT
Companion piece to inv. no. 729. Elisabeth was the daughter of the painter Cornelis Troost. This portrait was probably made in 1758 on the occasion of her wedding to Ploos van Amstel. Cleaned and restored in 2002.

Jan Mijtens

The Hague *c.*1614–1670 The Hague

113 *Portrait of Wolfert van Brederode (1649–1679), c.*1663–1665

Panel, 106.5 x 85.5 cm
Signed lower left, on the tree: *JANMijtens F.*
(JANM in ligature)
Dutch title: *Portret van Wolfert van Brederode (1649–1679)*

PROVENANCE
Unknown; transferred, in or before 1841

LITERATURE
Wagner 1924; Amsterdam 1984, no. 49; Bauer 2001, pp. 15–17, no. A 7

COMMENT
The painting is still in its original, elaborately carved frame, decorated with military attributes and various emblems and devices (see Amsterdam 1984). A replica of the painting, which was engraved by Theodor Matham (*c.*1605/6–1676), is in Dessau, Anhaltische Gemäldegalerie, inv. no. 622; copies are listed by Bauer. Van Brederode, the son of Johan Wolfert van Brederode and Louisa Christina of Solms-Braunfels, commanded troops at the age of seven. In 1673 he was appointed colonel of the Brederode regiment.

114 *Portrait of Maria of Orange (1642–1688), with Hendrik van Zuijlestein (d. 1673) and a servant, c.*1665

Canvas, 150 x 185.5 cm
Signed and dated middle right, on the tree:
JANMijtens F: 16[..] (JANM in ligature)
On the horse: *PVO* (in ligature; Princess of [=van] Orange)
Dutch title: *Portret van Maria van Oranje (1642–1688), met Hendrik van Zuijlestein (overleden in 1673) en een dienstbode*

PROVENANCE
Probably by inheritance to Albertine Agnes of Orange-Nassau, the sitter's sister, Oranienstein Palace, Diez, recorded in 1695 (see D/LS 1974–1976, vol 2, p. 160, no. 13); National Konst-Gallery, The Hague; found in the attic of the Mauritshuis, 1875

LITERATURE
Leeuwarden-Den Bosch-Assen 1979–1980, pp. 58–60, no. 18, p. 115, no. 214; Van Thiel 1981, p. 184, no. 13; Liedtke 1989, p. 101, note 17, p. 300, no. 182; Krefeld-Oranienburg-Apeldoorn 1999–2000, pp. 369–370; Bauer 2001, pp. 339–343, no. A 138

COMMENT
Maria of Orange was the youngest daughter of Stadholder Frederik Hendrik and Amalia of Solms-Braunfels. In 1666 she married Ludwig Heinrich of Simmern, Count Palatine. She is depicted here in a fashionable English male costume (cf. also her portrait by Van Honthorst, inv. no. 64). The little boy was identified by Bauer as Hendrik van Zuijlestein, the son of Maria's half-brother, Frederik of Nassau (1624–1672), Lord of Zuijlestein.

Nicolaes Moeyaert

Amsterdam 1592/93–1655 Amsterdam

115 *Hippocrates visiting Democritus*, 1636

Panel, 80 x 85 cm
Signed and dated lower right: *Cl. M. f. 1636* (Cl in ligature)
Dutch title: *Hippocrates bezoekt Democritus*

PROVENANCE
Purchased, 1873

LITERATURE
Tümpel 1974, pp. 92, 95, 103–104, 107, 142, note 248, 269, no. 191; Broos 1991a; Jacobs/Rütten 1998, pp. 116–117, fig. 10

394 *Mercury and Herse*, 1624

Panel, 53.8 x 84 cm
Signed and dated lower left: *CL Moeyaert. fe A° 1624*
(CL in ligature)
Dutch title: *Mercurius en Herse*

PROVENANCE
Kaiser Collection, Frankfurt am Main; purchased, 1874 (see comment to inv. no. 395)

LITERATURE
Tümpel 1974, pp. 78–82, 265, no. 167; Salerno 1977–1980, vol. 1, p. 162, no. 33.2; Mauritshuis 1993, p. 226

395 *The triumph of Bacchus*, 1624

Panel, 53 x 82.8 cm
Signed and dated lower left:
CL Moeyaert. fe A° 1624 (CL in ligature)
Dutch title: *De triomf van Bacchus*

PROVENANCE
Same as inv. no. 394

113 

 114

115 

 394

 395

LITERATURE

Weisner 1963, vol. 1, pp. 98–100, vol. 2, p. 21, note 5; Tümpel 1974, pp. 78, 81–82, 87, 105, 264, no. 156; Washington-Detroit-Amsterdam 1980–1981, no. 24; Mauritshuis 1993, no. 27; Athens-Dordrecht 2000–2001, no. 52; Den Bosch 2003–2004, pp. 72–73

COMMENT

Wrongly considered to be the companion piece of inv. no. 394, with which it was purchased in 1874.

Jan Miense Molenaer

Haarlem 1609/10–1668 Haarlem

407 *Merry peasants*, 1652?

Canvas, 111 x 148 cm
Signed and dated on the bench, next to the woman: *J. Molenaer 16[5?]2*
Dutch title: *Boerenfeest*

PROVENANCE

Neville Goldsmid, The Hague; purchased, 1876; on loan to the ICN

LITERATURE

Mauritshuis 1935, p. 210 (as dated 1653); Weller 1992, pp. 182–183 (as dated 1652)

572 *The five senses: Touch*, 1637

Panel, 19.5 x 24.2 cm
Signed and dated lower right: *IMR 1637* (IMR in ligature)
Dutch title: *De vijf zintuigen: Het gevoel*

PROVENANCE

M.F. Dittlinger, Helvoirt; purchased, 1893

LITERATURE

The Hague 1991–1992, pp. 45, 46; Christie/Wadum 1992; Weller 1992, pp. 133–136; Haarlem-Worcester 1993, no. 36; Raleigh-Columbus-Manchester 2002–2003, no. 26; Neumeister 2003, pp. 229–230

COMMENT

Belongs to a series of five panels (inv. nos. 573–576), all cleaned and restored in 1992.

573 *The five senses: Sight*, 1637

Panel, 19.6 x 23.9 cm
Signed at left, on the table: *IMR* (in ligature)
Dutch title: *De vijf zintuigen: Het gezicht*

PROVENANCE

Same as inv. no. 572

LITERATURE

Same as inv. no. 572

574 *The five senses: Sound*, 1637

Panel, 19.4 x 24.2 cm
Dutch title: *De vijf zintuigen: Het gehoor*

PROVENANCE

Same as inv. no. 572

LITERATURE

Same as inv. no. 572

575 *The five senses: Smell*, 1637

Panel, 19.5 x 24.3 cm
Signed at left, on the table: *IMR* (in ligature)
Dutch title: *De vijf zintuigen: De reuk*

PROVENANCE

Same as inv. no. 572

LITERATURE

Same as inv. no. 572

576 *The five senses: Taste*, 1637

Panel, 19.6 x 24.1 cm
Signed lower right, on the table: *IMR* (in ligature)
Dutch title: *De vijf zintuigen: De smaak*

PROVENANCE

Same as inv. no. 572

LITERATURE

Same as inv. no. 572

691 *Peasant wedding*

Panel, 43.5 x 56.7 cm
Dutch title: *Boerenbruiloft*

PROVENANCE

Bequest of Timon Hendrik Blom Coster, The Hague, 1904; on loan to the ICN

Louis de Moni

Breda 1698–1771 Leiden

116 *A lacemaker, with a boy blowing bubbles*, 1742

Panel, 39 x 42 cm
Signed and dated lower left: *L: De Moni f: / .1742*
Dutch title: *Een kantwerkster, met een bellenblazende jongen*

PROVENANCE

Estate of the painter, Leiden; his sale, 13 April 1772, lot 61; J. Bergeon, The Hague, 1789; Van Eyck Collection, 1829; purchased, 1829; on loan to the Stedelijk Museum De Lakenhal, Leiden, since 1922

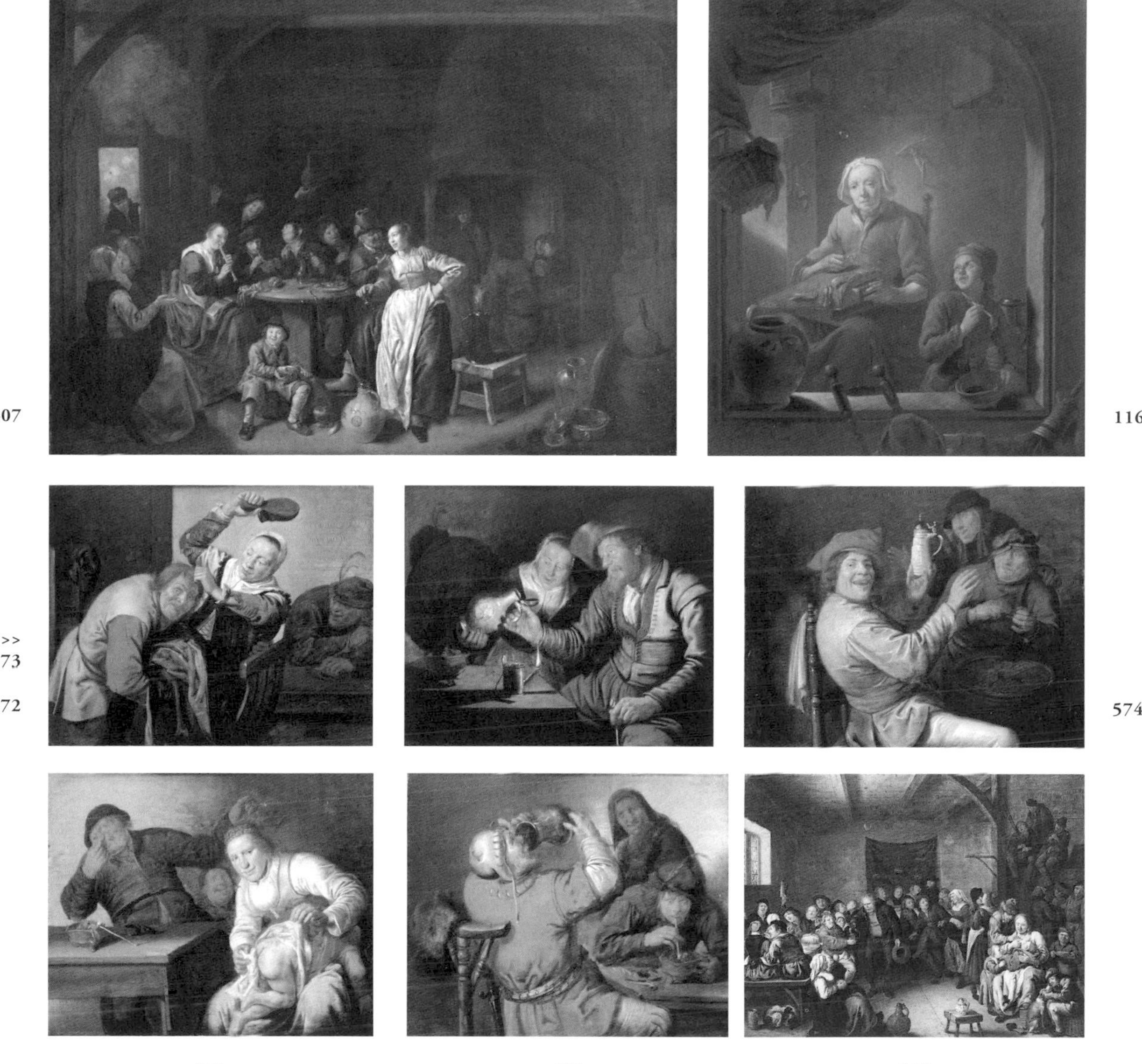

407

116

>>
573

572

574

575

576

691

LITERATURE
Lakenhal 1983, p. 227, no. 317; Leiden 1988, no. 52

COMMENT
The artist's mother, who died in 1743, may have been the model for the lacemaker (see Leiden 1988, pp. 178–179).

Anthonis Mor van Dashorst

Utrecht 1516/19–1575 Antwerp

117 *Portrait of Steven van Herwijck (c.1530–1565/67)*, 1564

Panel, 118 x 89 cm
Dated and inscribed upper right: *A[E]TATIS. XXXV. 1564*
Dutch title: *Portret van Steven van Herwijck (c.1530–1565/67)*

PROVENANCE
Sir Peter Lely, London; his sale (not in Lugt), London, 18 April 1682, unnumbered; possibly Allaert van Couwenhoven, Rotterdam, 1683; sale Nicolaes Anthonis Flinck, Rotterdam, 4 November 1754, lot 11; sale Hendrick van Kretschmar, Amsterdam, 29 March 1757, lot 13; Govert van Slingelandt, The Hague, 1754; the entire collection sold to Willem V in 1768; Prince Willem V, The Hague, 1768–1795

LITERATURE
Marlier 1934, p. 100, no. 28; Van Gelder 1947; Friedländer 1967–1976, vol. 13, p. 103, no. 368; Mauritshuis 1968, p. 41; D/LS 1974–1976, vol. 3, p. 222, no. 97; Amsterdam 1986, no. 214; *Portraits in the Mauritshuis*, no. 39

COMMENT
Steven van Herwijck was a portraitist and medallist from Utrecht who became master in the guild at Antwerp, the city in which he had presumably been apprenticed. In 1565 he went to England. This portrait may have had a companion piece, possibly *Seated woman with a parrot* (Glasgow, University of Glasgow, Hunterian Art Gallery).

Anthonis Mor van Dashorst (and studio)

559 *Portrait of a man*, 1561

Canvas, 69.2 x 55.8 cm
Signed and dated upper left:
Antonius morus / pingebat A° 1561
Dutch title: *Portret van een man*

PROVENANCE
E. Secrétan, Paris; his sale, Paris, 1 July 1889, lot 146; purchased, 1889

LITERATURE
Marlier 1934, p. 99, no. 25; Mauritshuis 1968, pp. 40–41; Friedländer 1969–1976, vol. 13, p. 103, no. 366; Bruyn 1999, pp. 125, 126 (fig. 15); Bruyn 2003, p. 88

COMMENT
Possibly the replica of a larger original. Only the head is autograph. Purchased as a portrait of Willem I of Orange.

Louis-Gabriel Moreau the Elder

Paris 1739–1805 Paris

861 *Fashionable company in a garden*

Panel, 30 x 25 cm
Dutch title: *Elegant gezelschap in een tuin*

PROVENANCE
Eugène Féral, Paris, before 1920; M.A. Beurdeley, Paris, 1920; Gibour Collection, Paris; David Weill, Paris, *c.*1923–1926; Fritz Mannheimer, Amsterdam; Adolf Hitler; Stichting Nederlands Kunstbezit; on loan to the Mauritshuis, 1948–1960; transferred, 1960

LITERATURE
Wildenstein 1923, p. 62, no. 50

Johannes Moreelse

Utrecht after 1602–1634 Utrecht

705 *Democritus, the laughing philosopher, c.1630*

Canvas, 84.5 x 73 cm
Signed on the globe:
JPM (the 'P' is presumably a later addition)
Dutch title: *Democritus, de lachende filosoof*

PROVENANCE
Gift of L. Nardus, Arnouville, 1906

LITERATURE
De Jonge 1938, p. 129, no. 3; Blankert 1967, pp. 52, 55–56, note 54, 98, no. 33; Fremantle 1974, pp. 618–620; Utrecht 2001, no. 37

COMMENT
This painting was probably accompanied by a companion piece with Heraclitus. A repetition, with a companion piece, is in an English private collection.

117 

 559

861 

 705

M

Paulus Moreelse

Utrecht 1571–1638 Utrecht

118 *Self-portrait, c.*1630

Panel, 71.5 x 62 cm
Bears signature lower right: *PM* (in ligature)
Dutch title: *Zelfportret*

PROVENANCE
François Henri Corneille, Baron van Heeckeren van Brandsenburg, Utrecht, 1869; dowager Christine Louise van Heeckeren van Brandsenburg, née Van Foreest van Heemse, Utrecht, 1869–1875; purchased by the State Advisory Board for Monuments of History and Art and transferred to the Mauritshuis, 1875

LITERATURE
De Jonge 1938, p. 11, 22, 64, 99, no. 123; Huys Janssen 1990, pp. 8–9; Domela Nieuwenhuis 2001, vol. 2, pp. 503–505; *Portraits in the Mauritshuis*, no. 41

655 *Portrait of a lady*, 1627

Canvas, 117.5 x 95 cm
Signed and dated upper right: *1627 / PM:* (PM in ligature)
Dutch title: *Portret van een dame*

PROVENANCE
Edward or William Gascoyne Bulwer, Wood Dalling and Heydon Hall, Norfolk, before 1901; Dowdeswell & Dowdeswell Gallery, London, 1901; Abraham Bredius, The Hague, 1901–1946 (on loan to the Mauritshuis since 1901); bequest of Abraham Bredius, 1946

LITERATURE
De Jonge 1938, p. 92, no. 89; The Hague 1991–1992, no. 8; Mauritshuis 1987, p. 122, fig. 3; Domela Nieuwenhuis 2001, vol. 2, pp. 472–473; *Portraits in the Mauritshuis*, no. 40

Jean Baptiste Morel (attributed to)

Antwerp 1662–1732 Brussels

702 *Portrait of a lady encircled by a wreath of flowers, c.*1690?

Panel, 36.8 x 27.6 cm
Dutch title: *Portret van een dame omringd door een bloemenkrans*

PROVENANCE
Bequest of Johanna Charlotte Hendrika Roels, The Hague, 1906

COMMENT
Companion piece to inv. no. 703. The portrait was painted by an unknown Flemish artist.

703 *Portrait of a man encircled by a wreath of flowers, c.*1690?

Panel, 37.3 x 28.8 cm
Dutch title: *Portret van een man omringd door een bloemenkrans*

PROVENANCE
Same as inv. no. 702

COMMENT
Companion piece to inv. no. 702. The portrait was painted by an unknown Flemish artist.

Giovanni Battista Moroni

Albino *c.*1525–1575 Bergamo

767 *Portrait of Vercellino Olivazzi, c.*1565?

Canvas, 98 x 81 cm
Dutch title: *Portret van Vercellino Olivazzi*

PROVENANCE
Olivazzi family, Bergamo, until *c.*1900; Countess P. Luppi-Olivazzi, Bergamo; J. Bischof Gallery, Paris; F. von Franz, Frankfurt am Main; Bachstitz Gallery, The Hague, 1921; purchased, 1922; on loan to the Rijksmuseum, Amsterdam (inv. no. SK-C-1365), since 1948

LITERATURE
Cugini 1939, p. 152, no. 99; RM 1976, p. 400; Bergamo 1979, pp. 220–222, 354; Boschloo/Van der Sman 1993, pp. 66–67, no. 53

COMMENT
The portrait has traditionally been identified as that of Vercellino Olivazzi, a senator of Bergamo. The Olivazzi family lived mainly in Milan.

Jan Mostaert?

Haarlem *c.*1475–1555/56 Haarlem

921 *Joseph explaining the dreams of the baker and the cupbearer, c.*1500

Panel, 31.1 x 24.5 cm
Dutch title: *Jozef verklaart de dromen van de bakker en de schenker*

118

655

703

702

767

921

PROVENANCE
Edouard Aynard, Lyons, before 1904–1913; Louis, Baron de Rotschild, Vienna, before 1930–1955; Rosenberg & Stiebel Gallery, New York, 1955; purchased, 1955

LITERATURE
Winkler 1959b, pp. 188–190, 192–193; Mauritshuis 1968, pp. 41–42; Mauritshuis 1970, no. 2; Rotterdam 1983, no. 273; Mauritshuis 1993, no. 45 (as North-Netherlandish School [Jan Mostaert or Jacob Jansz van Haarlem?]); Schwarz 2004, no. I/38

COMMENT
The attribution is uncertain.

Frederik de Moucheron

Emden 1633–1686 Amsterdam

121 *Italian landscape*

Canvas, 93.5 x 125 cm
Signed lower right: *Moucheron. ft.*
Dutch title: *Italiaans landschap*

PROVENANCE
Jan Willem van Arp, Amsterdam, 1800; Pieter de Smeth van Alphen, Amsterdam, 1810; Henry Croese, Amsterdam, 1811; Gerrit Muller, Amsterdam, 1827; De Vries Gallery, Amsterdam; purchased, 1827

LITERATURE
Blankert 1978, p. 222, no. 140; Salerno 1977–1980, vol. 2, p. 760; Mauritshuis 1980, pp. 58–59

COMMENT
The figures can be attributed to Johannes Lingelbach.

Frederik de Moucheron (attributed to)

122 *Landscape with travellers being attacked*

Canvas, 89 x 72.5 cm
Bears signature lower right: *Moucheron*
Dutch title: *Landschap waarin reizigers worden overvallen*

PROVENANCE
(?) Marin Collection, Paris, 1790; on loan to the ICN

LITERATURE
Mauritshuis 1980, p. 59 (as attributed to De Moucheron and possibly by Jan van Huysum)

COMMENT
The attribution is uncertain; the signature is not autograph.

Pieter Mulier the Elder

Haarlem *c.*1615–1670 Haarlem

549 *Choppy sea, c.*1640

Panel, 39.5 x 60.5 cm
Signed on a floating piece of wood: *.PML.* (in ligature)
Dutch title: *Stormachtige zee*

PROVENANCE
T. Humphrey Ward & Son Gallery, London, 1889; gift of Abraham Bredius, The Hague, 1889; on loan to the Nederlands Scheepvaartmuseum, Amsterdam, since 1981

LITERATURE
Bol 1973, p. 143; Mauritshuis 1980, p. 60; The Hague 1991–1992, no. 9

Bartolomé Esteban Murillo

Seville 1617–1682 Seville

296 *Madonna and Child, c.*1655–1660

Canvas, 188 x 137.5 cm
Dutch title: *Madonna met kind*

PROVENANCE
Jean A. Snijers, Antwerp; purchased by King Willem I for the Mauritshuis, 1818; on loan to the Rijksmuseum, Amsterdam (inv. no. SK-C-1366), since 1948

LITERATURE
Van Vliet 1966, pp. 1332–133, fig. 2; RM 1976, p. 403; Gaya Nuño 1978, p. 92, no. 66; Angulo-Iñiguez 1981, vol. 1, p. 280, vol. 2, no. 143; Madrid-London 1982–1983, no. 25

Michiel van Musscher

Rotterdam 1645–1705 Amsterdam

123 *Family portrait,* 1681

Canvas, 90 x 106 cm
Signed, dated and inscribed centre below, on a piece of paper: *A°:1681 in Amsterdam / Ml:v: Musscher. / Pinxit.*
Dutch title: *Familieportret*

PROVENANCE
Van Eyck Collection, 1829; purchased, 1829; on loan to the ICN

LITERATURE
Mauritshuis 1935, p. 454

121

122

296

549

123

748 *Portrait of Thomas Hees (1634–1692), with his nephews Jan (b. 1662/63) and Andries (b. 1669/70) Hees, and his servant Thomas*, 1687

Canvas, 83 x 76 cm
Signed and dated on the table-cloth: *Michiel v. Musscher. Pinxit. Anno M.DC.LXXXVII.*
Inscribed on the shield: *CONCORDIA RES PARVAE CRESCUNT* (Unity makes strength)
Bears inscription on the verso: *Thomas Hees 52 jaar, Jan Hees 16 jaar, Andries Hees 24 jaar en Thomas de neger 17 jaar*
Dutch title: *Portret van Thomas Hees (1634–1692) met zijn neven Jan (geboren 1662/63) and Andries (geboren 1669/70) Hees, en zijn bediende Thomas*

PROVENANCE
Bequest of *Jonkheren* Jacob Hendrik and Wiardus Hora Siccama, The Hague, 1914; on loan to the Rijksmuseum, Amsterdam (inv. no. SK-C-1215), since 1932

LITERATURE
Moes 1897–1905, vol. 1, p. 402, no. 3359; Edwards 1954, p. 148, no. 43; RM 1976, p. 404; Amsterdam 1992b, pp. 62, 295, note 42; Beumer 1999, p. 158, fig. 10; Noordervliet 1999, pp. 112–114, repr.; Dublin-Greenwich 2003–2004, p. 27

COMMENT
Thomas Hees was resident and commissioner of the States General to the governments of Algiers (1675–1680; 1682–1683), Tunis and Tripoli (1684–1685), as is indicated by the opened atlas on the table ('BARBARI[A]'), on which there are also a bible ('BIBLIA / SACRA') and a koran. A red velvet wallet with a tortoise shell comb (inv. nos. 748a–b), part of the same bequest as the painting, are also on loan to the Rijksmuseum.

Pieter Nason

Amsterdam *c.*1612–*c.*1688/90 The Hague

124 *Portrait of Stadholder Willem Frederik (1613–1664)*, 1662

Canvas, 121 x 93.6 cm
Signed and dated upper left: *Nason. f 1662*
Dutch title: *Portret van stadhouder Willem Frederik (1613–1664)*

PROVENANCE
Probably from one of the stadholder's palaces; found in the attic of the Mauritshuis, 1875; on loan to the Paleis Het Loo Nationaal Museum, Apeldoorn

LITERATURE
Van der Ploeg 1997, p. 18 (repr.); Krefeld-Oranienburg-Apeldoorn 1999–2000, no. 10/2; Mulder-Radetzky 2003, p. 241; The Hague 2004, p. 37

COMMENT
Based on Adriaen Hanneman (see comment to MINIATURES, after Hanneman, inv. no. 1024, a portrait of the same sitter). Engraved by Abraham Bloteling (1640–1690). Willem Frederik, Count of Nassau-Dietz, became Stadholder of Friesland in 1640, and of Groningen in 1650. In 1652 he married Albertine Agnes, daughter of Stadholder Frederik Hendrik.

Peter Neeffs the Younger

Antwerp 1620–1675 Antwerp

With Frans Francken III
Antwerp 1607–1667 Antwerp

248 *Interior of the Onze Lieve Vrouwekerk in Antwerp*, in or after 1654

Panel, 34 x 47.6 cm
Signed on a pillar at left: *Peeter / neeffs / ffrank*
Inscribed on the statue of the Virgin at right: *S. MARIA . MATRI VIERGI / NE APOSTOLO / RVM. 1654*
Inscribed on the statue of St Paul at the next column, and on a little monument at left: *D.O.M. / PET[R]US / VAN / HOREN*
Dutch title: *Interieur van de Onze Lieve Vrouwekerk in Antwerpen*

PROVENANCE
Prince Willem V, The Hague, 1763–1795

LITERATURE
D/LS 1974–1976, vol. 3, p. 19, no. 14, p. 223, no. 104; Jantzen 1979, p. 230, no. 339

COMMENT
The figures were painted by Francken III. Cleaned and restored in 1987.

Aert van der Neer

Gorinchem 1604–1677 Amsterdam

682 *Landscape at sunset, c.*1645–1650

Panel, 46.5 x 37.8 cm
Dutch title: *Landschap bij zonsondergang*

PROVENANCE
T. Sheffield, London, *c.*1872; F. Kleinberger Gallery, Paris, 1900; purchased with the support of the Rembrandt Society, 1903

LITERATURE
HdG 1907–1928, vol. 7, pp. 408–409, no. 196; The Hague-

748

124

248

682

London 1970–1971, no. 83; Mauritshuis 1980, p. 62; Schulz 2002, p. 221, no. 358

787 *Winter landscape with houses, c.1645–1650*

Panel, 25 x 36.5 cm
Signed and dated at left: *AVDN / 7 fe[bruaris] 16[.]5*
(AV and DN in ligature; date not original)
Dutch title: *Winterlandschap met huizen*

PROVENANCE
Theodor Lang, Paris; Jules Porgès, Paris, F. Kleinberger Gallery, Paris; A. de Ridder and heirs, Kronberg, 1910–1924; purchased with the support of the Rembrandt Society and private individuals, 1924

LITERATURE
HdG 1907–1928, vol. 7, pp. 481–482, no. 494; Mauritshuis 1980, pp. 61–62; Bachmann 1982, p. 115; Schulz 2002, p. 131, no. 21 (as dated 1655)

COMMENT
The date has been read as 1635, 1655 and 1675.

912 *River landscape, c.1650*

Panel, 44.8 x 63 cm
Signed lower right: *AVDN* (AV and DN in ligature)
Dutch title: *Rivierlandschap*

PROVENANCE
(?) Blok Collection, Haarlem, 1765; (?) Andreas Bonn, Amsterdam; Jean Gisbert Verstolk van Soelen, The Hague, 1846; Thomas Baring, London; Thomas George Baring, Earl of Northbrook, London, 1889; E.A. Veltman, Bussum; Wertheimer Gallery, Basel; purchased, 1953

LITERATURE
HdG 1907–1928, vol. 7, p. 376, no. 54; Mauritshuis 1970, no. 30; Mauritshuis 1980, pp. 62–63; Bachmann 1982, p. 106; Schulz 2002, p. 220, no. 356 (mistakenly referred to as inv. no. 913)

COMMENT
Cleaned and restored in 2002. Formerly regarded as a companion piece to inv. no. 913.

913 *River landscape at sunset, c.1650*

Panel, 46 x 63.5 cm
Signed lower centre: *AVDN* (AV and DN in ligature)
Dutch title: *Rivierlandschap bij zonsondergang*

PROVENANCE
Same as inv. no. 912

LITERATURE
HdG 1907–1928, vol. 7, p. 376, no. 53; De Vries 1953a, pp. 82–83; Mauritshuis 1970, no. 31; Mauritshuis 1980, pp. 63–64; Bachmann 1982, p. 106; Schulz 2002, pp. 220–221, no. 357 (mistakenly referred to as inv. no. 912)

COMMENT
Cleaned and restored in 2002. Formerly regarded as a companion piece to inv. no. 912.

Eglon van der Neer

Amsterdam *c.*1634–1703 Düsseldorf

862 *Interior with a woman washing her hands, 1675*

Panel, 49 x 39.5 cm
Signed and dated lower right, under the column of the fireplace: *Eglon. vander. Neer. fe. 1675*
Dutch title: *Interieur met handenwassende vrouw*

PROVENANCE
Seger Tierens, The Hague, 1743; Hendrik van der Vugt, Amsterdam, 1745; Johan van der Linden van Slingelandt, Dordrecht, 1785; T.T. Cremer, Rotterdam, 1785–1816; W. Beckford, Fonthill Abbey, near Bath, 1823; F. Heusch, London, 1854; (?) Lord Northwick, Thirlestaine House, Cheltenham, 1859; Alfred de Rothschild, London; Victor de Rothschild, London; sale London, Sotheby's, 19–22 April 1937, lot 13, to Rosenberg, art dealers; Fritz Mannheimer, Amsterdam; Adolf Hitler, Führermuseum, Linz; Stichting Nederlands Kunstbezit; on loan to the Mauritshuis, 1948–1960; transferred, 1960

LITERATURE
HdG 1907–1928, p. 518, nr. 44; Amsterdam 1976, no. 48; Philadelphia-Berlin-London 1984, pp. 270–271; Haak 1984, p. 491; Gaehtgens 1987b, pp. 92–93; Slive 1995, p. 307; Washington-The Hague 1995–1996, pp. 40, 146, 148; Van der Ploeg *et al.* 2002, pp. 122–123; Schwarz 2004, no. III/37; Rotterdam-Frankfurt am Main 2004–2005, no. 76

Caspar Netscher

Prague or Heidelberg 1635/36–1684 The Hague

125 *Company making music, 1665*

Panel, 44 x 36 cm
Signed and dated on the back of the chair at left: *CNetscher. A° 1665* (CN in ligature)
Dutch title: *Muziekmakend gezelschap*

PROVENANCE
Sale Baron Schönborn, Amsterdam, 16 April 1738, lot 35; Willem Lormier, The Hague, 1738–1752; Govert van Slingelandt, The Hague, 1752; the entire collection sold to Willem V in 1768; Prince Willem V, The Hague, 1768–1795

LITERATURE
HdG 1907–1928, vol. 5, pp. 194–195, no. 115; D/LS 1974–1976, vol. 3, p. 222, no. 102; Philadelphia-Berlin-London 1984,

912 

 913

 787

862 

 125

pp. 274–275; Buijsen *et al.* 1998, p. 219; Korthals Altes 2000–2001, pp. 283–284, 305, no. 32; Wieseman 2002, no. 52

COMMENT
The background relief probably shows the abduction of Helen.

126 *Portrait of Maurits Le Leu de Wilhem (1643–1724)*, 1677

Canvas, 48.4 x 39.5 cm
Signed and dated lower right: *CNetscher. 1677* (CN in ligature)
Bears inscription on the verso: *de Walwijk* (presumably 19th-century)
Dutch title: *Portret van Maurits Le Leu de Wilhem (1643–1724)*

PROVENANCE
Probably by descent through the family of the sitter to Pauline Marie Constance de Forestier d'Orges van Waalwijk, née Le Leu de Wilhem, until 1846; bequest of Pauline Adrienne Philippine de Forestier d'Orges van Waalwijk, The Hague, 1855

LITERATURE
HdG 1907–1928, vol. 5, p. 227, no. 222; Haarlem 1986, no. 38; Slive 1995, p. 261; Wieseman 2002, no. 161; *Portraits in the Mauritshuis*, no. 42

COMMENT
Companion piece to the portrait of Maria Timmers (inv. no. 127), which was painted six years later on the occasion of her marriage to Le Leu de Wilhem. Maurits Le Leu de Wilhem came from a prominent family in The Hague. He worked as an advocate at the Court of Holland and became a member, and later president, of the Council of Brabant (1693–1717). In 1678 Maurits received the Spanish king's grant of nobility, which allowed him to call himself 'Le Leu de Wilhem'. Cleaned and restored in 1993.

127 *Portrait of Maria Timmers (1658–1753)*, 1683

Canvas, 48.2 x 39.7 cm
Signed and dated lower left: *CNetscher: fec / 1683* (CN in ligature)
Dutch title: *Portret van Maria Timmers (1658–1753)*

PROVENANCE
Same as inv. no. 126

LITERATURE
HdG 1907–1928, vol. 5, p. 227, no. 223; Haarlem 1986, no. 38; Slive 1995, p. 261; Wieseman 2002, no. 215; *Portraits in the Mauritshuis*, no. 43

COMMENT
Maria Timmers was the daughter of Paulus Timmers, burgomaster of Rotterdam and scion of a particularly influential and wealthy family. In 1683 she married Maurits Le Leu de Wilhem, portrayed on the companion piece (inv. no. 126). Cleaned and restored in 1993.

714 *Portrait of Elisabeth van Bebber (1643–1704)*, 1677?

Canvas, 49 x 40 cm
Signed and dated lower left: *C. Netsch[er] / 167[.]*
Dutch title: *Portret van Elisabeth van Bebber (1643–1704)*

PROVENANCE
Probably Michiel ten Hove and heirs, until 1907; bequest of *Jonkvrouw* Maria Johanna Singendonck, The Hague, 1907

LITERATURE
Wieseman 2002, no. 166; Wieseman 2004, p. 251

COMMENT
Companion piece to inv. no. 715. Elisabeth van Bebber married Michiel ten Hove in 1672 (see inv. no. 715). She was first married to the wealthy merchant Johannes Dierquens (see also Maes, inv. no. 718, and Van Haensbergen, inv. no. 720).

Caspar Netscher (studio of)

715 *Portrait of Michiel ten Hove (1640–1689)*, after 1689?

Canvas, 48.8 x 39.4 cm
Dutch title: *Portret van Michiel ten Hove (1640–1689)*

PROVENANCE
Same as inv. no. 714

LITERATURE
Lubberhuizen-Van Gelder 1947, p. 146; Wieseman 2002, no. C 149 (studio of Netscher)

COMMENT
Companion piece to inv. no. 714, to which this portrait was perhaps added after Ten Hove's death. Ten Hove was advocate of the West India Company, magistrate of Haarlem and was elected Grand Pensionary of Holland in 1688, but he died before he could take office. In 1672 he married Elisabeth van Bebber (inv. no. 714). Possibly executed by Constantijn Netscher, Caspar's son. Ten Hove's brother Cornelis was portrayed by Nicolaes Maes (inv. no. 717).

126 

 127

715 

 714

Caspar Netscher (after)

716 *Portrait of Johan de Witt (1625–1672)*

Canvas, 47 x 43 cm
Dutch title: *Portret van Johan de Witt (1625–1672)*

PROVENANCE
Bequest of *Jonkvrouw* Maria Johanna Singendonck, The Hague, 1907; on loan to the ICN

LITERATURE
Wieseman 2002, p. 217, no. 67a

COMMENT
Copy after a portrait by Netscher dated 1667 in a private collection (Wieseman 2002, no. 67). Statesman Johan de Witt was appointed Grand Pensionary of Holland in 1653. In 1672 Johan and his brother Cornelis de Witt (see De Baen, inv. no. 454) were stoned by a mob for opposing the House of Orange.

Constantijn Netscher

The Hague 1668–1723 The Hague

686 *Portrait of a man*, 1715

Canvas (oval), 52.5 x 43.1 cm
Signed and dated bottom right: *Const.s: Netscher / 1715*
Dutch title: *Portret van een man*

PROVENANCE
Netscher family, The Hague and Rotterdam, until 1903; bequest of Pieter Marinus Netscher, The Hague, 1903; on loan to the ICN

COMMENT
Since the last known owner of inv. no. 686 was a descendant of the painter, the sitter might well have been related to the latter.

721 *Portrait of Anna Maria Roman (1680–1758)*, 1710

Canvas, 57.5 x 46 cm
Signed and dated lower left: *Const. Netscher 17[10]*
Dutch title: *Portret van Anna Maria Roman (1680–1758)*

PROVENANCE
Bequest of *Jonkvrouw* Maria Johanna Singendonck, The Hague, 1907; on loan to the ICN

LITERATURE
Buijsen *et al.* 1998, p. 223

COMMENT
Companion piece to Johan van Haensbergen's portrait of Pieter Dierquens (inv. no. 720), whom Anna Maria Roman married in 1704. Until the discovery of the signature and date in 1971 attributed to Van Haensbergen.

Jan van Nickele?

Haarlem 1656–1721 Kassel

967 *Country house and park, c.*1690–1700?

Panel, 50.5 x 69.2 cm
Dutch title: *Buitenhuis en park*

PROVENANCE
Gift of Edward Speelman, London, 1963

LITERATURE
Mauritshuis 1970, no. 49 (as attributed to Johan Post); The Hague 2002, p. 214, note 31 (with present attribution)

COMMENT
To be compared with a painting that is evidently by the same hand (Buijsen *et al.* 1998, p. 337, repr.; panel, 24.8 x 31.1 cm, until 1995 at the New York Historical Society, cat. 1915, no. D-137; sale New York, Sotheby's, 12 January 1995, lot 48, as by Johan Post; HdG 1907–1928, vol. 8, p. 427, no. 229, as by Jan van der Heyden).

Adriaen van Nieulandt

Antwerp 1587–1658 Amsterdam

476 *Maurits (1567–1625) and Frederik Hendrik (1584–1647), Princes of Orange, on the beach at Scheveningen*

Canvas, 136.3 x 199.3 cm
Dutch title: *Maurits (1567–1625) en Frederik Hendrik (1584–1647), prinsen van Oranje, op het strand van Scheveningen*

PROVENANCE
C. de Snoy, Brussels, 1884; purchased, 1884

LITERATURE
Leeuwarden-Den Bosch-Assen 1979–1980, p. 49, no. 12, p. 115, no. 221; The Hague 1997–1998b, pp. 26, 79; Dessau 2003, no. II–13

COMMENT
A preliminary drawing is in Paris, Fondation Custodia, Frits Lugt Collection, inv. no. 5209. For biographical data on Maurits, who is wearing the Order of the Garter, see Van Mierevelt, inv. no. 99. For biographical data on Frederik Hendrik, see Van Honthorst, inv. no. 104. Cleaned and restored in 1990.

716

967

476

721

686

Pieter van Noort

Leiden (?) *c.*1600–1672 Zwolle

602 *Fish still life, c.*1640–1650

Canvas, 65 x 82 cm
Bears signature lower left: *A:Cuijp*
Dutch title: *Visstilleven*

PROVENANCE
Purchased, 1895; on loan to the ICN

LITERATURE
The Hague 1991–1992, pp. 38, 41, fig. 22

Jacob Ochtervelt

Rotterdam 1634–1682 Amsterdam

195 *A fishmonger at the door, c.*1667–1668

Canvas, 55.5 x 44 cm
Formerly signed at right at the door:
Jac^0 Ochtervelt (see Mauritshuis 1935, p. 237)
Dutch title: *Een visverkoper aan de deur*

PROVENANCE
S. Stinstra sale, Amsterdam, 26 March 1783, lot 191; G. van der Pals, Rotterdam, 1824; Van Roothaan Collection, Amsterdam; purchased, 1826

LITERATURE
Kuretsky 1979, no. 41; Philadelphia-Berlin-London 1984, p. 279, note 1; Nagasaki 1992–1993, no. 20; Dumas 1991, pp. 419, 422, notes 12 and 14; Dordrecht-Enschede 2000, p. 130; Rotterdam-Frankfurt am Main 2004–2005, no. 73

Hendrick ten Oever

Zwolle 1639–1716 Zwolle

681 *View of the Herengracht in Amsterdam, c.*1690?

Panel, 36.8 x 42 cm
Signed lower left: *H. Ten Oever fecit*
Dated on the verso: *1690* (probably not autograph)
Dutch title: *Gezicht op de Herengracht in Amsterdam*

PROVENANCE
Purchased, 1903

LITERATURE
Verbeek/Schotman 1957, no. 33; Zwolle 1997, no. 40

COMMENT
A second dog, which was not original, was removed during restoration in 1978.

Jan Olis

Gorinchem *c.*1610–1676 Heusden

537 *Portrait of Johan van Beverwijck (1594–1647) in his study, c.*1640

Panel, 25.7 x 20.5 cm
Signed lower left, on the edge of the table: *J olis*
Dutch title: *Portret van Johan van Beverwijck (1594–1647) in zijn studeerkamer*

PROVENANCE
Inventory of Johan van Beverwijck, Dordrecht, 22–23 February 1651: '1 conterfeytselken van heer Dr. Beverwijck zar. van Jan Olens' (1 portrait of the late Doctor Beverwijck by Jan Olens; see Loughman/Montias 2000); J.H. Cremer, Amsterdam, 1886; C.F. Roos & Cie, Amsterdam; purchased, 1887; on loan to the Dordrechts Museum, Dordrecht, since 2003

LITERATURE
Bernt 1969–1970, vol. 2, no. 615; Loughman/Montias 2000, pp. 79, 146

COMMENT
Van Beverwijck was one of the most remarkable men of his day: he was a medical scholar, local historian, poet and politician. In 1625 he was named the official town doctor of Dordrecht.

Jacob van Oost II (circle of)

Bruges 1637–1713 Bruges

297 *Bust of a young man*

Canvas, 45.7 x 40.3 cm
Dutch title: *Buste van een jonge man*

PROVENANCE
Bernard Eugène Rottiers, Antwerp, 1823; purchased by King Willem I for the Mauritshuis, 5 August 1823

LITERATURE
De Callatay 1971, pp. 95–98 (as by Van Mol); Meulemeester 1984, p. 397, no. C 33 (attribution to Van Oost doubtful)

COMMENT
A copy is in a private collection in Amsterdam. Formerly attributed to Pieter van Mol (1599–1650).

195

602

297

681

537

O

Maria van Oosterwyck

Nootdorp 1630–1693 Uitdam

468 *Flowers in a ornamental vase, c.1670–1675?*

Canvas, 62 x 47.5 cm
Signed lower centre on the edge of the table:
MARIA VAN OOSTERWYCK
Dutch title: *Bloemen in een versierde vaas*

PROVENANCE
Coninck de Mercken Collection, Ghent, 1856; Bernard du Bus de Gisignies, Brussels; purchased, 1882

LITERATURE
Bol 1969, pp. 318–319, fig. 291; Amsterdam-Den Bosch 1982, no. 52; Osaka-Tokyo-Sydney 1990, no. 54; Nagasaki 1992–1993, no. 21; Antwerp-Arnhem 1999–2000, no. 56

COMMENT
Cleaned and restored in 1990.

Adriaen van Ostade

Haarlem 1610–1685 Haarlem

128 *Peasants at an inn*, 1662

Panel, 47.5 x 39 cm
Signed and dated lower right: *Av. Ostade. / 1662*
(Av in ligature)
Dutch title: *Boeren in een herberg*

PROVENANCE
C. van Dyk, The Hague, 1713; F. van Bleyswyk, 1734; H. van Slingelandt, The Hague, 1734–1759; Van Slingelandt heirs, until 1768; Prince Willem V, The Hague, 1768–1795

LITERATURE
HdG 1907–1928, vol. 3, pp. 339–340, no. 636; D/LS 1974–1976, vol. 3, p. 223, no. 106; Paris 1986, no. 38; Mauritshuis 1987, no. 43; Romanko Gier 1990, pp. 1–3, 5–6, 11, 38, 45, 55

129 *The violinist*, 1673

Panel, 45 x 42 cm
Signed and dated lower right, on a plank:
Av. Ostade. / 1673 (Av in ligature)
Dutch title: *De vioolspeler*

PROVENANCE
Govert van Slingelandt, The Hague, after 1752; the entire collection sold to Willem V in 1768; Prince Willem V, The Hague, 1768–1795

LITERATURE
HdG 1907–1928, vol. 3, p. 277, no. 429; D/LS 1974–1976, vol. 3, p. 223, no. 105; Niemeijer 1980, pp. 262–263, no. 17; Schnackenburg 1981, pp. 124–125, no. 227

COMMENT
A watercolour by Van Ostade of a violinist, also dated 1673, is in the Pierpont Morgan Library, New York. Cornelis Ploos van Amstel made an engraving after this sheet.

580 *Peasants celebrating*, 1630s

Panel, 47.3 x 63.6 cm
Signed and dated on the bench:
Av Ostade 163[.] (Av in ligature)
Dutch title: *Boerenfeest*

PROVENANCE
Colnaghi Gallery, London; purchased, 1894

LITERATURE
HdG 1907–1928, vol. 3, p. 320, no. 565; Schnackenburg 1981, p. 83, no. 19; Romanko Gier 1990, pp. 11, 31, 41, 59, 74

807 *The merry drinkers*, 1659

Panel, 30.5 x 25 cm
Signed and dated lower right: *AV. Ostade. / 1659*
(AV in ligature)
Dutch title: *Vrolijke drinkers*

PROVENANCE
Jonkheer Johan Steengracht van Oostkapelle and heirs, The Hague, before 1840–1913; Jacques Goudstikker Gallery, Amsterdam; purchased, 1932

LITERATURE
HdG 1907–1928, vol. 3, p. 243, no. 325

Isack van Ostade

Haarlem 1621–1649 Haarlem

745 *Farmer with a pig*, 1644

Panel, 27.1 x 25.3 cm
Bears signature and date lower left: *Av ostade / 1644*
(Av in ligature)
Dutch title: *Boer met varken*

PROVENANCE
Johan Gualtherus van der Poort van Oostkapelle and heirs, Middelburg and The Hague, 1793–1913; purchased with the support of the Rembrandt Society; on loan to the Frans Hals Museum, Haarlem, since 1975

LITERATURE
HdG 1907–1928, vol. 3, p. 493, no. 122; Mauritshuis 1980, p. 66

468

807

745

580

128

129

COMMENT
Isack's signature was changed to that of his more famous brother.

789 *Travellers outside an inn*, 1645

Panel, 75 x 109 cm
Signed and dated lower centre: *Isack: van. Ostade 1645*
Dutch title: *Reizigers voor een herberg*

PROVENANCE
P.-L. Randon de Boisset, Paris, 1777; Radix Sainte-Foix Collection, Paris, 1777; D'Arney Collection, Paris, 1791; G. Robit, Paris, 1791–1801; Duchesse de Berry, Paris, 1837; Anatole Demidoff, San Donato, 1837–1868; Richard Seymour-Conway, 4th Marquess of Hertford, Paris, 1868; The Wallace Collection, London, 1890; Alfred de Rothschild, London, *c.*1891–1898; Kleykamp Gallery, The Hague, 1925; purchased with the support of the Rembrandt Society and private individuals, 1925

LITERATURE
HdG 1907–1928, vol. 3, p. 465, no. 22; Mauritshuis 1980, pp. 66–68; Mauritshuis 1987, no. 44; Ingamells 1992, pp. 12, 460, no. 50; Amsterdam 2000a, no. 87

864 *On the ice, c.*1640–1642

Panel, 34 x 49 cm
Signed lower right: *Isaak Ostade*
Dutch title: *IJsvermaak*

PROVENANCE
Marquis de Marigny, Paris; Marquis de Menars, Paris, 1772; Claude Tolozan, Paris, 1772–1801; Pieter van Winter and heirs, Amsterdam, 1801–1920; Frederik Muller & Co, Amsterdam; Fritz Mannheimer, Amsterdam; Adolf Hitler, Führermuseum, Linz; Stichting Nederlands Kunstbezit; on loan to the Mauritshuis, 1948–1960; transferred, 1960

LITERATURE
HdG 1907–1928, vol. 3, p. 543, no. 249; Mauritshuis 1980, p. 65; Priem 1997, p. 121, fig. 29, p. 221, no. 116; Schwarz 2004, no. III/47

Anthonie Palamedesz
Delft 1601–1673 Amsterdam

615 *Merry company dining and making music*, 1632

Panel, 47.4 x 72.6 cm
Signed and dated lower left: *A. palamedes. / 1632*
Dutch title: *Musicerend en dinerend gezelschap*

PROVENANCE
On loan from dowager J.K.H. de Jonge-de Kock, The Hague, 1897; her heir, *Jonkheer* A.H.W. de Jonge; purchased, 1900

LITERATURE
Baumgart 1944, pp. 245–248; Philadelphia-Berlin-London 1984, p. 292; New York-London 2001, no. 47

Giovanni Paolo Panini (follower of)
Piacenza 1691/92–1765 Rome

307 *Capriccio with ruins, c.*1750?

Canvas, 75.5 x 56.5 cm
Dutch title: *'Capriccio' met ruïnes*

PROVENANCE
Nationale Konst-Gallery, The Hague; transferred, in or before 1823

LITERATURE
Van Thiel 1981, p. 208, no. 171; Aikema *et al.* 1997, pp. 115–116, no. 130

COMMENT
Companion piece to inv. no. 308, both formerly attributed to Luca Carlevarijs. The building in the background is presumably the pyramid of Cestius.

308 *Capriccio with ruins, c.*1750?

Canvas, 75.5 x 56.5 cm
Bears inscription lower right, on the stone: *BELLOTTI / DIT / CANALETI / VENITIEN / PEINTRE / ROIAL*
Dutch title: *'Capriccio' met ruïnes*

PROVENANCE
Nationale Konst-Gallery, The Hague; transferred, in or before 1823

LITERATURE
Van Thiel 1981, p. 208, no. 173; Aikema *et al.* 1997, p. 117, no. 131

COMMENT
Companion piece to inv. no. 307.

Abraham de Pape
Leiden before 1621–1666 Leiden

130 *Old woman plucking a rooster*

789 

 307

864 

 308

130 

 615

Panel, 49 x 41 cm
Signed lower left: *A. DE PAPE*
Dutch title: *Oude vrouw die een haan plukt*

PROVENANCE
Gerrit Muller, Amsterdam, 1827; purchased, 1827

LITERATURE
Sumowski 1983–1995, pp. 501, 503, note 18; Leiden 1988, no. 62

COMMENT
Cleaned and restored in 1988.

Parmigianino (after)

Parma 1503–1540 Casal Maggiore

324 *The circumcision*

Panel, 45 x 33 cm
Dutch title: *De besnijdenis*

PROVENANCE
Count Edmund Bourke, Paris; purchased from his widow by King Willem I for the Mauritshuis, 1823

LITERATURE
Boschloo/Van der Sman 1993, no. 57; *Mauritshuis in focus* 11 (1998), nr. 2, p. 23, figs. 12–13; Vaccaro 2002, in no. 8

COMMENT
Old copy from the seventeenth or eighteenth century after *The circumcision* by Parmigianino in the Detroit Institute of Arts (Vaccaro 2002, no. 8).

354 *St Barbara*

Panel, 40 x 33 cm
Dutch title: *De heilige Barbara*

PROVENANCE
Martial Reghellini Schio, Venice and Brussels, until 1826; purchased by King Willem I for the Mauritshuis, 1831

LITERATURE
Boschloo/Van der Sman 1993, no. 58; Vaccaro 2002, in no. 3

COMMENT
Old copy after *St Barbara* by Parmigianino in Madrid, Museo Nacional del Prado (Vaccaro 2002, no. 3).

1135 **Giovanni Antonio Pellegrini**

–1149 Venice 1675–1741 Venice

Decoration of the Golden Room of the Mauritshuis, completed in 1718

Three ceiling paintings:

1135 *Apollo*

Canvas, 191.8 x 261.8 cm
Dutch title: *Apollo*

1136 *Aurora*

Canvas, 191.6 x 263 cm
Dutch title: *Aurora*

1137 *The dwindling night*

Canvas, 195 x 263 cm
Dutch title: *De nacht die op de vlucht wordt gejaagd*

Four paintings in grisaille:

1138 *The four elements: Fire*

Canvas, 261.1 x 113 cm
Dutch title: *De vier elementen: Vuur*

COMMENT
The woman is depicted with a vase from which a flame arises.

1139 *The four elements: Air*

Canvas, 264.4 x 113.1 cm
Dutch title: *De vier elementen: Lucht*

COMMENT
The woman is depicted with a peacock.

1140 *The four elements: Water*

Canvas, 260.8 x 112.8 cm
Dutch title: *De vier elementen: Water*

COMMENT
The woman is depicted with a scepter.

1141 *The four elements: Earth*

Canvas, 261.2 x 113.6 cm
Dutch title: *De vier elementen: Aarde*

COMMENT
The woman is depicted with a cornucopia, the horn of plenty.

324

1135

1136

354

1137

1138 1139 1140 1141

Two chimneypieces:

1142 *Mythological or allegorical representation*

Canvas, 235 x 189 cm
Dutch title: *Mythologische of allegorische voorstelling*

1143 *Allegorical representation, possibly a depiction of 'Raison d'Etat'*

Canvas, 235 x 186.6 cm
Signed lower right: *Pellegrin[i] F*
Inscribed lower right, on the spine of the book: *Republic[a]*
Dutch title: *Allegorische voorstelling, mogelijk een uitbeelding van de 'Raison d'Etat'*

PROVENANCE
All painted during the restoration of the Mauritshuis after the fire of 1704 and completed in 1718

LITERATURE
Olson 1994/1996, pp. 136–153, 269–271, nos. 11a–i; Knox 1995, pp. 137–144, figs. 111–115, p. 257, nos. P.394–P.402; Aikema/Mijnlieff 1993, pp. 224–228; Aikema *et al.* 1997, pp. 117–121, nos. 132a–i; Padua 1998–1999, p. 225

Giovanni Antonio Pellegrini (formerly attributed to)

Six flower pieces, all entitled:

1144 *Flowers in a vase*
– 1149 Canvas (round), all six 88.5 cm in diameter
Dutch title: *Bloemen in een vaas*

PROVENANCE
All six painted during the restoration of the Mauritshuis after the fire of 1704 and completed in 1718

LITERATURE
Mauritshuis 1991, p. 124, no. 834b (as Dutch *c.*1720); Olson 1994, p. 136; Aikema *et al.* 1997, p. 119 ('almost certainly not done by Pellegrini')

Antonio Francesco Peruzzini

Ancona 1668–*c.*1707

With Sebastiano Ricci?
Belluno 1659–1734 Venice

328 *Landscape with a hermit, a pilgrim, a peasant woman and other figures, c.1700–1710*

Canvas (oval), 138.5 x 109.8 cm
Dutch title: *Landschap met een kluizenaar, pelgrim, boerin en andere figuren*

PROVENANCE
Martial Reghellini Schio, Venice and Brussels, 1826; purchased by King Willem I for the Mauritshuis, 1831; on loan to the Rijksmuseum, Amsterdam (inv. no. SK-C-1356), since 1948

LITERATURE
Geiger 1949, p. 67, fig. 23 (Marco Ricci); RM 1976, pp. 359–360 (attributed to Alessandro Magnasco); Belluno 1993, no. 76; Muti/De Sarno Prignano 1994, pp. 45, 277, fig. 18; Muti/De Sarno Prignano 1996, p. 145, no. 2; Aikema *et al.* 1997, pp. 121–122, no. 133; Ancona 1997, no. 16

COMMENT
The staffage was probably painted by Sebastiano Ricci. Companion piece to inv. no. 329.

329 *Landscape with monks, a pilgrim and a peasant woman, c.1700–1710*

Canvas (oval), 138.5 x 109.8 cm
Dutch title: *Landschap met monniken, pelgrim en boerin*

PROVENANCE
Same as inv. no. 328; on loan to the Rijksmuseum, Amsterdam (inv. no. SK-C-1357), since 1948

LITERATURE
Geiger 1949, p. 67 (Marco Ricci); RM 1976, p. 360 (attributed to Alessandro Magnasco); Belluno 1993, no. 77; Muti/De Sarno Prignano 1994, pp. 45, 277; Muti/De Sarno Prignano 1996, p. 145, no. 1; Aikema *et al.* 1997, pp. 122–123, no. 134; Ancona 1997, no. 15

COMMENT
The staffage was probably painted by Sebastiano Ricci. Companion piece to inv. no. 328.

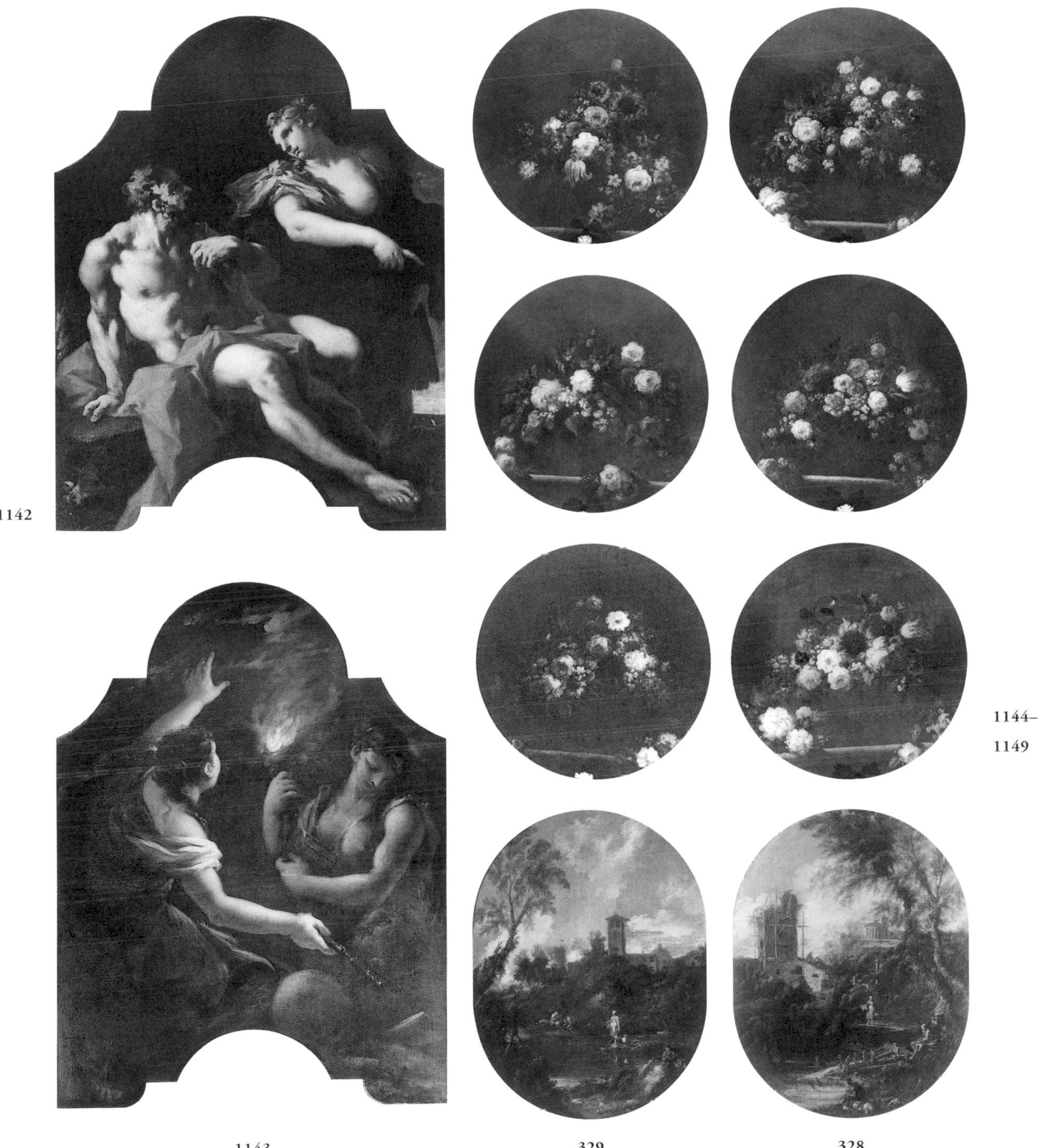

1142

1144–
1149

1143

329

328

P

Piero di Cosimo

See: Cosimo

474 Christoffel Pierson

The Hague 1631–1714 Gouda

Portrait of Joris Goethals (1584/86–1670), 1667

Panel, 37.2 x 28.2 cm
Signed and dated at right, on the edge of the table: *Chr: Pierson.1667*
Dutch title: *Portret van Joris Goethals (1584/86–1670)*

PROVENANCE
Elie Angély, Amsterdam, until 1797; Angély sale, The Hague, 5 April 1880, lot 6; W.N. Lantsheer, The Hague, 1880–1883; bequest of W.N. Lantsheer, The Hague, 1883

LITERATURE
Schiedam-Gouda 1986–1987, no. 4

COMMENT
Engraved by Reinier van Persijn (*c.*1614–1668). Joris Goethals was a clergyman of Blaricum and Hoorn.

4 Pieter Pietersz

Antwerp 1540/41–1603 Amsterdam

Portrait of Cornelis Cornelisz Schellinger (1551–1635), 1584?

Panel, 68 x 51 cm
Inscribed in cartouche: *Wert in dit Jaer tot / Delft doorschoten / Twelck veel me[n]sche[n] / heeft verdroten* (Was shot this year in Delft, which grieved many people); above the spinning-tops: *Obiit / A° 75* (died [15]75); lower left: *ELCK / SYN TYT* (To each his time)
Bears inscription: *AN°.1584. Æ.T.33.*
Dutch title: *Portret van Cornelis Cornelisz Schellinger (1551–1635)*

PROVENANCE
Sale Adriaan van der Willigen, Haarlem, 21 April 1874, lot 2 (as by Pieter Aertsen); purchased, 1874

LITERATURE
Wescher 1929, pp. 165–166; De Jongh 1967, pp. 78–79; Mauritshuis 1968, pp. 44–45; *Portraits in the Mauritshuis*, no. 44

COMMENT
The verses refer to the death of Willem I of Orange.

914 *Portrait of a man*, 1597

Panel (round), 42.5 cm in diameter
Inscribed at left: *A° ◊ 1597*; at right: *ÆT ◊ MEÆ ◊ 60 ◊*
Dutch title: *Portret van een man*

PROVENANCE
K. Fruwirth, Vienna, 1879; Albert Figdor, Vienna, 1930; Paul Cassirer Gallery, Berlin; Busch Gallery, Frankfurt am Main, *c.*1931; Mortimer Brandt Gallery, New York, *c.*1950; S. Nijstad Gallery, The Hague; purchased, 1953

LITERATURE
De Vries 1953b, pp. 79–80; Mauritshuis 1968, pp. 45–46; Mauritshuis 1970, no. 7; Van Suchtelen 1997b; Noble/Pottasch 1997

COMMENT
Companion piece to inv. no. 1109. Cleaned and restored in 1997.

1109 *Portrait of a woman*, 1597

Panel (round), 42 cm in diameter
Inscribed at left: *AN° ◊ 1597*; at right: *ÆTA ◊ MEÆ ◊ 60 ◊*
Dutch title: *Portret van een vrouw*

PROVENANCE
Sale Amsterdam, Christie's, 13 November 1995, lot 66 (unsold); gift of C.W. van Blijenburgh, Hilversum, 1996

LITERATURE
Van Suchtelen 1997b; Noble/Pottasch 1997

COMMENT
Companion piece to inv. no. 914. Cleaned and restored in 1997.

305 Simone Pignoni (after)

Florence 1611–1698 Florence

St Sebastian, 17th century

Canvas, 75.8 x 60 cm
Dutch title: *De heilige Sebastiaan*

PROVENANCE
Martial Reghellini Schio, Venice and Brussels, until 1826; purchased by King Willem I for the Mauritshuis, 1831

LITERATURE
Aikema *et al.* 1997, p. 123, no. 135

COMMENT
Presumably a contemporary copy after Pignoni, possibly originating in his studio, of a lost original.

474

305

4

914

1109

P

Adam Pijnacker

Schiedam 1620/22–1673 Amsterdam

132 *Mountainous landscape with waterfall,* 1660s

Canvas, 101 x 91 cm
Formerly signed lower right: *APijnacker* (AP in ligature)
Dutch title: *Berglandschap met waterval*

PROVENANCE
(?) Samuel van Huls, The Hague, 1737; Johan van der Marck, Leiden, until 1773; Adriaan Leonard van Heteren, The Hague, until 1800; Adriaan Leonard van Heteren Gevers, The Hague, 1800–1809; the entire collection bought by King Louis Napoleon for the Royal Museum, Amsterdam, 1809; acquired by exchange with the Rijksmuseum, Amsterdam, 1825

LITERATURE
HdG 1907–1928, vol. 9, p. 535, no. 54; Salerno 1977–1980, vol. 2, pp. 694, 760; Mauritshuis 1980, pp. 68–69; Harwood 1988, pp. 34, 97, no. 82; Utrecht-Frankfurt am Main 1993, no. 50

COMMENT
The figures, which appeared during a restoration in 1987, may not be by Pijnacker himself.

Egbert van der Poel

Delft 1621–1664 Rotterdam

133 *Beach with fishing boats at night, c.*1650–1660

Panel, 46.2 x 37 cm
Signed lower right: *E. van der Poel*
Dutch title: *Strand met vissersboten bij nacht*

PROVENANCE
Transferred, 1822; on loan to the Historisch Museum, Rotterdam, since 1986

LITERATURE
Mauritshuis 1980, pp. 70–71; Rotterdam 1994–1995, no. 35

698 *A fish market,* 1650

Panel, 61.3 x 75 cm
Signed and dated lower right: *Evander Poel / 1650*
Dutch title: *Vismarkt*

PROVENANCE
Gift of L. Nardus, Arnouville, 1905

LITERATURE
Mauritshuis 1980, p. 70; Delft 1996, ex catalogue

COMMENT
Possibly the market in Rotterdam.

Cornelis van Poelenburch

Utrecht *c.*1594/95–1667 Utrecht

134 *Mercury and Herse, c.*1625

Panel, 17.7 x 26.8 cm
Signed lower centre: *CP*
Dutch title: *Mercurius en Herse*

PROVENANCE
Jaques Meijers, Rotterdam, 1722; Prince Willem IV, Leeuwarden, before 1731; Prince Willem V, Stadholder's Court, The Hague, 1764

LITERATURE
D/LS 1974–1976, vol. 1, p. 696, note 23, vol. 3, p. 206, no. 18; Roethlisberger 1981, p. 38, no. 50; Sluijter-Seijffert 1984, p. 226, no. 25; Mauritshuis 1993, no. 28; London 2001, no. 84

COMMENT
In the past mistakenly attributed to Bartholomeus Breenbergh.

1065 *A gathering of gods in the clouds, c.*1630

Copper, 38 x 49 cm
Dutch title: *Godenbijeenkomst op de wolken*

PROVENANCE
Pierre Vigné de Vigny, Paris, 1773; Louis François de Bourbon, Prince de Conti, Paris, until 1776; Louis-César-Renaud de Choiseul, Duke de Praslin, Paris, 1793; Pierre Lafontaine Gallery, Paris, 1798; Bruno Meissner Gallery, Zürich; gift of Robert Noortman, Maastricht, 1983

LITERATURE
Sluijter-Seijffert 1984, p. 226, no. 20; Sluijter 1986, pp. 70, 209; Mauritshuis 1993, no. 29; San Francisco-Baltimore-London 1997–1998, no. 53

Bastiaan de Poorter

Meeuwen 1813–1880 Meeuwen

946 *Portrait of Jean Zacharia Mazel (1792–1884),* 1868–1869

Canvas, 116.5 x 87 cm
Signed and dated upper right: *B. de Poorter / ft. 1868. 9*
Dutch title: *Portret van Jean Zacharia Mazel (1792–1884)*

132 

 698

1065 

 133

946 

 134

PROVENANCE
Gift of the Mazel family, 1960

LITERATURE
Mauritshuis 1977, p. 182; Van Leeuwen 1990, p. 12

COMMENT
Jean Zacharia Mazel was director of the Mauritshuis from 1841 to 1874 (see p. 46).

Jan Porcellis

Ghent *c.*1583/84–1632 Zoeterwoude

969 *Shipwreck off the coast,* 1631

Panel, 36.5 x 66.5 cm
Signed and dated lower left: *JP 1631* (JP in ligature)
Dutch title: *Schipbreuk voor het strand*

PROVENANCE
Bruce Ingram, London, 1964; H. Cramer Gallery, The Hague; purchased by the Friends of the Mauritshuis Foundation, 1964 (on loan to the Mauritshuis, 1964–1989); purchased, 1989

LITERATURE
Mauritshuis 1970, no. 17; Mauritshuis 1980, pp. 71–72; Minneapolis-Toledo-Los Angeles 1990–1991, no. 23; Slive 1995, p. 217; Rotterdam-Berlin 1996–1997, no. 24

Frans Post

Haarlem *c.*1612–1680 Haarlem

706 *Brazilian landscape,* 1667

Panel, 50 x 69 cm
Signed and dated lower left: *F. POST / 1667*
Dutch title: *Braziliaans landschap*

PROVENANCE
Gift of P.J.D. van Dokkum, Utrecht, 1906

LITERATURE
Larsen 1962, pp. 113, 201, no. 112; De Sousa-Leão 1973, pp. 92–93, no. 52; Mauritshuis 1980, pp. 76–77; Washington etc. 1982–1984, no. 25

COMMENT
The painting depicts the landscape outside Mauritsstad on the landward side, with 'Park Vrijburg' on the left and on the plain various countryhouses of Dutch merchants.

915 *View of Itamaracà Island in Brazil,* 1637

Canvas, 63.5 x 88.5 cm
Signed and dated lower right: *F. POST 1637 1 / 3*
Bears inscription on the verso of the original canvas: *Het Eijlant ITamaraca gelijck / het selve int Zuijden ver thoont de / stadt legt boven op den Berg beneden / is het Fort orangien het welck leit / inden mont van de Zee op dese / manier sitten de Portugisen de peert / No 443* (The isle of Itamaraca as seen from the south, with the city on the top of the hill, and Fort Orange by the inlet. This is how the Portuguese ride their horses)
Dutch title: *Gezicht op het eiland Itamaracà in Brazilië*

PROVENANCE
Painted in Brazil for Johan Maurits; presumably part of his gift to King Louis XIV of France, 1679; Eugène Odinot, Paris, 1879; purchased by the Rijksmuseum, Amsterdam (inv. no. SK-A-4271), 1879; on loan from the Rijksmuseum since 1953

LITERATURE
Larsen 1962, pp. 96, 98, 136–138, 185, no. 2; De Sousa-Leão 1973, pp. 23, 54–55, no. 1; RM 1976, p. 452; The Hague 1979–1980, no. 87; Mauritshuis 1980, pp. 73–76; Whitehead/Boeseman 1989, pp. 179, 181, 186; The Hague 2004, no. 32

1127 *Brazilian landscape with a house under construction, c.*1655–1660

Panel, 46 x 70 cm
Signed lower right: *F. Post*
Dutch title: *Braziliaans landschap met een huis in aanbouw*

PROVENANCE
Probably private collection, Amsterdam, until 1891; Eduardo Prado, São Paulo; by inheritance to Paul Plinio Prado, São Paulo, 1962; Raphael Parisi, São Paulo; Brod Gallery, London; H.D. de Koster, Wassenaar; Robert Noortman Gallery, Maastricht, 1998; gift of Willem, Baron van Dedem to the Friends of the Mauritshuis Foundation, 2002

LITERATURE
Larsen 1962, p. 198, no. 92; De Sousa-Leão 1973, p. 117, no. 89; The Hague 1995–1996, no. 20; Sutton 2002, no. 40; Buvelot 2002a, pp. 22–24, no. 111

Pieter Post

Haarlem 1608–1669 The Hague

970 *Dune landscape with haystack,* in or before 1633

Panel, 53.3 x 79.5 cm
Signed and dated lower right: *P.Post 163[.]*
Dutch title: *Duinlandschap met een hooischelf*

969 

 706

970 

 915

1127 

PROVENANCE
C. Benedict Gallery, Berlin, 1938; Wilhelm Martin and his heirs, The Hague, 1938–1975 (on loan to the Mauritshuis, 1964–1966); purchased by the Friends of the Mauritshuis Foundation to mark the 70th birthday of A.B. de Vries, former director of the Mauritshuis, 1975

LITERATURE
Gudlaugsson 1954, pp. 59, 64; Mauritshuis 1980, pp. 79–80; Mauritshuis 1987, no. 46; The Hague 2002, p. 136

765 *Cavalry engagement*, 1631

Panel, 34.7 x 53.1 cm
Signed and dated lower left: *P.I. Post 1631*
Dutch title: *Ruitergevecht*

PROVENANCE
Van Diemen Gallery, The Hague; gift of Mr and Mrs A.F. Philips-de Jong, Eindhoven, 1922

LITERATURE
Gudlaugsson 1954, pp. 60–62, 66; Mauritshuis 1980, pp. 78–79; Delft 1998, no. 93

COMMENT
Companion piece to inv. no. 766.

766 *Attack on an army train*, 1631

Panel, 34.7 x 53 cm
Signed and dated lower right: *P.I. Post 1631*
Dutch title: *Aanval op een legertros*

PROVENANCE
Same as inv. no. 765

LITERATURE
Gudlaugsson 1954, pp. 60–62, 66; Mauritshuis 1980, pp. 78–79; Delft 1998, no. 93

COMMENT
Companion piece to inv. no. 765.

Hendrick Pot

Haarlem (?) *c.*1585–1657 Amsterdam

475 *Merry company in a brothel*

Panel, 41 x 56 cm
Signed on the bed: *H.P.*
Dutch title: *Vrolijk gezelschap in een bordeel*

PROVENANCE
Nahuijs and Royer-Kerst sale, Amsterdam, 14 November 1883, lot 122; purchased, 1883

LITERATURE
Bernt 1969–1970, vol. 2, no. 933; Kolfin 1998, p. 13

COMMENT
Cleaned and restored in 1986.

1075 *Portrait of Jean Fontaine (1608–1668), c.*1633

Panel, 18.2 x 15.1 cm
Dutch title: *Portret van Jean Fontaine (1608–1668)*

PROVENANCE
Probably by inheritance to Joan Fontaine and Petronella Calkoen, Amsterdam, until 1753, and Calkoen heirs, until 1900; bequest of Abraham, Baron Calkoen, to the Dutch State, 1966; on loan from the ICN (inv. no. C 1823), since 1987

LITERATURE
Amsterdam 1984, no. 16; Yamaguchi-Kumamoto-Tokyo-Rotterdam 1994–1995, no. 37A

COMMENT
Companion piece to inv. no. 1076. The work still has its original frame. Jean Fontaine, an Amsterdam merchant, married Anna Hooftman in 1633, on which occasion these portraits must have been painted.

1076 *Portrait of Anna Hooftman (1613–after 1645), c.*1633

Panel, 18.6 x 15.4 cm
Dutch title: *Portret van Anna Hooftman (1613–na 1645)*

PROVENANCE
Same as inv. no. 1075; on loan from the ICN (inv. no. C 1824), since 1987

LITERATURE
Amsterdam 1984, no. 16; Yamaguchi-Kumamoto-Tokyo-Rotterdam 1994–1995, no. 37B

COMMENT
Companion piece to inv. no. 1075. The work still has its original frame.

Hendrik Pothoven

Amsterdam 1726/28–1807 The Hague

764 *The main hall of the Binnenhof in The Hague, with the State Lottery Office*, 1779

Canvas, 57 x 65.7 cm
Signed and dated lower left, on the shop: *HPothoven P / A° 1779*
Dutch title: *De grote zaal op het Binnenhof te Den Haag, met het kantoor van de Staatsloterij*

765 

 766

1075 

 1076

475 

 764

PROVENANCE
Jan de Groot, Amsterdam, 1804; bequest of J.G. de Groot Jamin, Amsterdam, 1921; on loan to the Nederlands Kansspelmuseum, The Hague, since 1995

LITERATURE
Staring 1923, pp. 98–103; Dumas 1991, pp. 48, fig. 60, 589, 592, note 32

COMMENT
A preliminary drawing in the Gemeentearchief, The Hague (Dumas 1991, p. 588, fig. 8).

Paulus Potter

Enkhuizen 1625–1654 Amsterdam

136 *The bull*, 1647

Canvas, 235.5 x 339 cm
Signed and dated middle left, on the fence-rail: *Paulus. Potter. / f. 1647.*
Dutch title: *De stier*

PROVENANCE
Willem Fabricius d'Almkerk, Haarlem, 1749; Prince Willem IV, The Hague, 1749; Prince Willem V, The Hague, until 1795

LITERATURE
HdG 1907–1928, vol. 4, p. 635, no. 48; D/LS 1974–1976, vol. 3, p. 21, no. 42, p. 224, no. 114; Mauritshuis 1980, pp. 80–84; Paris 1986, no. 39; Mauritshuis 1987, no. 45; Dordrecht-Leeuwarden 1988–1989, no. 24; The Hague 1994–1995, no. 8; Slive 1995, pp. 208–210

COMMENT
Potter based his image on various studies of bulls of different ages (see The Hague 1994–1995).

137 *Cows reflected in the water*, 1648

Panel, 43.4 x 61.3 cm
Signed and dated centre right: *Paulus. Potter / f. i648*
Dutch title: *'Het spiegelende koetje'*

PROVENANCE
(?) De Wolf Collection, Amsterdam; Govert van Slingelandt, The Hague, in or before 1752; the entire collection sold to Willem V in 1768; Prince Willem V, The Hague, 1768–1795

LITERATURE
HdG 1907–1928, vol. 4, p. 649, no. 81; D/LS 1974–1976, vol. 3, p. 225, no. 115; Mauritshuis 1980, pp. 84–85; Dordrecht-Leeuwarden 1988–1989, pp. 21, 88, 91; The Hague 1994–1995, no. 14; Slive 1995, p. 210

COMMENT
Huis Binckhorst, Rijswijk and Delft can be seen in the distance, with the tower of Voorburg on the far left. Cleaned and restored in 2001.

138 *Cattle in a meadow*, 1652

Panel, 35.8 x 46.9 cm
Signed and dated middle right, on the barn: *Paulus Potter / f: 1652.*
Dutch title: *Vee in de weide*

PROVENANCE
Govert van Slingelandt, The Hague, after 1752; the entire collection sold to Willem V in 1768; Prince Willem V, The Hague, 1768–1795

LITERATURE
HdG 1907–1928, vol. 4, p. 643, no. 70; D/LS 1974–1976, vol. 3, p. 225, no. 116; Mauritshuis 1980, p. 85; The Hague 1994–1995, no. 25; Apeldoorn 2002, pp. 110–111

COMMENT
This painting belongs to a group of related works from the years 1651–1653, all of which are variations on the same theme of a peaceful meadow scene with cattle. Cleaned and restored in 2000.

Pieter Symonsz Potter

Enkhuizen 1597/1601–1652 Amsterdam

409 *Jacob urging Leah and Rachel to flee from Laban*, 1638

Panel, 54 x 81.5 cm
Signed and dated lower right: *P. Potter. f 1638.*
Dutch title: *Jacob haalt Lea en Rachel over te vluchten voor Laban*

PROVENANCE
Neville Goldsmid, The Hague; purchased, 1876

LITERATURE
Mauritshuis 1935, p. 457

136

137

138

409

P/R

Jan Provoost

Mons *c.*1464–1529 Bruges

783 *Triptych with the Virgin and Child, John the Evangelist and Mary Magdalene, c.*1520–1525

Exterior panels: imitation green and red porphyry (repr. in The Hague 1997, p. 47)
Panel, 44 x 30.5 cm (centre panel) and 49.5 x 15 cm (wings)
Dutch title: *Drieluik met Maria en kind, Johannes de Evangelist en Maria Magdalena*

PROVENANCE
Bequest of Cornelis Hoogendijk to the Rijksmuseum, Amsterdam (inv. no. SK-A-2570), 1912; on loan from the Rijksmuseum since 1924

LITERATURE
Friedländer 1967–1976, vol. 9b, no. 122; Mauritshuis 1968, pp. 46–47; Pottasch 1994; The Hague 1997, no. 3; Pottasch 1997; Bruges 1998, no. 28

COMMENT
Technical research revealed that several changes were made by Provoost to the centre panel. Four columns, to the left and right of the Virgin, were painted out, as well as a cloth over the balustrade. Preserved in its original frame. Cleaned and restored in 1997.

Jan Symonsz Pynas

Alkmaar 1581/82–1631 Amsterdam

131 *Mary and John at the cross*

Panel (rounded at the top), 116 x 84.5 cm
Signed lower right: *Jan.Pijnas*
Dutch title: *Maria en Johannes bij het kruis*

PROVENANCE
Van Gelder Collection, The Hague; purchased, 1874; on loan to the Museum Het Rembrandthuis, Amsterdam, since 1917

LITERATURE
Bernt 1969–1970, vol. 2, no. 953; Tümpel 1974, pp. 57–58

Pieter Jansz Quast

Amsterdam 1605/6–1647 Amsterdam

447 *The triumph of folly: Brutus playing the fool before King Tarquinius*, 1643

Panel, 69.5 x 99 cm
Signed and dated lower right, on the base of a column: *PQ 1643* (PQ in ligature)
Dutch title: *De triomf der zotheid: Brutus in de gedaante van een zot voor koning Tarquinius*

PROVENANCE
Sale Paris, 22 January 1879, lot 39; purchased, 1879; on loan to the Theatermuseum, Amsterdam, since 1959

LITERATURE
Heppner 1937; Stanton-Hirst 1982, p. 217

COMMENT
Probably based on a *tableau vivant* written for the Eglantine Chamber of Rhetoric in Amsterdam by Pieter Cornelis Hooft (1581–1647). An earlier version of the same subject in the Theatermuseum, Amsterdam.

658 *Card players, c.*1630–1640

Panel (almost round), 32.4 / 33.7 in diameter
Dutch title: *Kaartspelers*

PROVENANCE
Friedrich Schwartz Gallery, Vienna; purchased, 1901

LITERATURE
Bredius 1902, pp. 67–68; Schupbach 1978, p. 277 and fig. 7; The Hague 1991–1992, p. 31, fig. 5

COMMENT
The painting was originally oval and had more figures, as appears from a replica exhibited at the Rotterdamse Kunstkring in 1907.

Abraham Ragueneau (after)

London 1623–after 1681 (?)

498 *Portrait of Willem III (1650–1702) aged ten*, 1661

Panel, 73.9 x 59.7 cm
Dated and inscribed lower right: *A°. 1661. / Ætat:10.*
Dutch title: *Portret van Willem III (1650–1702), op 10-jarige leeftijd*

PROVENANCE
Prince Willem V, The Hague, 1763–1798; Nationale Konst-Gallery, The Hague, 1798; found in the attic of the Mauritshuis, *c.*1875

LITERATURE
Staring 1950–1951, pp. 167–168, fig. 7; D/LS 1974–1976, vol. 3, p. 27, no. 179

COMMENT
Other copies in the Frans Hals Museum, Haarlem, and in the Town Hall of Zwolle. For biographical data on Willem III, see Schalcken, inv. no. 158.

783

447

131

658

498

R

Raphael (after)

Urbino 1483–1520 Rome

339 *The Holy Family with St John the Baptist*

Panel, 32.5 25 cm
Dutch title: *De heilige familie met Johannes de Doper*

PROVENANCE
Victor de Rainer, Brussels, 1821; purchased by King Willem I for the Mauritshuis, 1821; on loan to the ICN

LITERATURE
Boschloo/Van der Sman 1993, p. 75, no. 67

COMMENT
One of many copies after Raphael's *Madonna della Quercia* in the Museo Nacional del Prado, Madrid.

357 *Madonna*, 17th century

Canvas, 49 x 40 cm
Dutch title: *Madonna*

PROVENANCE
Martial Reghellini Schio, Venice and Brussels, until 1826; purchased by King Willem I for the Mauritshuis, 1831

LITERATURE
Aikema *et al.* 1997, p. 181, no. 221

COMMENT
Based on Raphael's *Bridgewater Madonna*, Duke of Sutherland Collection, on loan to the National Gallery of Scotland, Edinburgh.

Jan Anthonisz van Ravesteyn

The Hague (?) *c.*1572–1657 The Hague

119 *Portrait of Catharina Belgica (1578–1648)*, 1617

Panel, 63.9 x 55.6 cm
Dated upper left: *Anno 1617*
Bears inscription upper left: *FIL' DE HANNAU*
Reverse: a brandmark with 'WM' (in ligature) with a crown on top, the mark of King-Stadholder Willem III and Mary, and the number '87'
Dutch title: *Portret van Catharina Belgica (1578–1648)*

PROVENANCE
Frederik Hendrik, Stadholder's Quarter, The Hague, 1632; by descent to Prince Willem V, Honselaarsdijk Palace, Naaldwijk, 1755; sold or taken from the stadholder's collection in or after 1795; purchased, 1820

LITERATURE
Drossaers 1932, pp. 256–257; D/LS 1974–1976, vol. 1, p. 223, no. 982, p. 536, no. 342 or 345, vol. 2, p. 508, no. 120 or 123

COMMENT
Catharina Belgica was the daughter of Prince Willem I of Orange and Charlotte de Bourbon. In 1596 she married Filips Lodewijk, Count of Hanau-Münzenberg. Formerly identified as a portrait of her daughter Amalia Elisabeth (1602–1651), Countess of Hanau.

120 *Portrait of Ernestine Yolande (1594–1663), Princess de Ligne*

Panel, 63.5 x 53.4 cm
Inscribed at the top: *Ernestina.Femme.de.Conte.Ian.de.Nass..* (possibly added later)
Dutch title: *Portret van Ernestine Yolande (1594–1663), prinses van Ligne*

PROVENANCE
Frederik Hendrik, Stadholder's Quarter, The Hague, 1632; by descent to Prince Willem V, Honselaarsdijk Palace, Naaldwijk, 1755; transferred, 1820

LITERATURE
Drossaers 1932, pp. 258–259; D/LS 1974–1976, vol. 1, p. 224, no. 1002, p. 536, no. 354, vol. 2, p. 508, no. 132

COMMENT
The sitter was a daughter of Lamoral de Ligne-Amblise and Marie de Melun-Espinay. In 1618 she married Jan III, Count of Nassau-Siegen, brother of Johan Maurits (see after Van Dyck, inv. no. 472 and Van Ravesteyn, inv. no. 418).

Jan Anthonisz van Ravesteyn (and studio)

139–144 *Series of 24 portraits of officers*, 1611–1624
414–426
438–439
455–457

For a 25th officer's portrait, see Fransise de Goltz, inv. no. 427
All on canvas, approximately 115 x 97 cm
Dutch title: *Serie van 24 officiersportretten*

PROVENANCE
Honselaarsdijk Palace, Naaldwijk, in or before 1694; Nationale Konst-Gallery, The Hague, 1804–1805; Nationaal Kabinet (Royal Museum), 'Besoigne-Kamer' (the Business Affair Room) and Picture Gallery of Prince Willem V, The Hague, 1805–1821; transferred, 1822 (excluding inv. nos. 438–439, both acquired in 1877)

LITERATURE
Moes/Van Biema 1909, pp. 39–40, nos. 1–7, 13–16, 18–20, 38–39, 41, p. 73, nos. 234–258, pp. 101–103, nos. 147–156, 236–237, 257–258, p. 136, no. 6 and p. 200; D/LS 1974–

119

120

339

357

1976, vol. 1, p. 455, nos. 9 and 19, p. 532, no. 226; Van Thiel 1981, pp. 175–176, 183–187, nos. 1–7, 14–15, 16–21, 23–24 and 26; Spruit 1997; Buijsen *et al.* 1998, p. 231; *Portraits in the Mauritshuis*, no. 45

COMMENT

Very probably painted on the instructions of Prince Maurits of Nassau (1567–1625), stadholder of the northern Netherlands provinces.

139 *Portrait of an officer, possibly Gaspard de Coligny (1584–1646)*, 1611?

Canvas, 116.5 x 97 cm
Formerly dated lower left: *A. 1611* (see Mauritshuis 1935, p. 458)
Bears inscription lower right: *23.*
Dutch title: *Portret van een officier, mogelijk Gaspard de Coligny (1584–1646)*

PROVENANCE

See above

LITERATURE

Spruit 1997, p. 25 and fig. 13; Amsterdam 2000–2001, no. 92

COMMENT

Tentatively identified by Spruit as a portrait of Gaspard de Coligny, Comte de Châtillon-sur-Loing, at the time colonel of a French regiment in the States army.

140 *Portrait of an officer*, 1611

Canvas, 114.9 x 93.5 cm
Dated lower left: *An 1611*
Bears inscription lower right: *23.*
Dutch title: *Portret van een officier*

PROVENANCE

See above; on loan to the Paleis Het Loo Nationaal Museum, Apeldoorn, since 1983

141 *Portrait of an officer*, 1611

Canvas, 118 x 97 cm
Signed and dated centre right: *An 1611 / R F*
Bears inscription lower left: *23.*
Dutch title: *Portret van een officier*

PROVENANCE

See above; on loan to the Paleis Het Loo Nationaal Museum, Apeldoorn, since 1984

LITERATURE

Van Thiel 1981, p. 186, no. 24

142 *Portrait of an officer*, 1616

Canvas, 117 x 97 cm
Dated lower left: *A: 1616*
Bears inscription lower right: *23.*
Dutch title: *Portret van een officier*

PROVENANCE

See above

LITERATURE

Van Thiel 1981, p. 185, no. 20

143 *Portrait of an officer*, 1612

Canvas, 117.5 x 96.4 cm
Signed and dated lower left: *R / An: 1612*
Bears inscription lower right: *23.*
Dutch title: *Portret van een officier*

PROVENANCE

See above

LITERATURE

Van Thiel 1981, p. 185, no. 19; Nagasaki 1992–1993, no. 22; Van Leeuwen 1993, pp. 25–26

COMMENT

Cleaned and restored in 1992.

144 *Portrait of an officer, possibly Adolf van Meetkerken (d. 1625)*, 1611

Canvas, 118 x 97.5 cm
Signed and dated lower left: *An 1611 / R F*
Bears inscription lower left: *23.*
Dutch title: *Portret van een officier, mogelijk Adolf van Meetkerken (gestorven 1625)*

PROVENANCE

See above; on loan to the Paleis Het Loo Nationaal Museum, Apeldoorn, since 1984

LITERATURE

Van Thiel 1981, p. 184, no. 14

COMMENT

Thought to be Van Meetkerken on the basis of a portrait in the Bentinck Collection, Amerongen Castle, De Steegh, which bears on the reverse the inscription 'De Heer van Meetkerken'. Van Meetkerken served in the States army from 1603.

414 *Portrait of an officer*, 1621

Canvas, 114.5 x 96.5 cm
Dated lower left: *A° 1621*
Bears inscription lower right: *23.*
Dutch title: *Portret van een officier*

>>
140
139
141

>>
143
142
144

414

PROVENANCE
See above; on loan to the Paleis Het Loo Nationaal Museum, Apeldoorn, since 1983

COMMENT
Spruit (1995, p. 43) has tentatively identified the sitter as the Scotsman Robert Henderson (d. 1622), in 1621 colonel in the States army.

415 *Portrait of an officer*, 1624

Canvas, 115 x 96.5 cm
Signed and dated upper right: *A°:1624 R:F*
Bears inscription lower right: *23.*
Dutch title: *Portret van een officier*

PROVENANCE
See above; on loan to the ICN

COMMENT
This officer's dress differs from that of most of the others in the series: he wears not a heavy harness but only a breast and backplate over a buff leather arming coat. His helmet, too, is far lighter. His weapon, a carbine, hangs from a sturdy shoulder belt or sling, which was why it was known as a *bandelierroer* (baldric). These elements identify the sitter as an officer in the light cavalry.

416 *Portrait of an officer*, 1611

Canvas, 114.6 x 96.5 cm
Signed lower right: *Ravesteijn F.*
Dated centre right: *A 1611*
Bears inscription lower right: *23.*
Dutch title: *Portret van een officier*

PROVENANCE
See above

417 *Portrait of an officer*, 1615

Canvas, 114.5 x 96.3 cm
Signed and dated lower left: *A° 1615 JR*
Bears inscription lower right: *23.*
Dutch title: *Portret van een officier*

PROVENANCE
See above

COMMENT
Spruit (1995, p. 44) tentatively identified the sitter as Willem Adriaan (d. 1625), Count of Hornes, Lord of Kessel and general of the Dutch artillery.

418 *Portrait of Jan III (1583–1638), Count of Nassau-Siegen*, 1611

Canvas, 115 x 97 cm
Signed and dated on the base of the column: *An° 1611. JvRavesteyn Fecit* (JvR and st in ligature)
Bears inscription lower right: *23.*
Dutch title: *Portret van Jan III (1583–1638), graaf van Nassau-Siegen*

PROVENANCE
See above; on loan to the Paleis Het Loo Nationaal Museum, Apeldoorn, since 1984

LITERATURE
Van Thiel 1981, p. 185, no. 16; Spruit 1997, p. 24

COMMENT
Jan III, Count of Nassau-Siegen —the brother of Johan Maurits, founder of the Mauritshuis— was a horse captain in the Dutch States army and is also known as Jan VIII (cf. also after Van Dyck, inv. no. 472). In 1618 he married Ernestine Yolande, also portrayed by Van Ravesteyn (see inv. no. 120). A portrait in the Honselaarsdijk series by Michiel van Mierevelt in the Rijksmuseum, with the inscription 'GRAEF JAN VAN NASSOU', shows the same person (RM 1976, p. 701, no. A 534).

419 *Portrait of Nicolaas Schmelzing (1561–1629)*, 1611

Canvas, 115 x 97 cm
Signed and dated lower right: *An° 16ii Ravest[...]*
Bears inscription lower right: *23.*
Dutch title: *Portret van Nicolaas Schmelzing (1561–1629)*

PROVENANCE
See above; on loan to the Koninklijk Nederlands Leger- en Wapenmuseum, Delft, since 1968

LITERATURE
Van Thiel 1981, p. 185, no. 18; Van Gruting 1995–1996, p. 65; Spruit 1997, p. 24; Amsterdam 2000–2001, no. 89

COMMENT
Schmelzing or Smelsinc was lieutenant-general of Overijssel. A portrait in the Honselaarsdijk series in the Rijksmuseum, with the inscription 'MONS. SMELSIN' (RM 1976, p. 703, no. C 1516), is obviously of the same person. The Rijksmuseum also possesses a replica of the Mauritshuis portrait (RM 1976, p. 464, no. A 259). Schmelzing took an active part in life at court in The Hague and assembled a substantial collection of portraits (see Von Gruting 1995–1996 and The Hague 1997–1998a, pp. 90–91).

420 *Portrait of Daniel de Hertaing (d. 1626)*, 1612

Canvas, 114.5 x 96.4 cm
Formerly dated lower left: *A 1612*
Bears inscription lower right: *23.*
Dutch title: *Portret van Daniel de Hertaing (overleden in 1626)*

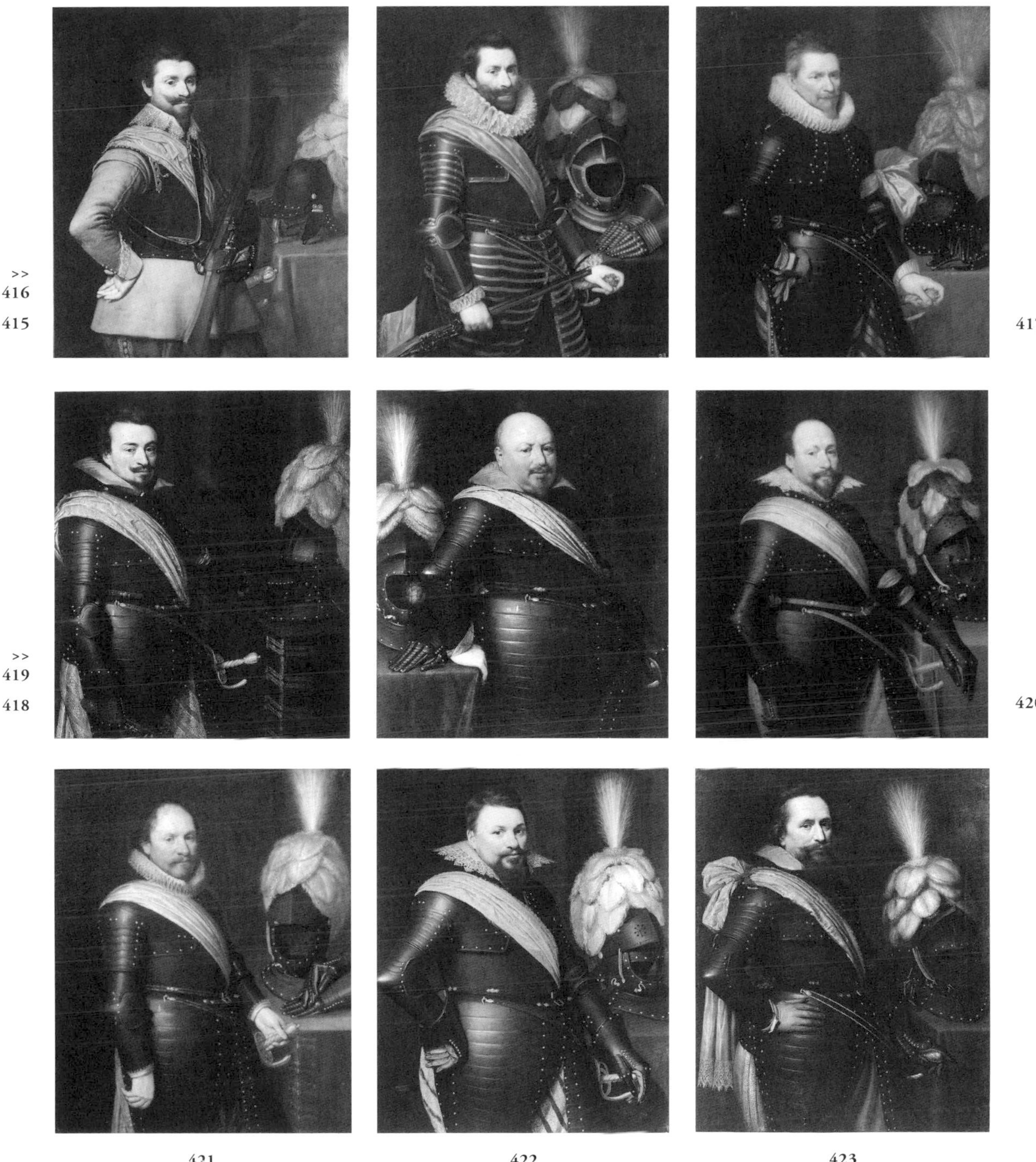

>> 416
415
417
>> 419
418
420
421
422
423

PROVENANCE
See above

LITERATURE
Spruit 1997, p. 24

COMMENT
Daniel de Hertaing was a lieutenant-general of cavalry. A painting in the Honselaarsdijk series in the Rijksmuseum (RM 1976, p. 703, no. A 564), with the inscription 'MONS^{r} DE MAR^{q}', is clearly of the same person.

< 421 *Portrait of an officer*, 1612

Canvas, 114.8 x 94.4 cm
Dated lower left: *A° 1612*
Bears inscription lower right: *23.*
Dutch title: *Portret van een officier*

PROVENANCE
See above

< 422 *Portrait of an officer*, 1612

Canvas, 115 x 96.5 cm
Signed and dated lower left: *JR / An° 1612 / R.F.*
Bears inscription lower right: *23.*
Dutch title: *Portret van een officier*

PROVENANCE
See above; on loan to the Paleis Het Loo Nationaal Museum, Apeldoorn, since 1983

COMMENT
Spruit (1995, p. 38) tentatively identified the officer as Horatio Vere (1565–1635), a general in the infantry.

< 423 *Portrait of an officer, presumably Anthonis van Utenhoven (d. 1625)*, 1611

Canvas, 113 x 93 cm
Signed and dated lower left: *An° 1611 / JRavesteyn* (JR in ligature)
Dutch title: *Portret van een officier, vermoedelijk Anthonis van Utenhoven (overleden in 1625)*

PROVENANCE
See above; on loan to the Paleis Het Loo Nationaal Museum, Apeldoorn, since 1984

LITERATURE
Van Thiel 1981, p. 187, no. 26; Spruit 1997, p. 25, fig. 11

COMMENT
Spruit (1995, p. 41; 1997, p. 25 and figs. 11–12) identified the officer as Anthonis van Utenhoven (d. 1625), from 1604 until 1625 colonel in the Utrecht regiment.

424 *Portrait of an officer*, 1615

Canvas, 114 x 94 cm
Signed and dated lower left: *JR 1615*
Dutch title: *Portret van een officier*

PROVENANCE
See above; on loan to the ICN

425 *Portrait of an officer*, 1612

Canvas, 114.5 x 97.5 cm
Dated lower left: *An: 1612*
Bears inscription lower right: *23.*
Dutch title: *Portret van een officier*

PROVENANCE
See above

426 *Portrait of an officer*, 1611

Canvas, 114.7 x 96.5 cm
Signed and dated lower left: *An:1611 / RF*
Bears inscription lower right: *23.*
Dutch title: *Portret van een officier*

PROVENANCE
See above; on loan to the Paleis Het Loo Nationaal Museum, Apeldoorn, since 1983

LITERATURE
Van Thiel 1981, p. 186, no. 23

438 *Portrait of an officer, presumably Johan Wolfert van Brederode (1599–1655)*

Canvas, 110 x 92 cm
The sash is decorated with flower motifs in various colours, a monogram ('AM'?) and the letter 's' with a diagonal stroke through it
Bears inscription lower right: *23.*
Dutch title: *Portret van een officier, vermoedelijk Johan Wolfert van Brederode (1599–1655)*

PROVENANCE
Until 1808: see above; transferred to the Royal Museum, Amsterdam, 1808–1815; Rijksmuseum, Trippenhuis, Amsterdam, 1815–1877; transferred, 1877; on loan to the Paleis Het Loo Nationaal Museum, Apeldoorn, since 1984

LITERATURE
Indianapolis-San Diego 1958, no. 64; Van Thiel 1981, p. 183, no. 1; Spruit 1997, p. 24; Braunschweig 2000, p. 12 and fig. 13

COMMENT
The officer was formerly identified as Reinout van Brederode (1597–1618), leader of a company of infantrymen in 1614. However, in light of Reinout's lowly rank it would seem more likely that the sitter is, as Spruit (1995,

>>
425

424

426

>>
439

438

455

456

457

719

pp. 34–35) suggested, in fact his younger brother Johan Wolfert, who was promoted to colonel in 1623. There are several portraits of him (Tiethoff-Spliethoff 1979; cf also Mijtens, inv. no. 113).

< 439 *Portrait of an officer*

Canvas, 110 x 92 cm
Bears inscription lower right: *23.*
Dutch title: *Portret van een officier*

PROVENANCE
See above; on loan to the Paleis Het Loo Nationaal Museum, Apeldoorn, since 1983

COMMENT
As in inv. no. 415, this officer's equipment differs from that seen in the other portraits. For the second decade of the seventeenth century his sleeveless leather jerkin is somewhat old-fashioned. The *bandelierroer*, or baldric, is a weapon characteristically used by cavalrymen, particularly senior officers.

< 455 *Portrait of an officer*, 1621

Canvas, 115 x 97 cm
Dated lower left: *A°. 1621*
Bears inscription lower right: *23.*
Dutch title: *Portret van een officier*

PROVENANCE
See above; on loan to the ICN

< 456 *Portrait of an officer*

Canvas, 113 x 90 cm
Bears inscription lower right: *23.*
Dutch title: *Portret van een officier*

PROVENANCE
See above; on loan to the ICN

< 457 *Portrait of an officer*

Canvas, 116 x 96.5 cm
Bears inscription lower right: *23.*
Dutch title: *Portret van een officier*

PROVENANCE
See above; on loan to the Paleis Het Loo Nationaal Museum, Apeldoorn, since 1984

COMMENT
The officer's clothes are decorated with fleurs-de-lys, possibly a clue to his identity.

Nicolaes van Ravesteyn

Zaltbommel 1661–1750 Zaltbommel (?)

< 719 *Portrait of a man, probably a member of the Mackay family*, c.1700

Canvas, 59.2 x 46.8 cm
Dutch title: *Portret van een man, waarschijnlijk een lid van de familie Mackay*

PROVENANCE
Bequest of *Jonkvrouw* Maria Johanna Singendonck, The Hague, 1907

Nicolas Regnier (attributed to)

Maubeuge 1591–1667 Venice

304 *St Sebastian tended by St Irene*, c.1615–1620

Canvas, 137.5 x 163.7 cm
Dutch title: *De heilige Sebastiaan verzorgd door de heilige Irene*

PROVENANCE
Martial Reghellini Schio, Venice and Brussels, 1826; purchased by King Willem I for the Mauritshuis, 1831

LITERATURE
Aikema *et al.* 1997, pp. 133–134, no. 154 (as Nicolas Regnier)

COMMENT
Several versions are known, amongst others a painting attributed to Regnier in the Musée des Beaux-Arts, Rouen, and in the Ferens Art Gallery, Kingston-upon-Hull.

Rembrandt van Rijn

Leiden 1606–1669 Amsterdam

145 *Simeon's song of praise*, 1631

Panel (rounded at the upper corners), 60.9 x 47.9 cm
Signed and dated lower right, on the side of the chair: *RHL. 1631* (RHL in ligature)
Dutch title: *Het loflied van Simeon*

PROVENANCE
Probably Stadholder Frederik Hendrik, The Hague, 1632–1647; Adriaan Bout, The Hague, 1696–1733; Prince Willem IV, Apeldoorn; by descent to Prince Willem V, The Hague, until 1795

145

304

LITERATURE
HdG 1907–1928, vol. 6, p. 48, no. 80; Bredius/Gerson 1969, no. 543; D/LS 1974–1976, vol. 1, p. 186, vol. 2, p. 643, no. 88, p. 652, no. m, vol. 3, p. 227, no. 129; Mauritshuis 1978, no. V; *Corpus*, vol. I (1982), no. A 34; Mauritshuis 1987, no. 47; Mauritshuis 1993, no. 30; Slive 1995, p. 58; The Hague 1997–1998a, no. 22; Kassel-Amsterdam 2001–2002, p. 278; Korthals Altes 2003, p. 44

COMMENT
When the painting was in the collection of Willem V, the upper corners were sawn off and an arched top was added so that the painting could be hung as a pendant to Dou's *Young mother* (inv. no. 32). In 1989, the missing upper corners were filled up. Cleaned and restored in 2004.

146 *The anatomy lesson of Dr Nicolaes Tulp*, 1632

Canvas, 169.5 x 216.5 cm
Signed and dated centre above: *Rembrant. f^v: 1632*
Dutch title: *De anatomische les van Dr. Nicolaes Tulp*

PROVENANCE
Commissioned by members of the Surgeons' Guild, Amsterdam, 1632; Surgeons' Widows' Fund, Amsterdam, 1798–1828; purchased by the Dutch State and placed in the Mauritshuis at the order of King Willem I, 1828

LITERATURE
HdG 1907–1928, vol. 6, pp. 387–388, no. 932; Bredius/Gerson 1969, no. 403; Heckscher 1958; Mauritshuis 1978, no. VI; Schupbach 1982; *Corpus*, vol. I (1982), no. A 51; Mauritshuis 1987, no. 48; Slive 1995, p. 61; The Hague 1998–1999; Amsterdam 2000a, no. 58; *Portraits in the Mauritshuis*, no. 47

COMMENT
The painting commemorates Tulp's second anatomy demonstration on 31 January 1632. For the names and more information on the other surgeons depicted, see *Portraits in the Mauritshuis*. The dead man is a convicted criminal, Adriaen Arisz (also known as Aris Kint) of Leiden. On 31 January 1632 he was hanged for the attempted theft of a coat. Cleaned and restored in 1998.

147 *Susanna*, 1636

Panel (enlarged at the right), 47.4 x 38.6 cm
Signed and dated lower right: *Rembr[ant f] / f 163[6]*
Dutch title: *Suzanna*

PROVENANCE
P.J. Sneijers, Antwerp, 1758; Govert van Slingelandt, The Hague, 1758; the entire collection sold to Willem V in 1768; Prince Willem V, The Hague, 1768–1795

LITERATURE
HdG 1907–1928, vol. 6, p. 37, no. 57; Bredius/Gerson 1969, no. 505; D/LS 1974–1976, vol. 3, p. 228, no. 130; Mauritshuis 1978, no. VIII; Paris 1986, no. 41; Mauritshuis 1987, no. 49; *Corpus*, vol. 3 (1989), no. A 117; Berlin-Amsterdam-London 1991–1992, no. 25; Mauritshuis 1993, no. 32; Melbourne-Canberra 1997–1998, no. 10; Edinburgh-London 2001, no. 69; Frankfurt am Main 2003, no. 26; Runia/Noble/Wadum 2003, pp. 14–19; Tokyo 2003, no. 9

COMMENT
Cleaned and restored in 2002. A strip of wood, 4 cm wide, was added to the panel at the right before 1758, probably to replace an original strip of wood, and the upper corners were filled in by a later hand, possibly in the eighteenth century. A drawing after the painting by Willem de Poorter (1608–after 1648) in Berlin is dated 1636 and provides a *terminus ante quem* for the painting, of which the last digit in the date was added later.

149 *'Tronie' of a man with a feathered beret*, *c.*1635–1640

Panel, 62.5 x 47 cm
Signed lower right: *Rembrandt. f:*
Dutch title: *Tronie van een man met gevederde baret*

PROVENANCE
Govert van Slingelandt, The Hague, in or before 1752; the entire collection sold to Willem V in 1768; Prince Willem V, The Hague, 1768–1795

LITERATURE
HdG 1907–1928, vol. 6, p. 238, no. 545; Bredius/Gerson 1969, no. 24; D/LS 1974–1976, vol. 3, p. 228, no. 131; Mauritshuis 1978, no. VII; Mauritshuis 1987, no. 50; *Corpus*, vol. 3 (1989), no. C 98; Nagasaki 1992–1993, no. 23; Blankert 1993, pp. 94–95; Buvelot/Wadum 1999, p. 33; London-The Hague 1999–2000, p. 54 and fig. 16; Frankfurt am Main 2003, no. 24 (as a self-portrait); *Portraits in the Mauritshuis*, no. 48

COMMENT
Cleaned and restored in 1999.

584 *Homer*, 1663

Canvas, 107 x 82 cm
Signed and dated upper left: *[Rembr]andt. f 1663*
Dutch title: *Homerus*

PROVENANCE
Commissioned by Don Antonio Ruffo, Messina; Ruffo family, Sicily, until *c.*1750; S.T. Smith Gallery, London, 1885; T. Humphrey Ward & Son Gallery, London, 1894; Abraham Bredius, The Hague, 1894–1946 (on loan to the Mauritshuis since 1894); bequest of Abraham Bredius, 1946

LITERATURE
HdG 1907–1928, vol. 6, p. 120, no. 217; Ricci 1918; Bredius/Gerson 1969, no. 483; Mauritshuis 1978, no. XII;

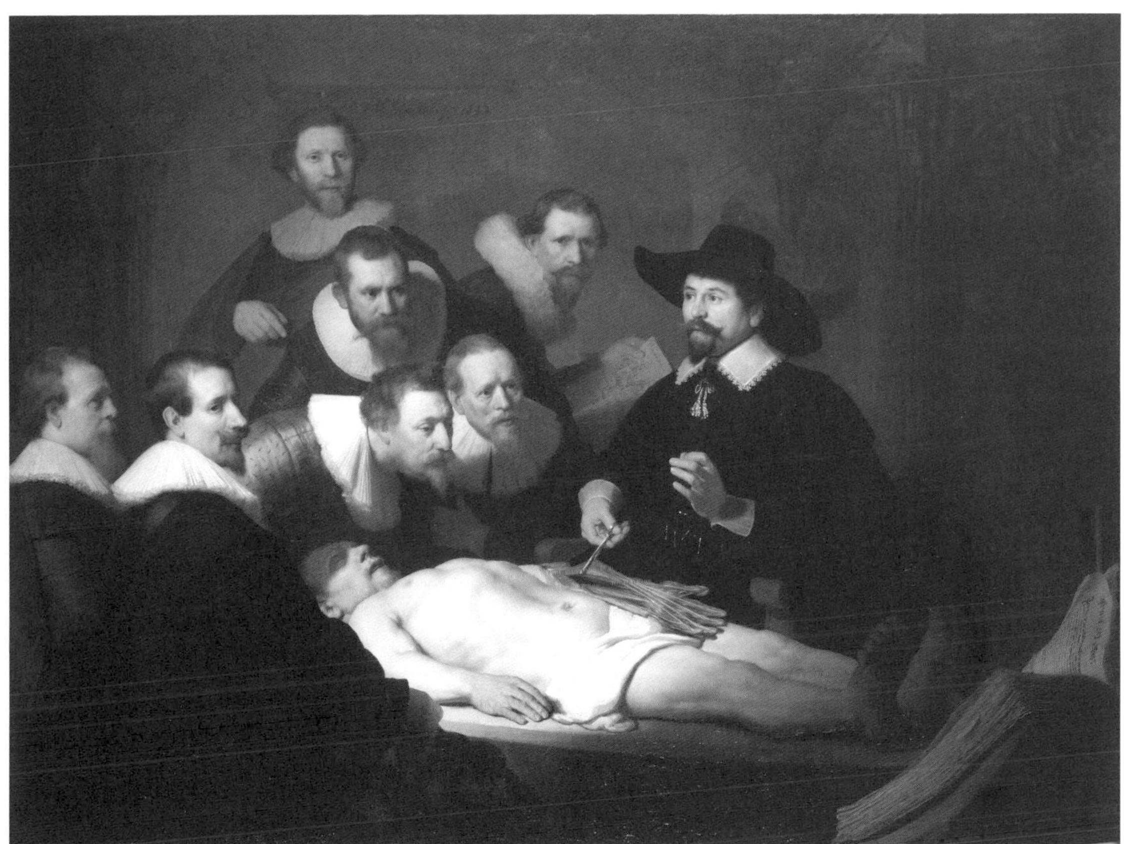
146

147

149

584

Mauritshuis 1987, no. 51; The Hague 1991–1992, no. 13; Mauritshuis 1993, no. 33; Giltaij 1996; Scallen 2004, pp. 148–150, 161

COMMENT

The canvas was reduced to its present size due to fire damage, after which it was cut down at all sides. Originally, the painting showed the poet teaching two pupils, as we see in the preliminary drawing (Stockholm, Nationalmuseum). Homer was painted after a well-known Hellenistic bust, which is recorded in Rembrandt's inventory of 1656. Commissioned by Don Antonio Ruffo of Messina, Sicily, as was the 1653 *Aristotle contemplating the bust of Homer*, now in The Metropolitan Museum of Art, New York, and *Alexander the Great* (possibly identical to the painting in the City Art Gallery and Museum, Glasgow). To be cleaned and restored in 2004–2005.

598 *The laughing man, c.*1629–1630

Copper (covered with gold foil), 15.3 x 12.2 cm
Dutch title: *De lachende man*

PROVENANCE

Sale Cornelia Steyn-Schellinger *et al.*, The Hague, 7–8 October 1783, lot 72; Gerard Munnicks van Cleeff, Utrecht, before 1860; sale Charles de Boissière, Paris, 19 February 1883, lot 40; F. Kleinberger Gallery, Paris, 1893–1894; Cornelis Hofstede de Groot, The Hague, 1894–1895; purchased, 1895

LITERATURE

HdG 1907–1928, vol. 6, pp. 236–237, no. 543; Bredius/Gerson 1969, no. 134; Mauritshuis 1978, no. II; *Corpus*, vol. I (1982), no. B 6; Schwartz 1984, p. 62, fig. 49; Mauritshuis 1987, p. 178, fig. 3; Stockholm 1992, no. 50; Phoenix-Kansas City-The Hague 1998–1999, no. 46; London-The Hague 1999–2000, p. 122 and fig. 18a; Kassel-Amsterdam 2001–2002, no. 79; *Portraits in the Mauritshuis*, no. 46

COMMENT

An etching by Jan Gillisz van Vliet (1609/10–1668) bears the inscription 'RHL jnuentor' (Amsterdam, Rijksmuseum, Rijksprentenkabinet). Cleaned and restored in 1998.

685 *Two moors*, 1661

Canvas, 77.8 x 64.4 cm
Bears signature and date upper right: *Rembrandt / f 1661*
Dutch title: *Twee moren*

PROVENANCE

De Montribloud Collection, Paris, 1784; Lord Berwick, Attingham Hall, Shrewsbury, 1784; Wertheimer Gallery, London; George Donaldson Gallery, London, 1902; Abraham Bredius, The Hague, 1903–1946 (on loan to the Mauritshuis since 1903); bequest of Abraham Bredius, 1946

LITERATURE

HdG 1907–1928, vol. 6, p. 166, no. 336; Bredius/Gerson 1969, no. 310; Mauritshuis 1978, no. X; Schwartz 1984, p. 315, no. 365; The Hague 1991–1992, no. 12; Slive 1995, p. 78

COMMENT

Two old copies of the painting are known, one of which is in the museum in Bucarest (The Hague 1991–1992, p. 76, fig. 1).

707 *Andromeda, c.*1630

Panel (trimmed before 1785), 34 x 24.5 cm
Dutch title: *Andromeda*

PROVENANCE

Charles de Proli, Antwerp, 1785; Armand de Mestral de St Saphorin, Vienna, 1805–1806; Countess d'Oultremont, Brussels; Richard Leeuwenhart van den Bosch, Brussels, 1905; Abraham Bredius, The Hague, 1906–1946 (on loan to the Mauritshuis since 1907); bequest of Abraham Bredius, 1946

LITERATURE

HdG 1907–1928, vol. 6, p. 109, no. 195; Bredius/Gerson 1969, no. 462; Mauritshuis 1978, no. IV; *Corpus*, vol. I (1982), no. A 31; The Hague 1991–1992, no. 10; Mauritshuis 1993, no. 31; Runia/Noble/Wadum 2003, pp. 8–13; Wadum 2003

COMMENT

Cleaned and restored in 2002 (see Wadum 2003 and Runia/Noble/Wadum 2003).

840 *Self-portrait*, 1669

Canvas, 63.5 x 57.8 cm
Signed and dated centre left, above the shoulder: *Rembrandt / f.1669*
Dutch title: *Zelfportret*

PROVENANCE

Sir Joseph Neeld, London, before 1850–1856; Sir John and Audley W. Neeld, Grittleton House, Red Lodge, Wiltshire, 1856–1899; R.L. Douglas Gallery, London; Knoedler Gallery, London; Marcus Kappel, Berlin, *c.*1912–*c.*1925; Kappel heirs, Ernest G. Rathenau and E. Ettlinger-Rathenau, Berlin, Oxford and New York, 1925–1947 (1925–1940 on loan to the Rijksmuseum, Amsterdam; 1940–1945 Adolf Hitler, Alt-Aussee, Salzburg); purchased from the Rathenau family with the support of the Rembrandt Society and private individuals, 1947

LITERATURE

HdG 1907–1928, vol. 6, pp. 230–231, no. 527; Bredius/Gerson 1969, no. 62; Mauritshuis 1970, no. 29; Mauritshuis 1978, no. XIII; Paris 1986, no. 42; Mauritshuis 1987, no. 52; Chapman 1990, pp. 128, 130–132, fig. 169; Berlin-Amsterdam-London 1991–1992, no. 51; London-The Hague 1999–2000, no. 86; Amsterdam 2002–2003a, no. 37; Frankfurt am

598

685

707

840

Main 2003, no. 48; Schwarz 2004, no. II/36; *Portraits in the Mauritshuis*, no. 50

1118 *Portrait of an elderly man*, 1667

Canvas, 81.9 x 67.7 cm
Signed and dated left of centre: *Rembrandt / f. 1667*
Dutch title: *Portret van een oude man*

PROVENANCE

Sampson Gideon, Erith, Kent, 1761; thence by descent to Sir Francis Edward Fremantle, until *c.*1885; Agnew's, London, 1919; bought by Lord Cowdray; The Trustees of the Cowdray Estate, 1999; purchased with the support of the Friends of the Mauritshuis Foundation, the Ministry of Education, Culture and Science, the Fund for National Cultural Heritage, the Sponsor Lottery, the Fonds 1818, the Rembrandt Society, the Prince Bernhard Culture Fund, ING Group, Prof. Dr Drs. A.C.R. Dreesmann, the Dr Hendrik Muller National Fund and private individuals, 1999

LITERATURE

HdG 1907–1928, vol. 6, p. 344, no. 829; Bredius/Gerson 1969, no. 323A; Melbourne-Canberra 1997–1998, no. 28; F. Duparc, P. van der Ploeg, P. Hecht, E. van de Wetering and H. van Os in *Mauritshuis in focus* 12 (1999), no. 2; *Portraits in the Mauritshuis*, no. 49

COMMENT

Duparc tentatively identifies the sitter as Lodewijk van Ludick (*c.*1606/7–1669), a merchant and art buyer who was one of Rembrandt's creditors (see *Portraits*, no. 49).

Rembrandt (attributed to)

560 *Study of an old man*, 1650

Canvas, 80.5 x 66.5 cm
Bears signature and date left of centre, next to the shoulder: *Rembrandt.f. / 1650*
Dutch title: *Studie van een oude man*

PROVENANCE

Jean-Baptiste-Pierre Lebrun, Paris, 1809–1810; Este sale, Paris, 28 April 1819, lot 64 (unsold; as kindly communicated by B. Fredericksen); Sébastien Erard, Paris, until 1832; Sir William Wellesley Knighton, Blendworth Lodge, Hampshire, 1885; Lesser Gallery, London; Sir John Robinson, London, 1889; Agnew's, London, 1890; Charles Sedelmeyer Gallery, Paris, 1890; purchased, 1891

LITERATURE

HdG 1907–1928, vol. 6, p. 184, no. 384; San Francisco-Toledo-Boston 1966–1967, no. 36; Bredius/Gerson 1969, no. 130; Mauritshuis 1978, no. IX; Tümpel 1986, p. 425, no. A 43; Tokyo-Chiba-Yamaguchi 1992, no. 72; Nagasaki 1992–1993, no. 24; Seoul 2003, no. 40; Scallen 2004, pp. 160–161, 354, note 84

COMMENT

Formerly thought to be a portrait of Rembrandt's brother, Adriaen van Rijn (1597/98–1652/53).

Rembrandt (and/or studio of)?

565 *'Tronie' of an old man*, *c.*1630–1631

Panel, 46.9 x 38.8 cm
Dutch title: *Tronie van een oude man*

PROVENANCE

Durand-Ruel Gallery, Paris; Harrison Collection, Sutton Place, Seaford, before 1891; Anders Zorn, Paris, 1891; Abraham Bredius, The Hague, 1892–1946 (on loan to the Mauritshuis since 1892); bequest of Abraham Bredius, 1946

LITERATURE

HdG 1907–1928, vol. 6, p. 287, no. 676; Bredius/Gerson 1969, no. 77; Mauritshuis 1978, no. III; *Corpus*, vol. I (1982), no. B 7; Schatborn 1986, p. 61; Broos 1990a; The Hague 1991–1992, no. 14; Buvelot/Wadum 1999, pp. 32–33 and fig. 19

COMMENT

Cleaned and restored in 1999. Formerly thought to be a portrait of Rembrandt's father, Harmen Gerritsz van Rijn (1569–1630).

Rembrandt (and/or studio of)?

621 *Saul and David*, *c.*1650–1655

Canvas, 130 x 164.5 cm
Dutch title: *Saul en David*

PROVENANCE

Victor de Riquet, Duke of Caraman, as Paris, before 1830; Didot de Saint-Marc Collection, Paris, 1835–1863; Alphonse Audry, Paris, 1863–1869; [Alexis-Joseph] Febure, Paris, *c.*1870; Durand-Ruel Gallery, Paris; Albert, Baron von Oppenheim, Cologne, 1876; Philippe George, Ay near Epernay, before 1890; Durand-Ruel Gallery, Paris, 1890–1898; Abraham Bredius, The Hague, 1898–1946 (on loan to the Mauritshuis since 1898); bequest of Abraham Bredius, 1946

LITERATURE

HdG 1907–1928, vol. 6, pp. 25–26, no. 36 (Rembrandt); Bredius/Gerson 1969, no. 526 (not by Rembrandt); Schmidt-Dörrenberg 1969; Mauritshuis 1978, no. XI (Rembrandt); Adams 1984, pp. 427–433, 435–436, 438 (Karel van der Pluym); Broos 1991a; The Hague 1991–1992, no. 11; Mauritshuis 1993, no. 34 (Rembrandt studio?); Slive 1995, p. 95; Bikker 2001, no. R 2; Scallen 2004, pp. 136, 161, 204

1118 

 565

560 

 621

COMMENT
The canvas was cut into two unequal pieces in the nineteenth century, probably with the intention of creating two paintings. The pieces were later reassembled, with the upper right section replaced by a fragment of an old portrait (see Mauritshuis 1993, p. 286, fig. 5). The attribution has been subject to debate as of 1969.

Rembrandt (studio copy)

148 *Portrait of Rembrandt (1606–1669) with a gorget,* after *c.*1629

Panel, 37.9 x 28.9 cm
Dutch title: *Portret van Rembrandt (1606–1669) met halsberg*

PROVENANCE
Govert van Slingelandt, The Hague, in or before 1752; the entire collection sold to Willem V in 1768; Prince Willem V, The Hague, 1768–1795

LITERATURE
HdG 1907–1928, vol. 6, pp. 237–238, no. 544; Bredius/Gerson 1969, no. 6; D/LS 1974–1976, vol. 3, p. 228, no. 132; Mauritshuis 1978, no. 1; *Corpus*, vol. 1 (1982), no. A 21; Paris 1986, no. 40; Mauritshuis 1987, p. 295 and fig. 1; Chapman 1990, pp. 34, 36, 38–40, 46, 131; Berlin-Amsterdam-London 1991–1992, no. 4; Buvelot/ Wadum 1999; London-The Hague 1999–2000, no. 14b; Buijsen 2000; Sluijter 2000b; Wadum 2000; Boston 2000–2001, no. 6; Frankfurt am Main 2003, no. 7; *Portraits in the Mauritshuis*, no. 51

COMMENT
Painted by an unknown artist in the studio of Rembrandt, after Rembrandt's self-portrait in Nuremberg, Germanisches Nationalmuseum (see London-The Hague 1999–2000, nos. 14a–b).

Rembrandt (studio of)

626 *Minerva, c.*1630

Panel, 61.7 x 53.5 cm
Dutch title: *Minerva*

PROVENANCE
Abraham Bredius, The Hague, 1899–1946 (on loan to the Mauritshuis since 1899); bequest of Abraham Bredius, 1946

LITERATURE
HdG 1907–1928, vol. 6, p. 467 (unnumbered); Mauritshuis 1978, no. 2 (circle of Rembrandt); Klessmann 1983, p. 176 (*ibid.*); Sumowski 1983–1995, vol. 1, p. 525, no. 242 (Gerrit Dou); The Hague 1991–1992, no. 16 (pupil of Rembrandt)

COMMENT
Cleaned and restored in 2002. Probably by the same hand as *A scholar at his desk* in Braunschweig, Herzog Anton Ulrich-Museum, formerly also mistakenly attributed to the young Gerrit Dou (see Klessmann 1983, p. 176, repr.).

Rembrandt (circle of)

579 *Travellers resting (The rest on the flight into Egypt?), c.*1629–1630

Paper on panel, 38 x 33.7 cm
Bears signature lower left: *Rembrandt. f.*
Dutch title: *Rustende reizigers (Rust tijdens de vlucht naar Egypte?)*

PROVENANCE
De la Roque Collection, Paris, 1745; Countess of Morton, Old Hall, Suffolk, 1850; W. Howgate, Leeds; purchased, 1894

LITERATURE
HdG 1907–1928, vol. 6, p. 55, no. 89; Bredius/Gerson 1969, no. 556; Mauritshuis 1978, no. 3; *Corpus*, vol. 1 (1982), no. C 12; Kassel-Amsterdam 2001–2002, no. 65; Scallen 2004, pp. 161–162

COMMENT
Probably by the same hand as *A man reading in a lofty room* in the National Gallery, London (Kassel-Amsterdam 2001–2002, no. 63). Cleaned and restored in 1985–1986.

Rembrandt (circle of)

828 *Study of an old man*

Panel, 26 x 21 cm
Dutch title: *Studie van een oude man*

PROVENANCE
Harrach Collection, Vienna; D.A. Hoogendijk Gallery, Amsterdam, 1935; Hans Ludwig Larsen, Wassenaar, 1935–1937; gift of the widow of H.L. Larsen in his memory, 1938

LITERATURE
Brown 1981, pp. 49, 129, no. A 1; Sumowski 1983–1995, vol. 2, p. 982, note 17, vol. 4, pp. 2876, 2883, note 32; The Hague 1992b, no. 40; The Hague-Schwerin 2004–2005, pp. 48–49 (in exhibition)

COMMENT
The same man is depicted in paintings in the Walker Art Gallery, Liverpool and the Musée du Louvre, Paris, which may be by the same hand (see The Hague 1992b, no. 40). Formerly attributed to Carel Fabritius. Cleaned in 2004. The painting is probably unfinished.

148

626

579

828

R

Rembrandt (circle of)

610 *Praying woman*, *c.*1660

Panel, 19.7 x 15.8 cm
Dutch title: *Biddende vrouw*

PROVENANCE
Sideroff Collection, St Petersburg; Abraham Bredius, The Hague, 1897–1946 (on loan to the Mauritshuis since 1897); bequest of Abraham Bredius, 1946

LITERATURE
HdG 1907–1928, vol. 6, pp. 156–157, no. 314 (as by Carel Fabritius); Brown 1981, p. 133, no. R 8; The Hague 1991–1992, no. 26

COMMENT
Formerly attributed to both Rembrandt and Fabritius.

Rembrandt (after)

556 *Study of an old woman*, 17th century

Panel, 18.4 x 14 cm
Dutch title: *Studie van een oude vrouw*

PROVENANCE
De Angelis sale, Brussels, 15 September 1763, lot 10; Boijmans sale, Utrecht, 31 August 1811, lot 79; C.J.H. Franssen, Grubbenvorst, 1890; Abraham Bredius, The Hague, 1890–1946 (on loan to the Mauritshuis since 1890); bequest of Abraham Bredius, 1946

LITERATURE
HdG 1907–1928, vol. 6, p. 290, no. 686; Bredius/Gerson 1969, no. 67 (after Rembrandt); Mauritshuis 1978, no. 1; *Corpus*, vol. I (1982), no. C 41; Broos 1990a; The Hague 1991–1992, no. 15; Scallen 2004, pp. 156–157, 161, 252, 259

COMMENT
One of many copies in existence after a lost painting that probably dated to 1631, traditionally identified as Rembrandt's mother, Neeltgen Willemsdr van Zuytbrouck (1568–1640). The other known copies are of a larger size and have an oval composition.

Jacob de Reyger

Amsterdam (?)–*c.*1645 England

608 *Portrait of a man*, 1635

Panel, 21.9 x 17.3 cm
Signed and dated lower right: *1635 / J.D. Reijger / .f.*
Dutch title: *Portret van een man*

PROVENANCE
Jacobson Gallery, London, 1897; purchased, 1897 (as by Thomas de Keyser)

LITERATURE
The Hague 1991–1992, p. 34, fig. 8, p. 47, notes 30, 31

COMMENT
Cleaned and restored in 1991.

Roelant Roghman

Amsterdam 1627–1692 Amsterdam

1124 *Mountainous landscape with waterfall*, *c.*1660–1670

Canvas, 83 x 102.3 cm
Bears inscription on the verso:
No 44 Landscape Rembrant van Rijn / Born 1606–[...]
Dutch title: *Berglandschap met waterval*

PROVENANCE
Possibly sale London, Greenwood, 8–9 May 1795, lot 44 or sale London, Foster, 13 April 1825, lot 44 (as by Rembrandt); Sir A. Chester Beatty, England; J. Leger & Sons, London, 1958; D. Cevat, Worthing, Sussex; S. Nijstad Gallery, The Hague, 1972; private collection, The Netherlands; partial and promised gift of Mr and Mrs De Koster-van Rijckevorsel, 2000

LITERATURE
The Hague 1982, no. 71; Sumowski 1983–1995, vol. 4, p. 2483, no. 1671; Kloek 1990, pp. 36, 41, no. 6; Buvelot 2002b

COMMENT
Cleaned and restored in 2002.

Johann Heinrich Roos

Otterberg 1631–1685 Frankfurt am Main

280 *Italian landscape*, 1670

Canvas, 64 x 53 cm
Signed and dated lower left: *JHRoos. fecit. / 1670.*
(JHR in ligature)
Dutch title: *Italiaans landschap*

PROVENANCE
Leeuwarden Palace; Prince Willem V, The Hague, 1795

LITERATURE
Jedding 1955, p. 220, no. 67; D/LS 1974–1976, vol. 3, p. 228, no. 134; Jedding 1998, p. 41, fig. 53

COMMENT
Cleaned and restored in 1992.

608 

 1124

610 

556

 280

R

Johannes Rosenhagen

Probably active in The Hague, mid-17th century

150 *Still life with fruit*, 1650s

Canvas, 55 x 70 cm
Signed at left, on the edge of the table:
Johannes. Rosenhagen. f
Dutch title: *Fruitstilleven*

PROVENANCE
David van der Kellen, Amsterdam; purchased, 1873

LITERATURE
Lunsingh Scheurleer 1971–1972, pp. 39–42, fig. 6

COMMENT
This painting, the only known work by 'Rosenhagen', was perhaps executed by Johannes Rosnagel (1640–1668), a still life painter from The Hague.

Matteo Rosselli (follower of)

Florence 1578–1650 Florence

355 *An evangelist, presumably St John the Evangelist*, 17th century

Canvas, 64 x 52 cm
Dutch title: *Een evangelist, waarschijnlijk Johannes de Evangelist*

PROVENANCE
Martial Reghellini Schio, Venice and Brussels, until 1826; purchased by King Willem I for the Mauritshuis, 1831

LITERATURE
Aikema *et al.* 1997, p. 136, no. 158

Hans Rottenhammer

Munich 1564–1624 Augsburg

284 *The fall of Phaeton*, 1604

Copper, 39 x 54.5 cm
Signed and dated lower left, on a stone:
1604 / H [?] O [?] Rottnh / F.
Dutch title: *De val van Phaëthon*

PROVENANCE
(?) Diego Duarte, Antwerp, before 1676; Jan van Beuningen, Amsterdam, 1716; Steven Theroude, dealer; Johan Hendrik, Count van Wassenaer Obdam, The Hague, 1716–1745; his sale, The Hague, 19 August 1750, lot 67; Govert van Slingelandt, The Hague, 1750; the entire collection sold to Willem V in 1768; Prince Willem V, The Hague, 1768–1795

LITERATURE
Peltzer 1916, p. 345, no. 30; Dogaer 1971, pp. 196–197, 200, note 15, p. 215, no. 138; D/LS 1974–1976, vol. 3, p. 228, no. 135; Mauritshuis 1993, no. 35 (background by Paulus Bril); Broos 1995c, p. 22 and fig. 11; Pijl 1998, p. 660 and note 9 (background by Rottenhammer); Korthals Altes 2003, pp. 40, 48, notes 25–26 and fig. 14

COMMENT
Cleaned and restored in 2001.

Hans Rottenhammer (attributed to)

281 *The encounter of David and Abigail*

Canvas, 165 x 203 cm
Dutch title: *De ontmoeting van David en Abigail*

PROVENANCE
Het Loo Palace, Apeldoorn, 1757; Nationale Konst-Gallery, The Hague; transferred, 1822

LITERATURE
Peltzer 1916, p. 354, no. 22 (perhaps Hendrik van Balen); D/LS 1974–1976, vol. 2, p. 640, no. 21; Van Thiel 1981, p. 183, no. 8

COMMENT
Possibly painted with the help of either Hendrik van Balen or Jan Brueghel the Elder.

Hans Rottenhammer (attributed to)

282 *The baptism of the chamberlain of the queen of Candace*

Panel, 160 x 194 cm
Dutch title: *De doop van de kamerling van de koningin van Candace*

PROVENANCE
Same as inv. no. 281

LITERATURE
Peltzer 1916, p. 354, no. 21; D/LS 1974–1976, vol. 2, p. 640, no. 28; Van Thiel 1981, p. 183, no. 9

COMMENT
See inv. no. 281. Cleaned and restored in 1990.

284

281

282

150

355

R

Peter Paul Rubens

Siegen 1577–1640 Antwerp

837 *The triumph of Rome: The youthful Emperor Constantine honouring Rome, c.1622–1623*

Panel, 54 x 69 cm
Dutch title: *De triomf van Rome: De jeugdige keizer Constantijn eert Rome*

PROVENANCE
M. de Calonne, Paris, 1795; John Charles Robinson, 1868; Sir Francis Cook, Doughty House, Richmond; by inheritance to Herbert Cook, Richmond, 1934; Adolf Hitler, Führermuseum, Linz; Stichting Nederlands Kunstbezit; gift of B. and N. Katz, Dieren and Basel, 1947

LITERATURE
Van Puyvelde 1939, p. 32, no. 7; Mauritshuis 1970, no. 9; London 1977, p. 79, in no. 85; Held 1980, vol. 1, pp. 84–85, no. 51; Nagasaki 1992–1993, no. 25; Schwarz 2004, no. II/3

COMMENT
Sketch for one of the twelve tapestries with scenes from the life of Constantine commissioned by King Louis XIII of France, around 1622–1623. This scene was never woven into a tapestry: it was replaced by a depiction of the death of Constantine.

926 *'Modello' for the Assumption of the Virgin, c.1622–1625*

Panel, 87.8 x 59.1 cm
Dutch title: *'Modello' voor de Hemelvaart van Maria*

PROVENANCE
M. de Calonne, Paris, 1795; Hope Collection, London, 1816; Knight Collection, London, 1819; John Webb, London, 1821; F.T. Davies, London, before 1955; Rosenberg & Stiebel Gallery, New York, 1955–1956; purchased with the support of the Friends of the Mauritshuis Foundation, 1956

LITERATURE
D'Hulst 1968, p. 97, no. 15; Mauritshuis 1970, no. 10; Held 1980, vol. 1, pp. 513–514, no. 377; Freedberg 1984, p. 178, note 26, pp. 178–180, no. 43a; Mauritshuis 1987, no. 53; Mauritshuis 1993, no. 36

COMMENT
This modello provided the basis for the final formulation of *The Assumption of the Virgin* on the high altar of Antwerp Cathedral (1626).

1131 *Portrait of a man, possibly Peter van Hecke (1591–1645), c.1630*

Panel, 114.5 x 90.5 cm
Dutch title: *Portret van een man, mogelijk Peter van Hecke (1591–1645)*

PROVENANCE
Vicomtesse de Spoelberch, Belgium; Léon Gauchez Gallery, Paris; sold to Edmond, Baron de Rothschild, Paris, before 1890; by inheritance to members of the Rothschild family, Château de Pregny, Geneva; Colnaghi Gallery, New York, 1983; Edward Speelman Gallery, London; on loan from a private collection, Switzerland, since 2000; purchased with the support of the Sponsor Lottery, the Ministery of Education, Culture and Science, the Friends of the Mauritshuis Foundation, the Fund for the National Cultural Heritage, the Mondriaan Foundation, the VSB Fund, the Rembrandt Society, supported by the Prince Bernhard Culture Fund, the Jaffé-Pierson Foundation, the Prince Bernhard Culture Fund and the Dr Hendrik Muller National Fund, 2003

LITERATURE
Rooses 1886–1892, vol. 4, pp. 192–193, no. 966; Vlieghe 1987, no. 107; Boston-Toledo 1993–1994, no. 15a; Van der Ploeg 2000; Van der Ploeg 2003c; Lille 2004, no. 70; *Portraits in the Mauritshuis*, no. 53

COMMENT
Max Rooses was the first to identify the couple in this painting and the companion piece (inv. no. 1132) as Peter van Hecke and Clara Fourment, who married in 1621 and belonged to the intimate family circle of the painter. Clara's younger sister Hélène married Rubens, and one of her brothers, Daniel Fourment, was the husband of Clara Brant, a sister of Rubens's first wife Isabella. In October 1635 Rubens became the godfather of Ferdinandus, the youngest of Peter and Clara's seven children. A preparatory drawing for the male portrait is in London, British Museum.

1132 *Portrait of a woman, possibly Clara Fourment (1593–1643), c.1630*

Panel, 114.5 x 90.5 cm
Dutch title: *Portret van een vrouw, mogelijk Clara Fourment (1593–1643)*

PROVENANCE
Same as inv. no. 1131

LITERATURE
Rooses 1886–1892, vol. 4, p. 160, no. 934; Vlieghe 1987, no. 108; Boston-Toledo 1993–1994, no. 15b; Van der Ploeg 2000; Van der Ploeg 2003c; Lille 2004, no. 71; *Portraits in the Mauritshuis*, no. 54

COMMENT
Companion piece to inv. no. 1131.

1131

1132

926

837

252 *Portrait of Michael Ophovius (1570–1637), c.1615–1617*

Canvas, 111.5 x 82.5 cm
Dutch title: *Portret van Michael Ophovius (1570–1637)*

PROVENANCE
Dominican monastery, Antwerp, *c.*1615/1617–*c.*1795; J.F. de Vinck van Wesel, Antwerp, 1813; Henricus-Josephus, Baron Stier van Aertselaer, Antwerp, 1814–1822; purchased by King Willem I for the Mauritshuis, 1822

LITERATURE
Vlieghe 1987, no. 126; Boston-Toledo 1993–1994, no. 23; Tax/Tax-Coolen 1995; Braunschweig 2004, no. 57; *Portraits in the Mauritshuis*, no. 52

COMMENT
Michael Ophovius (Michiel van Ophoven) was one of the strongest champions of the Counter-Reformation, and a good friend of Rubens. A closely similar version, presumably executed in Rubens's studio, is in the Rubenshuis, Antwerp, on loan from a private collection.

Peter Paul Rubens (and studio)

250 *Portrait of a young woman*, 1620s

Panel, 97 x 67.8 cm
On the verso: 'MV', the mark of the Antwerp panel-maker Michiel Vriendt
Dutch title: *Portret van een jonge vrouw*

PROVENANCE
Govert van Slingelandt, The Hague, in or before 1752; the entire collection sold to Willem V in 1768; Prince Willem V, The Hague, 1768–1795

LITERATURE
Oldenbourg 1921, pp. 442, 472; D/LS 1974–1976, vol. 3, p. 227, no. 126; Vlieghe 1983, pp. 106–107, fig. 3

COMMENT
Restoration completed in 2000. The head is autograph, the clothing and the hands were painted by a studio assistant. Another version is in the Wallace Collection, London (Ingamells 1992, pp. 333–335, no. P30). Formerly identified as Isabella Brant (1591–1626), the first wife of the painter.

Peter Paul Rubens (and studio)

251 *Portrait of a young woman*, 1620s

Panel, 98 x 76 cm
On the reverse: 'MV', the mark of the Antwerp panel-maker Michiel Vriendt
Dutch title: *Portret van een jonge vrouw*

PROVENANCE
Govert van Slingelandt, The Hague, 1752; the entire collection sold to Willem V in 1768; Prince Willem V, The Hague, 1768–1795

LITERATURE
Oldenbourg 1921, p. 436; D/LS 1974–1976, vol. 3, p. 227, no. 127; Müller Hofstede 1983, pp. 318 and 321, note 66; Muller 1989, p. 115, in no. 102

COMMENT
Formerly identified as Hélène Fourment (1614–1673), the second wife of the painter. During the restoration, completed in 2004, many overpaintings from the eighteenth century were removed. Possibly only the head is autograph. On the basis of the 'A' on the verso of the panel, the portrait may be dated to around 1621–1622 (see Wadum 1998, pp. 192, 198).

Peter Paul Rubens (studio copy)

254 *Venus attempting to keep Adonis from the hunt*, 17th century

Panel, 59 x 81 cm
Dutch title: *Venus poogt Adonis van de jacht te weerhouden*

PROVENANCE
Govert van Slingelandt, The Hague, in or before 1752; the entire collection sold to Willem V in 1768; Prince Willem V, The Hague, 1768–1795

LITERATURE
D/LS 1974–1976, vol. 3, p. 227, no. 124; Broos 1990b; Sillevis-Chodzinska 1990

COMMENT
This copy, which closely resembles the painting in the State Hermitage Museum in St Petersburg, was probably executed in Rubens's studio. Rubens derived the subject from a painting by Titian (Madrid, Museo Nacional del Prado). Cleaned and restored in 1987–1988.

Peter Paul Rubens (after)

246 *Nymph and satyr*, 17th century

Panel, 108 x 78 cm
Dutch title: *Nimf en sater*

PROVENANCE
Gift of Jonkheer J.L. Cremer van den Bergh, Heemstede, 1844

252

254

246

250

251

COMMENT

One of many copies after a painting by Rubens, of which the version in a private collection in Madrid may well be the original (compare Antwerp 2004, no. 19).

Peter Paul Rubens (after)

247 *Sine Cerere et Baccho friget Venus (Without Ceres and Bacchus Venus grows cold)*

Canvas, 183 x 205 cm
Dutch title: *Sine Cerere et Baccho friget Venus (Zonder Ceres en Bacchus bevriest Venus)*

PROVENANCE

Het Loo Palace, Apeldoorn, 1757; Nationale Konst-Gallery, The Hague; transferred to the Mauritshuis, 1822

LITERATURE

Moes/Van Biema 1909, p. 215; Snoep 1969, p. 280, fig. 7, p. 288; D/LS 1974–1976, vol. 2, p. 641, no. 42; The Hague 1997–1998a, p. 203, note 11

COMMENT

One of many copies after the painting in the Musée des Beaux-Arts in Brussels, in which the left section was replaced at a later date by Vulcan at his forge. The original left section, depicting an old woman and two children with hot coals, is in the Gemäldegalerie, Dresden.

Peter Paul Rubens (after)

255 *Angelica spied on by the hermit,* before 1637?

Panel, 42 x 56 cm
Dutch title: *Angelica bespied door de heremiet*

PROVENANCE

Probably Forchoudt Gallery, Antwerp (a number '8' is inscribed on the verso); Victor de Rainer, Brussels, 1821; purchased by King Willem I for the Mauritshuis, 1821

COMMENT

Weak, free copy after a painting by Rubens in Vienna, Kunsthistorisches Museum. The scene is taken from *Orlando furioso* by Ariosto. Next to the hermit is a devil, in the sky Ruggero rides a winged horse. The panel-maker's mark on the verso is that of Michiel Claessen (active 1615–1637), providing a *terminus ante quem* for the date of the copy (Wadum 1998, p. 191).

Jacob van Ruisdael

Haarlem 1628/29–1682 Amsterdam

153 *Chapel by a waterfall, c.*1670

Canvas, 69 x 53.3 cm
Signed lower left: *JvRuisdael* (JvR in ligature)
Dutch title: *Kapel bij een waterval*

PROVENANCE

Roelof Meurs Pruyssenaar, Amsterdam; purchased for the Nationale Konst-Gallery, The Hague, 5 May 1802; transferred to the Rijksmuseum, Amsterdam, 1808; acquired by exchange with the Rijksmuseum, Amsterdam, 1825

LITERATURE

HdG 1907–1928, vol. 4, p. 72, no. 225; Mauritshuis 1980, pp. 88–89; Slive 2001, no. 197

155 *View of Haarlem with bleaching grounds, c.*1670–1675

Canvas, 55.5 x 62 cm
Signed bottom right: *JvRuisdael* (JvR in ligature)
Dutch title: *Gezicht op Haarlem met bleekvelden*

PROVENANCE

Samuel Beyerman, Gouda, 1778; Gerrit Muller, Amsterdam, by 1822–1827; purchased, 1827

LITERATURE

HdG 1907–1928, vol. 4, p. 25, no. 65, p. 29, no. 79m; Fuchs 1973; Mauritshuis 1980, pp. 90–92; The Hague-Cambridge 1981–1982, no. 44; Paris 1986, no. 43; Mauritshuis 1987, no. 55; Walford 1991, pp. 128–129, 131, 154, 193; Slive 2001, no. 40; Amsterdam 2003, no. 30

728 *Road through a wooded landscape at twilight,* 1648?

Panel, 29.7 x 37.3 cm
Signed and dated lower left: *vRuisdael / 164[.]*
(vR in ligature; the last number has been read as 5, 6 or 8)
Dutch title: *Weg in een boslandschap bij schemering*

PROVENANCE

Samuel van Hasselt, Amsterdam, 1873; J.C. de Bruijn, The Hague, 1909; gift of Cornelis Hofstede de Groot, The Hague, 1909

LITERATURE

HdG 1907–1928, pp. 181–182, no. 614; Keyes 1975, vol. 1, pp. 99, 140, no. 70; Mauritshuis 1980, pp. 87–88; Slive 2001, no. 352; Hamburg-Haarlem 2002, p. 35, note 18

155

153

728

247

255

R

802 *Winter landscape, c.1660–1670*

Canvas, 37.3 x 32.5 cm
Signed lower left: *JvRuisdael* (JvR in ligature)
Dutch title: *Winterlandschap*

PROVENANCE
Possibly Gerret Braamcamp, Amsterdam, until 1771; possibly Huybert Ketelaar, Amsterdam, 1776; gift of Princess L. de Croy, born D'Espine, Paris, 1931

LITERATURE
HdG 1907–1928, vol. 4, p. 304, no. 1008d (?), p. 305, no. 1009c (?); Mauritshuis 1980, p. 89; Slive 2001, no. 673; The Hague 2001–2002, ex catalogue

803 *View of the Dam and Damrak in Amsterdam, c.1672–1675*

Canvas, 46.8 x 43 cm
Signed lower left: *v Ruisdael*
Dutch title: *Gezicht op de Dam en het Damrak te Amsterdam*

PROVENANCE
Johan Verkolje, Amsterdam, 1763; possibly Anna Elink, Amsterdam; her sale, 28 June 1802, lot 155 (as kindly communicated by B. Fredericksen, Los Angeles, 1997); gift of Princess L. de Croy, born D'Espine, Paris, 1931; on loan to the Amsterdams Historish Museum, Amsterdam, since 1999

LITERATURE
HdG 1907–1928, p. 13, no. 18; The Hague-Cambridge 1981–1982, p. 153; St Petersburg-Amsterdam 1996–1997, no. 22; Slive 2001, no. 6

COMMENT
Cleaned and restored in 1998.

Jacob van Ruisdael (after)

154 *Beach view, c.1675?*

Canvas, 53 x 64.5 cm
Dutch title: *Strandgezicht*

PROVENANCE
De Neufville brothers, Rotterdam; Gerrit van der Pot van Groeneveld, Rotterdam, 1785–1808; purchased by the Rijksmuseum, Amsterdam, 1808; acquired by exchange with the Rijksmuseum, Amsterdam, 1825

LITERATURE
HdG 1907–1928, p. 275, no. 924; Mauritshuis 1980, pp. 92–94; Davies 1992, no. 113 (with attribution to Jan van Kessel); Gibson 2000, p. 105; Slive 2001, no. dub145

COMMENT
This work may have been painted by Jan van Kessel after Van Ruisdael. A related painting in the Hermitage, St Petersburg (Slive 2001, no. 633), may have been the model (see Slive 2001, no. dub145).

Jacob van Ruisdael (manner of)

534 *View of the Vijverberg in The Hague*

Canvas, 62.5 x 80.5 cm
Bears signature lower right: *vR*
Dutch title: *Gezicht op de Vijverberg in Den Haag*

PROVENANCE
Count and Countess Bloudoff, Brussels; purchased, 1886; on loan to the ICN

LITERATURE
HdG 1907–1928, p. 22, no. 54; Dumas 1991, p. 694, no. 7; Slive 2001, p. 621, in no. dub21

COMMENT
A variant of a painting in a private collection in The Hague, possibly an old copy after a lost work by Van Ruisdael (Slive 2001, no. dub21).

Carl Borromäus Andreas Ruthart

Danzig *c.*1630–after 1703 Aquila

10 *Fox hunt*

Canvas, 59.5 x 85.5 cm
Dutch title: *Vossenjacht*

PROVENANCE
Acquired in or before 1841; on loan to the ICN

COMMENT
Formerly ascribed to Adriaen Beeldemaker, but convincingly attributed to Ruthart by F.G. Meijer, The Hague.

Rachel Ruysch

The Hague 1664–1750 Amsterdam

151 *Vase with flowers*, 1700

Canvas, 79.5 x 60.2 cm
Signed and dated lower left, on the edge of the table: *Rachel Ruysch F: 1700*
Dutch title: *Vaas met bloemen*

PROVENANCE
(?) Given by the painter to the Confrerie Pictura, The Hague; H.D. Loeff Gallery, The Hague; purchased, 1826

154

802

534

10

803

151

LITERATURE

HdG 1907–1928, vol. 10, p. 327, no. 22 A; Grant 1956, p. 30, no. 57; The Hague 1992a, no. 21; Berardi 1998, p. 318

Salomon van Ruysdael

Naarden 1600/3–1670 Haarlem

699 *River view with a man hunting ducks,* 1648?

Panel, 47.3 x 69 cm
Signed and dated lower left, on the boat with the hunter: *SVR 16[48?]* (VR in ligature)
Dutch title: *Riviergezicht met eendenjager*

PROVENANCE

F. Kleinberger Gallery, Paris; purchased, 1905

LITERATURE

Stechow 1975, p. 131, no. 398; Mauritshuis 1980, pp. 97–98; Paris 1986, no. 44; Washington etc. 1982–1984, no. 32; De Kinkelder 2000, p. 14

738 *River view with a church and a ferry,* 1649

Panel, 75 x 106.5 cm
Signed and dated lower centre, on the boat: *SVRuysdael 1649* (SVR in ligature)
Dutch title: *Riviergezicht met kerk en veerpont*

PROVENANCE

David Sellar, London, 1885; Charles Sedelmeyer Gallery, Paris, 1889; Rodolphe Kann, Paris, 1907; Duveen Brothers Gallery, New York, Paris and London, 1907; Abraham Bredius, The Hague, 1911–1946 (on loan to the Mauritshuis since 1912); bequest of Abraham Bredius, 1946

LITERATURE

Keyes 1975, vol. 1, pp. 86, 138; Stechow 1975, p. 124, no. 361; Mauritshuis 1980, pp. 96–97; The Hague 1991–1992, no. 17; De Kinkelder 2000, pp. 14, 17

COMMENT

Thanks to cleaning and restoration in 2001, the date can now clearly be read as '1649'.

941 *River bank with old trees,* 1633

Panel, 32.8 x 51.3 cm
Signed and dated to the left: *S VR 16[.]3*
Dutch title: *Rivieroever met geboomte*

PROVENANCE

Earl of Mar and Kellie, Alloa House, Scotland; P. de Boer Gallery, Amsterdam; purchased by the Friends of the Mauritshuis Foundation, 1960

LITERATURE

Mauritshuis 1970, no. 18; Stechow 1975, p. 146, no. 498–A; Mauritshuis 1980, pp. 95–96; Edinburgh 1992, no. 64; De Kinkelder 2000, p. 14

COMMENT

Cleaned and restored in 1986.

1044 *View of a lake with sailing ships,* c.1650–1651

Panel, 36.4 x 31.7 cm
Dutch title: *Meergezicht met zeilschepen*

PROVENANCE

Sale Amsterdam, Frederik Muller, 10 July 1923, lot 129; C.T.F. Thurkow, The Hague, 1923 (on loan to the Mauritshuis since 1972); bequest of L. Thurkow-van Huffel, The Hague, 1987

LITERATURE

Stechow 1975, p. 76, no. 46; Mauritshuis 1980, p. 98; Mauritshuis 1991, no. XXV; De Kinkelder 2000, p. 17

COMMENT

Cleaned and restored in 2000.

1115 *River landscape with sailing boats and a horse-drawn barge,* 1660

Panel, 45 x 68 cm
Signed and dated lower left: *SVR 1660* (SVR in ligature)
Dutch title: *Rivierlandschap met zeilboten en een trekschuit*

PROVENANCE

Lady Cochian, England; D. Katz Gallery, Dieren, 1939–1940; Adolf Hitler, Führermuseum, Linz; Stichting Nederlands Kunstbezit; on loan from the ICN (inv. no. NK 1678) for the Picture Gallery of Prince Willem V, The Hague, since 1992

LITERATURE

Stechow 1975, p. 151, no. 529 A; Tokyo-Kasama-Kumamoto-Leiden 1992–1993, no. 39; De Kinkelder 2000, p. 17; Schwarz 2004, no. IV/7

1117 *View of Beverwijk from the Wijkermeer,* c.1661

Panel, 41 x 35.5 cm
Dutch title: *Gezicht op Beverwijk vanaf het Wijkermeer*

PROVENANCE

L. Nardus, Arnouville, 1917; J.L. Laverge, Rotterdam, 1938; by inheritance to A. de Clercq, Johannesburg, 1966; gift (partial and promised) of Mr M. de Clercq to the American Friends of the Mauritshuis, 1999; on permanent loan from the American Friends of the Mauritshuis since 2000

699

738

941

1115

1044

1117

LITERATURE

Stechow 1975, p. 74, no. 33; De Kinkelder 2000; Burgemeister/Surh 2002, p. 64; Sutton 2002, p. 218

COMMENT

Cleaned and restored in 2000.

1128 *Winter landscape near Arnhem*, 1653

Panel, 56 x 80 cm
Signed and dated lower left, on the sleigh: *S.VR. 1653*
Dutch title: *Winterlandschap bij Arnhem*

PROVENANCE

François-Joseph, Duc de Caylus; Eugene Slatter Gallery, London, 1950; Diaz Estévez Collection, before 1983; sale London, Sotheby's, 6 July 1983, lot 78; gift of Willem, Baron van Dedem to the Friends of the Mauritshuis Foundation, 2002

LITERATURE

Stechow 1975, p. 69, no. 5B; The Hague 2001–2002, no. 25; Sutton 2002, no. 44; Buvelot 2002a, pp. 25–27, no. IV

François Ryckhals

Middelburg *c.*1609–1647 Middelburg

929 *Sleeping boy in a shed*, 1640

Panel, 36.3 x 32.2 cm
Signed and dated lower right: *FSRHALS 1640*
Dutch title: *Slapende jongen in een schuur*

PROVENANCE

Appleby Gallery, London; Vitale Bloch, The Hague; purchased, 1957

LITERATURE

Mauritshuis 1970, no. 37; Bol 1982, p. 23, fig. 6; Buma 1994, pp. 24–25, fig. 25, p. 46, no. 40

Pieter Saenredam

Assendelft 1597–1665 Haarlem

888 *The interior of the Cunerakerk in Rhenen*, 1655

Panel, 50 x 68.8 cm
Signed and dated centre below, on the tomb stone: *reensche kerck / Pieter Saenredam dit met schilderen volleijnt den / 30 april 1655* (Pieter Saenredam completed this painting of Rhenen Church on 30 April 1655)
Dutch title: *Het interieur van de Cunerakerk in Rhenen*

PROVENANCE

Carl von Aretin, Schloss Haidenburg, Munich, 1887; Museum Ferdinandeum, Innsbruck, 1928–1938 (cat. 1928, no. 679); Cassirer Gallery, Zürich; purchased with the support of the Rembrandt Society, 1951

LITERATURE

Swillens 1935, p. 124, no. 200; Mauritshuis 1970, no. 20; Jantzen 1979, p. 233, no. 415; Schwartz/Bok 1989, p. 271, no. 107

COMMENT

Several figures by a later hand were removed during restoration in 1938.

974 *The Mariaplaats with the Mariakerk in Utrecht*, 1659

Panel, 44 x 63 cm
Signed and dated centre below, on the pentice: *P.r Saenredam fecit A°. 1659. 11/20*
Inscribed above the pentice: *De St Maria kerck tot Utrecht.*
Dutch title: *De Mariaplaats met de Mariakerk in Utrecht*

PROVENANCE

Possibly W.A. Coats; Asscher and Welcker Gallery, London; Douwes Gallery, Amsterdam; Frits Lugt, Maartensdijk, 1927; J.W. Nienhuys, Bloemendaal, 1927; A.M. Nienhuys-Versteegh, Aerdenhout, 1948–1966; purchased with the support of the Rembrandt Society, the Prince Bernhard Culture Fund, the Openbaar Kunstbezit Foundation and the Friends of the Mauritshuis Foundation, 1966

LITERATURE

Mauritshuis 1970, no. 21; Mauritshuis 1987, no. 56; Schwartz/Bok 1989, p. 280, no. 147; Rotterdam 1991, no. 24; Giltaij 2000, pp. 44–45, figs. 14–15; Utrecht 2000–2001, no. 3; Los Angeles 2002, no. 3; The Hague 2002, p. 35

COMMENT

The preliminary drawing is in the Utrecht municipal archives (Utrecht 2000–2001, no. 2). Cleaned and restored in 2003.

Cornelis Saftleven

Gorinchem 1607–1681 Rotterdam

538 *Landscape with shepherds and cattle*, 1660

Panel, 36.3 x 49.5 cm
Signed and dated lower right: *1660. C. Saftleven*
Dutch title: *Landschap met herders en vee*

1128 

 538

974 

888 

 929

PROVENANCE
P. Tesse, Paris, 1876; J.H. Cremer, Brussels, 1887; purchased, 1887

LITERATURE
Schulz 1978, p. 212, no. 385; Mauritshuis 1980, pp. 99–100

Herman Saftleven

Rotterdam 1609–1685 Utrecht

1123 *Village on a river*, 1654

Panel, 30.5 x 45 cm
Signed and dated lower left: *HS 1654* (HS in ligature)
Inscribed at the back of the panel: *Bij Rijneck / Hermanus Saft Leven A Utrecht F / Anno 1654*
Dutch title: *Dorp aan een rivier*

PROVENANCE
Adriaan Leonard van Heteren, The Hague, until 1800; Adriaan Leonard van Heteren Gevers, The Hague, 1800–1809; the entire collection bought by King Louis Napoleon for the Royal Museum, Amsterdam, 1809; on loan from the Rijksmuseum, Amsterdam (inv. no. SK-A-363), since 2000

LITERATURE
RM 1976, p. 493; Schulz 1982, pp. 145–146, no. 80

Pieter van Santvoort

Amsterdam 1604/5–1635 Amsterdam

1096 *Dune landscape with a country road*, 1629?

Panel, 31.5 x 46 cm
Signed and dated lower left: *p. Santvoo[r]t 162[.]* (indistinct)
Dutch title: *Duinlandschap met een landweggetje*

PROVENANCE
D. Katz Gallery, Dieren, 1940; Jacques Goudstikker Gallery, Amsterdam; Hermann Göring, Berlin; Stichting Nederlands Kunstbezit; on loan from the Netherlands Institute for Cultural Heritage (inv. no. NK 2650), Amsterdam and Rijswijk, since 1993

LITERATURE
London 1986, no. 117; Beck 1991, p. 337, no. 1061; Tokyo-Kasama-Kumamoto-Leiden 1992–1993, no. 29; Buijsen/Van der Ploeg 1993, pp. 28–29, no. 8; Hamburg-Haarlem 2002, no. 4

Giovanni Battista Salvi, known as Sassoferrato (after)

Sassoferrato 1609–1685 Rome

336 *The Virgin in prayer*

Canvas, 48 x 36.5 cm
Dutch title: *Biddende Maria*

PROVENANCE
Victor de Rainer, Brussels, 1821; purchased by King Willem I for the Mauritshuis, 1821

LITERATURE
Aikema *et al.* 1997, p. 143, no. 168 (present attribution)

COMMENT
Mediocre copy after one of the artist's most successful compositions, now in the Musée des Beaux-Arts, Bordeaux. Another version at Robert Noortman Gallery, Maastricht, 1989.

Jacob Savery the Elder

Courtrai 1565/67–1603 Amsterdam

156 *The St Sebastian's Day Fair, c.*1598

Panel, 41.5 x 62 cm
Signed lower right: *Jaq.$^{s.}$ Savery*
Dutch title: *Sint Sebastiaanskermis*

PROVENANCE
Gift of Arnoldus Andries des Tombe, The Hague, 1874

LITERATURE
Mauritshuis 1968, p. 48; Franz 1969, p. 296, fig. 471

Roelant Savery

Courtrai 1576/78–1639 Utrecht

157 *Orpheus enchanting the animals with his music*, 1627

Panel, 62 x 131.5 cm
Signed lower centre: *ROELANDT / SAVERY FE / 1627*
Bears inscription on the verso: *Ein stick von Serwie.N.18*
Dutch title: *Orpheus betovert de dieren met zijn muziek*

PROVENANCE
Stadholder Frederik Hendrik, The Hague, 1632; Oranienstein Palace, Diez, 1775; by descent to Prince Willem V, The Hague

1096

157

1123

156

336

LITERATURE

D/LS 1974–1976, vol. 1, p. 192, no. 237, vol. 2, p. 372, no. 348, vol. 3, p. 240, no. 189; Bakker 1983, p. 50; Müllenmeister 1988, pp. 103, 139, 294, no. 206; The Hague 1997–1998a, pp. 204, 207, notes 3, 4

COMMENT

Cleaned and restored in 2002–2003.

1129 *Peasants dancing before a Bohemian inn, c.1610?*

Panel, 47 x 61 cm
Signed and dated lower left, beneath the sitting man with the jug: *R SAVERY FE / 16[..]*
Dutch title: *Dansende boeren voor een Boheemse herberg*

PROVENANCE

G.H.G. Braams, Arnhem, before 1918; his sale, Amsterdam, Frederik Muller, 24–26 September 1918, lot 195, for 4000 guilders to Jacobson for Houthakker; Gottschewski Collection, Berlin, 1927; Enthoven Collection; sale Amsterdam, Muller, 25 October 1932, lot 19; P. de Boer Gallery, Amsterdam, 1934; W. Paech Gallery, Amsterdam, 1936; B. de Geus van den Heuvel, Nieuwersluis, until 1976; his sale, Amsterdam, Sotheby Mak van Waay, 26–27 April 1976, lot 59; Richard Green Gallery, London, and J. Kraus, 1977; gift of Willem, Baron van Dedem to the Friends of the Mauritshuis Foundation, 2002

LITERATURE

Cologne-Utrecht 1985–1986, no. 3; Müllenmeister 1988, p. 186, no. 4; Sutton 2002, no. 47; Buvelot 2002a, pp. 28–30, no. V

Cornelis Symonsz van der Schalcke

Haarlem 1611–1671 Haarlem

800 *Slaughtered pig in a moonlit landscape, 1644*

Panel, 34 x 33 cm
Signed and dated centre below: *CS VD Schalck 1644* (VD in ligature)
Dutch title: *Geslacht varken in een maanverlicht landschap*

PROVENANCE

G.H.G. Braams, Arnhem, 1918; gift of C.W. Matthes, Breukelen, 1929

LITERATURE

Van Regteren Altena 1926, p. 52; Mauritshuis 1980, pp. 100–101

Godfried Schalcken

Made 1643–1706 The Hague

158 *Portrait of King-Stadholder Willem III (1650–1702), 1699*

Canvas, 163.2 149.9 cm
Signed and dated lower left: *G. Schalcken. 1699*
Dutch title: *Portret van koning-stadhouder Willem III (1650–1702)*

PROVENANCE

Nationale Konst-Gallery, The Hague, 1800–1808; Picture Gallery of Prince Willem V, The Hague, 1808–1821; transferred, 1822

LITERATURE

HdG 1907–1928, vol. 5, pp. 415–416, no. 333; Moes/Van Biema 1909, pp. 40, no. 43, 47, no. 8, 74, no. 261, 101, no. 146, 108, no. 221; Van Thiel 1981, p. 189, no. 38; Paris 1986, no. IV; Beherman 1988, pp. 44, 185–186, no. 86

COMMENT

Based on an official portrait by Godfrey Kneller of 1690, of which many copies exist. The ships could refer to the Peace of Rijswijk (1697), which ended the Nine-Years War between England, the Dutch Republic and Spain against France. On this occasion, France recognized Willem III as King of England. For biographical data on Willem III, see Bakhuysen, inv. no. 6.

159 *Lady in front of a mirror by candlelight, c.1685–1690*

Canvas, 76 x 64 cm
Signed lower left: *G S[.]h[.]lcken*
Dutch title: *Dame voor de spiegel bij kaarslicht*

PROVENANCE

Estate of the painter; his widow, Françoisia van Diemen, The Hague, 1733 (as kindly communicated by Dr. E. Korthals Altes); Benjamin da Costa, The Hague, 1764; Prince Willem V, The Hague, 1764–1795

LITERATURE

HdG 1907–1928, vol. 5, p. 393, no. 235; D/LS 1974–1976, vol. 3, p. 230, no. 144; De Jongh 1975–1976, p. 83, fig. 13; Beherman 1988, p. 303, no. 207; Nagasaki 1992–1993, no. 26

COMMENT

A mezzotint in reverse by Nicolaes Verkolje (1673–1746).

> **160** *A useless moral lesson, c.1680–1685*

Panel, 35 x 28.5 cm
Signed lower left: *G. Schalcken.*
Dutch title: *De nutteloze zedenles*

1129

800

158

159

162

PROVENANCE
Evert van Sypesteyn, Utrecht, until 1713 (portrayed by Schalcken, see Beherman 1988, no. 78); Adriaan Bout, The Hague, 1733; Prince Willem IV, The Hague; Prince Willem V, Apeldoorn and The Hague, 1757–1795

LITERATURE
HdG 1907–1928, vol. 5, p. 349, no. 92; D/LS 1974–1976, vol. 2, 644, no. 104, vol. 3, p. 230, no. 145; Amsterdam 1976, no. 58; Beherman 1988, pp. 268–269, no. 170; Hecht 1997, p. 94

COMMENT
Companion piece to inv. no. 161.

161 *The medical examination, c.*1680–1685

Panel, 35 x 28.5 cm
Signed lower left: *G. Schalcken.*
Dutch title: *Het onderzoek van de dokter*

PROVENANCE
Same as inv. no. 160

LITERATURE
HdG 1907–1928, vol. 5, p. 364, no. 144; D/LS 1974–1976, vol. 2, p. 644, no. 105, vol. 3, p. 230, no. 146; Amsterdam 1976, no. 59; Beherman 1988, p. 272, no. 175; Hecht 1997, p. 94

COMMENT
Companion piece to inv. no. 160. Cleaned and restored in 1989.

< 162 *Young woman with pigeons, c.*1680–1685

Panel, 21.5 x 17 cm
Dutch title: *Jonge vrouw met duiven*

PROVENANCE
Govert van Slingelandt, The Hague, in or before 1752; the entire collection sold to Willem V in 1768; Prince Willem V, The Hague, 1768–1795

LITERATURE
HdG 1907–1928, vol. 5, p. 346, no. 80; D/LS 1974–1976, vol. 3, p. 230, no. 147; Beherman 1988, p. 321, no. 231

708 *Portrait of Diederick Hoeufft (1648–1719), c.*1680

Copper, 42 x 34.2 cm
Signed lower left: *G. Schalcken*
Dutch title: *Portret van Diederick Hoeufft (1648–1719)*

PROVENANCE
Probably inherited in the family of the sitters; bequest of *Jonkvrouw* Maria Johanna Singendonck, The Hague, 1907

LITERATURE
HdG 1907–1928, vol. 5, p. 411, no. 308; Beherman 1988, pp. 170, 172, no. 71

COMMENT
Diederick Hoeufft, Lord of Fontaine-Pereuse and captain of the cavalry, was the son of Diederick Hoeufft and Maria de Witt (see: Anonymous, northern Netherlands, inv. nos. 710–711). He married Isabella Agneta Deutz in 1680, in which year Schalcken presumably portrayed him and his wife (see the companion piece, inv. no. 709).

709 *Portrait of Isabella Agneta Deutz (1658–1694/96), c.*1680

Copper, 42 x 34 cm
Signed at right, near the elbow: *G. Schalcken*
Dutch title: *Portret van Isabella Agneta Deutz (1658–1694/96)*

PROVENANCE
Same as inv. no. 708

LITERATURE
HdG 1907–1928, vol. 5, p. 411, no. 309; Beherman 1988, pp. 171–172, no. 72

COMMENT
Companion piece to inv. no. 708.

Hendrik Willem Schweickhardt

Hamm 1746–1797 London

669 *Vegetable seller,* 1790

Panel, 31.3 x 42.3 cm
Signed lower left: *W. Schweick[hardt]*
Dutch title: *Groentenverkoper*

PROVENANCE
Van Doorn Collection, 1884; bequest of Arnoldus Andries des Tombe, The Hague, 1903 (on loan to the Mauritshuis since 1884); on loan to the Rijksmuseum Twenthe, Enschede, since 2001

LITERATURE
Sluijter 1975, p. 172, 175, fig. 45, p. 211

COMMENT
According to the painter's 'memorieboek', containing a list of his work, executed in 1790.

160

161

708

709

669

S

Daniel Seghers

Antwerp 1590–1661 Antwerp

256 *Garland of flowers with a sculpture of the Virgin Mary*, 1645

Canvas, 151 x 122.7 cm
Signed and dated lower right: *D. Seghers. Soc*[tis] *Jesu / 1645*
Dutch title: *Bloemencartouche met Mariabeeld*

PROVENANCE
Stadholder Frederik Hendrik, The Hague, 1645–1647; Huis ten Bosch Palace, The Hague, 1654; Nationale Konst-Gallery, The Hague, 1800–1805; transferred, 1822

LITERATURE
Couvreur 1967, p. 104, no. 92, pp. 127, 137; D/LS 1974–1976, vol. 1, p. 281, no. 1179, vol. 2, p. 540, no. 19; Hairs 1985, pp. 143, 146, 174, 182, vol. 2, p. 42; Utrecht 1991, no. 58; Broos/Van Leeuwen 1992; The Hague 1992a, no. 24; The Hague 1997–1998a, no. 27; Vlieghe 1998, p. 210; Scholten 2003b, pp. 110–111

COMMENT
In 1654 this painting served as a chimneypiece in one of the rooms of Huis ten Bosch Palace where it was an integral part of the decorative scheme (The Hague 1997–1998a, p. 130, fig. 1). It is now built in as a chimneypiece in the Van Dyck Room. The sculpture of the Virgin Mary was painted by Thomas Willeboirts Bosschaert.

257 *Garland of flowers around the portrait of King-Stadholder Willem III (1650–1702)*, c.1660?

Canvas, 122.5 x 107 cm
Signed lower right: *D. Seghers. Soc*[tis]*. JESV*
Dutch title: *Bloemencartouche rond een beeld van koning-stadhouder Willem III (1650–1702)*

PROVENANCE
Constantijn Huygens and heirs, The Hague; transferred from the Huygens residence in 1842; on loan to the Paleis Het Loo Nationaal Museum, Apeldoorn, since 1984

LITERATURE
Couvreur 1967, p. 104, no. 91 (?); Hairs 1985, vol. 1, pp. 146–147, 172, 438, note 549, vol. 2, pp. 42–43 (as a portrait of Huygens); Broos/Van Leeuwen 1992, p. 16

COMMENT
The portrait, as usual not painted by Seghers himself, was possibly added around 1670.

Hercules Seghers

Haarlem 1589/90–1637/38 The Hague

1033 *River valley*, c.1620

Panel (possibly originally higher), 22.5 x 53 cm
Signed lower right: *hercūles segers*
Dutch title: *Rivierdal*

PROVENANCE
L. Sievers, Amsterdam, 1875; F. Görlitz, Amsterdam, 1901; (?) Count Cavens, Brussels, 1922; Paul Cassirer Gallery, Berlin; H. Coray-Stoop, Ellenbach and Zürich, *c.*1920; E.M.L. Kessler-Stoop, IJmuiden; purchased with the support of the Rembrandt Society, the Prince Bernhard Culture Fund, the Royal Dutch Foundries and Steel Mills Ltd, IJmuiden and the Friends of the Mauritshuis Foundation, 1969

LITERATURE
Van Gelder 1953, pp. 149–151; Collins 1953, pp. 84, 133; Rotterdam 1954, no. 2; Mauritshuis 1970, no. 28; Mauritshuis 1980, pp. 102–103; Amsterdam 1993–1994, no. 344; Pijl 1995, pp. 172–174, 178

COMMENT
The same scene appears in mirror image in an etching by Seghers (Haverkamp Begemann 1973, no. 4).

Jacob Seisenegger

Lower Austria (Linz?) 1505–1567 Linz

269 *Portrait of Elisabeth of Austria (1526–1545), aged four*, 1530

Panel, 43.4 x 34.7 cm
Signed upper right: *IS* (in ligature)
Inscribed: *ELISABET. FERDINANDI. HVNGARIE. ET. BOHEMIE. REGIS. / FILIA. ANNO.15.30. ETATIS . SVE. 4.*
Dutch title: *Portret van Elizabeth van Oostenrijk (1526–1545), op 4-jarige leeftijd*

PROVENANCE
Victor de Rainer, Brussels, 1821; purchased by King Willem I for the Mauritshuis, 1821

LITERATURE
Löcher 1962, pp. 18–20, 86, no. 20; Mauritshuis 1968, pp. 48–49

COMMENT
Elisabeth of Austria was a daughter of Emperor Ferdinand I. Seisenegger painted the portraits of Ferdinand's four children during the Diet of Augsburg, 1530 (see also inv. nos. 270 and 271). The portrait of his youngest son, Ferdinand, is lost.

256 

 257

1033 

 269

270 *Portrait of Anna of Austria (1528–1590), aged two*, 1530

Panel, 44.7 x 34.8 cm
Signed upper left: *IS* (in ligature)
Inscribed: *ANNA. FERDINANDI. HVNGARIE. ET. BOHEMIE. / REGIS. FILIA. ANNO. 15.30. ETATIS. SVE. 2.*
Dutch title: *Portret van Anna van Oostenrijk (1528–1590), op 2-jarige leeftijd*

PROVENANCE
Same as inv. no. 269

LITERATURE
Löcher 1962, pp. 18–20, 85, no. 13; Mauritshuis 1968, p. 49

271 *Portrait of Maximilian of Austria (1527–1576), aged three*, 1530

Panel, 43 x 34.4 cm
Signed upper right: *IS* (in ligature)
Inscribed: *MAXIMILIANVS. FERDINANDI. HVNGARIE. ET. / BOHEMIE. REGIS. FILIVS. PRIMO. GENITVS. ANNO. / 15.30. ETATIS. SVE. 3.*
Dutch title: *Portret van Maximiliaan van Oostenrijk (1527–1576), op 3-jarige leeftijd*

PROVENANCE
Same as inv. no. 269

LITERATURE
Löcher 1962, pp. 18–20, 90–91, no. 48; Mauritshuis 1968, pp. 49–50

Michel Sittow

Tallinn 1469–1525 Tallinn

832 *Portrait of a man*, *c.*1510

Panel, 35.9 x 25.9 cm
Dutch title: *Portret van een man*

PROVENANCE
Von Liphart family, Ratshof Castle, Tartu, Estonia, until 1918; Ernest, Baron von Liphart, Petrograd, 1918–1921; A.W. Volz, The Hague, 1921–1946; purchase made possible by the testamentary disposition of Mr Volz and with the support of the Rembrandt Society, 1946

LITERATURE
Mauritshuis 1970, no. 1; Trizna 1976, p. 58, notes 2–3, p. 100, no. 25; Bruges 1994, no. 93; Bruges 2002, no. 56; *Portraits in the Mauritshuis*, no. 55

Karel Slabbaert

Zierikzee 1618/19–1654 Middelburg

410 *Soldiers and other figures among the ruins of a castle, with a self-portrait of the artist in the foreground*, *c.*1650

Panel, 50.5 x 39 cm
Signed at left, on the wheel of the cannon: *K. Slabbaert.*
Dutch title: *Soldaten en andere figuren tussen de ruïnes van een kasteel, met een zelfportret van de kunstenaar in de voorgrond*

PROVENANCE
Jacobus Willemsen, Middelburg, 1780; Neville Goldsmid, The Hague; purchased, 1876

LITERATURE
Bol 1982, p. 587; The Hague 2002, pp. 165, 220, note 24

751 *Portrait of a man*, 1653

Panel, 68.1 x 57.3 cm
Signed and dated lower left: *K.Slabbaert f.*
Dated and inscribed upper right: *Aetis 50. An.° 1653. / N.L.S.* (last three letters possibly later addition)
Dutch title: *Portret van een man*

PROVENANCE
(?) Van Landschot Collection; gift of the Council of Indonesia, Batavia, 1916

LITERATURE
Bol 1982, p. 585

Frans Snijders

Antwerp 1579–1657 Antwerp

258 *Still life with huntsman*, *c.*1615

Canvas, 113.7 x 205.5 cm
Dutch title: *Stilleven met een jager*

PROVENANCE
Govert van Slingelandt, The Hague, in or before 1752; the entire collection sold to Willem V in 1768; Prince Willem V, The Hague, 1768–1795

LITERATURE
D/LS 1974–1976, vol. 3, p. 231, no. 149; Greindl 1983, p. 92 (as by Adriaen van Utrecht); Robels 1989, pp. 139, 151, 152, 185, no. 19, p. 407; Nagasaki 1992–1993, no. 28

COMMENT
The huntsman was possibly painted by a pupil of Anthony van Dyck. A preliminary drawing, without the

>>
270

271

832

>>
751

410

258

huntsman, in the Victoria and Albert Museum, London. Cleaned and restored in 1985–1986.

Frans Snijders (studio of)

794 *Still life with a dead stag*

Canvas, 121 x 180.3 cm
Dutch title: *Stilleven met een dode reebok*

PROVENANCE
Sale Amsterdam, A. Mak, 1 December 1925, lot 88; purchased with funds collected on the occasion of Wilhelm Martin's 25th anniversary as director, 1926

LITERATURE
Greindl 1983, p. 377, no. 173; Robels 1989, pp. 73, 164, 224, no. 65

COMMENT
Cleaned and restored in 1985–1986.

Francesco Solimena

Canale di Serino 1657–1747 Naples

340 *The annunciation, c.*1693

Canvas, 62 x 75 cm
Dutch title: *De annunciatie*

PROVENANCE
Victor de Rainer, Brussels, 1821; purchased by King Willem I for the Mauritshuis, 1821

LITERATURE
Rotterdam 1989–1990, no. 69; Nagasaki 1992–1993, no. 29; Aikema *et al.* 1997, pp. 144–145, no. 172

COMMENT
Cleaned and restored in 1989.

Jan Frans Soolmaker

Antwerp (?) *c.*1635–after 1665 Italy (?)

164 *Italian landscape with shepherds*

Canvas, 115 x 133 cm
Signed at left, on the pedestal of the fountain: *J. v. Soolmaker ff.*
Dutch title: *Italiaans landschap met herders*

PROVENANCE
Purchased, 1821; on loan to the ICN

LITERATURE
Mauritshuis 1980, p. 104; Wuestman 1998, p. 73

COMMENT
The staffage is derived rather conspicuously from the oeuvre of Nicolaes Berchem (see Wuestman 1998).

Pieter Soutman (attributed to)

Haarlem *c.*1580–1657 Haarlem

755 *Portrait of a lady, c.*1625–1630

Panel, 129.3 x 99.4 cm
Dutch title: *Portret van een dame*

PROVENANCE
Charles Crews, London, 1915; Jacques Goudstikker Gallery, Amsterdam, 1917; Abraham Bredius, The Hague, 1917–1946 (on loan to the Mauritshuis since 1918); bequest of Abraham Bredius, 1946

LITERATURE
The Hague 1991–1992, no. 18

Jan Steen

Leiden 1625/26–1679 Leiden

165 *A tooth-puller,* 1651

Canvas, 32.5 x 26.7 cm
Dated at right, on the scroll with a wax seal: *1651*
Dutch title: *De kiezentrekker*

PROVENANCE
Wannaar Collection; Willem Lormier, The Hague, 1763; Prince Willem V, The Hague, 1763–1795

LITERATURE
HdG 1907–1928, vol. 1, p. 51, no. 180; D/LS 1974–1976, vol. 3, p. 229, no. 141; De Vries 1977, pp. 33–34, 155, no. 23; Braun 1980, p. 90, no. 32; Nagasaki 1992–1993, no. 30; De Boer *et al.* 1993, pp. 34–36, no. 9; Washington-Amsterdam 1996–1997, p. 185

166 *Portrait of Bernardina Margriet van Raesfelt, known as 'The poultry yard',* 1660

Canvas, 106.6 x 80.8 cm
Signed and dated lower left, on the timbering: *JSteen. / 1660* (JS in ligature)
Dutch title: *Portret van Bernardina Margriet van Raesfelt, bekend als 'De hoenderhof'*

794

340

164

755

165

166

PROVENANCE
Anna van den Bongard, Lokhorst Castle, 1660; her heirs, Warmond Castle, until 1763; Prince Willem V, The Hague, 1769–1795

LITERATURE
HdG 1907–1928, vol. 1, pp. 79–80, no. 330; D/LS 1974–1976, vol. 3, p. 230, no. 143; De Vries 1977, p. 160, no. S 79; Braun 1980, pp. 100–101, no. 113; Paris 1986, no. 46; Mauritshuis 1987, no. 58; Slive 1995, p. 172; Washington-Amsterdam 1996–1997, no. 12; Haarlem-Antwerp 2000–2001, pp. 25–27 and fig. 8; Apeldoorn 2002, p. 95; *Portraits in the Mauritshuis*, no. 56

COMMENT
Van Raesfelt, born around 1650, was a daughter of Wennemar van Raesfelt, who died in 1656. Bernardina was taken in as a foster-child by the childless Anna van den Bongard and her second husband, Johan van Raesfelt, who died in 1657. From that year until 1663 Anna and Bernardina lived in Lokhorst Castle, the house shown in this painting. The portrait was formerly thought to be of Jacoba Maria van Wassenaer (1654–1683). Aert Schouman made a drawing after the painting in 1774 for Cornelis Ploos van Amstel (private collection).

167 *'The sick girl', c.*1660–1662

Panel, 58 x 46.5 cm
Signed lower right: *JSteen.* (JS in ligature)
Dutch title: *'Het zieke meisje'*

PROVENANCE
Govert van Slingelandt, The Hague, in or before 1752; the entire collection sold to Willem V in 1768; Prince Willem V, The Hague, 1768–1795

LITERATURE
HdG 1907–1928, vol. 1, p. 39, no. 131; D/LS 1974–1976, vol. 3, p. 229, no. 142; De Vries 1977, pp. 42–43, 159, no. 61; Braun 1980, p. 114, no. 203; Washington-Amsterdam 1996–1997, p. 40; Petterson 2000, p. 516, no. 51 and p. 631; Copenhagen-Amsterdam 2001, p. 110; Madrid 2003, no. 30

COMMENT
Cleaned and restored in 1999.

168 *The doctor's visit, c.*1660–1662

Panel, 60.5 x 48.5 cm
Signed lower right: *JSteen.* (JS in ligature)
Dutch title: *Het doktersbezoek*

PROVENANCE
Johan van Schuylenburch, The Hague, 1735; I. Hoogenbergh, Amsterdam, 1743; Willem Lormier, The Hague, 1743–1763; Prince Willem V, The Hague, 1763–1795

LITERATURE
HdG 1907–1928, vol. 1, p. 39, no. 130; D/LS 1974–1976, vol. 3, p. 229, no. 140; Amsterdam 1976, no. 63; De Vries 1977, pp. 59, 64, 164, no. 124; Braun 1980, p. 132, no. 318; Philadelphia-Berlin-London 1984, p. 314, note 4; Petterson 1987, pp. 205, 208, 219; Petterson 2000, pp. 516–517, no. 53 and p. 631; Copenhagen-Amsterdam 2001, no. 65

COMMENT
The painting in the background depicts the battle of the Lapiths and centaurs. Cleaned and restored in 1986.

169 *'As the old sing, so twitter the young', c.*1663–1665

Canvas, 84 x 92.6 cm
Signed lower right, on the mortar: *.STEEN.*
Inscribed on the mantle: *Soo de Oude Songe, Soo pypen de Jonge* (As the old sing, so twitter the young)
Dutch title: *'Zo de ouden zongen, zo piepen de jongen'*

PROVENANCE
Prince Willem V, The Hague, until 1795

LITERATURE
HdG 1907–1928, vol. 1, p. 25, no. 90; D/LS 1974–1976, vol. 3, p. 229, no. 138; Braun 1980, p. 114, no. 200; Nagasaki 1992–1993, no. 31

COMMENT
Two heads were damaged during a restoration in Antwerp before 1889; they were subsequently repainted by David Bles (1821–1899).

170 *The life of man, c.*1665

Canvas, 68.2 x 82 cm
Signed at right, on a column: *JSteen* (JS in ligature)
Dutch title: *Het leven van de mens*

PROVENANCE
Adriaan Bout, The Hague, 1733; Benjamin da Costa, The Hague, 1764; Prince Willem V, The Hague, 1764–1795

LITERATURE
HdG 1907–1928, vol. 1, p. 143, no. 595; The Hague 1958–1959, no. 53; D/LS 1974–1976, vol. 3, p. 229, no. 139; Amsterdam 1976, no. 62; De Vries 1977, pp. 60, 165, no. 129; Braun 1980, p. 122, no. 261; Mauritshuis 1987, p. 348 and fig. 2; Washington-Amsterdam 1996–1997, p. 43; De Jongh 1997, p. 41

COMMENT
The painting is an allegory on the vanity of life: in the background a little boy is blowing bubbles, with a skull besides him (see De Jongh 1997, p. 41, fig. 17a).

779 *Woman playing the sistrum, c.*1662

Panel, 31 x 27.5 cm
Signed lower right: *JSteen* (JS in ligature)
Dutch title: *Sisterspelende vrouw*

167

168

779

169

170

PROVENANCE
G. Smith, London, 1880; P.J. Heseltine, London; Frits Lugt, Maartensdijk, 1919; E.G. Verkade, Delft (on loan to the Mauritshuis since 1919); purchased with contributions from private individuals, 1928

LITERATURE
HdG 1907–1928, vol. 1, p. 103, no. 441a; The Hague 1958–1959, no. 19; De Vries 1977, pp. 57, 163, no. 111; Braun 1980, p. 104, no. 132; Washington-Amsterdam 1996–1997, p. 192; The Hague 2002, p. 19

COMMENT
Traditionally identified as the wife of the painter, Grietje van Goyen.

553 *Dancing peasants at an inn, c.1646–1648*

Panel, 40 x 58 cm
Signed lower left: *JSteen* (indistinct)
Dutch title: *Dansende boeren bij een herberg*

PROVENANCE
Maria Beukelaar, The Hague, 1742; Nicolaas van Bremen, The Hague, 1769; J.A.A. de Lelie, Amsterdam, 1845; W. Gruyter, Amsterdam, 1882; Hermann Wirz, Cologne, 1890 (as by Pieter de Bloot); Abraham Bredius, The Hague, 1890–1946 (on loan to the Mauritshuis since 1890); bequest of Abraham Bredius, 1946

LITERATURE
HdG 1907–1928, vol. 1, p. 151, no. 624; De Vries 1977, pp. 30, 33, 154, no. 1; Braun 1980, p. 86, no. 5; The Hague 1991–1992, no. 19; Washington–Amsterdam 1996–1997, p. 111; Buijsen *et al.* 1998, p. 239

COMMENT
Cleaned and restored in 2004.

664 *Village fair, c.1648*

Panel, 47.2 x 66 cm
Signed lower centre: *JSteen* (JS in ligature)
Dutch title: *Dorpskermis*

PROVENANCE
Hennin Collection, Paris, 1764; A. Visscher-Boelger, Basel; Jos Schall Gallery, Baden-Baden; J.E. Goedhart Gallery, Amsterdam, 1901; Abraham Bredius, The Hague, 1901–1946 (on loan to the Mauritshuis since 1901); bequest of Abraham Bredius, 1946

LITERATURE
HdG 1907–1928, vol. 1, pp. 151–152, no. 625; De Vries 1977, pp. 30, 32, 33, 154, no. 3; Braun 1980, p. 8, no. 81; The Hague 1991–1992, no. 20; Buijsen *et al.* 1998, p. 239

736 *'A pig belongs in the sty', c.1674–1678*

Canvas, 86 x 72 cm
Signed lower right: *JSteen* (JS in ligature)
Dutch title: *'Wie een varken is, moet in het kot'*

PROVENANCE
G. Vogel, Rotterdam, 1755; (?) Pieter Foucquet, London, 1773; Henry Doetsch, London, 1895; Abraham Bredius, The Hague, 1895–1946 (on loan to the Mauritshuis since 1911); bequest of Abraham Bredius, 1946

LITERATURE
HdG 1907–1928, vol. 1, p. 189, no. 753; De Vries 1977, pp. 69, 168, no. 167; Braun 1980, p. 140, no. 362; The Hague 1991–1992, no. 21; Washington-Amsterdam 1996–1997, p. 55

COMMENT
The scene with the drunken woman, who is being put in the sty because of her dissolute ways, illustrates a well-known proverb.

742 *'The way you hear it, is the way you sing it', c.1665*

Canvas, 134 x 163 cm
Formerly bore signature on the wall, lower left: *J. Steen fect* (see Mauritshuis 1935, p. 333; removed in 1953)
Inscribed on the sheet held by the old woman: *Liet / Soo voer gesongen soo / na gepepen dat is al lang / g[e]bleken ick sing u vo[or] / so[o] volcht ons na[er] / van een tot hon[derd] jaar* (The way you hear it, is the way you sing it, that's been known for long, I'll sing and you follow, from a baby to a hundred-year old)
Dutch title: *'Soo voer gesongen, soo na gepepen'*

PROVENANCE
Hermina Jacoba, Baroness van Leyden, Warmond, 1816; *Jonkheer* Johan Steengracht van Oostkapelle and heirs, The Hague, 1816–1913; purchased with the support of the Rembrandt Society, 1913

LITERATURE
HdG 1907–1928, vol. 1, pp. 129–130, no. 529; De Vries 1977, pp. 57–58, 61, 164, no. 118; Braun 1980, p. 114, no. 201; Paris 1986, no. 47; Mauritshuis 1987, no. 59; Slive 1995, p. 175; Washington-Amsterdam 1996–1997, no. 23; Buvelot *et al.* 1998, pp. 196, 198

COMMENT
According to tradition, the sitters are members of Jan Steen's family. The laughing man with hat and pipe is certainly a self-portrait. Cleaned and restored in 2003.

742

553

664

736

S

818 *Girl eating oysters, c.*1658–1660

Panel (rounded at the top), 20.5 x 14.5 cm
Signed upper left, above the door: *IS* (in ligature)
Dutch title: *'Het oestereetstertje'*

PROVENANCE
Pieter Locquet, Amsterdam, 1783; Pieter van Winter and heirs, Amsterdam; Six Collection, Amsterdam, until 1928; gift of Sir Henri W.A. Deterding, London, 1936

LITERATURE
HdG 1907–1928, vol. 1, p. 218, no. 853; De Vries 1977, pp. 48, 161, no. 84; Braun 1980, pp. 27, 98–99, no. 92; Paris 1986, no. 45; Mauritshuis 1987, no. 57; Washington-Amsterdam 1996–1997, no. 9

920 *An old couple preparing a beverage, c.*1665–1670

Panel, 41 x 31.5 cm
Signed lower right: *JSteen* (JS in ligature)
Dutch title: *Een oud echtpaar bezig met kandeel maken*

PROVENANCE
Jan Jacob Brants, Amsterdam, 1813; Baron van Verschuere, The Hague, until 1901; M.C. van den Honert, Hilversum (on loan to the Mauritshuis since 1954); gift of Miss M.C. van den Honert, Hilversum, 1957

LITERATURE
HdG 1907–1928, vol. 1, p. 84, no. 351; The Hague 1958–1959, no. 45; Mauritshuis 1970, no. 36; De Vries 1977, pp. 41, 43, 159, no. 59; Braun 1980, p. 98, no. 95

1111 *The fortune teller, c.*1650–1654

Canvas, 73.5 x 60 cm
Signed lower right: *J. Steen*
Dutch title: *De waarzegster*

PROVENANCE
M.J. Roelofs Thijssen, Amsterdam, 1891; Baron Königswärter, Vienna; August Janssen, Amsterdam; Jacques Goudstikker Gallery, Amsterdam, 1919; P.W. Janssen, Amsterdam, 1926; M.J. IJzerloo, Rijswijk, 1941; P. de Boer Gallery, Amsterdam, 1941; M.F. de Vries, Amsterdam, 1941; G.B. Lanz, Laren, 1941; D. Katz Gallery, Dieren, 1941; Adolf Hitler, Führermuseum, Linz; Stichting Nederlands Kunstbezit; on loan from the ICN (inv. no. NK 2727) for the Picture Gallery of Prince Willem V, since 1992

LITERATURE
HdG 1907–1928, vol. 1, p. 59, no. 225; De Vries 1976, p. 29, fig. 5; Braun 1980, p. 166, no. B–52 (as by Gerard ter Borch); Tochigi-Sakura-Gunma-Nagasaki 1997–1998, no. 41; Schwarz 2004, no. IX/35

Hendrick van Steenwijck the Younger

Antwerp *c.*1580–1649 Leiden or The Hague

171 *An imaginary city square,* 1614

Copper, 47 x 70 cm
Signed and dated centre left, below the balustrade: *H.V S / 1614*
Dutch title: *Een plein met gefantaseerde gebouwen*

PROVENANCE
Ewout van Dishoeck, Middelburg, before 1744; Prince Willem IV, 1745; thence by descent to Prince Willem V, The Hague, until 1795

LITERATURE
D/LS 1974–1976, vol. 2, p. 640, no. 29, vol. 3, p. 232, no. 155; Jantzen 1979, pp. 36–37, 235, no. 457; Rotterdam 1991, no. 6; Boston-Toledo 1993–1994, no. 76

Dirck Stoop

Utrecht *c.*1610–1686 Utrecht

172 *View of Belem monastery near Lisbon,* 1660s

Canvas, 111.5 x 179 cm
Dutch title: *Gezicht op het klooster Belem bij Lissabon*

PROVENANCE
S.E. Lin, Venice; Martial Reghellini Schio, Venice and Brussels, until 1826; purchased by King Willem I for the Mauritshuis, 1831

LITERATURE
Gerson 1983, p. 530, fig. 130 (as by Isaac Mijtens)

COMMENT
A comparable painting of the same subject in the Museu Nacional de Arte Antigua, Lissabon (canvas, 112.5 x 184.5 cm).

Abraham Storck

Amsterdam 1644–1708 Amsterdam

> 173 *Moorage,* 1683

Panel, 22 x 31 cm
Signed and dated lower right: *A: Storck / F. A° 1683*
Dutch title: *Aanlegplaats met boten*

818

920

1111

172

291

171

PROVENANCE
Prince Willem IV, Leeuwarden, 1731; by descent to Prince Willem V, The Hague, until 1795

LITERATURE
D/LS 1974–1976, vol. 2, p. 405, no. 507, vol. 3, p. 231, no. 153; Mauritshuis 1980, p. 105

COMMENT
Companion piece to inv. no. 174.

174 *Beach view*, 1683

Panel, 22.5 x 31 cm
Signed and dated lower left: *A: Storck. F. / A° 1683*
Dutch title: *Strandgezicht met boten*

PROVENANCE
Same as inv. no. 173

LITERATURE
D/LS 1974–1976, vol. 2, p. 405, no. 507, vol. 3, p. 231, no. 152; Mauritshuis 1980, p. 105

COMMENT
Companion piece to inv. no. 173.

Herman van Swanevelt

Woerden *c.*1600–1655 Paris

< 291 *Wooded landscape with shepherds*, *c.*1630–1640

Canvas on panel, 52.5 x 75.5 cm
Dutch title: *Boslandschap met herders*

PROVENANCE
Het Loo Palace, Apeldoorn, 1712; Prince Willem V, The Hague, until 1795

LITERATURE
D/LS 1974–1976, vol. 1, p. 677, no. 830, p. 698, no. 77, vol. 2, p. 70, no. 24, p. 639, no. 3, vol. 3, p. 220, no. 87; Rome 1983, no. 15; The Hague 1988–1989, no. 11

Michael Sweerts

Brussels 1618–1664 Goa

657 *A man defleaing himself and a sleeping boy*, *c.*1650–1654

Canvas, 78.5 x 71 cm
Dutch title: *Een man die zich vlooit en een slapende jongen*

PROVENANCE
Purchased, 1901

LITERATURE
Kultzen 1996, p. 104, no. 54

886 *Peasant family, with a man defleaing himself*, *c.*1656–1660

Canvas, 66.5 x 50 cm
Dutch title: *Boerenfamilie, met een een man die zich vlooit*

PROVENANCE
Vitale Bloch, Paris and The Hague; purchased, 1951

LITERATURE
Mauritshuis 1970, no. 13; Kultzen 1996, p. 108, no. 66

1121 *Draughts players*, 1652

Canvas, 48 x 38 cm
Signed and dated lower right:
Michael Sweerts / fecit añ 1652 / Roma.
Dutch title: *De damspelers*

PROVENANCE
John Everett Millais, England; bequest of Cornelis Hoogendijk to the Rijksmuseum, Amsterdam (inv. no. SK-A-2574), 1912; on loan from the Rijksmuseum since 2000

LITERATURE
RM 1976, p. 532; Kultzen 1996, p. 101, no. 46; Amsterdam-San Francisco-Hartford 2002, no. XVI; Blankert 2004, p. 296

COMMENT
Cleaned and restored in 2001.

Abraham van den Tempel

Leeuwarden 1622/23–1672 Amsterdam

396 *Portrait of Jan Antonides van der Linden (1609–1664)*, 1660

Canvas, 88.5 x 71 cm
Signed and dated lower right: *ABv Tempel ft.1660*
Inscribed on the book: *HIPP OPE* (Hippocrates's Opera)
Dutch title: *Portret van Jan Antonides van der Linden (1609–1664)*

PROVENANCE
L. Lippmann von Lissingen, Vienna, 1876; purchased, 1876; on loan to the Stedelijk Museum De Lakenhal, Leiden, since 1922

LITERATURE
Wijnman 1959, p. 67, no. 3; Ekkart 1977, pp. 152–153, no. 147; Lakenhal 1983, p. 333, no. 428

COMMENT
Companion piece to inv. no. 397. A replica is in the Senaatskamer of Leiden University. Engraved by Rembrandt (B. 264). Cleaned and restored in 1988.

173

174

886

1121

657

396

397

Van der Linden was professor of medicine at Franeker and later at Leiden. In 1634 he married Helena Grondt, who is portrayed in the companion piece.

< 397 *Portrait of Helena Grondt (1613/14–after 1665), c.*1660

Canvas, 88.5 x 71 cm
Signed and dated lower right: *AB v. Tempel f 166[.]*
Dutch title: *Portret van Helena Grondt (1613/14–na 1665)*

PROVENANCE
Same as inv. no. 397; on loan to the Stedelijk Museum De Lakenhal, Leiden, since 1922

LITERATURE
Wijnman 1959, p. 67, no. 4; Lakenhal 1983, p. 334, no. 429

COMMENT
Companion piece to inv. no. 396. Cleaned and restored in 1988.

David Teniers the Younger

Antwerp 1610–1690 Brussels

260 *Kitchen interior, 1644*

Copper, 57 x 77.8 cm
Signed lower right: *DAVID. TENIERS. F*
Dated at right, on the drawing above the fireplace: *A° 1644*
Dutch title: *Keukeninterieur*

PROVENANCE
Johan van Schuylenburch, The Hague, 1735; Govert van Slingelandt, The Hague, in or before 1752; the entire collection sold to Willem V in 1768; Prince Willem V, The Hague, 1768–1795

LITERATURE
D/LS 1974–1976, vol. 3, p. 232, no. 156; Davidson 1980, pp. 5, 14–15; Antwerp 1991, no. 36; Phoenix-Kansas City-The Hague 1998–1999, no. 58; Fransen 1997, p. 148

COMMENT
Thought to portray the artist's wife Anna and their son David Teniers III. Cleaned and restored in 1998.

261 *The alchemist*

Panel, 26.6 x 37.5 cm
Signed lower right: *D. Teniers: Fec*
Dutch title: *De alchemist*

PROVENANCE
Prince Willem IV, thence by descent to Prince Willem V, The Hague, 1754–1795

LITERATURE
D/LS 1974–1976, vol. 2, p. 480, no. 33, vol. 3, p. 232, no. 157; Davidson 1980, pp. 14, 32–34; Nagasaki 1992–1993, no. 32

848 *Country inn*

Panel, 35 x 32.5 cm
Signed lower centre, on a leg of the table: *DT* (in ligature)
Dutch title: *Boerenherberg*

PROVENANCE
Nationale Konst-Gallery, The Hague, 1808; Rijksmuseum, Amsterdam (inv. no. SK-A-400), since 1883; on loan from the Rijksmuseum since 1948

LITERATURE
Moes/Van Biema 1909, pp. 129 (?), 165, 221; RM 1976, p. 536

COMMENT
A falsely signed copy is in the Musée de Dijon, Dijon, with a man added at the right. Cleaned and restored in 1987.

1092 *Monkeys' guardroom, c.*1633

Panel, 41.5 x 58 cm
Bears signature lower left: *D. TENIERS. FEC.*
Dutch title: *Apenkortegaard*

PROVENANCE
H. Steinmeyer Gallery, Lucerne, 1924; Reinhardt Collection, New York, 1927; M. Schloss Collection; Jacques Goudstikker Gallery, Amsterdam; Hermann Göring, Berlin; Stichting Nederlands Kunstbezit; on loan from the Netherlands Institute for Cultural Heritage (inv. no. NK 1897), Amsterdam and Rijswijk, since 1992

LITERATURE
Antwerp 1991, no. 6; Buijsen/Van der Ploeg 1993, pp. 29–30, no. 9

COMMENT
Reproduced by Teniers in a painting dated 1635 (private collection) depicting an art cabinet (Antwerp 1991, no. 11).

Mattheus Terwesten

The Hague 1670–1757 The Hague

1042 *Allegory of peace, c.*1740?

Canvas (oval; originally rectangular), 118 x 79 cm
Dutch title: *Allegorie op de vrede*

PROVENANCE
Served as a chimneypiece in the so-called Late Cabinet on the first floor of the Mauritshuis until 1982 (see Wansink 1991, fig. 8)

LITERATURE
Wansink 1990, pp. 284–285, fig. 23; Wansink 1991

260 

261 

 1092

848 

 1042

T

Gillis van Tilborgh

Brussels *c.*1625–*c.*1678 Brussels

262 *Family portrait, c.*1665

Canvas, 80.3 x 104 cm
Signed lower right: *TILBORGH*
Dutch title: *Familieportret*

PROVENANCE
A.L.C.H.T. de l'Espinasse de Langeac, Paris, 1815; P.F. Tiberghien, Brussels, 1827; purchased by King Willem I for the Mauritshuis, 1827

LITERATURE
Brussels-Niederösterreich 1991, no. 223; Boston-Toledo 1993–1994, pp. 56, 66, 194, 203; Braunschweig 1993–1994, no. IX.29; Vlieghe 1998, p. 148

COMMENT
A similar room is depicted in a painting sold in London, Christie's, 23 March 1973, lot 9 (repr.).

Anton Wilhelm Tischbein

Haina 1730–1804 Hanau

232 *Portrait of Carolina Wilhelmina of Orange (1743–1787) and her children*

Canvas, 104.5 x 149 cm
Dutch title: *Portret van Carolina Wilhelmina van Oranje (1743–1787) en haar kinderen*

PROVENANCE
Found in the attic of the Mauritshuis, 1875; on loan to the Paleis Het Loo Nationaal Museum, Apeldoorn, since 1977

LITERATURE
Leeuwarden-Den Bosch-Assen 1979–1980, no. 269

COMMENT
Other versions in The House of Orange-Nassau Historic Collections Trust, The Hague, and a private collection. Carolina Wilhelmina, Princess of Orange, was the eldest daughter of Stadholder Willem IV and Anne of Hannover, and sister of Stadholder Willem V (see MINIATURES, Mussard, inv. no. 1012). In 1760 she married Karl Christian of Nassau-Weilburg. The children depicted from left to right are: Carolina Louise Frederika (1770–1828); Amalia Charlotte Wilhelmina Louise (1776–1841); Karel Frederik Willem (1775–1807); Wilhelmina Louise (1765–1837); Augusta Maria Carolina (1764–1802); and Frederik Willem (1768–1816).

Johann Friedrich August Tischbein

Maastricht 1750–1812 Heidelberg

286 *Portrait of Frederika Louise Wilhelmina of Prussia (1774–1837)*

Pastel on paper (oval), 64.8 x 53.5 cm
Dutch title: *Portret van Frederika Louise Wilhelmina van Pruisen (1774–1837)*

PROVENANCE
Nationale Konst-Gallery, The Hague; found in the attic of the Mauritshuis, 1841

LITERATURE
Moes/Van Biema 1909, p. 121, no. 28, p. 127, no. 375 (?); Staring 1978, p. 37; Dekking *et al.* 1987, pp. 35, 97, no. 145

COMMENT
Probably a copy after the portrait in the Rijksmuseum, Amsterdam, inv. no. SK-A-413. Another version of the painting, signed and dated 1789, is in The House of Orange-Nassau Historic Collections Trust, The Hague. Reproduced in aquatint by Charles Melchior Descourtis (1753–1820). Cleaned and restored in 2001. Frederika Louise Wilhelmina, Princess of Prussia, was the daughter of the Prussian king Friedrich Wilhelm II and Friederike of Hesse-Darmstadt. In 1791 she married Willem Frederik of Orange-Nassau, later King Willem I.

464 *Portrait of Princess Frederika Sophia Wilhelmina (1751–1820)*, 1789

Canvas, 172 x 135 cm
Signed and dated lower right, on the music instrument: *Tischbein. / p:1789*
Dutch title: *Portret van prinses Frederika Sophia Wilhelmina (1751–1820)*

PROVENANCE
Nationale Konst-Gallery, The Hague, 1808; Picture Gallery of Prince Willem V, The Hague, 1808–1821; transferred, 1822

LITERATURE
Moes/Van Biema 1909, p. 102, no. 228, p. 127, no. 372 (?); Van Thiel 1981, p. 179; Dekking *et al.* 1987, pp. 32, 88, no. 122

COMMENT
One of the many versions of this portrait. Frederika Sophia Wilhelmina, Princess of Prussia, was the daughter of Prince August Wilhelm of Hohenzollern and Luise Amalie of Braunschweig-Wolfenbüttel. Her brother was the Prussian king Friedrich Wilhelm II. In 1767 she married Prince Willem V of Orange.

262

232

286

464

T

Johann Friedrich August Tischbein (after)

504 *Portrait of Princess Anne of Hannover (1709–1759)*

Canvas, 82 x 70 cm
Dutch title: *Portret van prinses Anna van Hannover (1709–1759)*

PROVENANCE
Found in the attic of the Mauritshuis, 1841; on loan to the ICN

COMMENT
Anne of Hannover was the eldest daughter of the English king George II Augustus and Wilhelmine Christine von Brandenburg. In 1734 she married Stadholder Willem IV.

Titian (after)

Pieve di Cadore *c.*1488–1567 Venice

343 *Venus with an organist and a dog*

Canvas, 157 x 213 cm
Dutch title: *Venus met een orgelspeler en een hond*

PROVENANCE
Lucien Bonaparte; Joseph, Cardinal Fesch, Rome, 1839; King Willem II, *c.*1845–1849; by descent to Prince Hendrik (on loan to the Mauritshuis, February 1868); gift of Sophie, Grand Duchess of Saxe-Weimar-Eisenach, 1883

LITERATURE
Wethey 1975, vol. 3, p. 200; Hinterding/Horsch 1989, pp. 45, 112, no. 185; Boschloo/Van der Sman 1993, p. 100, no. 99

COMMENT
Old copy after the painting by Titian in Madrid, Museo Nacional del Prado.

358 *Portrait of Emperor Charles V (1500–1558)*, 17th century

Canvas, 67.5 x 54 cm
Dutch title: *Portret van keizer Karel V (1500–1558)*

PROVENANCE
Victor de Rainer, Brussels, 1821; purchased by King Willem I for the Mauritshuis, 1821

LITERATURE
Boschloo/Van der Sman 1993, p. 100, no. 98

COMMENT
Copy after a lost original by Titian of 1548 (Wethey 1975, vol. 2, pp. 193–194, no. L-5). Charles V was Holy Roman Emperor, King of Spain and Archduke of Austria.

Gerrit Toorenburgh

Amsterdam 1732–1785 Nijkerk

178 *View of the Amstel in Amsterdam*

Canvas, 39 x 47 cm
Signed lower left: *Toorenburgh / Pinxit*
Dutch title: *Gezicht op de Amstel te Amsterdam*

PROVENANCE
Purchased after 1817

Cornelis Troost

Amsterdam 1696–1750 Amsterdam

179 *Pretended virtue exposed: The discovery of Volkert in the laundry basket*, 1739

Pastel and brush in gouache on paper, 60.5 x 49 cm
Signed and dated upper right, on the cupboard: *C. Troost / 1739*
Dutch title: *De ontdekte schijndeugd: De ontdekking van Volkert in de mand*

PROVENANCE
Jeronimus Tonneman, Amsterdam, 1754; Johan van der Marck, Amsterdam, 1773; J.S. de Neufville Brants, Amsterdam, 1829; purchased, 1829

LITERATURE
Niemeijer 1973, p. 273, no. 400 T; The Hague 1993, no. 9

COMMENT
One of a series of four pastels representing scenes from David Lingelbach's 1687 comedy *De ontdekte schyndeugd* (Pretended virtue exposed). Only the Mauritshuis pastel is known today – the compositions of the remaining three have survived thanks to the gouaches Sara Troost (1732–1803) made after her father's designs. Prints by William Hogarth (1697–1764) and François Boucher (1703–1770) were used as models for the figures (see The Hague 1993).

180 *Jan Claasz or the supposed servant girl: The marriage proposal to Saartje Jans*, 1738

Pastel and brush in colours on paper, 61 x 48.5 cm
Signed and dated left of centre, on the window: *C. Troost 1738* (twice, over each other, in red and black)
Dutch title: *Jan Claasz of de gewaande dienstmaagd: Saartje Jans ten huwelijk gevraagd*

PROVENANCE
Jeronimus Tonneman, Amsterdam, 1754; Jan de Bruyn,

504

179

343

358

178

180

Amsterdam, 1754; by inheritance to Jan Jacob de Bruyn, Amsterdam, 1798; J.S. de Neufville Brants, Amsterdam, 1829; purchased, 1829

LITERATURE

Niemeijer 1973, pp. 255–256, no. 346 T; The Hague 1993, no. 12; Washington-Amsterdam 1996–1997, p. 46

COMMENT

Scene from Thomas Asselijn's highly successful 1682 comedy *Jan Klaa[s]z of Gewaande Dienstmaagt* (Jan Claasz or the supposed servant girl). Troost rendered the three most significant scenes in numerous variants (see also inv. nos. 181–182).

181 *Jan Claasz or the supposed servant girl: Reinier Adriaansz's declaration of love,* 1737

Pastel and brush in gouache on paper, 60.5 x 52 cm
Signed and dated lower right, on the edge of the stoop: *C. Troost 1737*
Dutch title: *Jan Claasz of de gewaande dienstmaagd: De liefdesverklaring van Reinier Adriaansz*

PROVENANCE

Same as inv. no. 180

LITERATURE

Niemeijer 1973, p. 261, no. 362 T; The Hague 1993, no. 13

COMMENT

See inv. no. 180.

182 *Jan Claasz or the supposed servant girl: The discovery of Jan Claasz,* 1738

Pastel and brush in gouache on paper, 60.5 x 49 cm
Signed and dated left of centre, on the chair: *C. Troost / 1738*
Dutch title: *Jan Claasz of de gewaande dienstmaagd: De ontdekking van Jan Claasz*

PROVENANCE

Same as inv. no. 180

LITERATURE

Niemeijer 1973, p. 265, no. 379 T; The Hague 1993, no. 14

COMMENT

See inv. no. 180.

183 *Harlequin, magician and barber: The deceived rivals,* 1738

Pastel and brush in gouache on paper, 62 x 50 cm
Signed and dated lower left: *C. Troost / 1738*
Dutch title: *Arlequin, tovenaar en barbier: De bedrogen rivalen*

PROVENANCE

Jan Jacob de Bruyn, Amsterdam, 1798; J.S. de Neufville Brants, Amsterdam, 1829; purchased, 1829; on loan to the J. Paul Getty Museum, Los Angeles, since 2002

LITERATURE

Niemeijer 1973, p. 239, no. 282 T; The Hague 1993, no. 19

COMMENT

Scene from Willem van der Hoeven's 1730 farce *Arlequin, tovenaar en barbier* (Harlequin, magician and barber).

184 *Captain Ulrich or greed deceived: Disguised, Godefroy and his servant put Captain Ulrich to flight,* 1738

Pastel and brush in gouache on paper, 55.5 x 72.5 cm
Signed and dated centre right, on the mantelpiece: *C. Troost / 1738*
Dutch title: *Hopman Ulrich of de bedrogen gierigheid: Godefroy en zijn knecht verjagen in vermomming hopman Ulrich*

PROVENANCE

J.S. de Neufville Brants, Amsterdam, 1829; purchased, 1829; on loan to the J. Paul Getty Museum, Los Angeles, since 2002

LITERATURE

Niemeijer 1973, pp. 251–252, no. 329 T; The Hague 1993, no. 18

COMMENT

Scene from Willem van Paffenrode's 1661 farce *Hopman Ulrich of de Bedroge Gierigheid* (Captain Ulrich or greed deceived). Troost drew inspiration from a print by William Hogarth (1697–1764).

185 *Pefroen and the sheep's head,* 1739

Pastel and brush in colours on paper, 63 x 50.5 cm
Signed and dated lower left, on a step of the stairs: *C. Troost 1739*
Dutch title: *Pefroen met het schaapshoofd*

PROVENANCE

Same as inv. no. 183

LITERATURE

Niemeijer 1973, pp. 277–278, no. 419 T; The Hague 1993, no. 20

COMMENT

Scene from Ysbrand Vincent's 1669 comedy *Pefroen met het schaapshoofd* (Pefroen and the sheep's head), an adaption of Raymond Poisson's 1661 *Lubin ou le sot vangé.*

181

182

183

185

184

T

186 *'Nemo loquebatur' (No one spoke)*, 1740

Pastel and brush in gouache on paper, 56.5 x 72.5 cm
Signed and dated lower right, on a plinth: *C. Troost 1740*
Dutch title: *'Nemo loquebatur' (Niemand sprak er)*

PROVENANCE
Probably commissioned by Theodoor van Snakenburg, Leiden, 1739–1740; J. Tak, Zoeterwoude, 1781; J.A. Bennet, Leiden, 1829; purchased, 1829

LITERATURE
Niemeijer 1973, pp. 337–338, no. 653 A/E; The Hague 1993, nos. 27–31; Slive 1995, p. 311; Laan 2003, pp. 150–156

COMMENT
One of a series of five pastels (inv. nos. 186–190) known as the 'NELRI series', a humorous portrayal of a gathering of seven gentlemen which derives its name from the first letters of the Latin titles found in the cartouches on the original decorative frames (see Mauritshuis 2000, pp. 136–139). Troost made four drawings for this scene (The Hague 1993, nos. 23–26).

187 *'Erat sermo inter fratres' (The brothers were having a conversation)*, 1740

Pastel and brush in gouache on paper, 56.5 x 72.5 cm
Signed and dated lower left, on the base of a pilaster: *C. Troost 1740*
Dutch title: *'Erat sermo inter fratres' (De vrienden raakten in gesprek)*

COMMENT
See above. A preparatory study is preserved in the Koninklijk Oudheidkundig Genootschap, Amsterdam (The Hague 1993, p. 86, repr.).

188 *'Loquebantur omnes' (Everyone was speaking)*, 1740

Pastel and brush in gouache on paper, 56.5 x 72.5 cm
Signed and dated left of centre, on the base of a pilaster: *C. Troost / 1740*
Dutch title: *'Loquebantur omnes' (Iedereen voerde het woord)*

COMMENT
See above. A preparatory study is preserved in the Koninklijk Oudheidkundig Genootschap, Amsterdam (The Hague 1993, p. 88, repr.).

189 *'Rumor erat in casa' (There was a commotion in the house)*, 1740

Pastel and brush in gouache on paper, 57 x 73 cm
Signed lower left, on a plinth: *C. Troost*
Dutch title: *'Rumor erat in casa' (Het werd rumoerig in huis)*

COMMENT
See above. A preparatory study is preserved in the Koninklijk Oudheidkundig Genootschap, Amsterdam (The Hague 1993, p. 90, repr.). Troost drew inspiration from a print by William Hogarth (1697–1764).

190 *'Ibant qui poterant, qui non potuere cadebant' (Those who could walk did, the others fell)*, 1739

Pastel and brush in gouache on paper, 56.5 x 72.5 cm
Signed and dated lower left, on the kerb: *C. Troost 1739*
Inscribed next to the door: *Leveraard Biberius*
Dutch title: *'Ibant qui poterant, qui non potuere cadebant' (Wie nog kon lopen ging heen, wie dat niet meer kon, viel om)*

COMMENT
See above. A preparatory study is preserved in the Koninklijk Oudheidkundig Genootschap, Amsterdam (The Hague 1993, p. 92, repr.).

191 *The mathematicians or the young lady who ran away: The dispute between doctors Raasbollius and Urinaal*, 1741

Pastel and brush in colours on paper, 64 x 83.5 cm
Signed and dated lower left, on the tablecloth: *C. Troost / 1741*
Dutch title: *De wiskunstenaars of 't gevluchte juffertje: Het dispuut van de doktoren Raasbollius en Urinaal*

PROVENANCE
Same as inv. no. 183

LITERATURE
Niemeijer 1973, pp. 289–290, no. 450 T; The Hague 1993, no. 21; Buijsen 1993b; Smit 2000, pp. 84–85, 232–233; *Mauritshuis in focus* 14 (2001), no. 1, pp. 6–7

COMMENT
Scene from Pieter Langendijk's 1715 farce *De wiskunstenaars of 't gevlugte juffertje* (The mathematicians or the young lady who ran away). Troost represents the play's most spectacular scene: Raasbollius ('Loudmouth'), in the foreground at the right, is engaged in a heated debate with Urinaal ('Urinal') concerning the orbits of the planets.

192 *Singing round the star on Twelfth Night*

Pastel and brush in gouache on paper, 56 x 74 cm
Signed lower right, on the stairs: *C. Troost* (twice)
Inscribed left, on a piece of paper: *O starre je moet er soo / stille niet staan / [je] moet met [ons] / na[ar] Beth[lehem] gaan* (Oh star do not stand still, to Bethlehem with us if you will; see Mauritshuis 1935, p. 356)
Dutch title: *Het zingen bij de ster op Driekoningen*

186

188

187

189

190

191

192

PROVENANCE
Same as inv. no. 184

LITERATURE
Niemeijer 1973, pp. 344–345, no. 668 T; Den Bosch 1992, no. 44; The Hague 1993, no. 3

COMMENT
Twelfth Night, or Epiphany, is still celebrated on 6 January in some parts of the northern and southern Netherlands with a procession illuminated by torches and lanterns.

193 *The wedding of Kloris and Roosje*

Pastel and brush in gouache on paper, 64 x 83 cm
Signed lower left: *C. Troost*
Inscribed on the piece of paper: *Ter Bruyloft / van / Kloris / en / Roosje* (see Mauritshuis 1935, p. 357)
Dutch title: *De bruiloft van Kloris and Roosje*

PROVENANCE
Same as inv. no. 183

LITERATURE
Niemeijer 1973, pp. 246–247, no. 314 T; The Hague 1993, no. 11; Enschede 1996, pp. 73, 93; Smit 2000, p. 233; *Mauritshuis in focus* 14 (2001), no. 1, pp. 6–7

COMMENT
Scene based on Dirk Buysero's 1688 *De bruiloft van Kloris en Roosje* (The wedding of Kloris and Roosje) and Pieter Langendijk's *Don Quichot op de bruiloft van Kamacho* (Smit 2000). Drawings with the same subject are in the Theater Instituut Nederland, Amsterdam, and the British Museum, London. A third drawing, with the couple dancing to the tune of a flute player, is in the Koninklijk Oudheidkundig Genootschap, Amsterdam (The Hague 1993, p. 52, repr.).

194 *Self-portrait*, 1745

Pastel, brush in gouache on parchment, 62 x 52 cm
Signed and dated lower left: *C. Troost. / 1745*
Dutch title: *Zelfportret*

PROVENANCE
(?) Jeronimus Tonneman, Amsterdam, 1754; (?) Jan de Bruyn, Amsterdam, 1754; D. van Dyl, Amsterdam, 1814; Van Oosthuyse van Rijsenburg-de Jongh Collection, The Hague, 1847; W. Gruyter, Amsterdam, 1847–1867; C.C.J. de Ridder, Rotterdam, 1874; purchased, 1874

LITERATURE
Niemeijer 1973, p. 155, no. 2 T; The Hague 1993, no. 1; Grijzenhout 1993, pp. 27–28, 89; *Portraits in the Mauritshuis*, no. 58

COMMENT
Troost gave up acting when his painting career began to take shape in 1724, but the stage would inspire him throughout his life. The unfinished painting on the easel depicts an episode in the biblical story of Solomon's idolatry. Troost may have intended it to represent a scene from Joost van den Vondel's 1648 biblical drama *Solomon*.

411 *Lady with cupid and a songbook*, 1745

Pastel, brush in gouache on parchment, 47.5 x 61.5 cm
Signed and dated lower right: *C. Troost. / 1745*
Inscribed on the songbook: *Maar wagt u zoet Meysje voor 't eerste snoeprysje op* (But beware, sweet girl, of the first jaunt; see Mauritshuis 1935, p. 358)
Dutch title: *Dame met cupido en een liedboek*

PROVENANCE
(?) N. Albrechts, Amsterdam, 1772; J.W. Heybroek, Rotterdam, 1788; C.C.J. de Ridder, Rotterdam, 1874; S.C. Snellen van Vollenhoven, The Hague, 1876; purchased, 1876

LITERATURE
Niemeijer 1973, pp. 302–303, no. 514 T

COMMENT
The music sheet shows the refrain of a song from the book *Vermakelijk boerenleven* (Peasant diversions).

609 *The organ grinder*

Pastel on paper, 51.7 x 68.7 cm
Dutch title: *De liereman*

PROVENANCE
Hendrik Verschuring, The Hague, 1751; F. van de Velde, Amsterdam, 1775; J. Smies, Amsterdam, 1834; gift of Miss G.J.L. van Dijk, The Hague, 1897

LITERATURE
Niemeijer 1973, p. 350, no. 684 T; The Hague 1993, no. 6

COMMENT
The preliminary sketch, in the Rijksmuseum, Rijksprentenkabinet, Amsterdam, reveals that Troost reduced the number of figures and replaced a street singer with the organ grinder.

1034 *Allegory on the war with France in 1747*, 1747

Canvas, 82 x 102 cm
Signed and dated lower left, on the table: *Cornelis Troost fecit 1747*
Inscribed on the mantlepiece: *JE MAINTIENDRAI*
Dutch title: *Allegorie op de oorlog met Frankrijk in 1747*

PROVENANCE
David Ietswaart, Amsterdam, 1749; Johan van der Marck, Leiden, 1749–1773; Hendrik Twent, Leiden, 1789; J. Hoofman van Diepenbroek, Haarlem; M. Hoofman, Haarlem; L.J. Quarles van Ufford, Haarlem, 1874;

193 

 194

1034 

609 

 411

C.F. van de Poll, Heemstede (temporarily on loan to the Mauritshuis); E. Boreel; W.M.F. Boreel, Laren (on loan to the Maurits-huis since 1968); purchased by the Friends of the Mauritshuis Foundation, 1980

LITERATURE
Niemeijer 1973, pp. 354–356, no. 694; Paris 1986, no. 48; Mauritshuis 1987, no. 60; The Hague 1993, no. 4

COMMENT
The scene makes reference to the War of the Austrian Succession (1740–1748), which was initiated by the question of who would succeed the German emporer Charles VI. Troost wanted to give vent to either his own —or his patron's— pro-Orange inclinations, since the motto of Stadholder Willem IV is depicted on the mantlepiece underneath the medallion with his portrait. Various preliminary studies are known, one of which is in the Musée des Beaux-Arts et d'Archeologie, Besançon (The Hague 1993, p.38, repr.).

1068 *Portrait of a man*, 1730?

Canvas, 90 x 71.5 cm
Signed and dated lower left: *C. Troost. f 17[3?]o*
Dutch title: *Portret van een man*

PROVENANCE
Nancy Stutterd, Papatoetoe, New Zealand, 1985; J. Hoogsteder Gallery, The Hague; purchased, 1986

LITERATURE
Mauritshuis 1991, no. XIX; The Hague 1993, no. 2; *Portraits in the Mauritshuis*, no. 57

COMMENT
Possibly the companion piece to a portrait of a woman dated 1730 in Düsseldorf, Kunstmuseum (The Hague 1993, p. 34, repr.).

Alessandro Turchi

Verona 1578–1649 Rome

342 *Allegory of the power of love ('Omnia vincit Amor')*, c.1620–1630

Canvas, 100 x 123 cm
Dutch title: *Allegorie op de macht van de liefde ('Omnia vincit Amor')*

PROVENANCE
Philips de Flines, Amsterdam, until 1700; King-Stadholder Willem III, Het Loo Palace, Apeldoorn, 1700; by descent to Prince Willem V, Apeldoorn and The Hague; on loan to the Paleis Het Loo Nationaal Museum, Apeldoorn, since 1984

LITERATURE
D/LS 1974–1976, vol. 3, p. 234, no. 161 (?); Rotterdam 1989–1990, no. 48; Aikema *et al.* 1997, pp. 165–167, no. 190; Verona 1999, no. 28

COMMENT
A preliminary drawing in the National Gallery of Scotland, Edinburgh. A pen and ink drawing after the painting made by Jan de Bisschop around 1665 in the Rijksmuseum, Rijksprentenkabinet, Amsterdam (Amsterdam 1992a, no. 32).

Jacob van der Ulft

Gorinchem 1621–1689 Noordwijk

196 *Army advancing among Roman ruins*, 1671

Canvas, 81.8 x 133.3 cm
Signed and dated left of centre: *Jacob van der Ulft F / 1671*
Dutch title: *Optrekkend leger te midden van Romeinse ruïnes*

PROVENANCE
Pieter de Klok, Amsterdam, 1744; Pieter de Smeth van Alphen, Amsterdam, 1810; H. van der Werf, Dordrecht; H.D. Loeff Gallery, The Hague, 1825; purchased, 1825

LITERATURE
Mauritshuis 1980, p. 106; Tissink/De Wit 1987, pp. 34–35

COMMENT
A similar painting in the Museum Boijmans Van Beuningen, Rotterdam, dated 1674.

Domenico Antonio Vaccaro

Naples 1678–1745 Naples

359 *God the Father and the Holy Ghost*, c.1700–1710

Canvas, 64 x 42 cm
Dutch title: *God de vader en de heilige geest*

PROVENANCE
Nationale Konst-Gallery, The Hague, 1801–1809; found in 1875 in the attic of the Mauritshuis

LITERATURE
Moes/Van Biema 1909, p. 211 (as Gaule Bacier); Aikema *et al.* 1997, p. 167, no. 191 (present attribution)

COMMENT
This painting probably served as a *modello* for a more worked up version.

342 

 359

1068 

 196

V

Raffaello Vanni (attributed to)

Siena 1587–1673 Siena

309 *The Holy Family and St Anne, c.*1650

Canvas, 99 x 74.5 cm
Dutch title: *De heilige familie en de heilige Anna*

PROVENANCE
Count Edmund Bourke, Paris; purchased from his widow by King Willem I for the Mauritshuis, 1823; on loan to the Rijksmuseum, Amsterdam (inv. no. SK-C-1345), since 1948

LITERATURE
RM 1976, p. 178 (attributed to Pietro da Cortona); Rotterdam 1989–1990, no. 57; Aikema *et al.* 1997, pp. 167–168, no. 192 (present attribution)

Adriaen van de Velde

Amsterdam 1636–1672 Amsterdam

197 *Wooded landscape with cattle*, 1663

Panel, 29 x 35.5 cm
Signed and dated lower right: *A. V. Velde / 1663* (name indistinct)
Dutch title: *Boslandschap met vee*

PROVENANCE
Possibly Floris Drabbe, Leiden, 1743; Willem Lormier, The Hague, 1752–1763; Pieter Leendert de Neufville, Amsterdam, 1763–1765; Prince Willem V, The Hague, 1765–1795

LITERATURE
HdG 1907–1928, vol. 4, p. 521, no. 140; D/LS 1974–1976, vol. 3, p. 234, no. 164; Mauritshuis 1980, pp. 107–108; Rome 1983, no. 16; Utrecht-Frankfurt am Main 1993, no. 53

198 *Beach view*, 1663 or 1665

Panel, 42 x 54 cm
Signed and dated bottom left: *Av velde f / 166[3 or 5?]*
Dutch title: *Strandgezicht*

PROVENANCE
Jeronimus Tonneman, Amsterdam, 1754; Coenraad van Heemskerck, The Hague, 1765; Govert van Slingelandt, The Hague; the entire collection sold to Willem V in 1768; Prince Willem V, The Hague, 1768–1795

LITERATURE
HdG 1907–1928, vol. 4, pp. 586–587, no. 356; The Hague-London 1970–1971, no. 106; D/LS 1974–1976, vol. 3, p. 234, no. 165; Mauritshuis 1980, pp. 108–109; Paris 1986, no. 49; Mauritshuis 1987, no. 61; Amsterdam-Boston-Philadelphia 1987–1988, no. 103; Madrid 1994–1995, no. 68

Esaias van de Velde

Amsterdam 1587–1630 The Hague

199 *Merry company in the park*, 1614

Panel, 28.5 x 40 cm
Signed and dated lower right: *E. VANDEN. VELDE. / 1614*
Dutch title: *Vrolijk gezelschap in een park*

PROVENANCE
David van der Kellen, Amsterdam; purchased, 1873

LITERATURE
Keyes 1984, pp. 80–81, 136, no. 63; De Jongh 1997, pp. 43–44; Rodney 2003, pp. 57–58; Nehlsen-Marten 2003, pp. 69–70; Haarlem-Hamburg 2003–2004, no. 1

673 *Winter landscape with farmhouse*, 1624

Panel, 26 x 32 cm
Signed and dated lower right: *E. v. Velde. 1624*
Dutch title: *Winterlandschap met boerderij*

PROVENANCE
Bequest of Arnoldus Andries des Tombe, The Hague, 1903

LITERATURE
Mauritshuis 1980, p. 110; Keyes 1984, p. 70–71, 140, no. 77; Paris 1986, no. 50; Mauritshuis 1987, no. 62; Madrid 1994–1995, no. 70; De Jongh 1997, p. 27; The Hague 2001–2002, no. 32

Jan van de Velde III

Haarlem 1620–1662 Enkhuizen

533 *Still life with levelling glass*, 1660

Canvas, 54 x 47.5 cm
Signed and dated lower right, on the edge of the tabletop: *IANVANDEVELDE· An°.* 1660 */ Fecit/* (name in ligature)
Dutch title: *Stilleven met pasglas*

PROVENANCE
P. Verloren van Themaat, Amsterdam; purchased, 1885

LITERATURE
Mauritshuis 1935, p. 368

309 

 533

199 

 197

673 

 198

V

Willem van de Velde the Younger

Leiden 1633–1707 Greenwich

200 *Ships in the roads, c.1658*

Canvas, 66.5 x 77.2 cm
Signed at right, across the ribbon on the yacht's tafferel: *W vande velde f.*
Dutch title: *Schepen op de rede*

PROVENANCE
Govert van Slingelandt, The Hague, in or before 1752; the entire collection sold to Willem V in 1768; Prince Willem V, The Hague, 1768–1795

LITERATURE
HdG 1907–1928, vol. 7, p. 36, no. 109; D/LS 1974–1976, vol. 3, p. 135, no. 168; Mauritshuis 1980, pp. 111–112; Paris 1986, no. 51; Mauritshuis 1987, no. 63; Robinson 1990, vol. 1, pp. 324–325, no. 1; Rotterdam-Berlin 1996–1997, pp. 337–338, in no. 76

COMMENT
Probably a view on the Zuiderzee outside Amsterdam. On the right is a yacht of the admiralty.

201 *Ships in the roads, c.1658*

Canvas (cut at the left and below?), 66.2 x 77.5 cm
Signed at right, on the barrel: *w / v. v.*
Dutch title: *Schepen op de rede*

PROVENANCE
Pieter Leendert de Neufville, Amsterdam, 1765; Prince Willem V, The Hague, 1765–1795

LITERATURE
HdG 1907–1928, vol. 7, pp. 10–11, no. 19; D/LS 1974–1976, vol. 3, p. 235, no. 167; Mauritshuis 1980, pp. 112–114; Mauritshuis 1987, p. 375 and fig. 1; Robinson 1990, vol. 1, p. 326, no. 2.1; Minneapolis-Toledo-Los Angeles 1990–1991, no. 35; Rotterdam-Berlin 1996–1997, no. 76

COMMENT
Left of centre is a States yacht with the arms of Willem II, built for Frederik Hendrik in 1645–1647. In the eighteenth century, this painting was regarded as a companion piece to inv. no. 200.

Willem van de Velde the Younger (studio of)?

471 *Conquest of the 'Royal Prince',* early 18th century?

Canvas, 42 x 52 cm
Dutch title: *Verovering van de 'Royal Prince'*

PROVENANCE
Henry Richard Wellesley; C. de Waspick, Brussels, 1852; Bernard du Bus de Gisignies, Brussels; purchased, 1882; on loan to the ICN

LITERATURE
HdG 1907–1928, vol. 7, p. 13, no. 26; Mauritshuis 1980, p. 115; Robinson 1990, vol. 1, pp. 151–152, no. 136

COMMENT
Episode from the Four-Day Battle at sea, 13 June 1666, showing the moment when the Dutch took down the flags of the 'Royal Prince' after it had run aground on a sandbank.

Willem van de Velde the Younger (studio of)?

563 *Sunset at sea, c.1680*

Canvas, 35 x 60.6 cm
Bears signature lower left: *w. v.velde J*
Dutch title: *Zonsondergang op zee*

PROVENANCE
T. Humphrey Ward & Son Gallery, London, 1890; Abraham Bredius, The Hague, 1890–1946 (on loan to the Mauritshuis since 1892); bequest of Abraham Bredius, 1946

LITERATURE
HdG 1907–1928, vol. 7, p. 57, no. 193; Mauritshuis 1980, p. 116; Robinson 1990, vol. 1, pp. 453–454, no. 137; The Hague 1991–1992, no. 22

Adriaen van de Venne

Delft 1589–1662 The Hague

202 *Dancing beggars,* 1635

Panel, 12 x 28 cm
Dated and signed lower right: *1635. A P:v:Venne*
Inscribed bottom right: *All om Arm* (All-round-Poor)
Dutch title: *Dansende bedelaars*

PROVENANCE
Adriaan van der Willigen, Haarlem; his sale, Haarlem, 20 April 1874, lot 99; purchased by the State Advisory Board for Monuments of History and Art and transferred to the Mauritshuis, 1875

LITERATURE
Francken 1878, p. 53, no. 24; Bol 1958, p. 130, fig. 19; Bol 1983, p. 60, fig. 78; Westermann 1999, p. 42 and fig. 8

200

201

471

563

202

Pieter Verbeecq

Haarlem *c.*1610/15–*c.*1654 Haarlem

611 *Two horsemen by a stream, c.*1635

Panel, 27.5 x 35.2 cm
Signed lower right: *P.VB.* (VB in ligature)
Dutch title: *Twee ruiters bij een bron*

PROVENANCE
Emil Goldschmidt, Frankfurt am Main; J. de Kuijper Gallery, Rotterdam; purchased, 1897

LITERATURE
Gerson 1940, pp. 183, 189, no. 6, fig. 204; Mauritshuis 1980, pp. 116–117; The Hague 1991–1992, pp. 38, 40, fig. 20

Jan Verkolje

Amsterdam 1650–1693 Delft

865 *The messenger ('t kan verkeren'),* 1674

Canvas, 59 x 53.5 cm
Signed and dated at left, the plinth next to the door: *I. Verkolje 1674*
Dutch title: *De boodschapper ('t kan verkeren')*

PROVENANCE
Van Loon Collection, Amsterdam; Alfred de Rothschild, London; Victor de Rothschild, London; sale London, Sotheby's, 19–22 April 1937, lot 19, as signed and dated 1678, to S. and R. Rosenberg, art dealers; Fritz Mannheimer, Amsterdam; Adolf Hitler, Führermuseum, Linz; Stichting Nederlands Kunstbezit; on loan to the Mauritshuis, 1948–1960; transferred, 1960

LITERATURE
Amsterdam 1976, no. 70; Philadelphia-Berlin-London 1984, pp. 335–336, fig. 1; Paris 1986, no. 52; Mauritshuis 1987, no. 64; New York-London 2001, no. 63; Dublin-Greenwich 2003–2004, no. 42; Schwarz 2004, no. III/38

COMMENT
In the background a painting depicting the death of Adonis.

Johannes Vermeer

Delft 1632–1675 Delft

92 *View of Delft, c.*1660–1661

Canvas, 96.5 x 115.7 cm
Signed lower left, on the boat: *IVM* (in ligature)
Dutch title: *Gezicht op Delft*

PROVENANCE
(?) Pieter Claesz van Ruijven and heirs, Delft; Jacob Dissius (with his father Abraham Dissius, 1685–1694), Delft, 1682–1695; Dissius sale, Amsterdam, 16 May 1696, lot 31; Willem Philip Kops and heirs, Haarlem, before 1805–1822; included in the Stinstra sale, Amsterdam, 22 May 1822, lot 112; purchased, 1822

LITERATURE
HdG 1907–1928, vol. 1, p. 607, no. 48; Paris 1986, no. 53; Mauritshuis 1987, no. 65; Wheelock 1988, no. 13; Blankert/Montias/Aillaud 1992, no. 10; Chong 1992b; Wadum/Hoppenbrouwers/Struick van der Loeff 1994; Broos 1995d; Slive 1995, p. 145; Wheelock 1995, pp. 1, 2, 5, 18, 72–83, 126, 139, 154, 159, 174; Washington-The Hague 1995–1996, no. 7; Broos *et al.* 1996

COMMENT
Cleaned and restored in 1994.

406 *Diana and her nymphs, c.*1653–1654

Canvas, 97.8 x 104.6 cm
Signed lower left, on the rock, between the dog and the thistle: *JVMeer* (VM in ligature)
Dutch title: *Diana en haar nimfen*

PROVENANCE
Dirksen Gallery, The Hague, before 1866; Neville Goldsmid, The Hague, 1866–1875; his widow, Eliza Garey, The Hague and Paris; sold in Paris, 4 May 1876, lot 68, as by Nicolaes Maes; purchased, 1876

LITERATURE
HdG 1907–1928, vol. 1, pp. 588–589, no. 3; Blankert/Montias/Aillaud 1992, no. 2; M. de Boer in Mauritshuis 1993, no. 37; Wheelock 1995, pp. 21, 25, 26, 27, 28–37, 55, 163, 164, 170; Washington-The Hague 1995–1996, no. 3; Rotterdam-Frankfurt am Main 1999–2000, no. 62; Krempel 2000, pp. 349–350, no. C 14; New York-London 2001, no. 64; Van der Ploeg 2001b; Kolfin/Pottasch/Hoppe 2002; Pottasch/Hoppe 2003

COMMENT
A section of blue sky in the upper right corner, probably added in the beginning of the nineteenth century, was concealed during the restoration of the painting in 1999–2000. Originally, the painting must have been approximately 12 cm larger at the right side (see Van der Ploeg 2001b, figs. 12–14).

92

865

611

406

670 *Girl with a pearl earring*, *c.*1665

Canvas, 44.5 x 39 cm
Signed upper left: *IVMeer* (IVM in ligature)
Dutch title: *Meisje met de parel*

PROVENANCE

(?) Dissius sale (see inv. no. 92), Amsterdam, 16 May 1696, lot 38, 39 or 40; Braams sale, The Hague, day and month unknown, 1881; bequest of Arnoldus Andries des Tombe, The Hague, 1903 (on loan to the Mauritshuis in 1881)

LITERATURE

HdG 1907–1928, vol. 1, p. 606, no. 44; Paris 1986, no. 54; Mauritshuis 1987, no. 66; Blankert/Montias/Aillaud 1992, no. 18; Wadum/Hoppenbrouwers/Struick van der Loeff 1994; Slive 1995, pp. 151–152; Wheelock 1995, pp. 103, 123, 124, 178; Washington-The Hague 1995–1996, no. 15; Van der Ploeg *et al.* 2002, p. 167; Buvelot 2004, pp. 28–29; *Portraits in the Mauritshuis*, no. 59

COMMENT

Cleaned and restored in 1994.

Jan Vermeer van Haarlem

Haarlem 1628–1691 Haarlem

724 *Landscape on the edge of the dunes*, 1648

Panel, 52 x 68 cm
Signed and dated left of the middle: *Jvmeer / 1648* (Jv in ligature)
Dutch title: *Landschap aan de duinzoom*

PROVENANCE

Private collection, London; purchased, 1907

LITERATURE

Stechow 1966, pp. 48–49, 195, note 54; Bol 1969, pp. 217–218; Mauritshuis 1980, p. 117

COMMENT

Companion piece to inv. no. 809.

809 *A farm near the dunes*, 1648

Panel, 52 x 68 cm
Signed lower left: *JVMee*r (JVM in ligature)
Dutch title: *Boerderij bij de duinen*

PROVENANCE

Private collection, London; Frederik Muller Gallery, Amsterdam; purchased by the Rijksmuseum, Amsterdam (inv. no. SK-A-2351), with the support of the Rembrandt Society, 1908; on loan from the Rijksmuseum since 1933

LITERATURE

Stechow 1966, pp. 48–49; Bol 1969, pp. 217–218; RM 1976, p. 375; Mauritshuis 1980, pp. 117–118

COMMENT

Companion piece to inv. no. 724.

Jan Vermeulen

Recorded in Haarlem between 1651 and 1655

402 *Still life with books and musical instruments*, *c.*1660

Panel, 81.5 x 63.5 cm
Signed lower right, on the drawing: *JVM*
Dutch title: *Stilleven met boeken en muziekinstrumenten*

PROVENANCE

J.K. van der Haagen, The Hague; Neville Goldsmid, The Hague, 1868; purchased, 1876 (as by Gerrit Dou)

LITERATURE

Leiden 1970, no. 34; The Hague 1991–1992, p. 102

662 *Still life with books, a globe and musical instruments*, *c.*1660

Panel, 30 x 38.5 cm
Signed upper centre, on the base of the column: *J. V.Meulen*
Inscribed on the piece of paper below the standing book: *Vanitas*, at right next to the base of the column: *Cantor*
Dutch title: *Stilleven met boeken, een globe en muziekinstrumenten*

PROVENANCE

Henry Pfungst Gallery, London, 1901; Abraham Bredius, The Hague, 1901–1946 (on loan to the Mauritshuis since 1901); bequest of Abraham Bredius, 1946

LITERATURE

Martin 1935–1936, vol. 1, pp. 418–419; The Hague 1991–1992, no. 23

COMMENT

Several versions are known (see photographs at the RKD, The Hague).

670

402

662

809

724

V

Claude-Joseph Vernet

Avignon 1714–1789 Paris

292 *An Italian harbour in stormy weather, c.1740–1750*

Canvas, 101 x 138 cm
Dutch title: *Een Italiaanse haven bij stormachtig weer*

PROVENANCE
Cardinal Valenti Gonzaga, Rome, until 1763; Prince Willem V, The Hague, 1764–1795

LITERATURE
Ingersoll-Smouse 1926, no. 200; D/LS 1974–1976, vol. 3, p. 235, no. 169; Den Bosch-Heino-Haarlem 1984, no. 170; Dijon-Paris-Rotterdam 1992–1993, no. 43; Philadelphia-Houston 2000, no. 300

COMMENT
Companion piece to inv. no. 293.

293 *The waterfalls near Tivoli, with the villa of Maecenas, c.1740–1750*

Canvas, 101 x 138 cm
Dutch title: *De watervallen bij Tivoli met de villa van Maecenas*

PROVENANCE
Same as inv. no. 292

LITERATURE
Ingersoll-Smouse 1926, no. 199; D/LS 1974–1976, vol. 3, pp. 235–236, no. 170; Den Bosch-Heino-Haarlem 1984, no. 147; Dijon-Paris-Rotterdam 1992–1993, no. 44; Philadelphia-Houston 2000, no. 300

COMMENT
Companion piece to inv. no. 292.

Bonifazio (de' Pitati) Veronese

Verona 1487–1553 Venice

344 *A martyr, c.1545*

Canvas on panel (oval), 53.1 x 41.2 cm
Reverse: a wax seal of Johan Willem Friso (see The Hague 1988–1989, p. 89, fig. a)
Dutch title: *Een martelares*

PROVENANCE
King Charles I, London, until 1649; King-Stadholder Willem III, Het Loo Palace, Apeldoorn, *c.*1700; thence by descent to Prince Willem V, The Hague; Nationale Konst-Gallery, 1801–1809; transferred, 1875

LITERATURE
Westphal 1931, pp. 66–67; Van Thiel 1981, p. 198, no. 120; The Hague 1988–1989, no. VI; Boschloo/Van der Sman 1993, p. 35, no. 15

COMMENT
Fragment of a larger painting, a copy of which is preserved in a private collection (see The Hague 1988–1989, p. 91, fig. b).

Paolo Veronese (after)

Verona 1582–1588 Venice

312 *The martyrdom of Saints Primus and Felicianus*

Paper on canvas (rounded at the top), 94 x 49 cm
Dutch title: *Het martelaarschap van de heiligen Primus en Felicianus*

PROVENANCE
Martial Reghellini Schio, Venice and Brussels, until 1826; purchased by King Willem I for the Mauritshuis, 1831; on loan to the ICN

LITERATURE
Pignatti 1976, no. A 134; Boschloo/Van der Sman 1993, p. 115, no. 112

COMMENT
Copy after a much larger painting by Veronese in the Museo Civico, Padua.

Hendrik Verschuring

Gorinchem 1627–1690 Dordrecht

606 *Hunters and dogs in an Italianate landscape, c.1656–1660*

Panel, 41.3 x 31.5 cm
Signed lower left: *H. verschuring f.*
Dutch title: *Zuidelijk landschap met jagers en honden*

PROVENANCE
Gift of A. Stengelin, Katwijk, 1897; on loan to the ICN

LITERATURE
Bol 1969, p. 266; Mauritshuis 1980, pp. 118–119

606

292

312

293

344

V

Johannes Verspronck

Haarlem 1606/9–1662 Haarlem

948 *Portrait of André de Villepontoux (1616–1663)*, 1651

Panel, 55.6 x 45 cm
Signed and dated lower right: *Joh. vSpronck an° 1651*
Dutch title: *Portret van André de Villepontoux (1616–1663)*

PROVENANCE
By inheritance to Anna Maria du Peyrou-de Villepontoux, daughter of the sitter; J. van Breugel-du Peyrou; C. Baron van Breugel Douglas, The Hague; on loan to the Mauritshuis since 1961

LITERATURE
Ekkart 1979, no. 80; Amsterdam 1984, pp. 143–144

COMMENT
Companion piece to inv. no. 949. In its original frame. André de Villepontoux married Maria Hammius in 1650.

949 *Portrait of Maria Hammius*, 1651

Panel, 55.6 x 45 cm
Signed and dated at left, above the fan:
Joh. vSpronck a° 1651
Dutch title: *Portret van Maria Hammius*

PROVENANCE
Same as inv. no. 948

LITERATURE
Ekkart 1979, no. 81; Amsterdam 1984, pp. 143–144

COMMENT
Companion piece to inv. no. 948. In its original frame. Maria Hammius (dates unknown) married André de Villepontoux in 1650.

Anthonie Verstralen

Gorinchem *c.*1594–1641 Amsterdam

659 *Winter scene*, 1623?

Panel, 26.2 x 43 cm
Signed and dated lower right: *AVS 16[.]3*
(AVS in ligature)
Dutch title: *Winterlandschap*

PROVENANCE
Gift of Cornelis Hofstede de Groot, The Hague, 1901

LITERATURE
Mauritshuis 1980, p. 119

David Vinckboons

Malines 1576–*c.*1632 Amsterdam

542 *Country fair*, 1629

Panel, 40.5 x 67.5 cm
Signed and dated at right, on the door:
Dvinck=Boons / AN° 1629 (Dv and AN in ligature)
Inscribed on a sign: *Sotcap* (Fool's cap)
Dutch title: *Boerenkermis*

PROVENANCE
Bos de Harlingen Collection, Amsterdam; purchased, 1888

LITERATURE
Goossens 1954, pp. 126–133; Philadelphia-Berlin-London 1984, no. 122; Essen-Vienna 2003–2004, p. 202

Simon de Vlieger

Rotterdam (?) *c.*1601–1653 Weesp

558 *Beach view*, 1643

Panel, 60.6 x 83.5 cm
Signed and dated lower right: *S. DE VLIEGER / A 1643*
Dutch title: *Strandgezicht*

PROVENANCE
H. Roxard de la Salle, Nancy, 1881; G. Rothan, Paris, 1890; Abraham Bredius, The Hague (on loan to the Mauritshuis since 1890); purchased, 1892

LITERATURE
Bol 1973, pp. 182–183; Mauritshuis 1980, pp. 120–121; The Hague 1991–1992, pp. 29–30; Gibson 2000, p. 105 and fig. 76

COMMENT
Cleaned and restored in 2000.

Hendrick van Vliet

Delft 1611/12–1675 Delft

203 *Interior of the Oude Kerk in Delft*, after 1665

Canvas, 77.5 x 68.2 cm
Signed indistinctly on the base of a column in the centre:
H. (the rest illegible; see Mauritshuis 1935, p. 383)
Dutch title: *Gezicht in de Oude Kerk te Delft*

PROVENANCE
Purchased, 1819

542

659

558

948

949

203

LITERATURE

Jantzen 1979, pp. 102, 238, no. 550; Liedtke 1982, pp. 65, 106, no. 50

Karel van Vogelaer (attributed to)

Maastricht 1653–1695 Rome

677 *Portrait of a man (Self-portrait?)*

Canvas, 90 x 72 cm
Dutch title: *Portret van een man (Zelfportret?)*

PROVENANCE

Hendrik Willem Cramer, Amsterdam and Cleves, until 1867; sold to Arnoldus Andries des Tombe, The Hague, 1867–1902; bequest of Arnoldus Andries des Tombe, The Hague, 1903; on loan to the ICN

LITERATURE

Bad Homburg-Wuppertal 1995, p. 150, in no. 58

COMMENT

The thistle in the man's right hand may be a reference to Van Vogelaer's bent name, 'Distelblom'. Van Vogelaer specialised in still-life painting.

Arie de Vois

Utrecht *c.*1632–1680 Leiden

204 *Self-portrait as a hunter, c.1660*

Panel, 28.7 x 21.8 cm
Signed lower right: *ADVois f.* (ADV in ligature)
Dutch title: *Zelfportret als jager*

PROVENANCE

Samuel van Huls, The Hague, 1737; Gerard Block, The Hague, 1754; Willem Lormier, The Hague, 1754–1763; Gerret Braamcamp, Amsterdam, 1763–1771; Prince Willem V, The Hague, 1771–1795

LITERATURE

Bille 1961, vol. 1, pp. 39, 112, fig. 252, vol. 2, pp. 61–61a, 127, no. 252; D/LS 1974–1976, vol. 3, p. 236, no. 171; Leiden 1988, no. 91; Amsterdam 1989–1990, no. 49; *Portraits in the Mauritshuis*, no. 60

COMMENT

Companion piece to *Shepherdess with a rose* in Dresden, Gemäldegalerie Alte Meister (Amsterdam 1989–1990, no. 50).

Elias Vonck

Amsterdam 1605–1652 Amsterdam

404 *Dead birds*

Panel, 35.5 x 54 cm
Formerly signed on the table: *[...]CK*
Dutch title: *Dode vogels*

PROVENANCE

Neville Goldsmid, The Hague (as by Dirck de Heem); purchased, 1876

Maerten de Vos

Antwerp 1532–1603 Antwerp

249 *Moses showing the tablets of the law to the Israelites, with portraits of members of the Panhuys family, their relatives and friends,* 1574–1575

Panel, 153 x 237.5 cm
Dated by two inscriptions on the clothing of the members of the Panhuys family: *MARGARITA PANHUYS. ÆTATIS . SUÆ.30 1575.* and *MARGARITA / PANHUYS.Æ / .6. ANO 1574* (for a complete record of the inscriptions, see Dijkstra *et al.* 2002, p. 91)
Inscribed on the original frame: *ALS MOYSI DEN TWEEDEMAAL DIE TAFELEN DES WEETS VAN DEN HEERE OP DEN BERCH SYNAI ONTFANGEN / HADDE IS NEDERGHECOMEN EN HEEFT GHEHEEL ISRAEL VERGAEDERT / ENDE HEEFT HAER DIE GHEBODEN DES HEEREN VOER GHEHOUDEN OPDAT SY MAKEN SOUDEN ALLEN SIERATEN / DES TABERNAKELS DIE DE HEERE BEVOLEN HADDE MOYSI TE DOENE. EXODUS 34.35* (When Moses came down from Mount Sinai the second time with the tablets of the law the Lord had given him, he gathered all the children of Israel and held up the Lord's commandments. For them to make all the adornments for the tabernacle as the Lord had commanded Moses)
For the text of the tablets of the law, see Dijkstra *et al.* 2002, p. 91
Dutch title: *Mozes toont de tafelen der wet aan de Israëlieten, met portretten van leden van de familie Panhuys, hun verwanten en vrienden*

PROVENANCE

Made for members of the Panhuys family; bequest of *Jonkheer* Pieter van Panhuys, Leiden, 1836; on loan to the Museum Catharijneconvent, Utrecht, since 1982

LITERATURE

Mauritshuis 1968, pp. 51–53; Zweite 1980, pp. 288–290,

249

404

204

677

no. 59; Zondervan 1982; Dijkstra *et al.* 2002, pp. 90–92; Defoer *et al.* 2003, no. 34

COMMENT
This painting contains portraits of the Calvinist Panhuys family: Peeter (1529–1585) and Margarita Panhuys, their children, relatives and friends (see Zondervan 1982).

Paul de Vos

Hulst 1595–1678 Antwerp

With Jan Wildens
Antwerp 1586–1653 Antwerp

259 *Deer hunt*

Canvas, 212 x 349 cm
Dutch title: *Hertenjacht*

PROVENANCE
Pieter de la Court van der Voort and heirs, Leiden, 1685–1766; Gerret Braamcamp, Amsterdam, until 1771; Prince Willem V, The Hague, 1771–1795

LITERATURE
Bille 1961, vol. 1, p. 105, vol. 2, p. 118, no. 207; D/LS 1974–1976, vol. 3, p. 231, no. 148; Adler 1980, p. 126, no. A 5; Robels 1989, p. 478, no. A 271; De Poorter/Jansen/Giltaij 1990, p. 49 and fig. 7.1

COMMENT
The animals were formerly attributed to Frans Snijders. The landscape was painted by Jan Wildens. A study of the dog is in the Koninklijk Museum van Schone Kunsten, Antwerp. Based on a sketch by Anthony van Dyck in the Museum Boijmans Van Beuningen, Rotterdam (see De Poorter/Jansen/Giltaij 1990, no. 7).

740 *Hunting dogs chasing up partridges*

Canvas, 112.5 x 251.3 cm
Dutch title: *Jachthonden sporen patrijzen op*

PROVENANCE
Bequest of R.T. Baron van Pallandt van Eerde, 1913; on loan to the ICN

COMMENT
Several versions are known.

Huygh Pietersz Voskuyl

Amsterdam or Leiden 1592/93–1665 Amsterdam

955 *Self-portrait*, 1638

Panel, 42.2 x 31.9 cm
Signed, dated and inscribed lower right: *HP voskuijl / fe. A°. 1638 / ÆTATIS / SVÆ 46* (HP in ligature)
Dutch title: *Zelfportret*

PROVENANCE
Edward Speelman Gallery, London; S. Nijstad Gallery, The Hague; purchased, 1963

LITERATURE
Van Eeghen 1963, pp. 123, 124, 128; Delft-Antwerp 1964–1965, no. 116; Mauritshuis 1970, no. 22

COMMENT
Cleaned and restored in 1997. The artist is wearing his working attire.

Roelof Jansz van Vries

Haarlem 1630/31–after 1681 Amsterdam

205 *Herdsmen with cattle*, 1650s

Canvas, 66 x 80.5 cm
Signed lower right: *R. Vries*
Dutch title: *Herders met vee*

PROVENANCE
David van der Kellen, Amsterdam; purchased, 1873; on loan to the ICN

LITERATURE
Mauritshuis 1980, p. 121

Jan Weenix

Amsterdam 1642–1719 Amsterdam

206 *Dead swan*

Canvas, 245.5 x 294 cm
Signed lower right: *J. Weenix fc*
Dutch title: *Dode zwaan*

PROVENANCE
Painted for a room in the 'Garnalendoelen' (a civic guard room) in Amsterdam; St Sebastiaansdoelen, Amsterdam; purchased, 1821

LITERATURE
Ginnings 1970, p. 304, no. 258

259

740

955

206

205

COMMENT

Cleaned and restored in 1987. A copy attributed to Dirk Valkenburg (1675–1721) in sale Berlin, Lepke, 8 April 1913, lot 34.

207 *Hunting still life*, 1706 or 1708

Canvas, 79.2 x 69.5 cm
Dutch title: *Jachtstilleven*

PROVENANCE

Commissioned by Pieter de la Court van der Voort, Leiden; his heirs, until 1766; Prince Willem V, The Hague, 1766–1795

LITERATURE

D/LS 1974–1976, vol. 1, p. 238, no. 176, vol. 3, p. 238, no. 176; Ginnings 1970, p. 283, no. 218; Nagasaki 1992–1993, no. 33

COMMENT

Originally accompanied by a companion piece dated 1706 or 1708, Bachstitz Gallery, The Hague, 1922–1924.

642 *Dead hare*, 1689

Canvas, 115.3 x 92.3 cm
Signed and dated upper right: *J. Weenix. f 1689*
Dutch title: *Dode haas*

PROVENANCE

On loan from Count and Countess van Lynden van Pallandt, 1899; gift of dowager C.J. van Lynden van Pallandt, 1900; on loan to the Fondation Custodia, Paris

LITERATURE

Ginnings 1970, p. 256, no. 164

Jan Baptist Weenix

Amsterdam 1621–1659/61 De Haar

901 *Italian landscape with inn and ruins*, 1658

Panel, 68.2 x 87.2 cm
Signed lower centre: *Gio Batta Weenix f.*
Dated and inscribed lower right:
A° 16[5]8 10m / 20d in het huys ter Mey
Dutch title: *Italiaans landschap met herberg en antieke ruïnes*

PROVENANCE

P.-L. Randon de Boisset, Paris, 1777; Antoine Poullain, Paris, until 1780; G. Robit, Paris, 1801; Van Pallandt Collection; Van Rechteren Limpurg Collection; S. Nijstad Gallery, The Hague, 1950; purchased, 1952

LITERATURE

Mauritshuis 1970, no. 44; Ginnings 1970, p. 186, no. 68; Blankert 1978, pp. 183–184, no. 105; Mauritshuis 1980, pp. 122–123; Schloss 1983, pp. 70, 78, 91, 94, note 12

COMMENT

The sheep and goat in the right corner also appear in a signed painting by Weenix in a private collection, 2003 (Schloss 1983, p. 91, fig. 29).

940 *Dead partridge hanging from a nail*, *c.*1650–1652

Canvas, 50.6 x 43.5 cm
Signed lower right: *Gio. Batta: Weenix f.*
Dutch title: *Dode patrijs, hangend aan een spijker*

PROVENANCE

Wttewaal van Stoetwegen Collection, Laren; S. Nijstad Gallery, The Hague; purchased by the Friends of the Mauritshuis Foundation, 1960

LITERATURE

Mauritshuis 1970, no. 45; Ginnings 1970, p. 172, no. 56; Paris 1986, no. 55; Mauritshuis 1987, no. 67; Slive 1995, p. 289; Karlsruhe 1999, no. 123; Washington 2002, no. 18

Adriaen van der Werff

Kralingen 1659–1722 Rotterdam

208 *Portrait of a man*, 1689

Canvas, 48.7 x 39.8 cm
Signed and dated upper right: *Adrⁿ· vand. / Werff fec / an°. 1689*
Dutch title: *Portret van een man*

PROVENANCE

Hugo Gevers, Dordrecht, 1797–1822, possibly acquired by inheritance; purchased, 1822

LITERATURE

HdG 1907–1928, vol. 10, p. 289, no. 201; Rotterdam 1973, no. 27; Gaehtgens 1987a, p. 383, no. 117

209 *The flight into Egypt*, 1710

Panel, 47 x 36.5 cm
Signed and dated lower right, on a stone:
*Chevr. / vr Werff. fe. / A*n° *1710*
Dutch title: *De vlucht naar Egypte*

PROVENANCE

Maria van der Werff, Rotterdam, 1710–*c.*1718; Johan van Schuylenburch, The Hague, *c.*1718–1735; Nicolaas Dierquens, The Hague, 1735; acquired by Prince Willem IV in or around 1745, thence by descent to Prince Willem V, The Hague

901

207

642

208

209

940

LITERATURE

HdG 1907–1928, vol. 10, pp. 247–248, no. 41; D/LS 1974–1976, vol. 2, p. 470, no. 357, p. 479, no. 26, vol. 3, p. 18, no. 11, p. 237, no. 174; Rotterdam 1973, no. 18; Gaehtgens 1987b, pp. 24, 155–156, 282, 321–322, no. 74, pp. 334, 464, no. 47; Broos/Wadum 1992; Mauritshuis 1993, no. 38

COMMENT

A preliminary drawing in the Musées Royaux des Beaux-Arts, Brussels (Mauritshuis 1993, p. 318, fig. 2).

Jan Westerbaen the Elder

The Hague 1600/2–1686 The Hague

210 *Portrait of Arnoldus Geesteranus (1593–1658)*, 1647

Panel, 67.7 x 57.3 cm
Signed and dated upper left: *A° 1647 W[...]*
Dutch title: *Portret van Arnoldus Geesteranus (1593–1658)*

PROVENANCE

Sale Rotterdam, Lamme, 14–16 May 1851, lot 179; gift of Herman Pieter van Ede van de Pals to King Willem III, Rotterdam, 1863; transferred, 1863

LITERATURE

Bilzen-Rijkhoven 1992–1993, no. II.2.7; Utrecht 1994, no. 164; Buijsen *et al.* 1998, p. 266

COMMENT

Engraved by Hendrick Bary as by Westerbaen. Arnoldus Geesteranus was a Remonstrant minister, who was imprisoned at Loevestein Castle from 1624 to 1631. From 1632 he was a preacher in The Hague. In 1627 he married Susanna Oostdijk, portrayed in the companion piece (inv. no. 211).

211 *Portrait of Susanna Pietersdr Oostdijk (b. 1597)*, 1647

Panel, 67.6 x 57.3 cm
Bears signature and date upper right:
I. WB. 1647 (WB in ligature)
Dutch title: *Portret van Susanna Pietersdr Oostdijk (geb. 1597)*

PROVENANCE

Same as inv. no. 210

LITERATURE

Utrecht 1994, no. 164

COMMENT

Companion piece to inv. no. 210.

Rogier van der Weyden (and studio)

Tournai 1399/1400–1464 Brussels

264 *The lamentation of Christ, c.*1460–1464?

Panel, 80.6 x 130.1 cm
Dutch title: *De bewening van Christus*

PROVENANCE

(?) College of Arras, Louvain, sixteenth century; Joseph Geedts, Louvain, 1805; C.L.G.J. Baron Keverberg van Kessel, Brussels, 1817–1827; purchased with an attribution to Hans Memling by order of King Willem I for the Mauritshuis, 1827

LITERATURE

Friedländer 1967–1976, vol. 2, p. 93, no. 46; Mauritshuis 1987, no. 68; Van Asperen de Boer/Dijkstra/Van Schoute *et al.* 1992, pp. 171–180, no. W 6; Mauritshuis 1993, no. 39; De Vos 1999, pp. 403–404, no. C 5 (as not autograph); Venice 1999–2000, no. 22

COMMENT

The painting, whose authorship has recently been questioned by De Vos, was presumably completed by pupils of Van der Weyden. Many figures are repeated in a sixteenth-century painting now in the Museum Catharijneconvent, Utrecht (Dijkstra *et al.* 2002, pp. 147–148, repr.). There has been some debate about the idenfication of the donor at the right (see Mauritshuis 1993, no. 39).

Rogier van der Weyden (follower of)

844 *Augustine sacrificing to an idol of the Manichaeans (?), c.*1480

Panel, 97.3 x 68.3 cm
Dutch title: *Augustinus offert aan een afgod van de Manicheeërs (?)*

PROVENANCE

Possibly W.A. Kien van Citters, Middelburg, 1787 (as Albrecht Dürer); C. Lambrechtsen van Ritthem, Middelburg; bequeathed by him to the Middelburg Drawing Academy, 1823; purchased by the Rijksmuseum, Amsterdam (inv. no. SK-A-2057), 1902; on loan from the Rijksmuseum since 1948

LITERATURE

Friedländer 1967–1976, vol. 4, no. 66; Mauritshuis 1968, p. 31; The Hague 1997, no. 4a

264

210

211

844

COMMENT

Painted in the style of Van der Weyden by an unknown master from Brussels and possibly the left wing of an altarpiece dedicated to St Augustine. Formed an ensemble with a panel by the same master now in the National Gallery of Ireland, Dublin (The Hague 1997, no. 4b).

Thomas Wijck

Beverwijk *c.*1616–1677 Haarlem

469 *The alchemist*

Panel, 48.5 x 41 cm
Signed lower centre: *TWijck* (TW in ligature)
Dutch title: *De alchemist*

PROVENANCE

De Waspick Collection; Bernard du Bus de Gisignies, Brussels; purchased, 1882

LITERATURE

Van Lennep 1966, p. 161, note 4

Jan Wijnants

Haarlem 1631/32–1684 Amsterdam

212 *Forest edge*, 1659

Canvas, 67 x 87 cm
Signed and dated lower right: *J Wijnants / 1659*
Dutch title: *Landschap met bosrand*

PROVENANCE

Van Eyck Collection, 1829; purchased, 1829

LITERATURE

HdG 1907–1928, vol. 8, p. 582, no. 481; Mauritshuis 1980, pp. 123–124; Tokyo-Kasama-Kumamoto-Leiden 1992–1993, no. 59; Buvelot *et al.* 1998, p. 248; Eisele 2000, no. 224

COMMENT

The figures may be the work of Johannes Lingelbach.

213 *Road in the dunes*, 1675

Canvas, 77.2 x 101.5 cm
Signed and dated lower right: *J. Wijnants. f. A° 1675*
Dutch title: *Weg in de duinen*

PROVENANCE

Noé Gallery; purchased, 1830; on loan to the ICN

LITERATURE

HdG 1907–1928, vol. 8, p. 595, no. 536; Mauritshuis 1980, p. 124; Eisele 2000, no. 303

Augustus Wijnantz

Düsseldorf 1795–after 1848 The Hague

1070 *View of the Mauritshuis*, 1830?

Panel, 22.5 x 27.5 cm
Signed and dated lower left: *A. Wynantz [..]3[.]*
Dutch title: *Gezicht op het Mauritshuis*

PROVENANCE

Gift of Hans Heinrich, Baron Thyssen-Bornemisza, Lugano, 1986

LITERATURE

Mauritshuis 1991, no. XXI

Adam Willaerts

Antwerp 1577–1664 Utrecht

1122 *Ships off a rocky coast*, 1621

Panel, 62 x 122.5 cm
Signed and dated on the boulder in the foreground: *A. Willarts. f / 1621*
Dutch title: *Schepen bij een rotsachtige kust*

PROVENANCE

Sale Amsterdam, Frederik Muller & Co, 6 November 1900, lot 351; purchased by the Rijksmuseum, Amsterdam (inv. no. SK-A-1927), 1900; on loan from the Rijksmuseum since 2000

LITERATURE

RM 1976, p. 605; San Francisco-Baltimore-London 1997–1998, no. 66; *Mauritshuis in focus* 13 (2000), no. 3, pp. 4–5

Willem Wissing

Amsterdam 1656–1687 Stamford

231 *Portrait of King-Stadholder Willem III (1650–1702)*

Canvas, 232 x 140 cm
Dutch title: *Portret van koning-stadhouder Willem III (1650–1702)*

PROVENANCE

(?) Prince Willem V, The Hague, 1763; transferred, in or before 1841; on loan to the ICN

LITERATURE

Collins Baker 1912, vol. 2, pp. 17–18; Staring 1950–1951, pp. 179–180; possibly D/LS 1974–1976, vol. 3, p. 22, no. 55; Amsterdam 1988, no. 3

469

231

212

213

1070

1122

COMMENT
After an original by Sir Peter Lely. For biographical data on Willem III, see Bakhuysen, inv. no. 6.

Jacob de Wit

Amsterdam 1695–1754 Amsterdam

731 *Apollo surrounded by the nine muses*, 1743

Canvas (oval), 395 x 636 cm (centre piece)
Signed and dated at left, on the lute:
IDWit F. / 1743 (IDW in ligature)
Dutch title: *Apollo omringd door de negen muzen*

PROVENANCE
Made with inv. nos. 732–735 for Rapenburg 48 in Leiden, the residence of Diederik van Leyden van Vlaardingen; purchased, 1910; installed in the ceiling of the Potter Room, 1912

LITERATURE
Staring 1958, pp. 79, 86, 112, 152; Amsterdam 2000b, p. 69, fig. 12

COMMENT
The following muses are depicted from left to right: Calliope, Euterpe, Terpsichore, Polyhymnia, Erato, Clio, Melpomene, Thalia and Urania. Surrounded by four cornerpieces (inv. nos. 732–735), painted in grisaille. The impressive chimney from the same house is in the Rijksmuseum, Amsterdam.

732 *The pastoral song*, 1743

Canvas (triangle), 270 x 398 cm
Dutch title: *De herderszang*

733 *The epos*, 1743

Canvas (triangle), 270 x 398 cm
Dutch title: *Het heldendicht*

734 *The comedy*, 1743

Canvas (triangle), 270 x 398 cm
Dutch title: *Het blijspel*

735 *The elegy*, 1743

Canvas (triangle), 270 x 398 cm
Dutch title: *Het treurdicht*

Emanuel de Witte

Alkmaar 1617–1692 Amsterdam

473 *Interior of an imaginary Catholic church*, 1668

Canvas, 110 x 85 cm
Signed and dated middle right: *E. De Witte fecit / A° 1668*
Dutch title: *Interieur van een gefantaseerde katholieke kerk*

PROVENANCE
Huybert Ketelaar, Amsterdam, 1776; V.L. Vegelin van Claerbergen, Leeuwarden, 1846; F. Rasponi, Brussels, 1880; purchased, 1883

LITERATURE
Manke 1963, pp. 46, 115, no. 156; Jantzen 1979, pp. 123, 241, no. 630; Liedtke 1982, pp. 89, 95, 96; Paris 1986, no. 56; Mauritshuis 1987, no. 69

824 *The Oude Kerk in Amsterdam during a service*, c.1654

Canvas, 50 x 41.5 cm
Dutch title: *De Oude Kerk in Amsterdam tijdens een dienst*

PROVENANCE
Semenoff Collection, St Petersburg; Jacques Goudstikker Gallery, Amsterdam, 1930; purchased with the support of the Rembrandt Society, 1936

LITERATURE
Manke 1963, p. 91, no. 59; Jantzen 1979, pp. 118–119, 241, no. 616; Liedtke 1982, pp. 87–88; Hamburg 1995–1996, no. 16

COMMENT
Said to have once been signed and dated 1654.

Victor Wolfvoet

Antwerp 1612–1652 Antwerp

267 *Abraham and Melchizedek*

Copper, 37.5 x 27.5 cm
Signed lower right: *V.W.*
Dutch title: *Abraham and Melchizedek*

PROVENANCE
Nationale Konst-Gallery, The Hague, 1801; transferred, in or after 1822; on loan to the ICN

LITERATURE
Held 1980, vol. 1, pp. 143–144; Van Thiel 1981, p. 199, no. 122

COMMENT
Companion piece to inv. no. 268. Copy after a sketch by Rubens in the Fitzwilliam Museum, Cambridge.

732

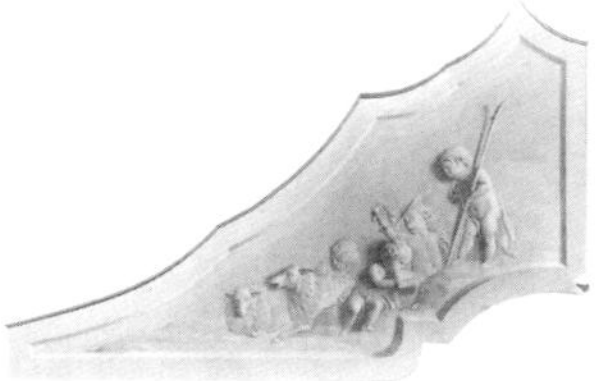

731

733

734

473

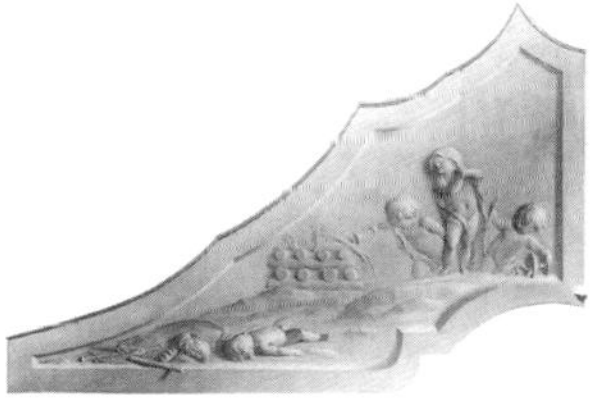

735

824

267

268 *The rain of manna*

Copper, 37.5 x 27.5 cm
Dutch title: *De manna-regen*

PROVENANCE
Same as inv. no. 267; on loan to the ICN

LITERATURE
Held 1980, vol. 1, p. 148; Van Thiel 1981, p. 198, no. 118

COMMENT
Companion piece to inv. no. 267. Copy after a sketch by Rubens in the Musée Bonnat, Bayonne.

Philips Wouwerman

Haarlem 1619–1668 Haarlem

214 *'The arrival in the stable'*, 1660s

Panel, 43 x 58.8 cm
Signed twice lower right: *PHILS. W.* (PHILS in ligature)
Dutch title: *'De aankomst in de stal'*

PROVENANCE
Govert van Slingelandt, The Hague, after 1752; the entire collection sold to Willem V in 1768; Prince Willem V, The Hague, 1768–1795

LITERATURE
HdG 1907–1928, vol. 2, p. 394, no. 487; D/LS 1974–1976, vol. 3, p. 239, no. 184 or 185; Mauritshuis 1980, p. 129

COMMENT
Companion piece to inv. no. 215. Cleaned and restored in 2003.

215 *'The departure from the stable'*, 1660s

Panel, 43 x 59 cm
Signed at right: *PHILS. W.* (PHILS in ligature)
Dutch title: *'Het vertrek uit de stal'*

PROVENANCE
Same as inv. no. 214

LITERATURE
HdG 1907–1928, vol. 2, pp. 394–395, no. 488; D/LS 1974–1976, vol. 3, p. 239, no. 185 or 184; Mauritshuis 1980, pp. 129–130

COMMENT
Companion piece to inv. no. 214. Cleaned and restored in 2004.

216 *Falconry*, 1660s

Panel, 39.5 x 50.5 cm
Signed lower right: *PHILS. W* (PHILS in ligature)
Dutch title: *Valkenjacht*

PROVENANCE
Prince De Carignan, Paris, 1749; Prince Willem V, Het Loo Palace, Apeldoorn, 1757, and The Hague, until 1795

LITERATURE
HdG 1907–1928, vol. 2, p. 453, no. 652, p. 461, no. 676; D/LS 1974–1976, vol. 2, p. 644, no. 96, vol. 3, p. 18, no. 4, p. 239, no. 182; Mauritshuis 1980, pp. 127–128

217 *The riding school*, 1660s

Canvas, 66 x 76.2 cm
Signed lower left: *PHILS. W.* (PHILS in ligature)
Dutch title: *De rijschool*

PROVENANCE
Govert van Slingelandt, The Hague, in or before 1752; the entire collection sold to Willem V in 1768; Prince Willem V, The Hague, 1768–1795

LITERATURE
HdG 1907–1928, vol. 2, p. 265, no. 51; D/LS 1974–1976, vol. 3, p. 239, no. 183; Mauritshuis 1980, p. 217

218 *The hay wagon,* after *c.*1650

Panel, 40 x 48 cm
Signed at left: *PHILS. W* (PHILS in ligature)
Dutch title: *De hooiwagen*

PROVENANCE
Samuel van Huls, The Hague, 1737; Willem Lormier, The Hague, 1737–1763; Govert van Slingelandt, The Hague, 1763; the entire collection sold to Willem V in 1768; Prince Willem V, The Hague, 1768–1795

LITERATURE
HdG 1907–1928, vol. 2, p. 558, no. 937; D/LS 1974–1976, vol. 3, p. 239, no. 186; Mauritshuis 1980, pp. 126–127

219 *Cavalry battle, c.*1655–1660

Canvas, 127 x 245 cm
Signed lower right: *PHILS. W* (PHILS in ligature)
Dutch title: *Veldslag*

PROVENANCE
Benjamin da Costa, The Hague, 1764; Prince Willem V, The Hague, 1764–1795

LITERATURE
HdG 1907–1928, vol. 2, pp. 484–485, no. 746; D/LS 1974–1976, vol. 3, p. 28, no. 192, p. 238, no. 177; Mauritshuis 1980, p. 126

COMMENT
Cleaned and restored in 1990.

216

268

217

214

218

215

219

220 *Army camp*, probably 1660s

Canvas, 70 x 100 cm
Signed lower right: *PHILS.W* (PHILS in ligature)
Dutch title: *Legerkamp*

PROVENANCE
Adriaan Bout, The Hague, 1733; Prince Willem V, Het Loo Palace, Apeldoorn, 1757

LITERATURE
HdG 1907–1928, vol. 2, pp. 526–527, no. 853; D/LS 1974–1976, vol. 2, p. 644, no. 95, p. 652, no. D, vol. 3, p. 18, no. 3, p. 238, no. 180; Mauritshuis 1980, pp. 128–129; Nagasaki 1992–1993, no. 34; De Boer *et al.* 1993, pp. 37–38, no. 10

COMMENT
Cleaned and restored in 1986.

221 *Hunting party at rest, c.*1650–1655

Panel (slightly cut down to the right), 35 x 40.5 cm
Signed lower right: *PHILS* (in ligature; the 'W' has disappeared)
Dutch title: *Rust tijdens de jacht*

PROVENANCE
(?) Adriaan Bout, The Hague, 1733; (?) Govert van Slingelandt, The Hague, 1752 (not in the 1768 sale); Prince Willem V, The Hague, until 1795

LITERATURE
HdG 1907–1928, vol. 2, pp. 453–454, no. 653; D/LS 1974–1976, vol. 3, p. 238, no. 179; Mauritshuis 1980, p. 127

222 *Hunters at rest, c.*1645

Panel, 35 x 44 cm
Signed at left: *PH W* (PH in ligature)
Verso: wax-seal of Johan Willem Friso
Dutch title: *Rustende jagers*

PROVENANCE
Stadholder Johan Willem Friso, Het Loo Palace, Apeldoorn, 1757; Prince Willem V, The Hague, until 1795

LITERATURE
HdG 1907–1928, vol. 2, p. 454, no. 654; D/LS 1974–1976, vol. 2, p. 640, no. 34, p. 652, no. C, vol. 3, p. 18, no. 6, p. 238, no. 181; Mauritshuis 1980, pp. 125–126

Moyses van Wtenbrouck

The Hague (?) *c.*1590/1600–*c.*1647 The Hague

1059 *Landscape with shepherds*, 1626

Panel, 42.5 x 67.5 cm
Signed and dated right of centre: *M. V WB FE 1626* (WB in ligature)
Dutch title: *Landschap met herders*

PROVENANCE
H. Girardet, Kettwich; purchased, 1979

LITERATURE
Weisner 1963, p. 223, no. 41; Mauritshuis 1991, no. XI

1097 *Wooded pool with Salmacis and Hermaphroditus*, 1627?

Panel, 43 x 66 cm
Signed and dated lower right: *Mo v WB / 162[7?]* (WB in ligature)
Dutch title: *Bosvijver met Salmacis and Hermaphroditus*

PROVENANCE
J.H. Gosschalk, The Hague, 1931 (on loan to the Gemeentemuseum, The Hague, 1935); Vitale Bloch, The Hague, 1942; Stichting Nederlands Kunstbezit; on loan from the ICN (inv. no. NK 2532), since 1992

LITERATURE
Amsterdam-Boston-Philadelphia 1987–1988, no. 123; Tokyo-Kasama-Kumamoto-Leiden 1992–1993, no. 66; Buijsen/Van der Ploeg 1993, pp. 31–32, no. 10; Mauritshuis 1993, p. 29; Buijsen *et al.* 1998, pp. 272–273; Athens-Dordrecht 2000–2001, no. 84; Schwarz 2004, no. XXIV/9

Joachim Wtewael

Utrecht 1566–1638 Utrecht

223 *Mars and Venus surprised by Vulcan*, 1601

Copper, 20.8 x 15.7 cm
Signed and dated lower centre: *IOACHIM WTE / WAEL [F]ECIT 1601*
Dutch title: *Mars en Venus betrapt door Vulcanus*

PROVENANCE
(?) Melchior Wijntgis, Middelburg, 1604; Prince Willem V, Het Loo Palace, Apeldoorn, 1757; transferred, *c.*1822

220

223

1059

1097

221

222

LITERATURE

D/LS 1974–1976, vol. 2, p. 646, note 146; Lowenthal 1986, no. A 18; Paris 1986, no. 57; Mauritshuis 1987, no. 70; Mauritshuis 1993, no. 40; Keers 1994, pp. 137, 138, 140, note 14; Lowenthal 1995, pp. 13, 21, 35, 66–67; San Francisco-Baltimore-London 1997–1998, no. 47; Phoenix-Kansas City-The Hague 1998–1999, no. 65a; Munich 2001, no. 14

COMMENT

A preparatory drawing in Florence, Galleria degli Uffizi (Mauritshuis 1993, p. 336, fig. 3).

Antonio Zanchi

Este 1631–1722 Venice

335 *Sisyphus, c.*1660–1665

Canvas, 110.4 x 119.8 cm
Dutch title: *Sisyphus*

PROVENANCE

Dukes of Mantua; Martial Reghellini Schio, Venice and Brussels, 1826; purchased by King Willem I for the Mauritshuis, 1831

LITERATURE

Rotterdam 1989–1990, no. 13; Aikema *et al.* 1997, pp. 170–171, no. 196

COMMENT

Companion piece to *Tityus* by Giovanni Battista Langetti (inv. no. 334). Restoration completed in 1989.

Johann Georg Ziesenis

Copenhagen 1716–1776 Hannover

462 *Portrait of Stadholder Willem V (1748–1806), c.*1768–1769

Canvas, 141 x 101 cm
Dutch title: *Portret van stadhouder Willem V (1748–1806)*

PROVENANCE

Royal Museum, The Hague, 1808; transferred, in or before 1841

LITERATURE

Moes/Van Biema 1909, p. 126, no. 338; Paris 1986, no. VI; Nagasaki 1992–1993, no. 35; Schrader 1995, pp. 75, 242–243, no. 204a

COMMENT

A smaller autograph repetition in the Staatliche Schlösser und Gärten, Berlin. A replica of the same size in The House of Orange-Nassau Historic Collections Trust, The Hague. Willem V, Prince of Orange-Nassau, was hereditary stadholder from 1751, until 1766 under regency. In 1767 he married Frederika Sophia Wilhelmina, portrayed in the companion piece (inv. no. 463).

463 *Portrait of Princess Frederika Sophia Wilhelmina (1751–1820), c.*1768–1769

Canvas, 140 x 101 cm
Dutch title: *Portret van prinses Frederika Sophia Wilhelmina (1751–1820)*

PROVENANCE

Same as inv. no. 462

LITERATURE

Moes/Van Biema 1909, p. 126, no. 339; Nagasaki 1992–1993, no. 36; Schrader 1995, pp. 75, 244–245, no. 207a

COMMENT

Companion piece to inv. no. 462. A smaller autograph repetition in the Staatliche Schlösser und Gärten, Berlin. A replica of the same size in The House of Orange-Nassau Historic Collections Trust, The Hague. An anonymous miniature copy in the Rijksmuseum, Amsterdam, inv. no. SK-A-4453. For biographical data of Frederika Sophia Wilhelmina, see Tischbein, inv. no. 464.

Francesco Zuccarelli

Pitigliano 1702–1788 Florence

350 *A ford in a forest, c.*1751–1762

Canvas, 110.7 x 131.7 cm
Dutch title: *Een doorwaadbare plaats in een bos*

PROVENANCE

Martial Reghellini Schio, Venice and Brussels, 1826; purchased by King Willem I for the Mauritshuis, 1831; on loan to the ICN

LITERATURE

Aikema *et al.* 1997, p. 172, no. 198

COMMENT

Autograph variant of an identical representation and composition, formerly in the collection of F. Asta, Venice, 1930.

463 

 462

335 

 350

Z

Bernard Zwaerdecroon

Utrecht after 1616–1654 Utrecht

675 *Portrait of two children as shepherds, c.1645*

Canvas, 143.5 x 158 cm
Signed lower left: *BZ* (in ligature)
Dutch title: *Portret van twee kinderen in pastorale kleding*

PROVENANCE
Pabst Collection, Utrecht, before 1881; bequest of Arnoldus Andries des Tombe, The Hague, 1903; on loan to the Centraal Museum, Utrecht (inv. no. 6571), since 1931

LITERATURE
Utrecht-Frankfurt am Main 1993–1994, no. 59; Helmus 1999, pp. 258–261

MASTERS WITH ACQUIRED NAMES

Master of Alkmaar (follower of or after)

Active *c.*1500, Alkmaar and Haarlem

790 *Triptych with the adoration of the magi*

Outer wings: at left, the departure of the three magi; at right, a group of riders; with on the versos Saints Anthony (left) and Adrian (right) in grisaille
Panel (rounded at the top), 48 x 36.8 cm (centre), 48.5 x 14 cm (wings)
Marked on the middle panel lower left and right and on the versos of the wings with a master's mark, 'A' (?) and 'V' (in ligature)
Dutch title: *Triptiek met de aanbidding van de koningen*

PROVENANCE
A.H. Buttery Gallery, London, 1925; gift of J.H. van Heek, Lonneker, 1926, in honour of the 25th anniversary of Wilhelm Martin's directorship of the Mauritshuis; on loan to the Rijksmuseum, Amsterdam (inv. no. SK-C-1364), since 1948

LITERATURE
Van Gelder-Schrijver 1930, pp. 115–117; Mauritshuis 1935, p. 193; Hoogewerff 1936–1947, vol. 2, pp. 369–370 and figs. 174–177 (as studio of Cornelis Buys); Friedländer 1967–1976, vol. 10, pp. 25, 73–74, no. 49; Philippot 1970, p. 132; RM 1976, p. 629; Cologne 1982–1983, no. 82

COMMENT
Although the versos of the two wings bear the same painter's mark as the centre panel, they were in fact painted by another artist. Wouter Kloek suspects that the triptych is a seventeenth-century copy after a lost original of the Master of Alkmaar, while the versos may indeed originate from the sixteenth century (written communication, 21 September 2004).

Master of the Brandon Portrait (attributed to)

Active *c.*1515–1530?

752 *Portrait of a man with a Samson medal, c.1515*

Panel, 33.8 x 24.4 cm
Dutch title: *Portret van een man met Samson-medaille*

PROVENANCE
A. Pallavicini-Grimaldi, Genoa, 1899 (as by Lucas van Leyden); L. Nardus, Arnouville and Paris (as by Petrus Christus); Frederik Muller Gallery, Amsterdam; purchased with the support of the Rembrandt Society and private individuals, 1917

LITERATURE
Friedländer 1937, p. 12; Mauritshuis 1968, pp. 32–33; *Portraits in the Mauritshuis*, no. 34

Master of the female half-lengths

Active in the southern Netherlands, *c.*1520–1540

845 *Madonna and Child*

Panel, 24 x 19 cm
Dutch title: *Madonna en kind*

PROVENANCE
A. de Stuers, Amsterdam, 1932; purchased by the Rijksmuseum, Amsterdam (inv. no. SK-A-3130), 1932; on loan from the Rijksmuseum since 1948

LITERATURE
Friedländer 1967–1976, vol. 12, p. 96, no. 61, p. 144, note 61; Mauritshuis 1968, pp. 36–37; RM 1976, p. 633

Master of the female half-lengths (circle of)

846 *The judgement of Paris, c.1532*

Panel, 10 x 15.5 cm
Dutch title: *Het oordeel van Paris*

675 

 846

752 

 845

790 

 790

PROVENANCE
Gift of Sir Henri W.A. Deterding to the Rijksmuseum, Amsterdam (inv. no. SK-A-3255), 1936; on loan from the Rijksmuseum since 1948

LITERATURE
Friedländer 1967–1976, vol. 12, p. 100, no. 109; Mauritshuis 1968, p. 37; Koch 1968, p. 56, note 3, p. 61; RM 1976, p. 633 (as signed and dated 'L.D.H. (?) 1532')

Master of Frankfurt

Active in the southern Netherlands and Frankfurt am Main, *c.*1490–1520

854 *St Catherine, c.*1510–1520

Panel, 158.7 x 70.8 cm
Dutch title: *De heilige Catherina*

PROVENANCE
George Grenville, first Marquess of Buckingham, Stowe, before 1783, and his heirs; George Donaldson Gallery, London, before 1914; Walter von Pannwitz, Berlin, *c.*1914–1920; Catharina von Pannwitz, Bennebroek and Heemstede, 1920–1940; Hermann Göring, Berlin; Stichting Nederlands Kunstbezit; on loan to the Mauritshuis, 1948–1960; transferred, 1960

LITERATURE
Friedländer 1967–1976, vol. 7, p. 77, no. 137; Mauritshuis 1968, pp. 34–35; Goddard 1984, pp. 141–142, nos. 44–45; Mauritshuis 1993, no. 42; The Hague 1997, no. 5

COMMENT
Left wing of a triptych, based on a prototype by Jan Gossaert in the Museu Nacional de Arte Antiga, Lisbon. The right wing is also in the Mauritshuis (inv. no. 855), the middle section with the Holy Family and music-making angels is now in the Walker Art Gallery in Liverpool.

855 *St Barbara, c.*1510–1520

Panel, 158.7 x 70.8 cm
Dutch title: *De heilige Barbara*

PROVENANCE
Same as inv. no. 854

LITERATURE
Same as inv. no. 854

COMMENT
Originally part of the same triptich as inv. no. 854.

872 *St Christopher, c.*1500?

Panel, 46 x 31 cm
Dutch title: *De heilige Christoffel*

PROVENANCE
O. Mayer, Berlin, 1929; Paul Cassirer Gallery, Amsterdam, 1942; Stichting Nederlands Kunstbezit; on loan to the Mauritshuis, 1948–1960; transferred, 1960

LITERATURE
Friedländer 1967–1976, vol. 7, p. 79, no. 155; Mauritshuis 1968, p. 34; Goddard 1984, p. 162, no. 121

Master of the Solomon triptych

Active *c.*1520, probably in Antwerp

433 *Triptych with the history of Solomon, c.*1525

Outer wings: angels supporting escutcheons with coats of arms
Panel, 107.5 x 77 cm (centre), 107.5 x 32.5 cm (wings)
Dutch title: *Triptiek met de geschiedenis van Salomon*

PROVENANCE
Willem Simonsz, Lord of Stavenisse and Cromstrijen, after 1521–1557 (his coat of arms is depicted on the left outer wing, those of his wife, Adriana van Duyveland, on the right outer wing); Stavenisse family, Zierikzee and Bruinisse, 1557–1783; Jacob Verheije van Citters, Popkensburg, 1782–1823; bequest of *Jonkheer* Jacob de Witte van Citters, The Hague, 1876

LITERATURE
Friedländer 1967–1976, vol. 11, p. 73, no. 64; Mauritshuis 1993, no. 43; The Hague 1997, no. 7; Noble 1997; Van den Brink 1997, no. 21; Wolff 2004, pp. 288, 290

COMMENT
The composition is based on a woodcut showing Solomon's idolatry by Lucas van Leyden. The frames of the wings are original (see Noble 1997).

433

433

854

855

872

ANONYMOUS

France

432 *Portrait of the brothers Gaspard (1519–1572), Odet (1517–1571) and François (1512–1569) de Coligny,* before 1579

Canvas, 191 x 163 cm
Dutch title: *Portret van de broers Gaspard (1519–1572), Odet (1517–1571) en François (1512–1569) de Coligny*

PROVENANCE
Frederik Hendrik, Noordeinde Palace, The Hague, 1632; thence by descent to Prince Willem V, The Hague, 1763; transferred, in or before 1841; on loan to the Stedelijk Museum Het Prinsenhof, since 1931

LITERATURE
Paris 1972–1973, no. 401; D/LS 1974–1976, vol. 1, p. 202, no. 489, p. 492, no. 204, p. 545, no. 28, vol. 3, p. 26, no. 159; Lunsingh Scheurleer 1979, p. 171 and note 42

COMMENT
Gaspard de Châtillon-Coligny was Count of Coligny and Châtillon-sur-Loing and leader of the Huguenots. His daughter, Louise de Coligny, married Willem I of Orange. Odet was Cardinal of Châtillon and Bishop and Count of Beauvais, and François de Coligny was Lord of Andelot. Several prints after this portrait are known, the earliest by Marc Duval (*c.*1530–1581), which is dated 1579.

Germany

897 *The birth of Mary, c.*1520

Panel (rounded at the top), 110 x 97 cm
Dutch title: *De geboorte van Maria*

PROVENANCE
Friedrich Lippmann, Berlin, before 1903–1912; Walter von Pannwitz, Berlin, 1912–1920; Catharina von Pannwitz, Bennebroek and Heemstede, 1920–1940; Hermann Göring, Berlin; Stichting Nederlands Kunstbezit; on loan to the Rijksmuseum, Amsterdam, 1948–1951; on loan to the Mauritshuis, 1951–1960; transferred, 1960

LITERATURE
Basel 1960, no. 445; Mauritshuis 1968, p. 6; Mauritshuis 1993, no. 44

COMMENT
Formerly attributed to Hans Suess von Kulmbach and Sigmund Holbein.

Italy

290 *Cavalry engagement,* 17th century

Copper, 12 x 15 cm
Dutch title: *Veldslag*

PROVENANCE
Victor de Rainer, Brussels, 1821; purchased by King Willem I for the Mauritshuis, 1821

LITERATURE
Aikema *et al.* 1997, pp. 174–175, no. 202 ('may have originated in the circle of Francesco Graziani')

COMMENT
Formerly attributed to Jacques Courtois. Painted on the verso of an engraved copperplate showing a scene of a doctor blood-letting a male patient with the help of an assistant. An —unsigned— print of the plate is in the Mauritshuis curatorial archives.

317 *Christ,* 16th century

Panel, 51 x 41.5 cm
Dutch title: *Christus*

PROVENANCE
Martial Reghellini Schio, Venice and Brussels, until 1826; purchased by King Willem I for the Mauritshuis, 1831; on loan to the ICN

COMMENT
Formerly considered a copy after either Bonifazio Veronese or Carlo Dolci.

327 *Portrait of a man, c.*1550–1600

Canvas, 110 x 91 cm
Dutch title: *Portret van een man*

PROVENANCE
Victor de Rainer, Brussels, 1821; purchased by King Willem I for the Mauritshuis, 1821; on loan to the ICN

LITERATURE
Boschloo/Van der Sman 1993, p. 133, no. 142 (as Venetian school)

COMMENT
The sitter's attire is that of a Venetian senator. Formerly catalogued as in the style of or after Tintoretto.

432

317

897

327

290

290 verso

330 *Landscape with the penitent Mary Magdalene, c.*1800?

Canvas, 39.5 x 56 cm
Dutch title: *Landschap met de boetvaardige Maria Magdalena*

PROVENANCE
Victor de Rainer, Brussels, 1821; purchased by King Willem I for the Mauritshuis, 1821; on loan to the ICN

LITERATURE
Aikema *et al.* 1997, p. 176, no. 207

COMMENT
Companion piece to inv. no. 331.

331 *Landscape with St Paul of Thebes as a hermit, c.*1800?

Canvas, 39.5 x 56 cm
Dutch title: *Landschap met de heilige Paulus van Thebe als kluizenaar*

PROVENANCE
Same as inv. no. 330; on loan to the ICN

LITERATURE
Aikema *et al.* 1997, p. 176, no. 208

COMMENT
Companion piece to inv. no. 330.

349 *Female figure (A goddess?), c.*1500–1550

Leather (oval) and canvas (additions on the corners), 67.5 x 51.3 cm
Dutch title: *Vrouwelijke figuur (Een godin?)*

PROVENANCE
Victor de Rainer, Brussels, 1821; purchased by King Willem I for the Mauritshuis, 1821

LITERATURE
Boschloo/Van der Sman 1993, pp. 116–117, no. 115

COMMENT
Possibly depicting Venus.

351 *The adoration of the shepherds, c.*1575–1600

Panel, 40 x 50.5 cm
Dutch title: *De aanbidding der herders*

PROVENANCE
Count Edmund Bourke, Paris; purchased from his widow by King Willem I for the Mauritshuis, 1823; on loan to the ICN

LITERATURE
Boschloo/Van der Sman 1993, p. 117, no. 117

811 *Portrait of a man, c.*1550–1600

Canvas, 59.5 x 45 cm
Dutch title: *Portret van een man*

PROVENANCE
Jacques Goudstikker Gallery, Amsterdam, 1933; purchased, 1933

LITERATURE
Boschloo/Van der Sman 1993, pp. 131–132, no. 140 (as Venetian school)

COMMENT
Formerly catalogued as in the style of or after Tintoretto.

Northern Netherlands

105 *Portrait of James I (1566–1625), King of England,* 1614

Canvas, 62 x 51.5 cm
Inscribed upper left and right: *1614. JACQVES. ROY. DE. LA. GRANDE / BRETAIGNE*
Dutch title: *Portret van Jacobus I (1566–1625), koning van Engeland*

PROVENANCE
(?) Honselaarsdijk Palace, Naaldwijk; transferred, *c.*1875; on loan to the Stedelijk Museum Het Prinsenhof, Delft, since 1957

LITERATURE
Delft 1948, no. 395; Amberg-The Hague 2003–2004, no. 2.6

COMMENT
James I, the son of Mary, Queen of Scots and Henry Stuart, became King of Scotland in 1567 and King of England in 1603. He is here depicted wearing the Order of the Garter (see also MINIATURES, Hilliard, inv. no. 1015).

229 *Simeon and the Christ child, c.*1700?

Copper, 17 x 14 cm
Dutch title: *Simeon met het kind Jezus*

PROVENANCE
Unknown; first recorded in 1895

386 *Portrait of a man,* 18th century

Panel (oval), 25.5 x 21 cm
Dutch title: *Portret van een man*

PROVENANCE
Unknown; transferred, in or before 1895; on loan to the ICN

351 349 >> 811 330 105 331 229 386

448 *Portrait of François de Virieu (d. 1596), c.1580–1590*

Panel, 95.5 x 71.5 cm
Dutch title: *Portret van François de Virieu (overleden in 1596)*

PROVENANCE
By inheritance in the family of the sitter; gift of Coenraad Leemans on behalf of the heirs of F.W. de Virieu, 1879; on loan to the ICN

LITERATURE
Delft 1984, p. 27, no. 10/35

COMMENT
De Virieu, majordomo of Willem I of Orange, married Françoise de Witte in 1574. She is portrayed in the companion piece.

449 *Portrait of Françoise de Witte (d. 1605/6), c.1580–1590*

Panel, 95.5 x 71.5 cm
Dutch title: *Portret van Françoise de Witte (overleden 1605/6)*

PROVENANCE
Same as inv. no. 448; on loan to the ICN

LITERATURE
Delft 1984, p. 27, no. 10/36

COMMENT
Companion piece to inv. no. 448.

496 *Portrait of Cornelis Haga (1578–1654), c.1645*

Panel (oval), 62 x 46.5 cm
Dutch title: *Portret van Cornelis Haga (1578–1654)*

PROVENANCE
(?) A.D. Schinkel, The Hague; J. Scheltema, Utrecht, 1836; J.E. Dibbits, Utrecht, 1836–1873; gift of A.J.S. Dibbits-Kaas in memory of her son J.E. Dibbits, 1873; on loan to the Rijksmuseum, Amsterdam (inv. no. SK-C-1225), since 1933

LITERATURE
RM 1976, p. 661; Amsterdam 1984, p. 135, in no. 21, p. 154, in no. 29, fig. N3

COMMENT
Haga was a Dutch legate to Constantinople and Stockholm.

540 *Portrait of Adriana Johanna van Heusden (1741–1800), c.1780*

Pastel, 35.5 x 28.5 cm
Bears illegible inscription at right
Dutch title: *Portret van Adriana Johanna van Heusden (1741–1800)*

PROVENANCE
Gift of Victor Eugène Louis de Stuers, The Hague, 1887; on loan to the Nederlands Scheepvaartmuseum, Amsterdam, since 1931

COMMENT
Van Heusden married Vice-Admiral Johan Arnold Zoutman in 1768. He was portrayed in 1781 by De la Croix (see inv. no. 539).

547 *Merry company*

Panel, 38.5 x 54 cm
Formerly falsely signed on the frame of the painting on the wall: *G. Metsu*
Dutch title: *Vrolijk gezelschap*

PROVENANCE
F. Kaiser; purchased, 1889

561 *Portrait of Prince Willem V (1748–1806)*

Pastel on paper (oval), 54 x 52.5 cm
Dutch title: *Portret van prins Willem V (1748–1806)*

PROVENANCE
Nationale Konst-Gallery, The Hague, 1809; transferred, in or before 1841

LITERATURE
Moes/Van Biema 1909, p. 126, no. 335 or p. 127, no. 355 (?), p. 136, no. 16

COMMENT
For biographical data on Willem V, see Ziesenis, inv. no. 462. Cleaned and restored in 1989.

603 *A child of the Honigh family on its deathbed*

Panel, 45.5 x 58 cm
Dutch title: *Kind uit de familie Honigh op het sterfbed*

PROVENANCE
Probably Johan Honigh, Hillegonda van Vierssen and heirs, Middelburg; gift of Constant L.M. Lambrechtsen van Ritthem, Middelburg, 1895

LITERATURE
Bremmer 1917, pp. 80–81, no. 54; Haarlem 1998, p. 212 (as possibly by Anthonie Palamedesz); *Mauritshuis in focus* 12 (1999), no. 1, pp. 11–12

COMMENT
The parents of the child depicted were probably Johan Honigh (1629–1692) and Hillegonda van Vierssen, who married in 1682 and had no surviving children. Cleaned and restored in 1999.

603

540

>>
449

448

496

547

561

654 *Vanitas still life, c.1650*

Canvas, 45 x 56 cm
Dutch title: *Vanitas-stilleven*

PROVENANCE
Carel Vosmaer, The Hague, 1881 (as by Rembrandt); Tersteeg Collection, The Hague, after 1888; Jacob Maris, The Hague; Abraham Bredius, The Hague, 1901–1946 (on loan to the Mauritshuis since 1901); bequest of Abraham Bredius, 1946

LITERATURE
The Hague 1991–1992, no. 25

COMMENT
Cleaned and restored in 1989.

680 *Donkey and children at play*

Canvas, 113 x 122.5 cm
Dutch title: *Spelende kinderen met een ezel*

PROVENANCE
Bequest of Arnoldus Andries des Tombe, The Hague, 1903; on loan to the ICN

701 *Old man with a tankard and pipe,* 1660s?

Panel, 31 x 24.5 cm
Dutch title: *Oude man met kan en pijp*

PROVENANCE
Gift of L. Nardus, Arnouville, 1906; on loan to the ICN

LITERATURE
Naumann 1981, vol. 2, p. 18

710 *Portrait of Diederick Hoeufft (1610–1688), c.1680?*

Panel, 43.5 x 32.5 cm
Dutch title: *Portret van Diederick Hoeufft (1610–1688)*

PROVENANCE
Bequest of *Jonkvrouw* Maria Johanna Singendonck, The Hague, 1907; on loan to the Museum Simon van Gijn, Dordrecht, since 1926

COMMENT
Hoeufft was commander of the West India Company since 1644. In 1641 he married Maria de Witt, who is portrayed in the companion piece (inv. no. 711). Perhaps painted around 1680 after an original of around 1650. The sitter's son Diederick was portrayed around 1680 by Godfried Schalcken (inv. no. 780).

711 *Portrait of Maria de Witt (1620–1681), c.1680?*

Panel, 43.5 x 32.5 cm
Dutch title: *Portret van Maria de Witt (1620–1681)*

PROVENANCE
Same as inv. no. 710; on loan to the Museum Simon van Gijn, Dordrecht, since 1926

COMMENT
Companion piece to inv. no. 710. Maria de Witt was the daughter of Jacob de Witt, and the sister of Johan and Cornelis de Witt (see De Baen and [after] Netscher, inv. nos. 454 and 716).

831 *Portrait of Lysbeth van Duvenvoorde (d. 1472), c.1430*

Parchment, 32.5 x 20.5 cm
Inscribed on the scroll: *mi verdriet lange te hopen wie is hi die sijn hert hout open* (To hope for long grieves me who is keeping his heart free)
Bears inscription on the verso of the panel: *Afbeeltsel van Juffer Lysbeth van Duvenvoorde, Heer Dircks dochter. Sij troude den 19. Meert anno 1430 aen Symon van Adrichem, Ridder, Heer Floris soon, en stierf op ons Heeren Hemelvaerts Avond anno 1472 en is begraven in de Beverwijck int Reguliersconvent voor het H. Cruijs Autaer dat hij hadde doen maken* (Picture of Miss Lysbeth van Duvenvoorde, daughter of Lord Dirck. She married Symon van Adrichem, Knight, son of Lord Floris, on 19 March 1430, and died in the year 1472, in the evening, on Ascension Day, and is buried in the Reguliersconvent in Beverwijk before the Altar of the Holy Cross that was ordered by her husband)
Dutch title: *Portret van Lysbeth van Duvenvoorde (overleden in 1472)*

PROVENANCE
Joannes M.C. van Blaauwsonnevelt van den Bergh, Haarlem, 1897; Herman J. Heshuysen, Haarlem; Henri Teixeira de Mattos, Haarlem and Vogelenzang, 1915–1916; Margaretha A. Teixeira de Mattos and Pierre van Son, Aerdenhout, 1937; sale Amsterdam, Frederik Muller & Co, 25–28, 31 January-1 February 1944, lot 34; purchased, 1944; on loan to the Rijksmuseum, Amsterdam (inv. no. SK-C-1454), since 1959

LITERATURE
RM 1976, p. 651; Van Os 1979, p. 136; Châtelet 1980, p. 203, no. 36; RM 2000, pp. 50–51, no. 2

COMMENT
In 1430 Lysbeth van Duvenvoorde married Symon van Adrichem, a bailiff and member of the Water Control Board of Rijnland. Originally, her portrait formed a diptych with a portrait of Van Adrichem which is now considered lost.

701

654

831

710

711

680

Southern Netherlands

227 *Portrait of a deceased man,* 1617

Panel, 39.5 x 32 cm
Dated upper left: *1617*
Dutch title: *Portret van een overleden man*

PROVENANCE
Gift of Van Eersel, Antwerp, to King Willem I, 1817; transferred by King Willem I, 1817

230 *Portrait of Ludwig Heinrich of Nassau-Dillenburg (1594–1662)*

Canvas, 89 x 69 cm
Dutch title: *Portret van Ludwig Heinrich van Nassau-Dillenburg (1594–1662)*

PROVENANCE
Acquired in or before 1875

LITERATURE
Vliegenthart 1981, p. 154, note 1

COMMENT
Other version in the collection of the Fürsten zu Salm-Salm, Anholt Castle (as in the manner of Karel van Mander III). Engraved by Pierre Philippe.

235 *Banquet of the gods,* before *c.*1637

Panel, 53 x 77.5 cm
On the verso: 'MV' (in ligature), the mark of the Antwerp panel-maker Michiel Vriendt
Dutch title: *Godenbanket*

PROVENANCE
Martial Reghellini Schio, Venice and Brussels, until 1826; purchased by King Willem I for the Mauritshuis, 1831

LITERATURE
Ertz 1979, pp. 415, 536, note 670; Härting 1983, no. B 222 (as attributed to Jan van Balen, with the landscape by Lucas van Uden)

COMMENT
Cleaned and restored in 1986. The mark of Vriendt, active *c.*1615–1637, provides a *terminus ante quem* for the estimated date (Wadum 1998, pp. 191–192).

353 *Sleeping cupid*

Canvas, 62 x 65 cm
Dutch title: *Slapende cupido*

PROVENANCE
Nationale Konst-Gallery, The Hague, 1800; transferred to the Picture Gallery of Prince Willem V, The Hague, *c.*1816; transferred, 1822

LITERATURE
Van Thiel 1981, p. 210, no. 185; De Jongh 1981–1982, p. 151 and fig. 6

431 *The penitent Magdalene*

Canvas, 137 x 121 cm
Dutch title: *De boetvaardige Magdalena*

PROVENANCE
Gift of dowager L.V.S. Baroness van Rijckevorsel van Rijsenburg-Dommer van Poldersveld, 1887; on loan to the ICN

536 *Landscape with soldiers at rest*

Canvas, 93 x 86 cm
Dutch title: *Landschap met rustende soldaten*

PROVENANCE
Cabinet of Her Majesty the Queen, Korte Vijverberg, The Hague; transferred, 1886; on loan to the ICN

COMMENT
Formerly attributed to Johannes Pietersz Schoeff (1609?–after 1660).

694 *Vanitas still life, c.*1530?

Panel (rounded at the top; cut at all sides), 34.2 x 26 cm
Inscribed lower centre: *MEMENTO MORI*
Dutch title: *Vanitas-stilleven*

PROVENANCE
Bequest of Timon Hendrik Blom Coster, The Hague, 1904

LITERATURE
Skreiner 1963, p. 93, no. 60; Mauritshuis 1968, pp. 50–51; Dülberg 1990, p. 289, no. 316

COMMENT
Dülberg proposed that the panel originally formed the verso of another painting, presumably a portrait.

235 

 431

536 

 353

227

230

694

695 *Portrait of a lady, c.1615*

Canvas, 112.3 x 94 cm
Inscribed lower right, on the skull: *sum quod eris*
(I am what you shall be)
Dutch title: *Portret van een dame*

PROVENANCE

Bequest of Timon Hendrik Blom Coster, The Hague, 1904

LITERATURE

Greindl 1944, p. 107; Held 1965, p. 113; Haarlem 1986, pp. 84 and 86, note 8; Caen 1990, no. F.49; Bikker *et al.* 2003, p. 267, note 30

COMMENT

Formerly attributed to Cornelis de Vos.

1031 *The sudarium of St Veronica*

Panel, 53.5 x 48 cm
Dutch title: *De zweetdoek van de heilige Veronica*

PROVENANCE

Transferred in or before 1908

COMMENT

Possibly by an artist from the circle of Marten de Vos.

695

1031

The miniatures were all given on loan by the Rijksmuseum in 1952, and all have the same provenance: originally owned by members of the House of Orange (see Schaffers-Bodenhausen/Tiethoff-Spliethoff 1993, pp. 48–57), they were transferred to the Koninklijk Kabinet van Zeldzaamheden (Royal Cabinet of Curiosities), housed in the Mauritshuis, in 1822. They were transferred to Amsterdam in 1883. Unless otherwise noted, all miniatures are painted in watercolour.

Miniatures

Benjamin Arlaud (attributed to)

Geneva *c.*1670–1719? London

997 *Portrait of King-Stadholder Willem III (1650–1702)*

Watercolour and oil on vellum (oval), stuck to table-book leaf, 9.4 x 7.1 cm
Dutch title: *Portret van koning-stadhouder Willem III (1650–1702)*

PROVENANCE

Rijksmuseum, Amsterdam (inv. no. SK-A-4296), since 1883

LITERATURE

Delft 1966, no. 19; RM 1976, pp. 750–751; Schaffers-Bodenhausen/Tiethoff-Spliethoff 1993, p. 94, in no. 12

COMMENT

Probably after Sir Godfrey Kneller, Windsor Castle, inv. no. 217. For biographical data on Willem III, see Bakhuysen, inv. no. 6.

Louis van der Bruggen

Paris 1614/15–1658 Paris

1021 *Portrait of François Duquesnoy (1594–1643)*

Vellum (oval), stuck to table-book leaf, 7.6 x 5.9 cm
Bears inscription on the verso: *Paintet [sic] / by / Oliver / 1613*
Dutch title: *Portret van François Duquesnoy (1594–1643)*

PROVENANCE

Rijksmuseum, Amsterdam (inv. no. SK-A-4353), since 1883

LITERATURE

Long 1929, p. 322; De Ranitz 1971, pp. 8–10, fig. 5; RM 1976, p. 763 (as attributed to Peter Oliver II); RM 1992, p. 108 (with present attribution)

COMMENT

After the portrait of Duquesnoy by Anthony van Dyck in the Palais des Beaux-Arts, Brussels, inv. no. 3928. Attributed to Louis (Hans) van der Bruggen by the late Jim Murrell, former Head of Conservation at the Victoria and Albert Museum in London (written communication, 1984). The sculptor Duquesnoy —'Il Fiammingo'— was a pupil of his father Jérôme Duquesnoy and of Gian Lorenzo Bernini (1598–1680). He stayed in Italy from 1618 onwards and was befriended with the artist Nicolas Poussin (1593–1665).

Alexander Cooper (attributed to)

London 1609–*c.*1660 Stockholm (?)

998 *Portrait of Elizabeth (1618–1680), Princess Palatine, c.*1645

Vellum (oval), stuck to table-book leaf, 4.5 x 3.8 cm
Dutch title: *Portret van Elizabeth (1618–1680), prinses van de Palatijn*

PROVENANCE

Rijksmuseum, Amsterdam (inv. no. SK-A-4314), since 1883

LITERATURE

Long 1929, p. 123; RM 1976, p. 754; New York 1979, no. 36; RM 1992, p. 108 (with present attribution and identification); Schaffers-Bodenhausen/Tiethoff-Spliethoff 1993, pp. 19, 49, fig. 2, p. 90; The Hague 1997–1998b, pp. 51, 52, fig. 38

COMMENT

The sitter, the third child of Friedrich V of Bohemia, became abbess of the Protestant Nunnery in Herford in 1667. She was the sister of Henriette Marie (inv. no. 999). Formerly attributed to David des Granges and identified as a portrait of Mary I Stuart (1631–1660), wife of Prince Willem II.

999 *Portrait of Henriette Marie (1626–1651), Princess Palatine, c.*1650

Vellum (oval), stuck to plain card, 4.5 x 3.9 cm
Dutch title: *Portret van Henriette Marie (1626–1651), prinses van de Palatijn*

PROVENANCE

Rijksmuseum, Amsterdam (inv. no. SK-A-4315), since 1883

LITERATURE

Long 1929, p. 123; RM 1976, p. 755; New York 1979, no. 28; RM 1992, p. 109 (with present attribution and identification); Schaffers-Bodenhausen/Tiethoff-Spliethoff 1993, pp. 19, 49, fig. 2, p. 90; The Hague 1997–1998b, p. 52, fig. 39; Judson/Ekkart 1999, p. 280, in no. 377

COMMENT

Based on a painting by Gerrit van Honthorst of *c.*1648–1650 (whereabouts unknown). The sitter, the ninth child of Friedrich V of Bohemia, married Sigismund Rakoczy in 1651 but died within six months after the wedding. She was the sister of Elizabeth (inv. no. 998). Formerly attributed to David des Granges and identified as a portrait of Albertina Agnes (1634–1687), wife of Stadholder Willem Frederik.

997

1021

998

999

C

Alexander Cooper (attributed to)

1008 *Portrait of Willem II (1626–1650), Prince of Orange*

Watercolour and oil on vellum (oval), stuck to table-book leaf, 4.4 x 3.5 cm
Dutch title: *Portret van Willem II (1626–1650), prins van Oranje*

PROVENANCE
Rijksmuseum, Amsterdam (inv. no. SK-A-4303), since 1883

LITERATURE
Staring 1943, pp. 93–94, fig. 9 (with present identification); RM 1976, p. 752; RM 1992, p. 108

COMMENT
For biographical data on Willem II, see Van Honthorst (studio), inv. no. 63.

Samuel Cooper

London 1608?–1672 London

991 *Portrait of a lady*, 1643

Watercolour and oil on vellum (oval), stuck to table-book leaf, 6.7 x 5.5 cm
Signed and dated lower left: *SC:fe: / 1643.*
Dutch title: *Portret van een dame*

PROVENANCE
Rijksmuseum, Amsterdam (inv. no. SK-A-4306), since 1883

LITERATURE
Foskett 1974, p. 108, fig. 8; London 1974, no. 13; RM 1976, p. 753

COMMENT
Possibly based on Anthony van Dyck's *Portrait of Catherine, Countess of Chesterfield* (Glück 1931, p. 444, repr.).

992 *Portrait of George Gordon (d. 1649)*

Vellum (oval), stuck to table-book leaf, 5.5 x 4.5 cm
Dutch title: *Portret van George Gordon (overleden in 1649)*

PROVENANCE
Rijksmuseum, Amsterdam (inv. no. SK-A-4305), since 1883

LITERATURE
Delft 1966, no. 16; Foskett 1974, p. 111; London 1974, no. 10; RM 1976, pp. 752–753

COMMENT
Based on a portrait by Anthony van Dyck in a private collection (Glück 1931, p. 446). The signature and date 'SC 16[..]', mentioned in RM 1976, could not be found during examination in September 2003. George Gordon, second Marquess of Huntley, supported Charles I. He was captured by Colonel Menzies in 1647 and beheaded in Edinburgh in 1649.

993 *Portrait of Charles II (1630–1685) in royal robes*, 1665

Vellum (oval), stuck to table-book leaf, 17 x 13.2 cm
Signed and dated right of centre: *1665 / SC* (in ligature)
Dutch title: *Portret van Karel II (1630–1685) in koninklijke dracht*

PROVENANCE
Rijksmuseum, Amsterdam (inv. no. SK-A-4307), since 1883

LITERATURE
London 1974, no. 112; RM 1976, p. 753; Murdoch 1981, p. 113, fig. 128; The Hague 1991, no. 26

COMMENT
A larger, rectangular version, also signed and dated 1665, is in a private collection (London 1974, no. 111). Charles II, the son of Charles I and Henrietta Maria, lived in exile after the execution of his father in 1649. He became king of England, Scotland and Ireland in 1660. In 1662 he married Catherine of Braganza, daughter of King John IV of Portugal. He is wearing the sash and the Order of the Garter.

995 *Portrait of Henrietta (1644–1670), Duchess of Orléans*, 1670

Vellum (oval), stuck to table-book leaf, 6.8 x 5.7 cm
Signed and dated lower right: *SC: 1670* (SC in ligature)
Dutch title: *Portret van Henrietta (1644–1670), hertogin van Orléans*

PROVENANCE
Rijksmuseum, Amsterdam (inv.no. SK-A-4309), since 1883

LITERATURE
Foskett 1974, pp. 25–26, 118, fig. 70; London 1974, no. 130; RM 1976, p. 753; RM 1992, p. 109; London-New Haven 2001–2002, no. 5

COMMENT
Henrietta –'Minette'– was a sister of Charles II and the fifth daughter of Charles I and Henrietta Maria. In 1661 she married Philippe, Duc d'Orléans.

996 *Portrait of Frances Teresa Stuart (1647–1702), in male costume*, 1666

Watercolour on vellum (oval), stuck to table-book leaf, 8.5 x 6.9 cm
Signed and dated lower left: *SC: 1666*
Dutch title: *Portret van Frances Teresa Stuart (1647–1702), gekleed als man*

1008 991 992

993 995 996

PROVENANCE
Rijksmuseum, Amsterdam (inv. no. SK-A-4308), since 1883

LITERATURE
De Vries 1969a, p. 168; Foskett 1974, pp. 79, 117; London 1974, no. 19; RM 1976, p. 753; The Hague 1991, no. 40; Wadum 1991, p. 6, fig. 4; RM 1992, p. 109

COMMENT
Another miniature of Frances Stuart in male attire, but without the hat, is in the English Royal Collection. Frances Teresa Stuart, Duchess of Richmond and Lennox, was called 'La Belle Stuart'. She grew up at the French court of Queen Henrietta Maria, and was maid of honour to Queen Catherine of Braganza, wife of Charles II. She later became one of the mistresses of Charles II. In 1666 she married Charles Stuart, 4th Duke of Richmond and 6th Duke of Lennox.

Richard Gibson (attributed to)

England 1605/15–1690 London

994 *Portrait of Mary II Stuart (1662–1695) as a child, c.1670*

Vellum (oval), stuck to plain card, 5.7 x 4.9 cm
Dutch title: *Portret van Mary II Stuart (1662–1695) als kind*

PROVENANCE
Rijksmuseum, Amsterdam (inv. no. SK-A-4312), since 1883

LITERATURE
Delft 1966, no. 12; RM 1976, p. 754 (as by Nicolas Dixon); RM 1992, p. 110 (with present attribution)

COMMENT
Mary, a daughter of the English king James II and Anne Hyde of Clarendon, married King-Stadholder Willem III in 1677. Gibson was Mary's drawing master and travelled with her to Holland.

Adriaen Hanneman (after)

The Hague *c.*1604–1671 The Hague

1024 *Portrait of Stadholder Willem Frederik (1613–1664), c.*1665

Enamel on gold (octagonal), 7 x 6.1 cm
Monogrammed on the frame: 'FWF' with two hearts and a royal crown
Dutch title: *Portret van stadhouder Willem Frederik (1613–1664)*

PROVENANCE
Rijksmuseum, Amsterdam (inv. no. SK-A-4436), since 1883

LITERATURE
RM 1976, p. 782; New York 1979, no. 29; RM 1992, p. 120

COMMENT
After a 1661 portrait by Adriaen Hanneman in the Staatliche Kunstsammlungen, Schlossmuseum, Weimar (Ter Kuile 1976, no. 66). For biographical data on Willem Frederik, see Nason, inv. no. 124, which is based on the same portrait by Hanneman. Presumably painted posthumously, given the skull and bones on the original frame.

Nicholas Hilliard

Exeter *c.*1547–1619 London

1000 *Portrait of Queen Elizabeth I (1533–1603)*

Vellum (oval), stuck to plain card, 4 x 3.2 cm
Dutch title: *Portret van koningin Elizabeth I (1533–1603)*

PROVENANCE
Rijksmuseum, Amsterdam (inv. no. SK-A-4321), since 1883

LITERATURE
Auerbach 1961, pp. 92, 296, note 54; De Vries 1969a, p. 166, fig. 3; RM 1976, p. 756

COMMENT
Elizabeth I, the daughter of King Henry VIII and his second wife Anne Boleyn, became queen of England in 1588.

1023 *Portrait of Lady Margaret Douglas (1515–1578),* 1575

Vellum (round), stuck to plain card, 4.5 cm in diameter
Dated and inscribed at left and right: *Año. Dni. 1575. / Ætatis. Suæ. [age missing]*
Dutch title: *Portret van Lady Margaret Douglas (1515–1578)*

PROVENANCE
Presumably King Charles I, London, the sitter's great grandson (see London 1983); Rijksmuseum, Amsterdam (inv. no. SK-A-4323), since 1883

LITERATURE
Auerbach 1961, pp. 68–69, 291, note 25; RM 1976, p. 757; London 1983, no. 64; Schaffers-Bodenhausen/Tiethoff-Spliethoff 1993, pp. 16, 50; James 1998, p. 17 and fig. 3

COMMENT
A severely damaged replica in the Fitzwilliam Museum, Cambridge, inv. no. 3851. Lady Margaret Douglas, Countess of Lennox, was the daughter of Archibald Douglas, Earl of Angus, and Margaret Tudor. She was the granddaughter of King Henry VII of England. She was first married to Lord Thomas Howard and in 1544 she married Matthew Stuart, 4th Earl of Lennox.

994

1024

1000

1023

H

Nicholas Hilliard (and/or studio of)?

1015 *Portrait of James I (1566–1625), King of England, c.*1610?

Vellum (heart-shaped), stuck to plain card, 5.4 x 4.6 cm
Dutch title: *Portret van Jacobus I (1566–1625), koning van Engeland*

PROVENANCE
Rijksmuseum, Amsterdam (inv. no. SK-A-4322), since 1883

LITERATURE
Long 1929, p. 318; Auerbach 1961, pp. 164, 317, note 173; RM 1976, p. 756; London 1983, no. 241; The Hague 1991, no. 23; RM 1992, p. 111 (as attributed to Lawrence Hilliard)

COMMENT
Strong attributed this portrait to Lawrence Hilliard (1582–1647/48), Nicholas's son, and dated it around 1620 (see London 1983). The sitter, James I of England and VI of Scotland, wearing the Order of the Garter, was the son of Mary, Queen of Scots and Henry Stuart, Lord Darnley. In 1567 he became king of Scotland and in 1603 king of England. In 1589 he married Anne of Denmark.

Gerrit van Honthorst (after)

Utrecht 1592–1656 Utrecht

981 *Portrait of Amalia of Solms-Braunfels (1602–1675) as a widow,* after *c.*1651–1652

Vellum (oval), stuck to table-book leaf, 4.7 x 3.8 cm
Verso: a memento mori
Inscribed on the verso: *AMELIE / D ORANGE*
Dutch title: *Portret van Amalia van Solms-Braunfels (1602–1675) als weduwe*

PROVENANCE
Rijksmuseum, Amsterdam (inv. no. SK-A-4437), since 1883

LITERATURE
RM 1976, pp. 782–783; Amsterdam 1988

COMMENT
Based on a portrait by Gerrit van Honthorst, painted around 1651–1652 for the cupola of the Oranjezaal, Huis ten Bosch Palace, The Hague, now in the Gemäldegalerie, Berlin (Judson/Ekkart 1999, no. 178). For biographical data on Amalia, see Van Honthorst, inv. no. 104.

John Hoskins

Wells (?) *c.*1590/95–1664/65 London

1004 *Portrait of Queen Henrietta Maria (1609–1669), wife of Charles I,* 1632

Vellum (round), stuck to plain card, glued to panel, 17.6 cm in diameter
Signed and dated lower right: *1632 / iH,* with a crowned monogram 'HMR'
Dutch title: *Portret van koningin Henrietta Maria (1609–1669), echtgenote van Karel I*

PROVENANCE
King Charles I, London, inventoried by Charles van der Doort in 1639; Rijksmuseum, Amsterdam (inv. no. SK-A-4326), since 1883

LITERATURE
London 1974, no. 145; RM 1976, p. 757; Murdoch 1981, p. 101, fig. 110; Larsen 1988, vol. 2, p. 318, in no. 806; Schaffers-Bodenhausen/Tiethoff-Spliethoff 1993, pp. 42, note 37, p. 50 and fig. 3

COMMENT
Based on a portrait by Anthony van Dyck, of which two versions are accepted as autograph: one in the English Royal Collection, and one in an English private collection (Glück 1931, pp. 374, 376; Larsen 1988, vol. 2, nos. 806, 862). Influenced by Peter Oliver. Henrietta Maria was the daughter of King Henri IV of France and Maria de' Medici. In 1625 she married Charles I of England. After 1644 she lived in France. She returned to England after the Restoration, but resumed living in France until 1665.

1005 *Portrait of Queen Henrietta Maria (1609–1669), wife of Charles I*

Vellum (oval), stuck to a playing card with diamonds on the verso which have been covered with black paint, 6.1 x 5 cm
Signed lower right: *iH.f* (iH in monogram), with a crowned monogram 'HMR' (also monogrammed on the verso)
Dutch title: *Portret van koningin Henrietta Maria (1609–1669), echtgenote van Karel I*

PROVENANCE
Rijksmuseum, Amsterdam (inv.no. SK-A-4327), since 1883

LITERATURE
Lugt 1915, p. 158, fig. 19; RM 1976, pp. 757–758; Schaffers-Bodenhausen/Tiethoff-Spliethoff 1993, p. 199, in no. 180

COMMENT
Based on a portrait by Anthony van Dyck in the English Royal Collection (Glück 1931, no. 383). A smaller version in the House of Orange-Nassau Historic Collections Trust, The Hague. For biographical data on Henrietta, see inv. no. 1004.

1004

981

1015

1005

1006 *Portrait of Charles I (1600–1649), King of England, c.*1640

Vellum (oval), stuck to table-book leaf, 7.9 x 6.4 cm
Signed left of the middle: *iH· fe* (iH in monogram)
Dutch title: *Portret van Karel I (1600–1649), koning van Engeland*

PROVENANCE
Rijksmuseum, Amsterdam (inv. no. SK-A-4325), since 1883

LITERATURE
Lugt 1915, p. 152; Delft 1966, no. 8; RM 1976, p. 757; Schaffers-Bodenhausen/Tiethoff-Spliethoff 1993, p. 198, in no. 178

COMMENT
A smaller version in the House of Orange-Nassau Historic Collections Trust, The Hague; another signed version in the English Royal Collection. Charles I, here wearing the Order of the Garter, was the second son of King James I and Anne of Denmark. In 1625 he married Henrietta Maria and became king of England and Scotland. In 1649 Charles was convicted of treason and beheaded.

1007 *Portrait of Queen Henrietta Maria (1609–1669), wife of Charles I, c.*1630–1635

Vellum (oval), stuck to plain card, 6.2 x 3.3 cm
Said to be signed: *iH*
Dutch title: *Portret van koningin Henrietta Maria (1609–1669), echtgenote van Karel I*

PROVENANCE
Rijksmuseum, Amsterdam (inv. no. SK-A-4328), since 1883

LITERATURE
RM 1976, p. 758; Murdoch 1981, p. 101, fig. 112

COMMENT
For biographical data on Henrietta, see inv. no. 1004. Formerly identified as Elizabeth Stuart (1596–1662), sister of Charles I and wife of Friedrich V of Bohemia.

Johann Friedrich Hurter (attributed to)

Schaffhausen 1734–1799 Düsseldorf

1027 *Portrait of Cornelis Ploos van Amstel (1726–1798),* after 1766

Enamel on copper (oval), 4 x 3.5 cm
Bears inscription on the verso: *Cornelis Ploos van Amstel / Jacobs Cornelz / GEB. 4 JANUARIJ 1726 / TE / WEESP*
Dutch title: *Portret van Cornelis Ploos van Amstel (1726–1798)*

PROVENANCE
On loan from the Koninklijk Oudheidkundig Genootschap, Amsterdam, since 1951

LITERATURE
Staring 1948, p. 86; Niemeijer 1980, p. 78, fig. 35

COMMENT
After the portrait by Jacobus Buijs (1724–1801) dated 1766 in the Rijksmuseum, Amsterdam, inv.no. SK-C-515. For biographical data on Ploos van Amstel, see Van der Mijn, inv. no. 729.

Robert Mussard

Geneva 1713–1777 Paris

1010 *Portrait of Willem V (1748–1806) aged three,* 1751

Watercolour and oil on vellum, stuck to a playing card with clubs verso, 5.7 x 7.5 cm
Inscribed on the verso: *RMussard pinxit agé / de 3 ans e demi dans / l'année 1751* (RM in ligature)
Dutch title: *Portret van Willem V (1748–1806) op 3-jarige leeftijd*

PROVENANCE
Rijksmuseum, Amsterdam (inv. no. SK-A-4340), since 1883

LITERATURE
RM 1976, p. 761; New York 1979, no. 89; Schaffers-Bodenhausen/Tiethoff-Spliethoff 1993, p. 98

COMMENT
For biographical data on Willem V, see Ziesenis, inv. no. 462.

1011 *Portrait of Willem V (1748–1806) as a child, c.*1751

Watercolour and oil on vellum, stuck to a playing card with queen verso, 5.5 x 7.2 cm
Dutch title: *Portret van Willem V (1748–1806) als kind*

PROVENANCE
Rijksmuseum, Amsterdam (inv. no. SK-A-4343), since 1883

LITERATURE
RM 1976, p. 761; New York 1979, no. 89; Schaffers-Bodenhausen/Tiethoff-Spliethoff 1993, p. 98

COMMENT
For biographical data on Willem V, see Ziesenis, inv. no. 462.

1006 1007 1027

1010

1011

1012 *Portrait of Carolina Wilhelmina of Orange (1743–1787), sister of Willem V, c.1751*

Vellum, stuck to a playing card with clubs verso, 5.5 x 7.3 cm
Formerly signed: *R. Mussard* (see RM 1976)
Dutch title: *Portret van Carolina Wilhelmina van Oranje (1743–1787), zus van Willem V*

PROVENANCE
Rijksmuseum, Amsterdam (inv. no. SK-A-4342), since 1883

LITERATURE
RM 1976, p. 761; New York 1979, no. 89; Schaffers-Bodenhausen/Tiethoff-Spliethoff 1993, p. 98

COMMENT
Carolina Wilhelmina, the eldest daughter of Stadholder Willem IV and Anne of Hannover, was a sister of Stadholder Willem V. In 1760 she married Karl Christian of Nassau-Weilburg. Cf. also the portrait by Tischbein, inv. no. 232.

Isaac Oliver

Rouen *c.*1560/65–1617 London

1001 *Portrait of a lady, masqued as Flora, c.1605–1610*

Vellum (oval), stuck to a playing card with hearts verso, 5.2 x 4.1 cm
Dutch title: *Portret van een dame, uitgedost als Flora*

PROVENANCE
Rijksmuseum, Amsterdam (inv. no. SK-A-4347), since 1883

LITERATURE
London 1947, no. 181; RM 1976, p. 762; Finsten 1981, vol. 2, pp. 82–83, no. 51, fig. 51; London 1983, no. 223; Strong 1983, p. 178, fig. 233; The Hague 1991, no. 36; RM 1992, p. 113; London 1995–1996, no. 82

COMMENT
The sitter is wearing female masquing dress. The last masque for ladies took place in 1613, providing a *terminus ante quem* for the date of execution (for the phenomenon of court masques, see London 1995–1996, pp. 160–164). For other miniatures depicting ladies in allegorical masque costume, see London 1983, nos. 225, 227.

1002 *Portrait of a lady*

Watercolour and oil on vellum (oval), stuck to a playing card with diamonds verso, 5.2 x 4.3 cm
Dutch title: *Portret van een dame*

PROVENANCE
Rijksmuseum, Amsterdam (inv. no. SK-A-4346), since 1883

LITERATURE
London 1947, no. 148; RM 1976, p. 762; Finsten 1981, vol. 2, p. 58, no. 34, fig. 34; RM 1992, p. 113

1013 *Portrait of a man (Ludovic Stuart or Thomas Howard?)*

Watercolour and oil on vellum (oval), stuck to plain card, 4.9 x 3.9 cm
Dutch title: *Portret van een man (Ludovic Stuart of Thomas Howard?)*

PROVENANCE
Rijksmuseum, Amsterdam (inv. no. SK-A-4345), since 1883

LITERATURE
RM 1976, pp. 761–762; Finsten 1981, vol. 2, p. 69, no. 43, fig. 43; RM 1992, p. 113

COMMENT
R. Strong (written communication, 1961) identified the sitter as either Ludovic Stuart (1574–1623/24) or Thomas Howard (1561–1626). Stuart, a son of Esmee I Stuart, Duke of Lennox and Lady Katherine de Balsac, became 1st Duke of Richmond and 2nd Duke of Lennox. In 1621 he married Frances Howard. Thomas Howard was Earl of Suffolk, and in 1583 married Lady Catherine Knyvett. The sitter is wearing the Order of the Garter.

1014 *Portrait of a lady with flowing hair, thought to be Arabella Stuart (1575–1615)*

Vellum (oval), stuck to a playing card with hearts verso, 6.9 x 5.6 cm
Signed upper left: *·IO·* (in ligature)
Dutch title: *Portret van een dame met golvend haar, vermoedelijk Arabella Stuart (1575–1615)*

PROVENANCE
Rijksmuseum, Amsterdam (inv. no. SK-A-4344), since 1883

LITERATURE
RM 1976, p. 761; Finsten 1981, vol. 2, pp. 118–119, no. 77, fig. 77 (possibly 'finished by another hand')

COMMENT
Arabella Stuart, the daughter of Charles, Earl of Lennox, and Elizabeth Cavendish, was a cousin of King James I.

1012

1013

1001

1002

1014

O

Peter Oliver

London *c.*1589 (?)–1647 London

1016 *Portrait of Charles I (1600–1649) as Prince of Wales,* 1621

Vellum (oval), stuck to a playing card with hearts verso, 5.7 x 4.5 cm
Signed and dated bottom right: *PO / 1621* (PO in ligature)
Dutch title: *Portret van Karel I (1600–1649) als prins van Wales*

PROVENANCE
Rijksmuseum, Amsterdam (inv. no. SK-A-4348), since 1883

LITERATURE
Long 1929, p. 322; RM 1976, p. 762

COMMENT
Another version in the English Royal Collection, also signed and dated 1621. The sitter is wearing the Order of the Garter. For biographical data on Charles I, see MINIATURES, Hoskins, inv. no. 1006.

1017 *Portrait of George Villiers (1592–1628) in Roman dress, c.*1620?

Watercolour and oil on vellum (oval), stuck to table-book leaf, 5 x 4.1 cm
Dutch title: *Portret van George Villiers (1592–1628) in Romeinse dracht*

PROVENANCE
Rijksmuseum, Amsterdam (inv. no. SK-A-4352), since 1883

LITERATURE
Long 1929, p. 322; RM 1976, p. 763; RM 1992, p. 113; Schaffers-Bodenhausen/Tiethoff-Spliethoff 1993, p. 377, in no. 500

COMMENT
Possibly the companion piece to inv. no. 1018 (see below). After the miniature in the English Royal Collection, signed by Isaac Oliver. A larger, signed, version in the House of Orange-Nassau Historic Collections Trust, The Hague. Villiers, Duke of Buckingham, was an English nobleman and courtier. He was a powerful man at court, especially during the reign of King Charles I.

1019 *Portrait of Friedrich V (1596–1632), c.*1620

Vellum (oval), stuck to table-book leaf, 5.2 x 4.1 cm
Signed bottom right: *PO* (in ligature)
Dutch title: *Portret van Friedrich V (1596–1632)*

PROVENANCE
Rijksmuseum, Amsterdam (inv. no. SK-A-4349), since 1883

LITERATURE
RM 1976, p. 762

COMMENT
For biographical data on Friedrich V, see Van Mierevelt (studio of), inv. no. 101.

Peter Oliver (attributed to)

1018 *Portrait of Prince Henry Frederick (1594–1612) in Roman dress, before a niche,* after 1611

Vellum (oval), stuck to a playing card with spades verso, 5.1 x 4 cm
Dutch title: *Portret van prins Henry Frederick (1594–1612) in Romeinse dracht, voor een nis*

PROVENANCE
Rijksmuseum, Amsterdam (inv.no. SK-A-4351), since 1883

LITERATURE
Long 1929, p. 322; RM 1976, p. 762; London 1983, in no. 230

COMMENT
Possibly a companion piece to inv.no. 1017. Other versions in the National Portrait Gallery, London, inv. no. 1572; the Fitzwilliam Museum, Cambridge, inv. no. 3903 (signed; Strong 1983, p. 172, fig. 224); and in the English Royal Collection (see London 1983, no. 230). Henry, the eldest son of King James I and Anne of Denmark, was Prince of Wales. After his sudden death, his brother Charles became king of England and Scotland.

Peter Oliver (attributed to)

1020 *Portrait of Charles I (1600–1649) as Prince of Wales*

Watercolour and oil on vellum (oval), stuck to a playing card with a club verso, 5.4 x 4.1 cm
Dutch title: *Portret van Karel I (1600–1649) als prins van Wales*

PROVENANCE
Rijksmuseum, Amsterdam (inv.no. SK-A-4350), since 1883

LITERATURE
RM 1976, p. 762

COMMENT
Another version is in the English Royal Collection, with an attribution to Isaac Oliver. The sitter is wearing the Order of the Garter. For biographical data on Charles I, see MINIATURES, Hoskins, inv. no. 1006.

1016 1017 1018

1019 1020

'Le Chevalier' Phaff

active in the northern Netherlands, *c.*1808

1022 *Portrait of Frederika Sophia Wilhelmina (1751–1820), wife of Stadholder Willem V*

Watercolour and oil on ivory (oval), backed with paper, 10 x 7.7 cm
Signed lower right: *Le ch. Phaff*
Dutch title: *Portret van Frederika Sophia Wilhelmina (1751–1820), echtgenote van stadhouder Willem V*

PROVENANCE
Rijksmuseum, Amsterdam (inv. no. SK-A-4360), since 1883

LITERATURE
RM 1976, p. 764; RM 1992, p. 114

COMMENT
For biographical data on Frederika, see Tischbein, inv. no. 464. May be a portrait of Frederika Sophia Wilhelmina of Nassau-Dietz (1770–1819), the daughter of Willem V.

Nathaniel Thach

Barrow 1617–unknown

1009 *Portrait of King Charles II (1630–1685) as a young man,* 1650s

Vellum (oval), stuck to plain card, 4.5 x 3.7 cm
Signed and dated bottom right: *NThach / F / 165[.]* (NT in ligature)
Dutch title: *Portret van Karel II (1630–1685) op jonge leeftijd*

PROVENANCE
Rijksmuseum, Amsterdam (inv. no. SK-A-4369), since 1883

LITERATURE
De Ranitz 1971, pp. 7–8; Ter Kuile 1976, pp. 68–69, in no. 14; RM 1976, p. 766

COMMENT
After a lost original by Adriaen Hanneman. The sitter is wearing the Order of the Garter. For biographical data on Charles II, see MINIATURES, Cooper, inv. no. 993.

Henri Toutin

Châteaudun 1614–after 1683 Paris

1029 *Portrait of King Charles I (1600–1649),* 1636

Enamel on gold (oval with scalloped edge), 6.5 x 5.5 cm
Inscribed on the verso: *henry Toutin Orphevre / aparis afait ce cy lan. / 1636* (see Schaffers-Bodenhausen/Tiethoff-Spliethoff 1993, p. 20, fig. 12)
Dutch title: *Portret van koning Karel I (1600–1649)*

PROVENANCE
Rijksmuseum, Amsterdam (inv. no. SK-A-4370), since 1883

LITERATURE
RM 1976, p. 766; RM 1992, p. 116; Schaffers-Bodenhausen/Tiethoff-Spliethoff 1993, pp. 19, 20

COMMENT
The sitter is wearing the Order of the Garter. For biographical data on Charles I, see MINIATURES, Hoskins, inv. no. 1006.

Christian Friedrich Zincke

Dresden 1683–1767 London

1025 *Portrait of Anne of Hannover (1709–1759), wife of Stadholder Willem IV, c.*1734

Enamel on gold (oval), 7.6 x 6.1 cm
Dutch title: *Portret van Anna van Hannover (1709–1759), echtgenote van stadhouder Willem IV*

PROVENANCE
Rijksmuseum, Amsterdam (inv. no. SK-A-4375), since 1883

LITERATURE
RM 1976, p. 768; RM 1992, p. 116; Schaffers-Bodenhausen/Tiethoff-Spliethoff 1993, p. 100

COMMENT
A smaller version in the House of Orange-Nassau Historic Collections Trust, The Hague. For biographical data on Anne, see Tischbein (after), inv. no. 504.

1022

1009

1029

1025

MONOGRAMMISTS

Monogrammist RF

active 1606

1090 *Portrait of a man,* 1606

Copper (oval), 8.2 x 6.6 cm
Signed and dated lower left: *A 1606 / R.F*
Dutch title: Portret van een man

PROVENANCE
Private collection, Düsseldorf; Douwes Gallery, Amsterdam; gift of C.W. van Blijenburgh, Hilversum, 1992

LITERATURE
Leiden 1980, no. 39; Buijsen/Van der Ploeg 1993, pp. 32–33, no. 11

ANONYMOUS MINIATURES

England

989 *Portrait of a man, c.*1635?

Oil on copper (oval), 6 x 4.8 cm
Dutch title: *Portret van een man*

PROVENANCE
Rijksmuseum, Amsterdam (inv. no. SK-A-4395), since 1883

LITERATURE
RM 1976, p. 769; RM 1992, p. 117

England?

985 *Portrait of a lady, thought to be Mary Stuart (1542–1587),* 19th century?

Oil on copper (oval), 4.9 x 4 cm
Dutch title: *Portret van een dame, vermoedelijk Maria Stuart*

PROVENANCE
Rijksmuseum, Amsterdam (inv. no. SK-A-4392), since 1883

LITERATURE
Cust/Martin 1906–1907, p. 44; RM 1976, p. 768 (as English School); RM 1992, p. 117

COMMENT
Probably a nineteenth-century copy after an original in the Galleria degli Uffizi, Florence. Mary Stuart was the daughter of King James V of Scotland and Mary of Guise. She became queen of Scotland in 1542, when she was only six days old.

France

982 *Portrait of Edward (1537–1553), the future king of England, aged two or three,* 18th century?

Vellum (oval), without a card support, 4.8 x 3.5 cm
Dutch title: *Portret van Edward (1537–1553), de toekomstige koning van Engeland, op 2- of 3-jarige leeftijd*

PROVENANCE
Rijksmuseum, Amsterdam (inv. no. SK-A-4297), since 1883

LITERATURE
RM 1976, p. 751 (as attributed to John Bettes); RM 1992, p. 118 (with present attribution); Franke 1995

COMMENT
According to J. Murrell (see comment to MINIATURES, Bruggen, inv. no. 1021) it is plausible that inv. nos. 982, 983, 984, 986 and 987 are by the same hand – possibly that of a French eighteenth-century copyist making a dynastic series (written communication, 1984). There is no evidence to support an attribution to John Bettes. Edward VI (1537–1553), the son of Henry VIII and his third wife Jane Seymour (see Studio of Holbein, inv. no. 278), became king of England and Ireland in 1547, at the age of nine.

983 *Portrait of James I (1566–1625), the future king of England, as a child,* 18th century?

Oil on a playing card (oval), with one heart verso, 5 x 3.7 cm
Dutch title: *Portret van Jacobus I (1566–1625), de latere koning van Engeland, als kind*

PROVENANCE
Rijksmuseum, Amsterdam (inv. no. SK-A-4302), since 1883

LITERATURE
Auerbach 1961, p. 269, fig. 239, p. 332, note 274 (as attributed to Arnold van Brounckhurst, active in Scotland *c.*1565–1598); RM 1976, p. 752

COMMENT
See inv. no. 982. For biographical data on James I, see MINIATURES, Hilliard (attributed to), inv. no. 1015.

1090 989 985

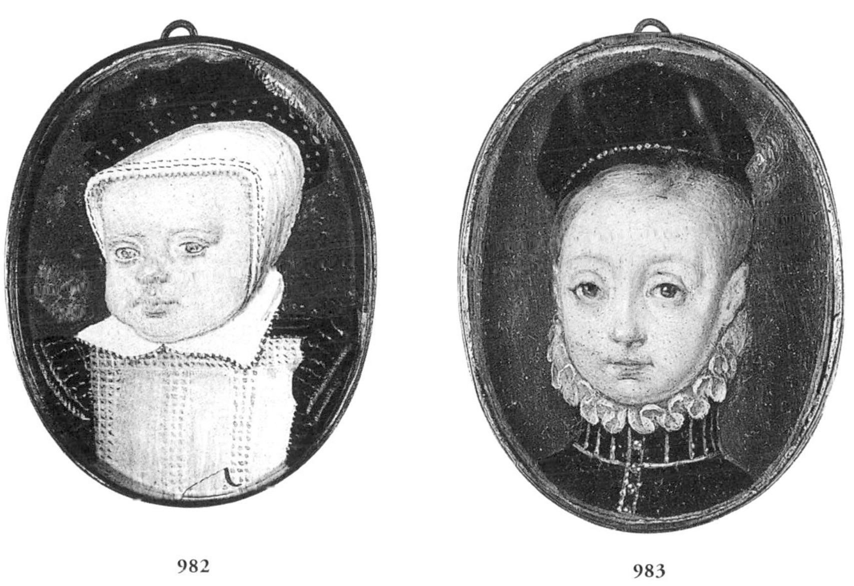

982 983

984 *Portrait of James Stuart (1566–1625), the future King James I of England, at about the age of ten,* 18th century?

Vellum (oval), without card backing, 4.5 x 3.6 cm
Dutch title: *Portret van James Stuart (1566–1625), de latere koning van Engeland, Jacobus I, op ongeveer 10-jarige leeftijd*

PROVENANCE
Rijksmuseum, Amsterdam (inv. no. SK-A-4390), since 1883

LITERATURE
RM 1976, p. 768 (as English school, *c.*1565); RM 1992, p. 118

COMMENT
See inv. no. 982; for biographical data on James I, see MINIATURES, Hilliard (attributed to), inv. no. 1015.

986 *Portrait of a lady, perhaps Mary Stuart (1542–1587),* 18th century?

Watercolour and oil on vellum (round), without card backing, 3.8 cm in diameter
Dutch title: *Portret van een dame, misschien Maria Stuart (1542–1587)*

PROVENANCE
Rijksmuseum, Amsterdam (inv. no. SK-A-4391), since 1883

LITERATURE
RM 1976, p. 769; RM 1992, p. 118

COMMENT
See inv. no. 982; for biographical data on Mary Stuart, see MINIATURES, England, inv. no. 985.

987 *Portrait of Henry Stuart (1547–1567),* 18th century?

Vellum (oval), without card backing, 5.1 x 4 cm
Dutch title: *Portret van Henry Stuart (1547–1567)*

PROVENANCE
Rijksmuseum, Amsterdam (inv. no. SK-A-4393), since 1883

LITERATURE
Cust/Martin 1906–1907, p. 47; RM 1976, p. 769; RM 1992, p. 118

COMMENT
See inv. no. 982. Henry Stuart, Lord Darnley, was the son of Matthew Stuart, 4th Earl of Lennox, and Margaret Douglas, granddaughter of King Henry VII of England (see MINIATURES, Hilliard, inv. no. 1023). In 1565 he married Mary Stuart, Queen of Scots (cf. inv. no. 986).

Northern Netherlands

1026 *Portrait of a lady, thought to be Princess Frederika Sophia Wilhelmina (1751–1820), c.*1775?

Enamel on copper (oval), 3.9 x 3.2 cm
Dutch title: *Portret van een dame, vermoedelijk prinses Frederika Sophia Wilhelmina (1751–1820)*

PROVENANCE
Rijksmuseum, Amsterdam (inv. no. SK-A-4458), since 1883

LITERATURE
RM 1976, p. 784

COMMENT
For biographical data, see Tischbein, inv. no. 464.

984

1026

986

987

Sculptures

Jan Blommendael

The Hague or Breda *c.*1650–1702 Amsterdam

360 *Full-length portrait of King-Stadholder Willem III (1650–1702),* 1676

White marble, height 79 cm
Signed and dated at left, on the pedestal:
J. Blommendael. / F: An: 1676.
Dutch title: *Portret van koning-stadhouder Willem III (1650–1702), ten voeten uit*

PROVENANCE
Nationale Konst-Gallery, The Hague, 1801–1808; transferred, *c.*1816

LITERATURE
Moes/Van Biema 1909, p. 53, no. 239, pp. 102, 109, 125; Neurdenburg 1948, p. 229 and fig. 185; Staring 1950–1951, p. 178; Von der Osten 1961, pp. 249–250; The Hague 1988–1989, ex catalogue

COMMENT
For biographical data on Willem III, see Bakhuysen, inv. no. 6.

361 *Bust of King-Stadholder Willem III (1650–1702),* 1699

White marble, height 80 cm
Signed, dated and inscribed on the pedestal:
J. Blommendael. F (at left) and
1699. / HAGÆ COMITIS. (at right)
Dutch title: *Buste van koning-stadhouder Willem III (1650–1702)*

PROVENANCE
Le Besconte Picard Gallery, Liège; purchased by King Willem I, 1820

LITERATURE
Staring 1950–1951, pp. 190–191; Von der Osten 1961, p. 249; Düsseldorf 1971, no. 199; New York 1979, no. 71; The Hague 1988–1989, ex catalogue; Amsterdam 2000a, no. 185; Wardle 2002, fig. 24

COMMENT
Willem III is wearing the Order of the Garter.
For biographical data, see Bakhuysen, inv. no. 6.

Bartholomeus Eggers (modern copy after)

Amsterdam *c.*1630–1692 Amsterdam

KN 20 *Bust of Johan Maurits, Count of Nassau-Siegen (1604–1679),* 1986

Imitation of white marble, height 132 cm
Dutch title: *Buste van Johan Maurits, graaf van Nassau-Siegen (1604–1679)*

PROVENANCE
Gift of Hans Heinrich, Baron Thyssen-Bornemisza, Lugano, 1987

LITERATURE
Mauritshuis 1991, p. 112, no. c; Scholten 2000, p. 25; The Hague 2004, no. 34

COMMENT
After the signed sculpture dated 1664 in the Fürstengruft, Siegen, which was originally made for the garden of the Mauritshuis (Cleves 1979, pp. 222–223; The Hague 1979–1980, no. 33; Scholten 1991, p. 189; Krefeld-Oranienburg-Apeldoorn 1999–2000, no. 7/3). For biographical data on Johan Maurits, see De Baen, inv. no. 5.

Etienne-Maurice Falconet

Paris 1716–1791 Paris

906 *Seated cupid: 'L'amour menaçant',* 1757

White marble, height 87 cm, including pedestal 185 cm
Signed and dated on the ribbon of the quiver:
ETIENNE-MAURICE FALCONET 1757
Inscribed on the pedestal: *Qui que tu sois, voicy ton Maître / Il l'est, le fut, ou le doit être* (Whoever you are, here is your master / He is, he was or he will be; verse adapted from Voltaire)
Dutch title: *Zittende amor: 'L'amour menaçant'*

PROVENANCE
Madame de Pompadour, Château de Bellevue, Paris; P.-L. Randon de Boisset, Paris, 1777; Duc de Rohan-Chabot, Paris, 1777–1787; Count Golovkine, Paris and/or St Petersburg, until 1796; Count Bezborodko, St Petersburg, 1796; his heirs, until 1870; A.P. Count Chouvalov, St Petersburg, 1870; Hermitage, St Petersburg, before 1929; Fritz Mannheimer, Amsterdam; Stichting Nederlands Kunstbezit; on loan to the Mauritshuis, 1953–1960; transferred, 1960; on loan to the Rijksmuseum, Amsterdam (inv. no. RBK 1963–101), since 1963

LITERATURE
RM 1973, pp. 429–431, no. 752; Scholten 1998a; Amsterdam 2002–2003b, p. 237, in no. 154; Versailles-Munich-London 2002–2003 (French ed.), pp. 311–312, in no. 137 (exhibited in London only)

360

361

KN 20

906

COMMENT
There are replicas in the Musée du Louvre, Paris, the State Hermitage Museum, St Petersburg, and a bronze version in the W.A. Clark Collection, Corcoran Gallery of Art, Washington, as well as other versions by Falconet and many copies by other masters (see Versailles-Munich-London 2002–2003, pp. 311–312 and Amsterdam 2002–2003b, no. 154).

Marie-Anne Falconet, born Collot

Paris 1748–1821 Morimont

379 *Bust of Stadholder Willem V (1748–1806)*, 1782

White marble, height 79 cm
Signed and dated at the back: *par M.A. falconet née Collot 1782.*
Dutch title: *Buste van stadhouder Willem V (1748–1806)*

PROVENANCE
Commissioned by Prince Willem V, The Hague; Royal Museum, The Hague, 1808; transferred to the Mauritshuis by order of King Willem I, 1816

LITERATURE
Moes/Van Biema 1909, pp. 103, 126; Verspeyck Mynssen 1918; Staring 1947, p. 87; Haarlem 1989, no. 86–a

COMMENT
For biographical data on Willem V, see Ziesenis, inv. no. 462. Companion piece to inv. no. 380.

380 *Bust of Princess Frederika Sophia Wilhelmina (1751–1820)*, 1782

White marble, height 84 cm
Signed and dated at the back: *par M.A. falconet. née Collot 1782*
Dutch title: *Buste van prinses Frederika Sophia Wilhelmina (1751–1820)*

PROVENANCE
Same as inv. no. 379

LITERATURE
Moes/Van Biema 1909, pp. 103, 126; Verspeyck Mynssen 1918; Staring 1947, p. 87; Haarlem 1989, no. 86–b; Potsdam-Sanssouci 1994, no. 142

COMMENT
For biographical data on Frederika, see Ziesenis, inv. no. 463. Companion piece to inv. no. 379.

Jean-Antoine Houdon

Versailles 1741–1828 Paris

373 *Bust of Pierre-André de Suffren (1726–1788)*, 1787

White marble, height 90.5 cm
Inscribed on the oval white plaque on the black marble pedestal: *PETRUS ANDREAS / DE SUFFREN, / GROOT KRUIS VAN ST.-JAN, / GENERAAL VAN MALTHA, / RIDDER VAN DE HN. GEEST, / VICE ADMIRAAL VAN / VRANKRYK, / VERDEDIGER VAN DE / NEDERLANDSE / COLONIËN, IN / OOSTINDIËN. / 1781* (Petrus Andreas de Suffren, Grand Cross of St John, General of Malta, Knight of the Holy Spirit, Vice-Admiral of France, Defender of the Colonies of Holland in the East Indies)
Dutch title: *Buste van Pierre-André de Suffren (1726–1788)*

PROVENANCE
Commissioned by the Dutch East India Company, Middelburg, 1787 (exhibited in the Paris Salon in 1787 and described in the sculptor's *livret*); transferred at an unknown date; on loan to the Hannema-de Stuers Fundatie, Heino, until August 2003; on loan to the Rijksmuseum, Amsterdam (BK-C-2003-3), 2003

LITERATURE
Staring 1947, p. 212; Réau 1964, no. 195; De Vries 1969b; Arnason 1975, pp. 79, 81, 116, note 197

COMMENT
The model in terracotta, signed and dated 1786, is in the museum in Aix-en-Provence. De Suffren was a French vice-admiral who aided the Dutch in defending the Cape Colony against the English and recaptured the colonies of Cuddalore in India and Trincomale in Ceylon (1781–1782). On his chest are the riband and cross of the Order of Saint-Esprit conferred on him by the French king in 1784.

Hendrick de Keyser

Utrecht 1565–1621 Amsterdam

362 *Bust of Willem I (1533–1584), Prince of Orange*

Terracotta, later gilded, height 80 cm
Dutch title: *Portret van Willem I (1533–1584), prins van Oranje*

PROVENANCE
Nationale Konst-Gallery, The Hague; transferred, *c.*1816; on loan to the Nationaal Museum Paleis Het Loo, Apeldoorn

LITERATURE
Neurdenburg 1930, pp. 99, 108, 152, note 209; RM 1973, p. 185, in no. 231

379

380

373

362

COMMENT
Partial replica of the sculpture of Willem I seated, placed on his tomb in the Nieuwe Kerk in Delft (depicted by Houckgeest, inv. nos. 57–58). Another version is in the Rijksmuseum, Amsterdam (RM 1973, no. 231). For biographical data on Willem I, see Key, inv. no. 225.

Ignatius van Logteren

Amsterdam 1685–1732 Amsterdam

1120 *Full-length portrait of Johan Maurits (1604–1679), Count of Nassau-Siegen,* 1727

Terracotta, height 35,4 cm
Signed and dated on the pedestal: *IVL 1727* (IVL in ligature)
Dutch title: *Portret van Johan Maurits (1604–1679), graaf van Nassau-Siegen, ten voeten uit*

PROVENANCE
Joannes de Bosch, Amsterdam, 1784; his sale, Amsterdam, 23 May 1785, lot 5; gift of Robert Noortman, Maastricht, 2000

LITERATURE
Scholten 2000; The Hague 2004, no. 33

COMMENT
For biographical data on Johan Maurits, see De Baen, inv. no. 5.

Martin-Claude Monnot

Paris 1738–1803 Paris

378 *Bust of King Friedrich Wilhelm II (1744–1797), c.*1782

White marble, height 85 cm
Dutch title: *Buste van koning Friedrich Wilhelm II (1744–1797)*

PROVENANCE
Stadholder's Quarter, Binnenhof, The Hague, 1796; Nationale Konst-Gallery, The Hague, 1808; transferred, *c.*1880

LITERATURE
Moes/Van Biema 1909, pp. 8, 107

COMMENT
King Friedrich Wilhelm II of Prussia, the son of August Wilhelm of Hohenzollern and Luise Amalie of Braunschweig-Wolfenbüttel, married Elisabeth Christine of Braunschweig-Wolfenbüttel in 1765. Four years later he remarried, this time to Friederike of Hesse-Darmstadt. Two similar plaster busts by Monnot, formerly in Schloss Monbijou in Berlin, are both signed. One bears the date 1782.

Theo van Reijn

Breda 1884–1954 Haarlem

812 *Bust of Abraham Bredius (1855–1946),* 1933

Bronze, height 68 cm
Signed and dated at left: *Theo van Reijn 1933*
Dutch title: *Portret van Abraham Bredius (1855–1946)*

PROVENANCE
Commissioned by the Government Advisory Committee for Creative Arts and donated to the Mauritshuis, 1933; on loan to the Museum Bredius, The Hague, since 1995

LITERATURE
Mauritshuis Annual Report 1933, p. 31

COMMENT
Bredius was a passionate collector as well as an eminent art historian and researcher. He was of great importance both to art history and to the Dutch museum world, especially the Mauritshuis. As the museum's director from 1889 to 1909, he acquired 35 paintings. In 1946 he bequeathed 25 paintings to the Mauritshuis (see The Hague 1991–1992, nos. 1–8, 10–26).

Johan Gregor van der Schardt

Nijmegen *c.*1530–after 1581 Nuremberg

550 *Portrait-bust of a man, c.*1570–1580

Earthenware and polychromy, height 40.5 cm
Dutch title: *Portretbuste van een man*

PROVENANCE
Gift of Henry Willett, Brighton, 1889; on loan to the Rijksmuseum, Amsterdam (inv. no. BK-C-1994-1), since 1994

LITERATURE
Mauritshuis 1968, p. 58; Amsterdam 1986, no. 364; Honnens de Lichtenberg 1991, pp. 150–152 (as possibly a portrait of Carolus Clusius [Charles de l'Ecluse]); Nijmegen 1994, ex catalogue; Scholten 2001, p. 315 and fig. 9; Wallert 2002

1120 378

550 812

Johann Heinrich Schepp

Diez 1736–after 1791

1069 *Relief with a portrait of Arnout Vosmaer (1720–1799), c.*1772

Terracotta, 31.5 x 26.5 cm
Dutch title: *Reliëf met het portret van Arnout Vosmaer (1720–1799)*

PROVENANCE
Gift of Mrs M.D. Vosmaer-Hudig, Leiden, 1986

LITERATURE
Bastet *et al.* 1989, p. 160, in fol. 1; Mauritshuis 1991, no. xx (with incorrect dates of Vosmaer); Nijmegen 1994, no. 36

COMMENT
The artist Vosmaer was curator of the collections of Prince Willem V; see Bastet *et al.* 1989, pp. 1–2 and Sliggers/Wertheim 1994, pp. 10–38.

Rombout Verhulst

Malines 1624–1698 The Hague

369 *Head of Michiel de Ruyter (1607–1676), c.*1677

Terracotta, colour-washed, height 37 cm
Dutch title: *Kop van Michiel de Ruyter (1607–1676)*

PROVENANCE
Bequeathed by the sculptor to 'Councillor Gool', 27 December 1692; Nationale Konst-Gallery, The Hague, 1804–1808; Royal Cabinet of Curiosities, housed in the Mauritshuis, 1825; on loan to the Rijksmuseum, Amsterdam (inv. no. BK-NM-13150), since 1923

LITERATURE
Van Notten 1907, p. 65; Neurdenburg 1948, p. 219; Van Luttervelt 1957, pp. 64–66; RM 1973, p. 239, no. 316; Scholten 1995, p. 54, in no. 24; Haarlem 1998, p. 59; Scholten 2003a, p. 65 and fig. 58

COMMENT
Probably a study for the 1677 tomb of Michiel de Ruyter in the Nieuwe Kerk, Amsterdam. For biographical data on De Ruyter, see Bol, inv. no. 585.

370 *Death portrait of Admiral Willem Joseph (1625–1672), Baron van Gendt,* before 1676

Terracotta, colour-washed, height 42 cm
Dutch title: *Doodsportret van admiraal Willem Joseph (1625–1672), baron van Gendt*

PROVENANCE
Nationale Konst-Gallery, The Hague, 1804–1808; Royal Cabinet of Curiosities, housed in the Mauritshuis, 1825; on loan to the Rijksmuseum, Amsterdam (inv. no. BK-NM-13151), since 1923

LITERATURE
Van Notten 1907, pp. 59–60; Neurdenburg 1948, p. 219; RM 1973, p. 239, no. 315; Nijmegen 1994, no. 25; Scholten 1995, p. 54, no. 24; Haarlem 1998, p. 59; Scholten 2003a, p. 65

COMMENT
Probably a study for the 1676 monument to Willem Joseph erected on the site of the former high altar in the choir of the Domkerk, Utrecht (Scholten 2003a, fig. 189).

Rombout Verhulst (studio of)

364 *Bust of Stadholder Frederik Hendrik (1584–1647),* 1683

White marble, height 77 cm
Signed and dated at the right side of the pedestal: *R.V.H. 1683 fe.*
Dutch title: *Buste van stadhouder Frederik Hendrik (1584–1647)*

PROVENANCE
Soestdijk Palace, 1799; Nationale Konst-Gallery, The Hague, 1801–1808; transferred, *c.*1816

LITERATURE
Moes/Van Biema 1909, p. 53, no. 235, pp. 102, 109, 125; Van Notten 1907, p. 85; Neurdenburg 1948, p. 221

COMMENT
Companion piece to inv. nos. 365–367. For biographical data on Frederik Hendrik, see Van Honthorst, inv. no. 104.

369

370

1069

364

Rombout Verhulst (studio of)

365 *Bust of Stadholder Willem II (1626–1650),* 1683

White marble, height 78 cm
Signed and dated at the right side of the pedestal:
R. V.H. 1683 fe.
Dutch title: *Buste van stadhouder Willem II (1626–1650)*

PROVENANCE
Same as inv. no. 364

LITERATURE
Moes/Van Biema 1909, p. 53, no. 236, pp. 102, 109, 125; Van Notten 1907, p. 85; Neurdenburg 1948, p. 221; Amsterdam 1988

COMMENT
Companion piece to inv. nos. 364, 366 and 367.
For biographical data on Willem II, see Van Honthorst (studio), inv. no. 63.

Rombout Verhulst (studio of)

366 *Bust of Mary II Stuart (1662–1695),* 1683

White marble, height 79 cm
Signed and dated at the right side of the pedestal:
R. V.H. 1683 fe.
Dutch title: *Buste van Mary II Stuart (1662–1695)*

PROVENANCE
Same as inv. no. 364

LITERATURE
Moes/Van Biema 1909, p. 53, no. 237, pp. 102, 109, 125; Van Notten 1907, p. 85; Neurdenburg 1948, p. 221; Amsterdam 1988, no. 147; The Hague 1988–1989, ex catalogue

COMMENT
Companion piece to inv. nos. 364, 365 and 367.
For biographical data on Mary, see MINIATURES, Gibson (attributed to), inv. no. 994.

Rombout Verhulst (studio of)

367 *Bust of King-Stadholder Willem III (1650–1702),* 1683

White marble, height 77 cm
Signed and dated at the right side of the pedestal:
R. V.H. 1683 fe.
Dutch title: *Buste van koning-stadhouder Willem III (1650–1702)*

PROVENANCE
Same as inv. no. 364

LITERATURE
Moes/Van Biema 1909, p. 53, no. 238, pp. 102, 109, 125; Van Notten 1907, p. 85; Neurdenburg 1948, p. 221; Staring 1950–1951, p. 182; Amsterdam 1988, no. 117; The Hague 1988–1989, ex catalogue

COMMENT
Companion piece to inv. nos. 364–366. For biographical data on Willem III, see Bakhuysen, inv. no. 6.

Jan Baptist Xavery

Antwerp 1697–1742 The Hague

371 *Bust of Stadholder Willem IV (1711–1751),* 1733

White marble, height 82 cm
Signed and dated at the right side of the pedestal:
J: B: XAVERŸ. F. / 1733
Dutch title: *Buste van stadhouder Willem IV (1711–1751)*

PROVENANCE
Oranjezaal, Huis ten Bosch Palace, The Hague; transferred, 1816

LITERATURE
D/LS 1974–1976, vol. 2, p. 690, no. 5; Hoetink 1962; Ozinga 1969, p. 170; Van der Klooster 1970, p. 108 and note 31; Scholten 1994, p. 116; Scholten 1995, p. 70, in no. 32; Baarsen 1998, p. 172, note 3, p. 173, fig. 14; Amsterdam 2001–2002, no. 20

COMMENT
The model in terracotta is in the Rijksmuseum, Amsterdam (RM 1973, no. 380; Scholten 1995, p. 70, no. 32). Companion piece to inv. no. 372. For biographical data on Willem IV, see Aved, inv. no. 461. The bust shows the prince with the badges of his rank: the ceremonial cuirass, the ermine cloak and the Order of the Garter.

372 *Bust of Princess Anne of Hannover (1709–1759),* 1736

White marble, height 85 cm
Signed and dated at the left side of the pedestal:
J: B: Xavery. F: 1736.
Dutch title: *Buste van prinses Anne van Hannover (1709–1759)*

PROVENANCE
Same as inv. no. 371

LITERATURE
Ozinga 1969, p. 170; Scholten 1994, p. 116; Amsterdam 2001–2002, no. 20

371

372

365

366

367

COMMENT
Companion piece to inv. no. 371. For biographical data on Anne, see Tischbein (after), inv. no. 504.

France

374 *Bust of Pierre Lyonet (1706–1789)*, 18th century

Terracotta, height 77 cm
Dutch title: *Buste van Pierre Lyonet (1706–1789)*

PROVENANCE
Gift of G.T.B. Croiset to King Willem I, The Hague; Royal Cabinet of Curiosities, housed in the Mauritshuis, 1825; on loan to the Haags Gemeentemuseum, The Hague, since 1990

LITERATURE
Staring 1947, p. 128; Van Seters 1947

COMMENT
Pierre (or Pieter) Lyonet was a jurist in The Hague, secretary to the States General, as well as an entomologist, draughtsman and engraver (see Dumas 1991, pp. 534–535). Formerly attributed to Jean-Baptiste Le Moyne, who remains the most likely candidate for the bust, as well as Jean-Jacques Caffieri and Marie-Anne Falconet. The donor, Croiset, was related to Lyonet.

Southern Netherlands
Brussels

973 *The Virgin Mary*, c.1475

Oak with polychromy, height 47.5 cm
Signed with a monogram on the right sleeve, below the letter 'N' (see Van Vlierden 2003)
Dutch title: *De maagd Maria*

PROVENANCE
Wertheimer Gallery, Paris; purchased, 1965; on loan to the Museum Catharijneconvent, Utrecht, since 1989

LITERATURE
Mauritshuis 1968, pp. 57–58; Mauritshuis 1970, no. 3; Van Vlierden 1997; Van Vlierden 1998; Scholten 1998b; Van Vlierden 2004, pp. 277–280 (with literature references)

COMMENT
Reunited at the Museum Catharijneconvent with another piece of a retable with a crucifixion by a Brussels master, acquired by the Utrecht museum in 1997. The three sculptures, all of high quality, were cut from the same piece of oak. Inspired by Rogier van der Weyden.

374

973

Prints and Drawings

Giovanni Antonio Pellegrini

Venice 1675–1741 Venice

834 *The wounded Porus before Alexander the Great,* c.1708–1710

Pen drawing, washed in sepia, 29 x 36 cm
Signed on the verso: *Di Antonio Pellegrini Veneziano*
Dutch title: *De gewonde Porus voor Alexander de Grote*

PROVENANCE

J.H. Wiegersma Gallery, Utrecht; gift of J.G. van Gelder, Utrecht, 1946

LITERATURE

Venice 1959, no. 65; Mauritshuis 1970, no. 50; Venice-Florence 1985, no. 68; Knox 1995, p. 275, no. D 114; Padua 1998–1999, pp. 93, 108, note 30

COMMENT

It is not entirely clear whether Porus or Darius is depicted. Related to Pellegrini's painting in the Casa di Risparmio, Padua. There is another related design in the Cini Collection, Venice. An oil sketch with a similar composition and the same subject is in the Accademia at Ravenna.

Pierre Philippe

Metz *c.*1635–1702 The Hague

1087 *Banquet in the Mauritshuis on the occasion of the visit of Charles II (1630–1685), King of England, 30 May 1660,* 1660

Etching and engraving, 40 x 49 cm
Inscribed centre right: *JTvielt [sic] in: Pierre Philippe Sculpsit.* (JT in ligature)
Dutch title: *Feestmaal in het Mauritshuis op 30 mei 1660 ter gelegenheid van het bezoek van Karel II (1630–1685), koning van Engeland*

PROVENANCE

Gift of H.J. Hijmersma, Den Bosch, 1987

LITERATURE

Hollstein, vol. 17, p. 99, no. 16; Mauritshuis 1991, no. XXIX; Mauritshuis 2000, p. 16

COMMENT

Engraved after Jacob Toorenvliet (1640–1719), published in Abraham de Wicquefort's *Verhael in forme Van Journael, van de reys Ende 't vertoeven Van den Seer Doorluchtige ende Machtige Prins Carel II,* The Hague 1660 and William Lower's *A Relation [...] of the Voiage and Residence which [...] Charles II [...] hath made in Holland,* The Hague 1660. For more details on the print, see Thornton 1978, p. 270, fig. 257, pp. 274, 412, note 257; Molenaar 1998, p. 52; Krefeld-Oranienburg-Apeldoorn 1999–2000, no. 7/11; Beijerman-Schols *et al.* 2000, p. 153.

Aert Schouman

Dordrecht 1710–1792 The Hague

1134 *Panorama near Arnhem,* 1776

Watercolour on paper, 34 x 43.1 cm
Inscription on the back: *Gezicht by Middagten en Dieren aan den Yzel; Hoog 13¼ dm / Breed 16¼ duim*; lower centre: *A: Schouman del 1776 / naar 't Schildery van Ad: vande Velden / berustende in't Kabinet van Zyne hoogheid Willem de 5e, Prins van Oranje*; bottom left: *A: Schouman fecit na. A. v. de Velden 1776*
Dutch title: *Panorama bij Arnhem*

PROVENANCE

Commissioned by Cornelis Ploos van Amstel, Amsterdam, 1776; acquired before 1931

LITERATURE

Duparc 1978, pp. 283–284 and fig. 2; Mauritshuis 1980, p. 38; Dufais 1998, repr.

COMMENT

Copy after the landscape by Joris van der Haagen (inv. no. 46), at the time attributed to Adriaen van de Velde.

Andy Warhol

Pittsburgh 1928–1987 New York

1080 *Portrait of Queen Beatrix,* 1985

Silkscreen print with diamond dust, 100 x 80 cm
Inscribed and signed lower right: *29/40 Andy Warhol*
Dutch title: *Portret van koningin Beatrix*

PROVENANCE

Lambert Tegenbosch Gallery, Amsterdam and Heusden, 1985; purchased by the Friends of the Mauritshuis Foundation, 1986

LITERATURE

Mauritshuis 1991, no. XXII

COMMENT

Beatrix (b. 1938) has been the reigning queen of the Netherlands since 1980.

1087 

 1080

834 

 1134

Appendices

Index by inventory number

Each work of art is allocated a Mauritshuis inventory number when it enters the collection. A gap in the sequence of numbers indicates that a work is no longer part of the collection (temporary loans to the museum were given numbers until 1975, since which time they have remained unnumbered).

1 Cornelisz van Oostsanen
2 Aelst
3 Aelst
4 Pietersz
5 Baen
6 Bakhuysen
8 Bakhuysen
9 Bassen
10 Ruthart
11 Berchem
12 Berchem
13 Berchem
14 Berchem
16 Bloemaert
17 Bloemaert
19 Bol
20 Both
21 Both
22 Cornelisz van Haarlem
23 Cornelisz van Haarlem
24 Cuylenborch
25 Cuyp
26 Bassen
27 Dijk
28 Dijk
29 Dijk
30 Dijk
31 Does
32 Dou
33 Dou
34 Droochsloot
35 Droochsloot
36 Koninck
37 Meytens
38 Meytens
39 Everdingen
40 Gelder
42 Goltzius
43 Goltzius
44 Goltzius
45 Govaerts
46 Haagen
47 Haagen
48 Heem
49 Heem
50 Heem
51 Heemskerck
52 Heemskerck
53 Heyden
54 Helst
55 Heusch
56 Heusch
57 Houckgeest
58 Houckgeest
59 Hondecoeter
60 Hondecoeter
61 Hondecoeter
62 Hondecoeter
63 Honthorst
64 Honthorst
65 Honthorst
66 Hoogstraten
67 Huchtenburgh
68 Huchtenburgh
69 Huchtenburgh
70 Huysum
71 Huysum
72 Huysum
73 Jardin
74 Jardin
75 Jardin
77 Keyser
78 Keyser
79 Keirincx
80 Koninck
81 Cooghen
82 Lairesse
83 Lairesse
84 Lapp
85 Lievens
86 Lingelbach
87 Lingelbach
88 Lingelbach
89 Lingelbach
90 Maes
91 Man
92 Vermeer
93 Metsu
94 Metsu
95 Metsu
96 Mierevelt
97 Mierevelt
98 Mierevelt
99 Mierevelt
100 Mierevelt
101 Mierevelt
104 Honthorst
105 Northern Netherlands
106 Mieris
107 Mieris
108 Mieris
109 Mieris
110 Mignon
111 Mignon
112 Mignon
113 Mijtens
114 Mijtens
115 Moeyaert
116 Moni
117 Mor
118 Moreelse
119 Ravesteyn
120 Ravesteyn
121 Moucheron
122 Moucheron
123 Musscher
124 Nason
125 Netscher
126 Netscher
127 Netscher
128 Ostade
129 Ostade
130 Pape
131 Pynas
132 Pijnacker
133 Poel
134 Poelenburch
135 Haensbergen
136 Potter
137 Potter
138 Potter
139 Ravesteyn
140 Ravesteyn
141 Ravesteyn
142 Ravesteyn
143 Ravesteyn
144 Ravesteyn
145 Rembrandt
146 Rembrandt
147 Rembrandt
148 Rembrandt
149 Rembrandt
150 Rosenhagen
151 Ruysch
153 Ruisdael
154 Ruisdael
155 Ruisdael
156 Savery
157 Savery
158 Schalcken
159 Schalcken
160 Schalcken
161 Schalcken
162 Schalcken
164 Soolmaker
165 Steen
166 Steen
167 Steen
168 Steen
169 Steen
170 Steen
171 Steenwijck
172 Stoop
173 Storck
174 Storck
176 Borch
177 Borch
178 Toorenburgh
179 Troost
180 Troost
181 Troost
182 Troost
183 Troost
184 Troost
185 Troost
186 Troost
187 Troost
188 Troost
189 Troost
190 Troost
191 Troost
192 Troost
193 Troost
194 Troost
195 Ochtervelt
196 Ulft
197 Velde
198 Velde
199 Velde
200 Velde
201 Velde
202 Venne
203 Vliet
204 Vois
205 Vries
206 Weenix
207 Weenix
208 Werff
209 Werff
210 Westerbaen
211 Westerbaen
212 Wijnants
213 Wijnants
214 Wouwerman
215 Wouwerman
216 Wouwerman
217 Wouwerman
218 Wouwerman
219 Wouwerman
220 Wouwerman
221 Wouwerman
222 Wouwerman
223 Wtewael
225 Key
226 Mierevelt
227 Southern Netherlands
228 Dittmers
229 Northern Netherlands
230 Southern Netherlands
231 Wissing
232 Tischbein
233 Brueghel
234 Brueghel
235 Southern Netherlands
236 Brueghel
237 Champaigne
238 Coques
239 Dyck
240 Dyck
241 Hanneman
242 Dyck
243 Dyck
244 Francken
245 Geeraerts
246 Rubens
247 Rubens
248 Neeffs
249 Vos
250 Rubens
251 Rubens
252 Rubens
253 Brueghel & Rubens
254 Rubens
255 Rubens
256 Seghers
257 Seghers
258 Snijders
259 Vos
260 Teniers
261 Teniers
262 Tilborgh
264 Weyden
266 Haecht
267 Wolfvoet
268 Wolfvoet
269 Seisenegger
270 Seisenegger
271 Seisenegger
272 Bury
273 Lapp
274 Lapp
275 Holbein
276 Holbein
277 Holbein
278 Holbein
279 Holbein
280 Roos
281 Rottenhammer
282 Rottenhammer
283 Brueghel
284 Rottenhammer
285 Brueghel
286 Tischbein
287 Cosimo
288 Cosimo
289 Lione
290 Italy
291 Swanevelt
292 Vernet
293 Vernet
294 Largillière
295 Escalante
296 Murillo
297 Oost
298 Mazo
299 Iriarte
300 Cerezo
301 Correggio
302 Correggio
303 Allori
304 Regnier
305 Pignoni
307 Panini
308 Panini
309 Vanni
310 Bordone
311 Farinato
312 Veronese
313 Cambiaso
314 Cambiaso
315 Carracci
316 Franceschini
317 Italy
319 Geldorp
320 Dughet
321 Giordano
322 Lauri
323 Mazzolino
324 Parmigianino
327 Italy
328 Peruzzini
329 Peruzzini
330 Italy
331 Italy
332 Magnasco
333 Magnasco
334 Langetti
335 Zanchi
336 Sassoferrato
339 Raphael
340 Solimena
342 Turchi
343 Titian
344 Veronese
347 Fogolino
348 Cleve
349 Italy
350 Zuccarelli
351 Italy
352 Giordano
353 Southern Netherlands
354 Parmigianino
355 Rosselli
356 Giordano
357 Raphael
358 Titian
359 Vaccaro
360 SCULPTURES Blommendael
361 SCULPTURES Blommendael
362 SCULPTURES Keyser
364 SCULPTURES Verhulst
365 SCULPTURES Verhulst
366 SCULPTURES Verhulst
367 SCULPTURES Verhulst
369 SCULPTURES Verhulst
370 SCULPTURES Verhulst
371 SCULPTURES Xavery
372 SCULPTURES

Xavery
373 SCULPTURES Houdon
374 SCULPTURES France
378 SCULPTURES Monnot
379 SCULPTURES Falconet
380 SCULPTURES Falconet
386 Northern Netherlands
387 Anspach
391 Begeyn
392 Codde
393 Lastman
394 Moeyaert
395 Moeyaert
396 Tempel
397 Tempel
398 Feti
399 Ast
400 Bega
401 Beyeren
402 Vermeulen
404 Vonck
405 Hondecoeter
406 Vermeer
407 Molenaer
408 Duyster
409 Potter
410 Slabbaert
411 Troost
414 Ravesteyn
415 Ravesteyn
416 Ravesteyn
417 Ravesteyn
418 Ravesteyn
419 Ravesteyn
420 Ravesteyn
421 Ravesteyn
422 Ravesteyn
423 Ravesteyn
424 Ravesteyn
425 Ravesteyn
426 Ravesteyn
427 Goltz
428 Honthorst
429 Hanneman
430 Honthorst
431 Southern Netherlands
432 France
433 Master of the Solomon triptych
437 Bray
438 Ravesteyn
439 Ravesteyn
440 Dusart
445 Codde
446 Lairesse
447 Quast
448 Northern Netherlands
449 Northern Netherlands
454 Baen
455 Ravesteyn
456 Ravesteyn
457 Ravesteyn
459 Hals
460 Hals
461 Aved
462 Ziesenis
463 Ziesenis
464 Tischbein
468 Oosterwyck
469 Wijck
470 Hackaert
471 Velde
472 Dyck
473 Witte
474 Pierson
475 Pot
476 Nieulandt
496 Northern Netherlands
498 Ragueneau
504 Tischbein
507 Mierevelt
530 Bol
531 Heyden
532 Marseus van Schrieck
533 Velde
534 Ruisdael
535 Bellevois
536 Southern Netherlands
537 Olis
538 Saftleven
539 Croix
540 Northern Netherlands
541 Beest
542 Vinckboons
543 Backer
544 Brakenburgh
545 Helst
546 Hillegaert
547 Northern Netherlands
548 Beyeren
549 Mulier
550 SCULPTURES Schardt
551 Goyen
553 Steen
554 Bois
556 Rembrandt
558 Vlieger
559 Mor
560 Rembrandt
561 Northern Netherlands
562 Brekelenkam
563 Velde
564 Leyster
565 Rembrandt
566 Goyen
567 Cappelle
568 Helst
569 Helst
572 Molenaer
573 Molenaer
574 Molenaer
575 Molenaer
576 Molenaer
579 Rembrandt
580 Ostade
584 Rembrandt
585 Bol
595 Memling
596 Heda
598 Rembrandt
599 Loo
601 Haensbergen
602 Noort
603 Northern Netherlands
605 Fabritius
606 Verschuring
607 Brouwer
608 Reyger
609 Troost
610 Rembrandt
611 Verbeecq
613 Heem
615 Palamedesz
618 Hals
621 Rembrandt
623 Hals
624 Goyen
626 Rembrandt
627 Hondecoeter
642 Weenix
654 Northern Netherlands
655 Moreelse
656 Chardin
657 Sweerts
658 Quast
659 Verstralen
662 Vermeulen
664 Steen
665 Beyeren
669 Schweickhardt
670 Vermeer
671 Berghe
672 Berghe
673 Velde
674 Goyen
675 Zwaerdecroon
676 Flinck
677 Vogelaer
678 Beyeren
679 Bosschaert
680 Northern Netherlands
681 Oever
682 Neer
685 Rembrandt
686 Netscher
687 Fijt
688 Jonson van Ceulen
689 Keyser
690 Berckheyde
691 Molenaer
692 Hals
693 Hanneman
694 Southern Netherlands
695 Southern Netherlands
696 Flinck
697 Beyeren
698 Poel
699 Ruysdael
701 Northern Netherlands
702 Morel
703 Morel
705 Moreelse
706 Post
707 Rembrandt
708 Schalcken
709 Schalcken
710 Northern Netherlands
711 Northern Netherlands
712 Dijk
713 Dijk
714 Netscher
715 Netscher
716 Netscher
717 Maes
718 Maes
719 Ravesteyn
720 Haensbergen
721 Netscher
722 Luttichuys
723 Alberts
724 Vermeer van Haarlem
725 David
728 Ruisdael
729 Mijn
730 Mijn
731 Wit
732 Wit
733 Wit
734 Wit
735 Wit
736 Steen
737 Gelder
738 Ruysdael
739 Bruyn
740 Vos
741 Emont
742 Steen
744 Borch
745 Ostade
746 Berckheyde
747 Backer
748 Musscher
749 Mierevelt
750 Mierevelt
751 Slabbaert
752 Master of the Brandon portrait
754 Calraet
755 Soutman
756 Hals
757 Gelder
759 Goyen
760 Jardin
762 Bouts
764 Pothoven
765 Post
766 Post
767 Moroni
770 Mancadan
771 Hals
772 Hals
773 Hals
774 Hals
775 Hals
776 Lagrenée
779 Steen
781 Koekkoek
782 Bakker Korff
783 Provoost
785 Avercamp
787 Neer
789 Ostade
790 Master of Alkmaar
791 Dijck
792 Humphrey
793 Humphrey
794 Snijders
795 Bol
796 Berckheyde
797 Borch
798 Dijck
799 Bois
800 Schalcke
801 Heerschop
802 Ruisdael
803 Ruisdael
806 Keyser
807 Ostade
808 Bray
809 Vermeer van Haarlem
810 Collier
811 Italy
812 SCULPTURES Reijn
813 Haag
814 Kipshaven
815 Heyden
816 Magnasco
817 Magnasco
818 Steen
819 Mieris
820 Cappelle
821 Cuyp
822 Cuyp
823 Dyck
824 Witte
825 Keil
826 Backer
827 Hendriks
828 Rembrandt
829 Cuyp
830 Gossaert
831 Northern Netherlands
832 Sittow
834 PRINTS AND DRAWINGS Pellegrini
835 Hooch
836 Aertsen
837 Rubens
838 Goyen
840 Rembrandt
841 Gossaert
842 Massys
843 David
844 Weyden
845 Master of the female half-lengths
846 Master of the female half-lengths
847 Brouwer
848 Teniers
849 Jordaens
854 Master of Frankfurt
855 Master of Frankfurt
856 Man
857 Codde
860 Mieris
861 Moreau
862 Neer
864 Ostade
865 Verkolje
866 Flinck
867 Fijt
868 Heyden
870 Lépicié
872 Master of Frankfurt
875 Bunel
883 Borch
885 Loo
886 Sweerts
887 Mancadan
888 Saenredam
889 Bruyn
890 Cranach
891 Cranach
895 Cleve
897 Germany
898 Barbari

899 Hobbema
901 Weenix
904 Kulmbach
905 Kulmbach
906 SCULPTURES Falconet
912 Neer
913 Neer
914 Pietersz
915 Post
917 Cranach
918 Cornelisz van Haarlem
919 Brouwer
920 Steen
921 Mostaert
923 Keynooghe
925 Fijt
926 Rubens
927 Kalf
928 Hals
929 Ryckhals
932 Breenbergh
936 Heda
937 Jordaens
940 Weenix
941 Ruysdael
943 Claesz
946 Poorter
947 Claesz
948 Verspronck
949 Verspronck
950 Asselijn
951 Lingelbach
953 Everdingen
955 Voskuyl
957 Eckhout
963 Cuyp
965 Beuckelaer
966 Brugghen
967 Nickele
968 Hondecoeter
969 Porcellis
970 Post
971 Kalf
972 Kalf
973 SCULPTURES Southern Netherlands
974 Saenredam
979 Goyen
981 MINIATURES Honthorst
982 MINIATURES France
983 MINIATURES France
984 MINIATURES France
985 MINIATURES England
986 MINIATURES France
987 MINIATURES France
989 MINIATURES England
991 MINIATURES Cooper
992 MINIATURES Cooper
993 MINIATURES Cooper
994 MINIATURES Gibson
995 MINIATURES Cooper
996 MINIATURES Cooper
997 MINIATURES Arlaud
998 MINIATURES Cooper
999 MINIATURES Cooper
1000 MINIATURES Hilliard
1001 MINIATURES Oliver
1002 MINIATURES Oliver
1004 MINIATURES Hoskins
1005 MINIATURES Hoskins
1006 MINIATURES Hoskins
1007 MINIATURES Hoskins
1008 MINIATURES Cooper
1009 MINIATURES Thach
1010 MINIATURES Mussard
1011 MINIATURES Mussard
1012 MINIATURES Mussard
1013 MINIATURES Oliver
1014 MINIATURES Oliver
1015 MINIATURES Hilliard
1016 MINIATURES Oliver
1017 MINIATURES Oliver
1018 MINIATURES Oliver
1019 MINIATURES Oliver
1020 MINIATURES Oliver
1021 MINIATURES Bruggen
1022 MINIATURES Phaff
1023 MINIATURES Hilliard
1024 MINIATURES Hanneman
1025 MINIATURES Zincke
1026 MINIATURES Northern Netherlands
1027 MINIATURES Hurter
1029 MINIATURES Toutin
1031 Southern Netherlands
1032 Hals
1033 Seghers
1034 Troost
1039 Hackaert
1042 Terwesten
1043 Bol
1044 Ruysdael
1045 Anraedt
1046 Bloemaert
1047 Gelder
1048 Eeckhout
1050 Borch
1055 Heijligers
1056 Beyeren
1057 Backer
1058 Berchem & Weenix
1059 Wtenbrouck
1060 Hals
1061 Hobbema
1062 Campen
1065 Poelenburch
1066 Ast
1067 Hemessen
1068 Troost
1069 SCULPTURES Schepp
1070 Wijnantz
1071 Mieris
1072 Brueghel
1073 Ast
1074 Lastman
1075 Pot
1076 Pot
1077 Gheyn
1078 Lataster
1079 Lataster
1080 PRINTS AND DRAWINGS Warhol
1081 Goyen
1082 Lataster
1083 Lataster
1084 Eeckhout
1087 PRINTS AND DRAWINGS Philippe
1088 Everdingen
1089 Campen
1090 MINIATURES Monogrammist RF
1091 Berchem
1092 Teniers
1093 Lisse
1094 Goyen
1095 Jardin
1096 Santvoort
1097 Wtenbrouck
1098 Breenbergh
1099 Heem
1100 Goyen
1101 Maes
1102 Laer
1104 Berg
1105 Hobbema
1106 Coorte
1107 Honthorst
1108 Ast
1109 Pietersz
1110 Bray
1111 Steen
1113 Huysum
1114 Huysum
1115 Ruysdael
1116 Flinck
1117 Ruysdael
1118 Rembrandt
1119 Geeraerts
1120 SCULPTURES Logteren
1121 Sweerts
1122 Willaerts
1123 Saftleven
1124 Roghman
1125 Claesz
1126 Kalf
1127 Post
1128 Ruysdael
1129 Savery
1131 Rubens
1132 Rubens
1133 Ter Borch
1134 PRINTS AND DRAWINGS Schouman
1135 Pellegrini
1136 Pellegrini
1137 Pellegrini
1138 Pellegrini
1139 Pellegrini
1140 Pellegrini
1141 Pellegrini
1142 Pellegrini
1143 Pellegrini
1144 Pellegrini
1145 Pellegrini
1146 Pellegrini
1147 Pellegrini
1148 Pellegrini
1149 Pellegrini

Paintings and sculptures no longer in the collection

The following paintings have been returned since the publication of *Mauritshuis 1985*

HANNEMA-DE STUERS FUNDATIE, HEINO

1085 Willem Bartel van der Kooi: *Portrait of King Willem I*

NEDERLANDS SCHEEPVAARTMUSEUM, AMSTERDAM

1063 Frans Post: *Brazilian landscape*

NETHERLANDS INSTITUTE FOR CULTURAL HERITAGE (ICN), AMSTERDAM AND RIJSWIJK

1086 Jacob Jordaens (circle of): *The expulsion from the temple*
1112 Gerrit Berckheyde: *View of Dam Square, Amsterdam, with the town hall*

RIJKSMUSEUM, AMSTERDAM

784 Southern Netherlands: *The building of the Tower of Babel*
788 Jan Weenix: *Still life with game and fruit*
853 Jan Provoost: *Madonna and Child enthroned, with Sts Jerome, John the Baptist and a kneeling monk*
880 Cornelis Cornelisz, known as Kunst: *The circumcision, with on the verso Mary in grisaille*
881 Pieter Pourbus: *Portrait of a young cleric*
884 Meindert Hobbema: *Watermill*
894 Joachim Patenir (manner of): *Landscape with the temptation of St Anthony*
896 France: *Dionysius the Areopagite in prayer*
944 Southern Netherlands: *The meeting of Abraham and Melchizedek* and *The synagogue*
945 Southern Netherlands: *Gathering the manna* and *Ecclesia*
958 Adriaen Isenbrant: *Madonna and Child*
959 Herri met de Bles: *Paradise*
960 Braunschweig Monogrammist: *'Ecce Homo'*
961 Quinten Massys: *The carrying of the cross*
962 Adriaen Brouwer: *The smoker*
1030 Henri Toutin (attributed to): *Portrait of Frederik Hendrik*

The following paintings have been de-accessioned

152 Rachel Ruysch: *Still life*, 1715
S. Nijstad Gallery, The Hague, 1964; Sydney van den Bergh, Wassenaar (De Vries 1968, no. 90); Leonard Koetser Gallery, London, 1971 (HdG 1907–1928, vol. 10, p. 313, no. 23; *Connoisseur* 176 (April 1971), no. 710, repr.)

403 Pieter Claesz: *Still life*, 1644
S. Nijstad Gallery, The Hague, 1961; E. Speelman Gallery, London; London, The Harold Samuel Collection (Sutton 1992, no. 15)

666 Attributed to Willem Kalf: *Still life*
S. Nijstad Gallery, The Hague, 1962; sale London, Christie's, 2 November 2001, lot 55, repr. (Grisebach 1974, no. 100a)

743 Meindert Hobbema: *Landscape with the water mills of Singraven at Denekamp*, *c.*1668
Ottawa, National Gallery of Canada, presented in 1950 by Queen Juliana of the Netherlands to the people of Canada to commemorate the part played by Canada in the Liberation of the Netherlands in 1944–1945 and Canada's hospitality to the Royal Family during the Second World War (Broulhiet 1938, no. 93; R. van Leeuwen in *Nieuwsbrief Mauritshuis* 5 (1992), no. 2, p. 7)

858 François-Hubert Drouais: *Portrait of two sons of Louis Arnaud*, 1761

859 François-Hubert Drouais: *Portrait of two sons of the Duc de Bouillon*
Rosenberg & Stiebel Gallery, New York, 1956; no. 859 was sold at Sotheby's, New York, 30 January 1997, lot 100

The following sculpture has been de-accessioned

922 Southern Netherlands: *Mourning woman from a passion scene*, *c.*1480
Purchased in 1955 by the Friends of the Mauritshuis Foundation (see Van Vlierden 2004, pp. 271–272).

Changed attributions

Works reattributed since the publication of Mauritshuis 1985, in alphabetical order

PAINTINGS AND PASTELS

836 Pieter Aertsen > Pieter Aertsen (attributed to)
723 Gerrit Alberts (attributed to) > Gerrit Alberts
234 Hendrick van Balen and school of Jan Brueghel the Elder > Jan Brueghel the Elder with an anonymous pupil of Rubens
898 Jacopo de' Barbari > Jacopo de' Barbari (attributed to)
10 Adriaen Beeldemaker > Carl Borromäus Andreas Ruthart
530 Ferdinand Bol (attributed to) > Ferdinand Bol (manner of)
762 Dieric Bouts (milieu of) > Dirk Bouts (circle of)
303 Agnolo Bronzino (studio of) > Alessandro Allori (circle of)
283 Jan Brueghel the Elder (attributed to) with Hendrick van Balen > Jan Brueghel the Elder and Hans Rottenhammer
285 Jan Brueghel the Younger and Hans Rottenhammer > Jan Brueghel the Elder and Hans Rottenhammer
236 Jan Brueghel the Elder (circle of) > Jan Brueghel the Younger?
875 François Bunel II > François Bunel II (attributed to)
307 Luca Carlevarijs > Giovanni Paolo Panini (follower of)
308 Luca Carlevarijs > Giovanni Paolo Panini (follower of)
237 Philippe de Champaigne > Philippe de Champaigne (circle of)
895 Joos van Cleve > Joos van Cleve (studio of)
348 Joos van Cleve (circle of) > Joos van Cleve (studio of)
238 Gonzales Coques > Gonzales Coques in collaboration with many other artists
918 Cornelis Cornelisz van Haarlem (attributed to) > Cornelis Cornelisz van Haarlem (after)
290 Jacques Courtois > Italy, 17th century
891 Lucas Cranach the Elder > Lucas Cranach the Elder (and/or studio?)
627 Aelbert Cuyp > Gijsbert Gillisz d'Hondecoeter
963 Aelbert Cuyp > Aelbert Cuyp (manner of)
821 Aelbert Cuyp (circle of) > Aelbert Cuyp (manner of)
829 Aelbert Cuyp > Aelbert Cuyp?
26 Dirck van Delen > Bartholomeus van Bassen (attributed to)
228 Henrich Dittmars > Heinrich Dittmers
957 Albert Eckhout > Albert Eckhout (attributed to)
798 Barent Fabritius > Abraham van Dijck (attributed to)
828 Carel Fabritius (attributed to) > Rembrandt (circle of)
687 Jan Fijt > Jan Fijt (attributed to)
244 Frans Francken the Younger and Paul Vredeman de Vries > Frans Francken the Younger, Paul Vredeman de Vries and an unidentified miniaturist
321 Luca Giordano (attributed to) > Luca Giordano
936 Gerrit Willemsz Heda > Willem Claesz Heda (attributed to)
275 Hans Holbein the Younger (attributed to) > Hans Holbein the Younger (formerly attributed to)
968 Melchior d'Hondecoeter > Melchior d'Hondecoeter?
63 Gerard van Honthorst > Gerrit van Honthorst (studio)
428 Gerard van Honthorst > Gerrit van Honthorst (and studio)
430 Gerard van Honthorst > Gerrit van Honthorst (after)
825 Bernhard Keil > Bernhard Keil (attributed to)
79 Alexander Keirincx with an artist from the circle of Cornelis van Poelenburgh > Alexander Keirincx with Cornelis van Poelenburch
776 Louis Lagrenée (attributed to) > Louis Lagrenée
273 Jan Willemsz Lapp (attributed to) > Jan Willemsz Lapp
274 Jan Willemsz Lapp (attributed to) > Jan Willemsz Lapp (manner of)
231 Peter Lely (copy after) > Willem Wissing
289 Andrea de Leone (attributed to) > Andrea de Lione (attributed to)
85 Jan Lievens > Jan Lievens (after?)
309 Benedetto Luti (attributed to) > Raffaello Vanni (attributed to)
328 Alessandro Magnasco > Antonio Francesco Peruzzini with Sebastiano Ricci
329 Alessandro Magnasco > Antonio Francesco Peruzzini with Sebastiano Ricci
842 Quinten Massys > Quinten Massys (and/or studio)
298 Juan Bautista Martinez del Mazo (attributed to) > Juan Bautista Martinez del Mazo (studio of?)
37 Martin Meytens the Younger > Martin Meytens the Younger (studio of)
38 Martin Meytens the Younger > Martin Meytens the Younger (studio of)
507 Michiel Jansz van Mierevelt (studio) > Michiel Jansz van Mierevelt (after)
297 Pieter van Mol (attributed to) > Jacob van Oost II (circle of)
559 Anthonis Mor van Dashorst > Anthonis Mor van Dashorst (and studio)
767 Giovanni Battista Moroni (attributed to) > Giovanni Battista Moroni
921 Jan Mostaert > Jan Mostaert?
715 Caspar Netscher > Caspar Netscher (studio of)
546 Hendrick Pacx > Pauwels van Hillegaert
1144 – 1149 Giovanni Antonio Pellegrini > Giovanni Antonio Pellegrini (formerly attributed to)
139 – 144; 414–426; 438–439; 455–457 Jan van Ravesteyn > Jan van Ravesteyn (and studio)
427 Jan van Ravesteyn > Fransise de Goltz
304 Nicolas Regnier (style of or after) > Nicolas Regnier (attributed to)
148 Rembrandt > Rembrandt (studio copy)
560 Rembrandt > Rembrandt (attributed to)
565 Rembrandt > Rembrandt (and/or studio of)?
621 Rembrandt > Rembrandt (and/or studio of)?
579 Rembrandt (imitator of) > Rembrandt (circle of)
250 Peter Paul Rubens > Peter Paul Rubens (and studio)
251 Peter Paul Rubens > Peter Paul Rubens (and studio)
254 Peter Paul Rubens (after) > Peter Paul Rubens (studio copy)
534 Jacob van Ruisdael > Jacob van Ruisdael (manner of)
566 Salomon van Ruysdael (circle of) > Jan van Goyen (attributed to)?
336 Sassoferrato > Sassoferrato (after)
794 Frans Snijders > Frans Snijders (studio of)
172 Dirck Stoop > Dirck Stoop (attributed to)
291 Herman van Swanevelt (attributed to) > Herman van Swanevelt
327 Tintoretto (style of or after) > Italy, 16th century
811 Tintoretto (style of or after) > Italy, 16th century
471 Willem van de Velde the Younger (attributed to) > Willem van de Velde the Younger (studio of)?
563 Willem van de Velde the Younger (milieu of) > Willem van de Velde the Younger (studio of)?
344 Bonifazio Veronese (milieu of) > Bonifazio Veronese
264 Rogier van der Weyden > Rogier van der Weyden (and studio)

MASTERS WITH ACQUIRED NAMES

790 Master of Alkmaar > Master of Alkmaar (follower of or after)
752 Master of the Brandon portrait > Master of the Brandon portrait (attributed to)
844 Master of the Legend of St Barbara > Rogier van der Weyden (follower of)
741 Monogrammist AVE >

Adriaen van Emont (attributed to)

692 Monogrammist BE > Frans Hals (follower of)

ANONYMOUS PAINTINGS

504 Dutch School > Johann Friedrich August Tischbein (after)

610 Dutch School > Rembrandt (circle of)

626 Dutch School > Rembrandt (studio of)

674 Dutch School > Jan van Goyen (manner of)

932 Dutch School > Bartholomeus Breenbergh (follower of)

967 Dutch School > Jan van Nickele?

1042 Dutch School > Mattheus Terwesten

319 Flemish School > Gortzius Geldorp the Elder

702 Flemish School > Jean Baptiste Morel (attributed to)

703 Flemish School > Jean Baptiste Morel (attributed to)

725 Flemish School > Gerard David (after)

305 Italian school > Simone Pignoni (after)

334 Italian school > Giovanni Battista Langetti

335 Italian school > Antonio Zanchi

352 Italian school > Luca Giordano (after)

355 Italian school > Matteo Rosselli (follower of)

356 Italian school > Luca Giordano (follower of)

359 Italian school > Domenico Antonio Vaccaro

MINIATURES

982 John Bettes (attributed to) > France, 18th century?

983 Arnold van Brounckhurst (attributed to) > France, 18th century?

998 David des Granges (attributed to) > Alexander Cooper (attributed to)

999 David des Granges (attributed to) > Alexander Cooper (attributed to)

1015 Nicholas Hilliard (studio of) > Nicholas Hilliard (and/or studio of)?

1017 Peter Oliver (attributed to) > Peter Oliver

1021 Peter Oliver (attributed to) > Louis van der Bruggen

1022 Loch Phaff > 'Le chevalier' Phaff

1009 Nathaniel Tach > Nathaniel Thach

1025 Christian Friedrich Zincke (attributed to) > Christian Friedrich Zincke

ANONYMOUS MINIATURES

981 Dutch School > Gerrit van Honthorst (after)

1024 Dutch School > Adriaen Hanneman (after)

985 French School > England, 19th century?

SCULPTURES

550 Jan Jorisz van der Schardt (attributed to) > Johan Gregor van der Schardt

List of catalogues of the Galerij Prins Willem V and Mauritshuis

List of catalogues of the Galerij Prins Willem V and the Koninklijk Kabinet van Schilderijen Mauritshuis, including catalogues of exhibitions held in or organised by the Mauritshuis, and other relevant publications and manuscripts, kept in the libraries and archives of the Mauritshuis, the Rijksmuseum, the Netherlands Institute for Art History and other institutions, excluding articles on new acquisitions or loans. For catalogues of the Koninklijk Kabinet van Zeldzaamheden, see Effert 2003.

by Quentin Buvelot

Galerij Prins Willem V

1768
Catalogue du Cabinet des Tableaux Delaissés par feu Monsieur Govert de Slingelandt, Receveur Général de la Hollande, &c. &c. &c., The Hague (House of Van Slingelandt), 18 May 1768 (the entire Van Slingelandt Collection was sold *en bloc* to Willem V; see Lugt 1938–1987, no. 1683; Van Riemsdijk 1892 and Hofstede de Groot 1892)

1770
P. Terwesten, *Catalogue D'une partie du superbe Cabinet de Tableaux de Son Altesse Sérenissime Monseigneur le Prince d'Orange et de Nassau / Catalogus Van een gedeelte van 't Vorstelyk Kabinet Schilderyen van Zyne Doorl. Hoogheid, den Heere Prince van Orange en Nassau*, The Hague 1770 (also published in G. Hoet, P. Terwesten, *Catalogus of naamlyst van schilderyen, met derzelve pryzen*, 3 vols, The Hague 1752–1770, vol. 3, pp. 689–720)

1775
J.F.C. Grimm, *Bemerkungen eines Reisenden durch Deutschland, Frankreich, England und Holland*, vol. 3, Altenburg 1775, pp. 273–274, 290

1781
J. Reynolds, 'Gallery of the Prince of Orange' [in 'A journey to Flanders and Holland in the year MDCCLXXXI'], in J. Reynolds, edited by H. Mount, *A Journey to Flanders and Holland*, Cambridge 1996, pp. 84–88 (see also 'Aanmerkingen op de Hollandsche Schilders en Schilderyen, van Joshua Reynolds, (Getrokken uit diens *Picturesque Journey t[h]rough Flandres and Holland.*)', *Nieuwe Algemene Konst- en Letter-Bode*, 14 December 1798, no. 259, pp. 186–187; and Broos 1994 cited below)

1783
H. Sanders, '[Das Gemäldekabinet[t] des Prinzen Erbstatthalters]', *Beschreibung seiner Reisen durch Frankreich, die Niederlande, Holland, Deutschland und Italien*, vol. 1, Leipzig 1783, pp. 504–506

1790
S. Ireland, *A Picturesque Tour through Holland, Brabant, and part of France; Made in the Autumn of 1789*, 2 vols, London 1790, vol. 1, pp. 71–72

before 1793?
[F. ten Dall, from notes by the late T.P.C. Haag], *Catalogus van het Kabinet Schilderijen van Zijne Doorl: Hoogheid den Heere Prince van Orange en Nassau enz. in 's Gravenhage*, Manuscript, The Hague [probably before 1793] (Royal Archives, The Hague; quoted after Drossaers/Lunsingh Scheurleer 1974–1976, vol. 3, pp. 203–242; to be compared with the other inventories by Ten Dall dated to 1815, see below)

1795
'Berigten: Nederlanden: 's Hage', *Nieuwe Algemene Konst- en Letter-Bode*, 27 March 1795, no. 65, p. 1

after 1795
Catalogus van de schoone verzameling Schilderijen die zig in den Haag bevonden in de Galerij van den voormaligen Stad-houder Willem den vijfden Prins van Orange etc. etc. en die in Frankrijk getransporteerd zijn voor en door de Fransche Natie als gereekend zijnde te behooren onder de geconquesteerde goederen van dien Prins in Mey 1795, Manuscript, The Hague [after 1795] (quoted after Mauritshuis 1914, p. XIII, note 2, no. II; whereabouts unknown)

1798
[Le Général Pommereul], 'Etat des objets d'arts envoyés aux divers musées français, et conquis par les armées de la République pendant la guerre de la liberté', [F. Milizia, ed.], *De l'art de voir dans les Beaux-Arts, traduit de l'italien de Milizia*, Paris [1798], pp. 275–316

1799
Notices des tableaux des écoles française et flamande, Exposés dans la grande Galerie du Musée central des Arts, Dont l'Ouverture a eu lieu le 18 Germinal an VII [7 April 1799], Paris 1799

'Schilderyen en Beeldhou[w]stukken: Parys', *Nieuwe Algemene Konst- en Letter-Bode*, 5 July 1799, no. 288, p. 5

1804–1815
A.M. Filhol, *Galerie du Musée Napoléon*, 10 vols, Paris 1804–1815

1815
[F. ten Dall, from notes by the late T.P.C. Haag], *Inventaris van de schilderijen van de Gallerij en Cabinet van zijne Doorluchtige Hoogheid den Heere Prince Erfstadhouder. &.&.&.*, Manuscript, The Hague [September-October 1815] (gift of J.Z. Mazel, probably 1882)

[F. ten Dall, from notes by the late T.P.C. Haag], *Catalogus van het Kabinet Schilderyen van Z:D:H: den Heere Prince van Orange & Nassau in 's Gravenhage*, Manuscript, The Hague [1815] (gift of W.A. Meijboom, Voorburg, 1934)

1816
Schilderijen van Parijs terug ontvangen, Manuscript, The Hague [1816]

1817
[J. Steengracht van Oostkapelle], *Lijst van het Koninklijk Kabinet van Schilderijen in 's Gravenhage*, [The Hague] 1817

[J. Steengracht van Oostkapelle], *Notice des Tableaux de la Galerie Royale a La Haye*, [The Hague] 1817

1818
J. Steengracht van Oostkapelle, *Catalogus van het Koninklijk Kabinet van Schilderijen in 's Gravenhage, bevattende de Schilderstukken der Oude Meesters, thans in de Groote Gallerij ten toon gesteld, benevens de Levensbeschrijvingen der Schilders*, Manuscript, The Hague [1818]

1891
W. Beckford, *The History of the Caliph Vathek; and European Travels*, London-New York-Melbourne 1891, pp. 108–109 (visited in 1780; see also G. Janzen (ed.), *William Beckford: Een dromer op reis: Een Grand Tour*, Amsterdam 1991, p. 46)

1902
C. Saunier, 'IV: Reprises de la Belgique et de la Hollande', *Les Conquêtes Artistiques de la Révolution et de l'Empire*, Paris 1902, pp. 113–129

1917
J.J. Marquet de Vasselot, *Répertoire des catalogues du Musée du Louvre (1793–1917) suivi de la liste des directeurs et conservateurs du musée*, Paris 1917, pp. 37–47 (list of catalogues of the Musée Central des Arts / Musée Napoléon, where the collection of Willem V was exhibited for 20 years; cf. also *ibid.*, *Répertoire des catalogues du Musée du Louvre (1793–1926)*, Paris 1927)

1933
A.W. de Vink, 'De kunstverzamelingen van Stadhouder Prins Willem V en hare lotgevallen sedert 1795', *Die Haghe* (1933), pp. 54–134

1942
H.E. van Gelder, 'Haagsche Kunstverzamelingen voor 1900', *Jaarboek Die Haghe* (1942), pp. 24–25, 28

1966
F. Boyer, 'Louis XVIII et la restitution des oeuvres d'art confisquées sous la révolution et l'empire', *Bulletin de la société de l'histoire de l'art français 1965*, Paris 1966, pp. 201–207

1967
H.E. van Gelder, 'De stadhouderlijke verzamelingen', *150 jaar Koninklijk Kabinet van Schilderijen Koninklijke*

Bibliotheek Koninklijk Penningkabinet, The Hague 1967, especially pp. 28–42

1971

F. Boyer, 'Le transfert à Paris des collections du stathouder (1795)', *Annales Historiques de la Révolution française* 43 (1971), no. 203, pp. 389–404

1972

F. Boyer, 'Une conquête artistique de la convention: Les tableaux du stathouder (1795)', *Bulletin de la société de l'histoire de l'art français [...] Année 1970*, Paris 1972, pp. 149–157

1974

I. Hasselgren, *Konstsamlaren Gustaf Adolf Sparre 1746–1794: Hans studieresa, våning, och konstsamling i Göteborg*, Göteborg 1974, pp. 33–41

1974–1976

S.W.A. Drossaers, T.H. Lunsingh Scheurleer, *Inventarissen van de inboedels in de verblijven van de Oranjes en daarmede gelijk te stellen stukken*, 3 vols, The Hague 1974–1976

1975

H. de Lussanet de la Sablonière, 'De restauratie van Buitenhof 34 tot en met 38 te 's-Gravenhage ten behoeve van de Tweede Kamer der Staten-Generaal', *Bulletin van de Koninklijke Nederlandse Oudheidkundige Bond* 74 (1975), pp. 97–126

1976

C.W. Fock, 'De schilderijengalerij van Prins Willem V op het Buitenhof te Den Haag (1)', *Antiek* 11 (1976), pp. 113–137

B. Brenninkmeyer-de Rooij, 'De schilderijengalerij van Prins Willem V op het Buitenhof te Den Haag (2)', *Antiek* 11 (1976), pp. 138–160

[B. Brenninkmeyer-de Rooij], 'Catalogus van het Kabinet Schilderijen, van Zijne Doorl: Hoogheid den Heere Prince van Orange en Nassau in 's-Gravenhage', *Antiek* 11 (1976), no. 2, pp. 161–176

A. Brejon de Lavergnée, J. Foucart, 'Nouvelles précisions sur la collection de tableaux du Stathouder', *Antiek* 11 (1976), pp. 177–185 (see below)

1977

[B. Brenninkmeyer-de Rooij], *Schilderijenzaal Prins Willem V [Visitor's guide]*, The Hague 1977

C.W. Fock, B.M.J. Brenninkmeyer-de Rooij, A. Brejon de Lavergnée, J. Foucart, with an introduction by R. de Haas, *De schilderijenzaal Prins Willem V te 's-Gravenhage*, The Hague 1977 (off-print of *Antiek* 11 (1976), no. 2, pp. 113–185)

E.J. S[luijter], '18de eeuw: [Review of] C. Willemijn Fock en Beatrijs Brenninkmeyer-de Rooij, "De schilderijengalerij van Prins Willem V op het Buitenhof te Den Haag"', *Oud Holland* 91 (1977), pp. 298–299

F.J. Duparc, '[The following paintings, which belonged to the Kabinet Willem V, have not been returned by the French in 1815]', *Mauritshuis: The Royal Cabinet of Paintings: Illustrated General Catalogue*, The Hague 1977, pp. 301–302 (with corrigenda in *Antiek* 13 (1978), see below)

1978

A. Brejon de Lavergnée, J. Foucart, 'Nieuwe gegevens over de schilderijen-verzameling van de Stadhouder', *Antiek* 13 (1978), pp. 273–281 (see above)

F.J. Duparc, 'De collectie van Stadhouder Willem V: Enkele aanvullingen', *Antiek* 13 (1978), pp. 282–284

J.G. van Gelder, 'De collectie van Stadhouder Willem V: Enkele aanvullingen', *Antiek* 13 (1978), pp. 285–290

1979

C.W. Fock, 'The Princes of Orange as Patrons of Art in the Seventeenth Century', *Apollo* 110 (1979), no. 214, pp. 466–475

1982

B.M.J. Brenninkmeyer-de Rooij, *Schilderijengalerij Prins Willem V / The Prince William V Gallery of Paintings*, The Hague 1982

1983

B. Brenninkmeyer-de Rooij, *Jan Davidsz. de Heem (1606–1683/84): Allegorisch portret van Prins Willem III*, The Hague 1983 (see Exhibitions, Galerij Prins Willem V)

H.J. Hijmersma, 'Princely collection, fashionable taste: Prince Willem V's Gallery, in The Hague', *Country Life*, 25 August 1983, pp. 74–75

1985

T. Coppens, 'Oranje als collectioneur: Waarom het hof niet beschikt over een eigen portretgalerij', *Elseviers Magazine*, 9 November 1985, pp. 102–105

1989

E. Hinterding, F. Horsch, '"A small but choice collection": The art gallery of King Willem II of the Netherlands (1792–1849)', *Simiolus* 19 (1989), p. 24

1991

B. Broos, 'Kabinetten, galerijen en het oudste museum van Nederland', *Mauritshuis Cahier* (1991), no. 2, pp. 12–20

1992

B. Broos, 'De vernieuwing van de Galerij Willem V', *Nieuwsbrief Mauritshuis* 5 (1992), nos. 3–4, pp. 12–13

1993

B. Broos, 'The Oldest Museum in the Netherlands', *Mauritshuis in focus* 6 (1993), no. 3, pp. 9–16

M. de Boer, B. Broos, E. Buijsen, R. van Leeuwen, P. van der Ploeg, 'Summary Catalogue of the Picture Gallery of Prince Willem V', *Mauritshuis in focus* 6 (1993), no. 3, pp. 22–38

1994

[P. van der Ploeg], *Galerij Prins Willem V [Visitor's guide]*, The Hague 1994

B. Broos, 'Een bezoek aan de Galerij van Prins Willem V in 1781', *Antiek* 28 (1994), pp. 346–351

1998

N. Dufais, 'Aert Schouman after Joris van der Haagen: A copy in watercolour', *Mauritshuis in focus* 11 (1998), no. 1, pp. 29–34

2000

F. Grijzenhout, *Een Koninklijk Museum: Lodewijk Napoleon en het Rijksmuseum 1806–1810*, Amsterdam (Rijksmuseum) 2000, pp. 61, 66, 67, 68

2001

K. van Strien, 'De verzamelingen van de prins van Oranje', *De ontdekking van de Nederlanden: Britse en Franse reizigers in Holland en Vlaanderen, 1750–1795*, Utrecht 2001, pp. 61–67

2002

M. Loonstra, with W. Gans, B. Winnubst and J. Bakker, edited by P. van der Ploeg, *Koninklijk Zilver: Hoogtepunten uit de verzamelingen van het Huis Oranje-Nassau*, The Hague-Zwolle 2002 (see Exhibitions, Galerij Prins Willem V)

H. Kraan, with I. Brons, *Dromen van Holland: Buitenlandse kunstenaars schilderen Holland, 1800–1914*, Zwolle-The Hague 2002, pp. 26–27, 34

Royal Picture Gallery Mauritshuis

1821

A. Falck, *Cataloque de la Collection de tableaux du chevalier De Rainer*, Manuscript, Brussels, 27 September 1821

1822

[J. Steengracht van Oostkapelle], *Notitie der Schilderyen van het Koninklyk Kabinet te 's Gravenhage*, The Hague 1822

[J. Steengracht van Oostkapelle], *Notice du Musée Royal de Tabl[e]aux à La Haye*, The Hague 1822

1823

[J. Steengracht van Oostkapelle], *Notitie der Schilderyen van het Koninklyk Kabinet te 's Gravenhage*, The Hague 1823

[J. Steengracht van Oostkapelle], *Notice du Musée Royal de Tabl[e]aux à La Haye*, The Hague 1823

J. Murray, '[The Musée or King's Collection of Paintings, at the Hague]', *Tour in Holland in the year MDCCCXIX*, London [1823], pp. 42–58

1826

Catalogue de Tableaux Précieux Formant la Collection de M. Reghellini de Schio, Précédé d'une Notice Historique sur l'Arrivée de ces Tableaux dans le Royaume des Pays-Bas, Brussels 1826

[G. Agar Ellis], 'The Hague: The musée, or academy', *Catalogue of the principal pictures of Flanders and Holland: 1822*, London 1826, pp. 40–47

1826–1830

J. Steengracht van Oostkapelle, *De voornaamste schilderijen van het Koninklijk Kabinet te 's Gravenhage, in omtrek gegraveerd, met derzelver beschrijving*, 4 vols, The Hague 1826–1830

J. Steengracht van Oostkapelle, *Les principaux tableaux du Musée Royal à La Haye, gravés au trait, avec leur description*, The Hague 1826–1830 (for these and other early illustrated catalogues of the Mauritshuis, see Ouwerkerk 2002, pp. 278–283)

1827

[J. Steengracht van Oostkapelle], *Notitie der Schilderyen van het Koninklyk Kabinet te 's Gravenhage*, The Hague [1827] (337 entries; reprinted in 1828 with an appendix, nos. 338–364; reprinted in 1829 with an appendix, nos. 365–388; reprinted in 1830 with an appendix, nos. 389–423, see below)

1830

[J. Steengracht van Oostkapelle], *Notitie der Schilderijen van het Koninklijk Kabinet te 's Gravenhage*, The Hague [1830] (423 entries)

1833

[J. Immerzeel], *Het koninklijk Museum van 's Gravenhage op steen gebragt, opgedragen aan Hare Majesteit De Koningin der Nederlanden / Musée Royal de La Haye lithographié, dédié à Sa Majesté la Reine des Paijs-Bas*, Amsterdam, Desguerrois et Cie, [1828–]1833

L. Wienbarg, 'Amsterdammer und Haager Gemäldesammlung', *Holland in den Jahren 1831 und 1832*, vol. 2, Hamburg 1833, pp. 88–95

1834

[J.] Duchesne Ainé, '[Le Musée de La Haye]', *Voyage d'un Iconophile: Revue des principaux cabinets d'estampes, bibliothèques et musées d'Allemagne, de Hollande et d'Angleterre*, Paris 1834, pp. 278–281

K. Schnaase, *Niederländische Briefe*, Stuttgart-Tübingen 1834, pp. 19–21

[Mrs H. Gunn, with D. Turner], *Letters written during a four-days' tour in Holland in the summer of 1834*, [London 1834], pp. 48–58

1835

K.F.H. Steltzer, *Fragmentarische Mittheilungen über eine Reise durch Holland und einen Theil von Belgien im Herbste 1834*, Cologne 1835, pp. 40–48

'Het Koninklijk Museum te 's Gravenhage', *Penning-magazijn voor de jeugd*, s.l. 1835, pp. 70–72

1838

[J. Steengracht van Oostkapelle], *Notitie der Schilderijen van het Koninklijk Kabinet te 's Gravenhage*, The Hague [1838] (282 entries)

[J. Steengracht van Oostkapelle], *Notice de Tableaux du Musée-Royal à La Haye*, The Hague [1838] (282 entries)

1839

[J. Steengracht van Oostkapelle], *Notitie der Schilderijen van het Koninklijk Kabinet te 's Gravenhage*, The Hague [1839] (1838 edition [282 entries] with supplement from 1839 [5 entries])

1841

[J.Z. Mazel], *Koninklijk Kabinet van Schilderijen te 's Gravenhage*, The Hague [1841] (301 entries) [annotated copy in Mauritshuis library with notes on restorations and cleanings by Nicolaas Hopman; see The Hague 1998–1999, p. 46]

A. Raczynski, *Ausflüge nach Holland, Belgien, England, Schweiz, Polen, Russland, Schweden, Dänemark und Nord-Amerika* in vol. 3 of *Geschichte der neueren Deutschen Kunst*, Berlin 1841, pp. 453–454

1843

H.F.C. ten Kate, 'Hoofdstuk V: Het Maurits-huis', *Physiologie van Den Haag door een Hagenaar*, The Hague 1843, pp. 36–42

circa 1850–1860?

Souvenir de la Galerie de Peinture du Musée de La Haye: Contenant 70 esquisses tracées d'après les plus beaux tableaux des maîtres les plus célèbres, Leiden, A. Arnz & Cie, [circa 1850–1860?]

1858

W. Bürger [T. Thoré], 'Musée de La Haye', *Musées de la Hollande*, vol. 1, Paris 1858, pp. 189–318

1859

M. du Camp, *En Hollande: Lettres à un ami: Suivies des catalogues des musées de Rotterdam, La Haye et Amsterdam*, Paris 1859, pp. 32–48 (also published in 1868)

L. Colet, *Promenade en Hollande*, Paris 1859, pp. 132–136

1860

L. Viardot, *Les musées d'Angleterre, de Belgique, de Hollande et de Russie: Guide et memento de l'artiste et du voyageur*, Paris 1860, pp. 253–266

before 1863

[J.Z. Mazel], *Koninklijk Kabinet van Schilderijen te 's Gravenhage*, The Hague [before 1863] (287 entries; does not yet catalogue the Westerbaen portraits [inv. nos. 210–211, acquired in 1863])

[J.Z. Mazel], *Koninklijk Kabinet van Schilderijen te 's Gravenhage*, The Hague [before 1863] (287 entries; identical to the catalogue described above but with different illustration on the title page)

[J.Z. Mazel], *Notitie der Schilderijen van het Koninklijk Kabinet te 's Gravenhage*, The Hague [before 1863] (287 entries)

[J.Z. Mazel], *Notice des Tableaux du Musée Royal à la Haye*, The Hague [before 1863] (287 entries)

1869

E. Montégut, *Les Pays-Bas: Impressions de voyage et d'art*, Paris 1869, pp. 210–228 (essay on Holbein written after a visit to the Mauritshuis)

1872

A. Lavice, 'Peintures du musée Royal', *Revue des musées de Belgique, de Hollande et de Russie*, Paris 1872, pp. 192–210

1873

V. de Stuers, 'Holland op zijn smalst', *De Gids* 37 (1873), pp. 320–403 (on the Mauritshuis, see pp. 325, 326, 337, 338, 342, 344, 346, 347, 350, 351–352; see also M. Beek *et al.* (eds.), *Victor de Stuers: Holland op zijn smalst*, Bussum 1975, esp. pp. 29, 154, 155)

1874

V. de Stuers, *Notice Historique et Descriptive des Tableaux et des Sculptures Exposés dans le*

Musée Royal de La Haye, The Hague 1874

C. Vosmaer, 'De eerste catalogus van het Haagsche Schilderijen-kabinet', *De Nederlandsche Spectator*, 5 September 1874, no. 36, pp. 289–290

1875

V. de Stuers, *Beknopte Beschrijving van de Kunst-voorwerpen tentoongesteld in het Koninklijk Kabinet van Schilderijen te 's Gravenhage*, The Hague 1875

C. Vosmaer, 'Het Mauritshuis', *De Nederlandsche Spectator*, 18 December 1875, no. 51, pp. 401–402

R. Gower, 'The Mauritz-huis, or National Gallery of Old Masters at The Hague', *A pocket guide to the public and private galleries of Holland and Belgium [Title on cover: Handbook to the art galleries public and private of Belgium & Holland]*, London 1875, pp. 30–55

1875–1926

J.K.J. de Jonge *et al.*, *Koninklijk Kabinet van Schilderijen: Register van aangevraagde en verleende verloven tot het kopiëren van kunstvoorwerpen in het Koninklijk Kabinet van Schilderijen Mauritshuis te 's Gravenhage [...]*, Manuscript, The Hague 1875–1926 (Register of copies after paintings in the Mauritshuis)

1876

V. de Stuers, *Beknopte Beschrijving van de Kunst-voorwerpen tentoongesteld in het Koninklijk Kabinet van Schilderijen te 's Gravenhage: Tweede uitgave*, The Hague 1876

V. de Stuers, *Beknopte Beschrijving van de Kunst-voorwerpen tentoongesteld in het Koninklijk Kabinet van Schilderijen te 's Gravenhage: Derde uitgave*, The Hague 1876

J.K.J. de Jonge, *Historische Nota betreffende Het Koninklijk Kabinet van Schilderijen, enz. met een aantal daartoe betrekkelijke documenten*, Manuscript, The Hague, 15 April 1876 (see Brenninkmeyer-de Rooij/Hartkamp 1988, p. 181)

E. Fromentin, *Les maîtres d'autrefois*, Paris 1876 (see the 1972 edition edited by P. Moisy; see also *Eugène Fromentin: De meesters van weleer / Les Maîtres d'autrefois*, edited by H. van de Waal, Rotterdam 1976 and E. Fromentin, *Œuvres complètes*, edited by G. Sagnes, Paris 1984, pp. 567–804, 1139–1143, 1709–1710)

1876–1879

J.K.J. de Jonge, *Inventaris der Kunst Voorwerpen van het Koninklijk Kabinet van Schilderijen*, Manuscript, The Hague, 1876–1879. According to a note on page 181 — signed by De Jonge and S. van den Berg, deputy director — this inventory of the collection was started on 15 March 1876. Entries were added until 13 December 1879. See also under 1880–1963.

1877

V. de Stuers, *Beknopte Beschrijving van de Kunst-voorwerpen tentoongesteld in het Koninklijk Kabinet van Schilderijen te 's Gravenhage: Vierde uitgave*, The Hague 1877

[V. de Stuers], *Notice historique et descriptive des tableaux et des sculptures exposés dans le Musée Royal de la Haye: Supplément Août 1877*, The Hague 1877

1878

F.H. Mylius, *Acht Tage in Holland: Reisenotizen über das Land und seine Kunstschätze*, Milan 1878 (ed. princ. 1876), pp. 52–68

1879

V. de Stuers, *Beknopte Beschrijving van de Kunst-voorwerpen tentoongesteld in het Koninklijk Kabinet van Schilderijen te 's Gravenhage: Vijfde uitgave*, The Hague 1879

[V. de Stuers], *Catalogue des Tableaux et des Sculptures du Musée Royal de La Haye*, The Hague 1879

J.K.J. de Jonge, *Petit Guide du Visiteur au Mauritshuis à La Haye*, The Hague 1879

1880

V. de Stuers, *Catalogue des Tableaux et des Sculptures du Musée Royal de La Haye: Deuxième édition*, The Hague 1880

1880–1963

S. van den Berg, C. Telders, A. Bredius, C. Hofstede de Groot, W. Martin, A.B. de Vries, *Vervolg Inventaris der Kunst Voorwerpen van het Koninklijk Kabinet van Schilderijen*, Manuscript, The Hague, 1880–1963 (this inventory of the collection is the second volume of the inventory mentioned above, see under 1876–1879)

1881

V. de Stuers, *Beknopte Beschrijving van de Kunst-voorwerpen tentoongesteld in het Koninklijk Kabinet van Schilderijen te 's Gravenhage: Zesde uitgave*, The Hague 1881

1882

V. de Stuers, *Catalogue des Tableaux et des Sculptures du Musee Royal de La Haye: Troisième édition*, The Hague 1882

1883

V. de Stuers, *Beknopte Beschrijving van de Kunst-voorwerpen tentoongesteld in het Koninklijk Kabinet van Schilderijen te 's Gravenhage: Zevende uitgave*, The Hague 1883

V. de Stuers, *Catalogue des Tableaux et des Sculptures du Musee Royal de La Haye: Quatrième édition*, The Hague 1883

1885

V. de Stuers, *Catalogue des Tableaux et des Sculptures du Musee Royal de La Haye: Cinquième édition*, The Hague 1885

1886

V. de Stuers, *Musée Royal de La Haye: Texte*, Dornach-Paris [Ad. Braun & Cie, Photographes-Éditeurs] 1886

1888

[V. de Stuers], *Beknopte Beschrijving van de Kunst-voorwerpen tentoongesteld in het Koninklijk Kabinet van Schilderijen te 's-Gravenhage: Achtste uitgave*, The Hague 1888

V. de Stuers, *Catalogue des Tableaux et des Sculptures du Musée Royal de La Haye: Sixième édition*, The Hague 1888

1890

A. Bredius, *Die Meisterwerke der königlichen Gemäldegalerie im Haag: Photogravure-Prachtwerk mit erläuterndem Text*, Munich [1890]

1891

A. Bredius, *Beknopte Catalogus der Schilderijen en Beeldhouwwerken in het Koninklijk Kabinet van Schilderijen (Mauritshuis) te 's-Gravenhage*, The Hague 1891

A. Bredius, *Catalogue Sommaire des Tableaux et Sculptures du Musée Royal de Tableaux (Mauritshuis) à La Haye*, The Hague 1891

1893

A. Bredius, C. Hofstede de Groot, *Catalogue of the Pictures and Sculpture in the Royal Picture Gallery (Mauritshuis) at The Hague*, The Hague 1893

1895

A. Bredius, C. Hofstede de Groot, *Musée Royal de La Haye (Mauritshuis): Catalogue Raisonné des Tableaux et des Sculptures*, The Hague 1895

1898

A. Bredius, *Beknopte Catalogus der Schilderijen en Beeldhouwwerken van het Koninklijk Kabinet van Schilderijen (Mauritshuis) te 's Gravenhage*, The Hague 1898 (the title page wrongly gives 1897, the cover 1898; the catalogue includes acquisitions until April 1898, as mentioned on p. 97; see also annual report 1897, pp. 71–72 and annual report 1898, p. 66)

G. Lafenestre, E. Richtenberger, 'La Haye: Musée Royal dit Mauritshuis', *La peinture en Europe: La Hollande*, Paris [1898], pp. 60–130

V. de Swarte, 'Musée Mauritshuis', *Au pays de Rembrandt et de Frans Hals: Coups de crayon sur un Carnet de voyage*, Lille 1898, pp. 19–27

1899

A. Bredius, *Abridged Catalogue of the Pictures and Sculpture in the Royal Picture Gallery (Mauritshuis) The Hague*, The Hague 1899

A. Bredius, edited by F.G. Waller, *Catalogue Abrégé des Tableaux et des Sculptures du Musée Royal de La Haye (Mauritshuis)*, The Hague 1899

circa 1900
C.L. Dake, *Mauritshuis Den Haag: Aangeboden als premie op hare artikelen tarwebloem en havermout onder het handelsmerk Standaard door de N.V.M. Witsenburg Jr Amsterdam*, Amsterdam [circa 1900]

1903
A. Bredius, edited by W. Martin, *Beknopte Catalogus der Schilderijen en Beeldhouwwerken in het Koninklijk Kabinet van Schilderijen (Mauritshuis) te 's Gravenhage*, The Hague 1903

A. Bredius, *Vereeniging tot bevordering van Beeldende Kunsten: Verzameling 'Mauritshuis'. [Premie-uitgave]*, [Amsterdam] 1903

K. Voll, *Die Meisterwerke der Königl. Gemälde-Galerie im Haag und der Galerie der Stadt Haarlem: 125 Kunstdrucke nach den Originalgemälden* (*Die Meisterwerke der bedeutendsten Galerien Europas*, vol. 5), London-Munich-New York [1903]

Het Mauritshuis 's Gravenhage: Uitgegeven door de firma Vinkenbos en Dewald – 's Gravenhage, The Hague [circa 1903] (Album with photographs of paintings in the Mauritshuis)

1904
A. Bredius, edited by W. Martin, *Abridged Catalogue of the Pictures and Sculpture in the Royal Picture Gallery (Mauritshuis) The Hague*, The Hague 1904

G. Geffroy, 'La Haye: Musée Royal (Mauritshuis)', *Les Musées d'Europe: La Hollande*, Paris [1904], pp. 85–125

1906
J.M. Schalekamp, *Les Chefs-d'oeuvre de l'école de peinture hollandaise classique: Musée de La Haye (Mauritshuis)*, Amsterdam [1906] ('12 planches en héliogravures sans texte')

1907
A. Bredius, edited by W. Martin, *Kurzgefasster Katalog der Gemälde- und Skulpturensammlung der Königlichen Gemälde Galerie (Mauritshuis) im Haag*, The Hague 1907

M.E. Waller, *Through the Gates of the Netherlands*, Boston 1907, p. 65

1908
D.C. Preyer, 'The Hague Galleries: The Mauritshuis', *The Art of the Netherland Galleries: Being a History of the Dutch School of Painting*, London 1908, pp. 304–327

E. Singleton, 'The Hague Gallery', *The Standard Galleries: Holland*, London 1908, pp. 3–107

1909
E.W. Moes, E. van Biema, *De Nationale Konst-Gallery en het Koninklijk Museum*, Amsterdam 1909

W. Martin, 'De werkzaamheid van Dr. A. Bredius aan het Mauritshuis', *Bulletin Nederlandschen Oudheidkundigen Bond* 2 (1909), pp. 109–116

1910
W. Martin, *Beknopte Catalogus der Schilderijen en Beeldhouwwerken in het Koninklijk Kabinet van Schilderijen (Mauritshuis) te 's-Gravenhage*, [The Hague] 1910

W. Martin, *Abridged Catalogue of the Pictures and Sculpture in the Royal Picture Gallery (Mauritshuis) The Hague*, The Hague 1910

1912
Rapport der Haagsche Museum-commissie, benoemd door de Vereeniging voor Handel, Nijverheid en Gemeentebelangen te 's-Gravenhage, The Hague 1912

1913
W. Martin, '[Renovation of the interior of the] Mauritshuis', *Bulletin Nederlandschen Oudheidkundigen Bond* 6 (1913), pp. 78–82

1914
W. Martin *et al.*, *Musée Royal de La Haye (Mauritshuis): Catalogue Raisonné des Tableaux et des Sculptures: Deuxième Édition*, The Hague 1914

C. Hofstede de Groot, 'De nieuwe catalogus van het Mauritshuis: Kritiek, zelfkritiek en aanvullingen', *Bulletin Nederlandsche Oudheidkundigen Bond* 7 (1914), pp. 77–85

J.C. van Dyke, 'The Hague Museum', *Amsterdam, The Hague, Haarlem: Critical Notes on the Rijks Museum, the Hague Museum [Mauritshuis], Halsmuseum*, New York 1914, pp. 69–106

1919
J.N. Jacobsen Jensen, *Reizigers te Amsterdam: Beschrijvende lijst van reizen in Nederland door vreemdelingen vóór 1850*, Amsterdam 1919 (repertory of travel journals written by foreigners, many of whom have visited the Gallery of Prince Willem V or the Mauritshuis)

1920
W. Martin, *Koninklijk Kabinet van Schilderijen, Mauritshuis: Beknopte Catalogus der Schilderijen en Beeldhouwwerken*, [The Hague 1920]

W. Martin, *Königliche Gemälde Galerie Mauritshuis: Kurzgefasster Katalog der Gemälde- und Skulpturensammlung*, The Hague 1920

1922
C. Hofstede de Groot, 'De schilderijenverzameling van het Mauritshuis tijdens het Stadhouderlijk Tijdperk', *Oudheidkundig Jaarboek* 2 (1922), pp. 1–4

W. Martin, 'Het Mauritshuis: 1822–januari–1922', *Oudheidkundig Jaarboek* 2 (1922), pp. 5–18

1923
W. Martin, *Royal Picture Gallery Mauritshuis, The Hague: Abridged Catalogue of the Pictures and Sculpture*, The Hague 1923

1925
W. Martin, *Koninklijk Kabinet van Schilderijen, Mauritshuis: Beknopte Catalogus der Schilderijen en Beeldhouwwerken*, The Hague 1925

1929
W. Martin, *Koninklijk Kabinet van Schilderijen, Mauritshuis: Beknopte Catalogus der Schilderijen en Beeldhouwwerken*, The Hague 1929

W. Martin, *Royal Picture Gallery Mauritshuis The Hague: Abridged Catalogue of the Pictures and Sculpture*, The Hague 1929

W. Martin, *Königliche Gemälde Galerie Mauritshuis: Kurzgefasster Katalog der Gemälde- und Skulpturensammlung*, The Hague 1929

G. Knuttel, *Oudhollandsche schilderijen in de Haagsche musea*, The Hague 1929

1934
E.H. ter Kuile, 'Het Mauritshuis onder het directeurschap van prof. Dr. W. Martin 30 Juni 1909–30 Juni 1934', *Oudheidkundig Jaarboek* 3 (1934), pp. 23–27

1935
W. Martin, H. Schneider, *Musée Royal de Tableaux Mauritshuis à La Haye: Catalogue Raisonné des Tableaux et Sculptures: Troisième Édition*, The Hague 1935

1936
W. Martin, with G.M. Becht, *Koninklijk Kabinet van Schilderijen, Mauritshuis: Beknopte Catalogus der Schilderijen en Beeldhouwwerken*, The Hague 1936

1938
W. Martin, *Royal Picture Gallery Mauritshuis The Hague: Abridged Catalogue of the Pictures and Sculpture*, The Hague 1938

1939
W. Martin, H. Schneider, *Musée Royal de Tableaux Mauritshuis à La Haye: Catalogue Raisonné des Tableaux et Sculptures: Supplément de 1939 à la Troisième Édition (1935)*, The Hague 1939

1942
[With an introduction by A. Seyss-Inquart and P. Giesler], *Kunst der Ruhrmark: Westfälisch-Niederrheinische Kunst: Gauausstellung Westfalen-Süd: Malerei, Graphik, Plastik*, [The Hague] 1942 (see Exhibitions)

1945
J.G. van Gelder, *Nederlandsche kunst van de XVde en XVIde eeuw*, The Hague 1945 (see Exhibitions)

Weerzien der meesters in het Rijksmuseum: Keuze van Schilderijen uit Rijksmuseum, Mauritshuis, Frans Halsmuseum, Dordrechts Museum, Amsterdam 1945 (also in English edition; see Exhibitions)

See the masters in the Rijksmuseum: Choice collection of pictures from: Rijksmuseum, Mauritshuis, Frans Halsmuseum, Dordrechts Museum, Amsterdam 1945

Schilderijententoonstelling Zuid ziet Noord [De tentoongestelde schilderijen zijn uit het bezit van het Rijksmuseum, Mauritshuis en Frans Halsmuseum en waren tijdens den oorlog in de Rijksbergplaats van den St. Pietersberg opgeborgen], Maastricht 1945

"Oude meesters op doorreis": Schilderijen uit het bezit van het Rijksmuseum te Amsterdam, het Mauritshuis te 's Gravenhage en het Frans-Halsmuseum te Haarlem, die tijdens den oorlog in den St. Pietersberg bewaard werden, Den Bosch 1945 (see Exhibitions)

1946

J.G. van Gelder *et al.*, *Koninklijk Kabinet van Schilderijen Mauritshuis: Beknopte Catalogus der Schilderijen en Beeldhouwwerken*, The Hague 1946

Musée Royal de Tableaux Mauritshuis à La Haye: Catalogue Raisonné des Tableaux et Sculptures: Illustrations, [The Hague 1946]

J.G. van Gelder, *Herwonnen kunstbezit: Tentoonstelling van uit Duitschland teruggekeerde Nederlandsche kunstschatten*, [The Hague] 1946 (see Exhibitions)

E.H. Ebels *et al.*, *Oude meesters in het Museum van Oudheden voor de Provincie en Stad Groningen: Keur van schilderijen uit het Rijksmuseum te Amsterdam en het Mauritshuis te 's-Gravenhage*, Groningen 1946 (see Exhibitions)

Oud-Hollandsche meesters komen naar Friesland: Tentoonstelling van meesterwerken uit het Rijksmuseum en het Mauritshuis, Leeuwarden 1946 (see Exhibitions)

J.G. van Gelder, 'Prof. Dr. W. Martin: Ter gelegenheid van zijn zeventigsten verjaardag', *Maandblad voor Beeldende Kunsten* 22 (1946), pp. 75–77

T.H. Lunsingh Scheurleer, 'Het Koninklijk Kabinet van Zeldzaamheden en zijn betekenis voor het Rijksmuseum', *Oudheidkundig Jaarboek* 13 (1946), pp. 50–67 (continued in *Bulletin Koninklijke Nederlandse Oudheidkundige Bond* 9 (1956), cols. 269–308)

1948

A.B. de Vries, A. Blunt, edited by S.J. Gudlaugsson, *Meesterwerken der Hollandse School uit de verzameling van Z.M. de Koning van Engeland ter gelegenheid van het 50-jarig regeringsjubileum van Koningin Wilhelmina*, The Hague 1948 (English edition: *Masterpieces of the Dutch School from the Collection of H.M. the King of England on the Occasion of the 50-Year Reign of Queen Wilhelmina*; see Exhibitions)

W. Martin, 'Gedachten over het koninklijk kabinet van schilderijen in het Mauritshuis', *Bulletin Nederlandse Oudheidkundige Bond* 47 (1948), pp. 33–42

1949

S.J. Gudlaugsson *et al.*, *Abridged Catalogue of the Pictures and Sculptures: Royal Picture Gallery Mauritshuis The Hague*, [The Hague] 1949

S.J. Gudlaugsson, B.J.A. Renckens *et al.*, *Beknopte Catalogus der Schilderijen en Beeldhouwwerken: Koninklijk Kabinet van Schilderijen, Mauritshuis / 's-Gravenhage*, [The Hague] 1949

1950

Vermeer thuis: Het Koninklijk Kabinet [van Schilderijen] "Het Mauritshuis" in het Museum "Het Prinsenhof" te Delft, Delft 1950 (see Exhibitions)

1951

W. Martin, 'Nog eens het Mauritshuis', *Bulletin Koninklijke Nederlandse Oudheidkundige Bond* 50 (1951), pp. 50–51

A.B. de Vries, 'Het Mauritshuis door andere bril', *Bulletin Koninklijke Nederlandse Oudheidkundige Bond* 50 (1951), pp. 52–54

1952

E.K.J. Reznicek *et al.*, *Abridged Catalogue of the Pictures and Sculptures; Royal Picture Gallery Mauritshuis The Hague*, [The Hague] 1952

1953

S.J. Gudlaugsson, *Mauritshuis 's Gravenhage: Geïllustreerde handleiding*, The Hague 1953 (also in English; German and French editions were published in 1954)

A.B. de Vries, with W.J. van Balen, J. de Sousa Leão, *Maurits de Braziliaan*, [The Hague] 1953 (see Exhibitions)

1954

A.B. de Vries *et al.*, *Beknopte Catalogus der Schilderijen en Beeldhouwwerken: Koninklijk Kabinet van Schilderijen, Mauritshuis / 's-Gravenhage*, [The Hague] 1954

1956

P.N.H. Domela Nieuwenhuis *et al.*, *Catalogue Abrégé des Tableaux et Sculptures: Musée Royal de Tableaux 'Mauritshuis' La Haye*, [The Hague 1956] (the foreword is dated July 1955, but the annual report mentions that this catalogue appeared in 1956)

1958

P.N.H. Domela Nieuwenhuis *et al.*, *Abridged Catalogue of the Pictures and Sculptures: Royal Picture Gallery Mauritshuis The Hague*, [The Hague] 1958

P.N.H. Domela Nieuwenhuis, with A. van Duinkerken and A.B. de Vries, *Jan Steen*, The Hague 1958 (see Exhibitions)

F.A. van Braam, *Art Treasures in the Benelux Countries, vol I: The Netherlands*, s.l. 1958

1959

[S.J. Gudlaugsson], *Mauritshuis Den Haag: Een rondgang door het Mauritshuis te 's-Gravenhage*, revised edition of the 1953 guide, [The Hague 1959 (?)] (also in English and German editions)

1960

L. von Weiher *et al.*, *Kurzgefasster Katalog der Gemälde und Skulpturensammlung: Königliche Gemälde Galerie Mauritshuis / Den Haag*, [The Hague] 1960

R. van Luttervelt, *Holland's Musea: Hoogtepunten der oude schilderkunst uit de collecties van het Rijksmuseum Amsterdam, Museum Boymans-van Beuningen Rotterdam, Frans Hals Museum Haarlem, Mauritshuis Den Haag*, The Hague 1960 (second edition: Paris 1974)

1963–

[Inventaris Mauritshuis]. This summary but complete inventory of the collection was started in 1963 (see also under 1880–1963) and is still used today by the curatorial department.

1964

[O. ter Kuile], *Supplément 1964 au Catalogue Abrégé 1954 des Peintures et des sculptures: Musée Royal des Peintures Mauritshuis — La Haye*, The Hague 1964

[O. ter Kuile], *Nachtrag 1964 zum Kurzgefassten Katalog der Gemälde und Skulpturensammlung: Königliche Gemälde Galerie Mauritshuis / Den Haag*, [The Hague 1964]

1965

[O. ter Kuile], *Supplement 1965 of the Abridged Catalogue of the Pictures and Sculptures from 1958: Royal Picture Gallery Mauritshuis The Hague*, [The Hague] 1965

1966

M.M. Tóth-Ubbens, with R. Huyghe and A.B. de Vries, *In het licht van Vermeer: Vijf eeuwen schilderkunst*, The Hague 1966 (French edition: *Dans la lumière de Vermeer: Cinq siècles de peinture*; English edition: *In the light of Vermeer: Five Centuries of Painting*; see Exhibitions)

H.E. van Gelder, C. Reedijk, A.B. de Vries, *150 jaar Koninklijk Kabinet van Schilderijen Koninklijke Bibliotheek Koninklijk Penningkabinet: Herdenkingstentoonstelling in het Mauritshuis*, The Hague 1966 (see Exhibitions)

1967

T.H. Lunsingh Scheurleer, A.B. de Vries, L. Brummel, H.E. van Gelder, *150 jaar Koninklijk Kabinet van*

Schilderijen Koninklijke Bibliotheek Koninklijk Penningkabinet, The Hague 1967

M.M. Tóth-Ubbens, *Mauritshuis Den Haag: Nederlandse schilderkunst: Met 48 kleurenreproducties*, Hannover 1967 (reprinted many times; also in English, German and French editions)

1968

M.M. Tóth-Ubbens, with contributions by E.K.J. Reznicek, L.R. Reznicek-Buriks, P.N.H. Domela Nieuwenhuis, O. ter Kuile, *Schilderijen en beeldhouwwerken 15e en 16e eeuw [Koninklijk Kabinet van Schilderijen Mauritshuis]: Catalogus 1*, The Hague 1968

L. de Vries *et al.*, *Koninklijk Kabinet van Schilderijen: Beknopte Catalogus van de schilderijen beeldhouwwerken en miniaturen: Mauritshuis*, The Hague 1968

1970

S.J. Gudlaugsson, with contributions by J.A. Bosmans, *1945 . 1970: Vijfentwintig jaar aanwinsten Mauritshuis*, The Hague 1970 (see Exhibitions)

J.A. Maravall, J. Baticle *et al.*, *Goya*, The Hague 1970 (also in French, German and English editions; see Exhibitions)

A.G.H. Bachrach, L. Thijssen, D. van Karnebeek-van Roijen, *Schok der Herkenning: Het Engelse landschap der Romantiek en zijn Hollandse Inspiratie*, The Hague 1970 (English edition: *"Shock of Recognition": The landscape of English Romanticism and the Dutch seventeenth-century school*; see Exhibitions)

1971

J. Bosmans *et al.*, *Koninklijk Kabinet van Schilderijen: Beknopte Catalogus van de schilderijen beeldhouwwerken en miniaturen: Mauritshuis*, The Hague 1971

M.M. Tóth-Ubbens, *Mauritshuis*, The Hague 1971 (Dutch/English edition; reprinted many times; also in a German/French edition)

1974

G. Langemeyer, with S.J. Gudlaugsson, J.P. Guépin, L. de Vries, P. Pieper, *Gerard Ter Borch Zwolle 1617 Deventer 1681*, The Hague 1974 (also in German edition; see Exhibitions)

1975

F.J. Duparc [Senior], '[Het Mauritshuis te 's-Gravenhage]', *Een eeuw strijd voor Nederlands Cultureel Erfgoed*, The Hague 1975, pp. 56–57, 116–123, 165–170, 210–213, 271–280

1977

H.R. Hoetink, F.J. Duparc, *Mauritshuis: The Royal Cabinet of Paintings: Illustrated General Catalogue*, The Hague 1977

1978

A.B. de Vries, M. Tóth-Ubbens, W. Froentjes, edited by D.B. Hensbroek-van der Poel, *Rembrandt in the Mauritshuis*, Alphen aan den Rijn 1978

1979

E. van den Boogaart, F.J. Duparc *et al.*, *Zo wijd de wereld strekt: Tentoonstelling naar aanleiding van de 300ste sterfdag van Johan Maurits van Nassau-Siegen op 20 december 1979*, The Hague 1979 (see Exhibitions)

E. van den Boogaart (ed.), *Johan Maurits van Nassau-Siegen 1604–1679: A Humanist Prince in Europe and Brazil. Essays on the occasion of the tercentenary of his death*, The Hague 1979

M. Tóth-Ubbens, *Mauritshuis* (third, revised edition, in Dutch and English), The Hague 1979

1980

F.J. Duparc, with contributions by R. Falkenburg, W. Schulz, *Mauritshuis: Hollandse schilderkunst: Landschappen 17de eeuw*, The Hague 1980

C. Wright, *Paintings in Dutch Museums: An Index of Oil Paintings in Public Collections in The Netherlands by Artists born before 1870*, Amsterdam 1980

1981

S. Slive, *Jacob van Ruisdael*, The Hague 1981 (also in English edition; see Exhibitions)

H.R. Hoetink, *Jacob van Ruisdael 1628/29–1682 [Album]*, The Hague 1981

P.J.J. van Thiel, 'De inrichting van de Nationale Konst-Gallery in het openingsjaar 1800', *Oud Holland* 95 (1981), pp. 170–227

1982

W. van de Watering, *Terugzien in bewondering / A Collectors' Choice*, The Hague 1982 (see Exhibitions)

H.R. Hoetink, F.J. Duparc, *Mauritshuis: Dutch Painting of the Golden Age*, The Hague 1982 (see Exhibitions)

N. Sluijter-Seijffert, *Schilderijen uit de collectie van het Mauritshuis in het Johan de Witthuis / Paintings from the collection of the Mauritshuis in the Johan de Witthuis*, The Hague 1982

1984

H.R. Hoetink, F.J. Duparc *et al.*, *Dutch Painting of the Golden Age from the Royal Picture Gallery Mauritshuis*, Tokyo-Nagoya-Sapporo 1984 (see Exhibitions)

1985

A. Blankert, A. Chong, R.E.O. Ekkart, E. Haverkamp Begemann, W.A. Liedtke, S. Segal, N.C. Sluijter-Seijffert, P.C. Sutton, H. Vlieghe, with contributions by R. van Leeuwen, J. van der Meer Mohr, M. Plomp, edited by H. Hoetink, *Art Treasures of Holland: The Royal Picture Gallery Mauritshuis*, Amsterdam-New York-The Hague 1985

F. Grijzenhout, 'Tempel voor Nederland: De Nationale Konst-Gallerij in 's-Gravenhage', *Het Rijksmuseum: Opstellen over de geschiedenis van een nationale instelling* (*Nederlands Kunsthistorisch Jaarboek* 1984), Weesp 1985, pp. 1–69

E. Bergvelt, 'Nationale, levende en 19de-eeuwse meesters: Rijksmusea en eigentijdse kunst (1800–1848)', *Het Rijksmuseum: Opstellen over de geschiedenis van een nationale instelling* (*Nederlands Kunsthistorisch Jaarboek* 1984), Weesp 1985, pp. 77–149

1986

B. Broos, with H. Hoetink, B. Brenninkmeyer-de Rooij, J. Lacambre, *De Rembrandt à Vermeer: Les peintres hollandais au Mauritshuis de La Haye*, Paris 1986 (see Exhibitions)

H.M. Cramer, *"Holland im Engadin": Dutch Painting of the Golden Age from the Royal Picture Gallery Mauritshuis and the galleries of Hans M. Cramer and John Hoogsteder, The Hague, Netherlands*, Zuoz 1986 (see Exhibitions)

P. Hecht, G. Luijten, 'Nederland verzamelt oude meesters: Tien jaar aankopen en achtergronden', *Kunstschrift* 30 (1986), p. 202

[F.L. Upmeijer, edited by R. van Leeuwen], *De geschiedenis van het fotoarchief van het Mauritshuis*, Manuscript [The Hague 1986]

1987

B. Broos, *Meesterwerken in het Mauritshuis*, The Hague 1987

B. Broos, *Aanwinsten van het Mauritshuis 1981–1987 / Acquisitions of the Mauritshuis 1981–1987*, [The Hague 1987] (brochure; see Exhibitions)

1988

B. Broos, *Mauritshuis 's-Gravenhage: Gids van het koninklijk kabinet van schilderijen / Mauritshuis The Hague: Guide to the royal cabinet of paintings*, The Hague 1988 (Dutch/English edition; also in French/Italian, Spanish/German, Japanese/English editions)

B. Brenninkmeyer-de Rooij, B. Broos, E. de Heer, B. Slot, edited by R. van Leeuwen, *Paintings from England: William III and the Royal Collections*, The Hague 1988 (see Exhibitions)

R. van Leeuwen, *Mauritshuis, vroeger en nu*, The Hague 1988 (brochure; also published in other languages)

B. Brenninkmeyer-de Rooij, A. Hartkamp,

'Oranje's erfgoed in het Mauritshuis', *Oud Holland* 102 (1988), pp. 181–235

J. Hoes, '"Het vee zooals het is en niet anders": De reputatie van Paulus Potter (1625–1654)', C. Boschma *et al.*, *Meesterlijk Vee: Nederlandse veeschilders 1600–1900*, Dordrecht (Dordrechts Museum), Leeuwarden (Fries Museum) 1988–1989, pp. 87–100

1989

[L.C. Brinkman], *"Een keuze": Een kleine en persoonlijke keuze van de gastconservator mr. drs. L.C. Brinkman uit de diverse aanwinsten die gedurende de laatste zeven jaar voor de Rijkscollectie zijn verworven*, The Hague 1989 (brochure; see Exhibitions)

B. Broos, *Een nieuwe aanwinst: Gerbrand van den Eeckhout: Isaak en Rebekka, 1665* (*Mauritshuis Cahier*, no. 1), The Hague 1989

E. Gombrich *et al.*, edited by H.R. Hoetink, *Gezicht op het Mauritshuis: Poëtische visies op een uitzonderlijk museum*, Amsterdam-The Hague 1989

[R. van Leeuwen, L. de la Mar], 'Geschiedenis van de presentatie na 1875', *Nieuwsbrief Mauritshuis* 2 (1989), no. 1, pp. 7–8

L. de la Mar, *De geschiedenis van de inrichting van het Koninklijk Kabinet van Schilderijen Mauritshuis na 1875 tot de Tweede Wereldoorlog*, Manuscript 1989

[R. van Leeuwen, C. Hogervorst], 'Het aankoopbeleid van 1815 tot 1875', *Nieuwsbrief Mauritshuis* 2 (1989), no. 2, pp. 5–6

C. Hogervorst, [*Het aankoopbeleid [van het Mauritshuis] van 1815 tot 1875*], Manuscript, The Hague 1989

[R. van Leeuwen, C. Haldar], 'Twee Koninklijke Kabinetten in een "ongunstig Locaal"', *Nieuwsbrief Mauritshuis* 2 (1989), no. 3, pp. 9–10

C. Haldar, *Twee Koninklijke Kabinetten in een 'ongunstig Locaal'*, Manuscript, The Hague 1989

[R. van Leeuwen], 'Het Mauritshuis en het RKD', *Nieuwsbrief Mauritshuis* 2 (1989), no. 4, p. 6

1990

B. Broos, with E. Buijsen, S. Donahue Kuretsky, W. Liedtke, L. Federle Orr, J. Roding, P.C. Sutton, edited by R. van Leeuwen, *Hollandse meesters uit Amerika*, The Hague-Zwolle 1990 (English edition: *Great Dutch Paintings from America*; see Exhibitions)

B. Broos, E. Buijsen, *Hollandse Meesters uit Amerika: Een beschrijving van 27 hoogtepunten*, The Hague 1990 (brochure; also in English edition)

R. van Leeuwen, 'De schoonmaakwoede van Mazel', *Nieuwsbrief Mauritshuis* 3 (1990), nos. 3–4, pp. 12–13

1991

B. Broos, R. van Leeuwen, with contributions by E. Buijsen, P. van der Ploeg, I. Scheltema-Hellingman, *Twee decennia Mauritshuis: Ter herinnering aan Hans R. Hoetink directeur 1972–1991*, The Hague-Zwolle 1991

M. Tiethoff, with K. Schaffers, *Portretten in miniatuur: Portretminiaturen uit de stadhouderlijke en koninklijke verzamelingen*, The Hague-Zwolle 1991 (also in Japanese edition; see Exhibitions)

M. de Boer, J. Leistra, B. Broos, *Bredius, Rembrandt en het Mauritshuis!!!: Een eigenzinnig directeur verzamelt*, The Hague-Zwolle 1991 (see Exhibitions)

M. de Boer, E. Buijsen, B. Broos, *Bredius, Rembrandt and the Mauritshuis!!!: A tenacious director collects: A guidebook to all the paintings Bredius acquired for or bequathed to the Mauritshuis*, The Hague 1991 (brochure)

E. Buijsen, B. Broos, W. Liedtke, P. Hecht, J. Eckstein, *Een symposium in Den Haag: De kunst van het verzamelen* (*Mauritshuis Cahier*, no. 2), The Hague 1991

R. van Leeuwen, 'De ruil van 1825', *Nieuwsbrief Mauritshuis* 4 (1991), no. 1, pp. 8–10

R. van Leeuwen, '175 jaar Koninklijk Kabinet van Schilderijen', *Nieuwsbrief Mauritshuis* 4 (1991), no. 2, pp. 9–10

1992

B. Brenninkmeyer-de Rooij, B. Broos, F.G. Meijer, P. van der Ploeg, *Mauritshuis in bloei: Boeketten uit de Gouden Eeuw / The Mauritshuis in Bloom: Bouquets from the Golden Age*, The Hague-Zwolle 1992 (reprinted many times; see Exhibitions)

B. Broos, with contributions by M. de Boer, E. Buijsen, R. van Leeuwen, P. van der Ploeg, *Princes and Paintings: Treasures from the Mauritshuis*, Nagasaki 1992 (see Exhibitions)

F. de Graaf, J. Wadum, *Een dansfestijn doorgrond: Technisch en kunsthistorisch onderzoek naar een Vlaams schilderij*, The Hague 1992 (see Exhibitions)

B. Broos, *Een portret van Huygens en zijn 'Sterre' voor het Mauritshuis*, [The Hague 1992] (brochure; see Exhibitions)

R. van Leeuwen, *Caesar van Everdingen: Venus en Adonis herenigd / Venus and Adonis reunited*, The Hague 1992 (brochure; see Exhibitions)

R. van Leeuwen, 'Jan Karel Jacob de Jonge, herschepper van het Mauritshuis', *Nieuwsbrief Mauritshuis* 5 (1992), no. 1, pp. 12–14

E. Bergvelt, *Aanwinsten van het Koninklijk Kabinet van Schilderijen onder Koning Willem I (1816–1840)*, Manuscript, [Amsterdam], 1992

1992–1993

R. v[an] L[eeuwen], *Chronologisch overzicht van catalogi Galerij [Prins] Willem V en Mauritshuis*, Manuscript, [The Hague] 1992–1993

1993

E. Buijsen, J. Niemeijer, with M. de Boer, *Cornelis Troost en het theater: Tonelen van de 18de eeuw / Cornelis Troost and the theatre of his time: Plays of the 18th century*, The Hague-Zwolle 1993

B. Broos, with a contribution by M. de Boer, *Liefde, list & lijden: Historiestukken in het Mauritshuis*, The Hague-Ghent 1993 (English edition: *Intimacies & Intrigues: History Painting in the Mauritshuis*; see also Exhibitions)

N. Sluijter-Seiffert, with R. van Leeuwen, J. van der Meer Mohr, M. Plomp, *Mauritshuis: Illustrated General Catalogue*, Amsterdam-The Hague 1993 (reprint of the catalogue in H. Hoetink *et al.*, *The Royal Picture Gallery Mauritshuis*, Amsterdam-New York 1985, with an appendix of new acquisitions by B. Broos and M. de Boer)

R. van Leeuwen, 'Provenance: House of Orange', *Mauritshuis in focus* 6 (1993), no. 1, pp. 21–26

F.J. Duparc, 'Acquisition policy', *Mauritshuis in focus* 6 (1993), no. 2, pp. 5–12

E. Bergvelt, 'Tussen geschiedenis en kunst: Nederlandse nationale kunstmusea in de negentiende eeuw', in E. Bergvelt *et al.* (eds.), *Verzamelen: Van rariteitenkabinet tot kunstmuseum*, Heerlen-Houten 1993, pp. 333–354

A.W.A. Boschloo, G.J.J. van der Sman (eds.), *Italian Paintings from the Sixteenth Century in Dutch Public Collections*, Florence 1993

1994

B. Broos, edited by Q. Buvelot, P. van der Ploeg and J. Havell, *Het Mauritshuis: Koninklijk Kabinet van Schilderijen en Galerij Prins Willem V*, London 1994 (also in English, French, German and Japanese editions)

J. Wadum, with R. Hoppenbrouwers and L. Struick van der Loeff, *Vermeer in het licht: Conservering, restauratie en onderzoek*, The Hague-Wormer 1994 (English edition: *Vermeer illuminated: Conservation,*

Restoration and Research; French edition published in 1995: *Vermeer en plein jour: Conservation, Restauration et Recherche*; see Exhibitions)

[C. Visser], *Vermeer in het licht*, The Hague [1994] (brochure)

E. Borger, with R. Hoppenbrouwers, *Vermeer in het licht: Conservering, restauratie en onderzoek*, The Hague 1994 (see Exhibitions)

A. Walsh, E. Buijsen, B. Broos, edited by Q. Buvelot, *Paulus Potter: Schilderijen, tekeningen en etsen*, The Hague-Zwolle 1994 (English edition: *Paulus Potter: Paintings, drawings and etchings*; see Exhibitions)

F.J. Duparc, 'The Rembrandt Society: A Devoted Friend of the Mauritshuis', *Mauritshuis in focus* 7 (1994), no. 2, pp. 15–16

R. van Koetsveld, 'The Mauritshuis goes independent', *Mauritshuis in focus* 7 (1994), no. 3, pp. 21–23

F. Keers, 'Bibliografische aantekeningen bij Ben Broos, *Liefde, list en lijden: Historiestukken in het Mauritshuis*', *Oud Holland* 108 (1994), pp. 137–140

P.H.J. Clemens, *Inventaris van het archief van het Koninklijk Kabinet van Schilderijen Mauritshuis: 1816–1952*, Manuscript, The Hague 1994

1995

P. van der Ploeg, *Meindert Hobbema. Boslandschap met boerenhoeven: Een monumentale aanwinst voor Nederland / Wooded landscape with cottages: A major acquisition for the Netherlands*, The Hague 1995 (brochure)

B. Broos, Q. Buvelot, F.J. Duparc, P. van der Ploeg, C. Vermeeren, *Uit de Schatkamer van de Verzamelaar: Hollandse Zeventiende-eeuwse Schilderijen uit Nederlands Particulier Bezit*, The Hague-Wormer 1995 (English edition: *The Amateur's Cabinet: Seventeenth-Century Dutch Masterpieces from Dutch Private Collections*; see Exhibitions)

B. Broos, 'Jan van Beuningen: A gentleman of standing in the art world', *Mauritshuis in focus* 8 (1995), no. 2, pp. 20–26

B. Broos, 'Vermeer's *View of Delft* in Bloemendaal', *Mauritshuis in focus* 8 (1995), no. 3, pp. 8–15

1995 and 1996

A.K. Wheelock, B. Broos, with A. Blankert and J. Wadum, *Johannes Vermeer*, The Hague-Washington-Zwolle 1995 and 1996 (also in English, French, German and Italian editions; see Exhibitions)

1996

B. Broos, with D. de Clercq, Y. Kuiper, C. Vermeeren, 'Het *Gezicht op Delft* en het Stinstra-mysterie', *Oud Holland* 110 (1996), pp. 35–46

1997

A. van Suchtelen, with E. Buijsen and Y. Bruijnen, *Kunst op vleugels: Rond een herenigd drieluik van Gerard David*, The Hague-Bussum 1997 (English edition: *Art on Wings: Celebrating the Reunification of a Triptych by Gerard David*; see Exhibitions)

P. van der Ploeg, C. Vermeeren, with B. Broos, C.W. Fock, S. Groenveld, J. Hein, M. Jonker, W. Savelsberg and J. van der Veen, *Vorstelijk Verzameld: De kunstcollectie van Frederik Hendrik en Amalia*, The Hague-Zwolle 1997 (English edition: *Princely Patrons: The Collection of Frederick Henry of Orange and Amalia of Solms in The Hague;* see Exhibitions)

B. Broos, M. Jonker, H. Kuiper, G. Sluiter, M. de Vet, *Diversity and Specialisation: Seventeenth-century Dutch Masters from the Mauritshuis,* Tochigi-Sakura-Gunma-Nagasaki 1997 (see Exhibitions)

C. Vermeeren, 'The search for a princely collection', *Mauritshuis in focus* 10 (1997), no. 3, pp. 25–30

[R. van Leeuwen], *Mauritshuis: Vroeger & nu*, The Hague 1997 (brochure; published in seven languages; ed. princ. 1988)

M. van Bohemen *et al.* (eds.), *Tien jaar Vrijwillig Thuis in het Mauritshuis 1987–1997*, The Hague 1997

F.J. Duparc, 'The Mauritshuis Collection', N. Phillips *et al.*, *The Art of Affluence sponsored by MeesPierson, private bankers since 1720*, Hong Kong 1997, pp. 85–91

B. Aikema, E. Mijnlieff, B. Treffers, *Italian Paintings from the Seventeenth and Eighteenth Centuries in Dutch Public Collections*, Florence 1997

1998

A. McNeil Kettering, edited by A. van Suchtelen, *Gerard ter Borch en de Vrede van Munster*, The Hague-Zwolle 1998 (English edition: *Gerard ter Borch and the Treaty of Münster*; see Exhibitions)

N. Middelkoop, P. Noble, J. Wadum, B. Broos, *Rembrandt onder het mes: De anatomische les van Dr Nicolaes Tulp ontleed*, The Hague-Amsterdam 1998 (English edition: *Rembrandt under the scalpel: The Anatomy Lesson of Dr Nicolaes Tulp Dissected*; see Exhibitions)

E. Bergvelt, *Pantheon der Gouden Eeuw: Van Nationale Konst-Gallerij tot Rijksmuseum van Schilderijen (1798–1896)*, Zwolle 1998, s.v.

A. Stott, *Hollandgekte: De onbekende Nederlandse periode in de Amerikaanse kunst en cultuur*, Amsterdam 1998 (translation of *Holland Mania: The unknown Dutch period in American art and culture*, Woodstock, New York 1998), pp. 27, 43, 134 and fig. 73

P.H.J. Clemens, *Inventaris Mauritshuis Archief 1953–1989 (1990)*, Manuscript, [The Hague 1998]

1999

M.K. Komanecky *et al.*, *Copper as Canvas: Two Centuries of Masterpiece Paintings on Copper 1575–1775*, Phoenix-New York-Oxford 1999 (see Exhibitions)

E. Runia, edited by P. van der Ploeg and Q. Buvelot, *Kunst op koper: Twee eeuwen meesterwerken op koperplaat*, The Hague 1999 (booklet; see Exhibitions)

C. White, Q. Buvelot (eds.), with essays by E. van de Wetering, V. Manuth and M. de Winkel, and entries by E. Buijsen, P. Schatborn, B. Broos and A. van Suchtelen, *Rembrandt zelf*, London-The Hague-Zwolle 1999 (English edition: *Rembrandt by Himself*; German edition: *Rembrandt selbst*; French edition: *Rembrandt par lui-même*; Italian edition: *Rembrandt stesso*; see Exhibitions)

C. Brown, *Scenes of everyday life: Dutch genre paintings from the Mauritshuis*, Oxford 1999 (see Exhibitions)

T.A. Carbone, '"Unexpected Opportunities": Coming of Age in The Hague', *Eastman Johnson: Painting America*, New York (Brooklyn Museum of Art), San Diego (San Diego Museum of Art) 1999, pp. 19–21

2000

B. Broos, Q. Buvelot, P. van der Ploeg, G. Sluiter, A. van Suchtelen, edited by Q. Buvelot, *Koninklijk Kabinet van Schilderijen Mauritshuis: Gids*, The Hague 2002 (also in English, French, German and Japanese editions)

A.K. Wheelock, C. Brown, *The Golden Age of Dutch and Flemish Painting: The Edward and Sally Speelman Collection*, Houston-The Hague 2000 (see Exhibitions)

R. Baer, with A. Wheelock and A. Boersma, *Gerrit Dou 1613–1675*, The Hague-Washington-Zwolle 2000 (English edition: *Gerrit Dou: Master Painter in the Age of Rembrandt*; see Exhibitions)

[P. van der Ploeg], *Treasure[s] from the Mauritshuis: The Royal Cabinet of Paintings*, Nagasaki 2000 (see Exhibitions)

2001

A. van Suchtelen, with F.J. Duparc, P. van der Ploeg and E. Runia, edited by P. van der Ploeg, *Winters van Weleer: Het Hollandse winterlandschap in de Gouden Eeuw*, The Hague-Zwolle 2001–2002 (English edition: *Holland Frozen in Time: The Dutch Winter Landscape in the Golden Age*; see Exhibitions)

Q. Buvelot, 'A decade at the Mauritshuis', *Mauritshuis in focus* 14 (2001), no. 2, pp. 6–39

2002

Q. Buvelot and H. Buijs, with an introduction by E. Reitsma, *A Choice Collection: Seventeenth-Century Dutch Paintings from the Frits Lugt Collection*, The Hague-Zwolle 2002 (see Exhibitions)

H. Kraan, with I. Brons, *Dromen van Holland: Buitenlandse kunstenaars schilderen Holland*, 1800–1914, Zwolle-The Hague 2002, pp. 26–27, 34, 80, 94, 97, 113, 119– 120, 125, 128, 129, 130, 134, 141, 144, 147, 163, 205, 208, 237, 277, 391–392

2003

S. Buck, J. Sander, A. van Suchtelen, Q. Buvelot, P. van der Ploeg, *Hans Holbein de Jonge 1497/98–1543*, The Hague-Zwolle 2003 (also in English, French and German editions; see Exhibitions)

G. Sluiter and B. van der Mark, edited by Q. Buvelot, *The Age of Rembrandt: 17th[-]Century Dutch Painting*, Seoul 2003 (see Exhibitions)

Q. Buvelot, 'The provenance of the Holbeins in the Mauritshuis', *Mauritshuis in focus* 16 (2003), no. 2, pp. 33–42

J. Stourton, 'Mauritshuis: The Hague', *Great Smaller Museums of Europe*, London 2003, pp. 150–157

R. Effert, *Volkenkundig verzamelen: Het Koninklijk Kabinet van Zeldzaamheden en het Rijks Etnographisch Museum 1816–1883* (diss. Leiden University), Leiden 2003

2004

Q. Buvelot, D.M. Teixeira, E. de Vries, F. Egmond, P. Mason, *Albert Eckhout: Een Hollandse kunstenaar in Brazilië*, The Hague-Zwolle 2004 (English edition: *Albert Eckhout: A Dutch Artist in Brazil*; see Exhibitions)

F.J. Duparc, with contributions by G. Seelig and A. van Suchtelen, *Carel Fabritius 1622–1654*, The Hague-Schwerin-Zwolle 2004 (also in English and German editions; see Exhibitions)

B. Broos, A. van Suchtelen, with contributions by Q. Buvelot, G. Sluiter, P. Noble, P. van der Ploeg, H. Vlieghe, F. Duparc, and an introductory essay by R. Ekkart, *Portraits in the Mauritshuis, 1430–1790*, The Hague-Zwolle 2004

Q. Buvelot, with contributions by C. Vermeeren, *Royal Picture Gallery Mauritshuis: A Summary Catalogue*, The Hague-Zwolle 2004

Q. Buvelot, 'On Des Tombe, donor of Vermeer's "Girl with a pearl earring"', *Mauritshuis in focus* 17 (2004), no. 1, pp. 22–30

Periodicals

'Bulletin van het Mauritshuis' in *Bulletin van het Rijksmuseum* 1–2 (1953–1954)

Nieuwsbrief Mauritshuis vol. 1–5 (1987/1988–1992)

Mauritshuis in focus vol. 6– (1993–) (with English translations)

Mauritshuis Cahier nos. 1–2 (1989–1991)

Musea rond de Haagse Hofvijver / Museums around the Hofvijver of The Hague (published by the Stichting Hofvijvermusea) 1–7 (1992–1998)

Annual Reports 1875 and 1876–1877 (printed seperately)

Verslagen omtrent 's Rijks Verzamelingen van Geschiedenis en Kunst (Reports of the state funded museums, published annually) 1–109 (1878–1987)

Jaarverslag Koninklijk Kabinet van Schilderijen Mauritshuis, Galerij Prins Willem V (with English summaries as of 1997) 1988–

List of exhibitions and presentations in the Mauritshuis and Galerij Prins Willem V

List of exhibitions and presentations in the Mauritshuis and Galerij Prins Willem V, including exhibitions organised or co-organised by the Mauritshuis on other locations

by Quentin Buvelot

[Still-lifes by Abraham Calraet]
September 1916 (no catalogue; see annual report 1916, p. 34; Bredius 1916; The Hague 1991–1992, p. 56)

[Weekly exhibitions of photographs of paintings in the Mauritshuis on the occasion of lectures given by the director]
October-December 1917 (see annual report 1917, p. 40)

[Weekly exhibitions of photographs of Italian sculpture on the occasion of lectures given by the director]
October-December 1918 (see annual report 1918, pp. 37–38)

[Three letters by Rembrandt]
December 1919–January 1920 (no catalogue; see annual report 1919, p. 36; *De Prins*, 20 December 1919; Bredius 1920)

[Paintings from private collections in The Hague and surroundings]
October 1920 (no catalogue; see annual report 1920, pp. 29–30)

[Portraits of Willem I of Orange]
Spring 1925 (no catalogue; see annual report 1925, p. 37)

[Photographs of the best known paintings in the Mauritshuis collection]
December 1940 (see annual report 1940, p. 37)

Het Duitsche Boek
15–30 November 1941 (see annual report 1941, pp. 85–86)

Het goud der zee
29 January-February 1942 (no catalogue; exhibition of amber objects; see annual report 1942, p. 84 and *De Tijd*, 29 January 1942, front page)

Kunst der Ruhrmark: Westfälisch-Niederrheinische Kunst: Gauausstellung Westfalen-Süd: Malerei, Graphik, Plastik
28 November–13 December 1942

Gemeenschapswerk
19 June–18 July 1943 (see annual report 1943, p. 58)

Weerzien der meesters in het Rijksmuseum: Keuze van Schilderijen uit Rijksmuseum, Mauritshuis, Frans Halsmuseum, Dordrechts Museum
Amsterdam, Rijksmuseum
15 July–30 September 1945

Schilderijententoonstelling Zuid ziet Noord [De tentoongestelde schilderijen zijn uit het bezit van het Rijksmuseum, Mauritshuis en Frans Halsmuseum en waren tijdens den oorlog in de Rijksbergplaats van den St. Pietersberg opgeborgen]
Maastricht, Provinciaal Oudheidkundig Museum
11 August–15 September 1945

Nederlandsche kunst van de XVde en XVIde eeuw
1 September–21 October 1945

"Oude meesters op doorreis": Schilderijen uit het bezit van het Rijksmuseum te Amsterdam, het Mauritshuis te 's Gravenhage en het Frans-Halsmuseum te Haarlem, die tijdens den oorlog in den St. Pietersberg bewaard werden
Den Bosch, Museum van het Provinciaal Genootschap van Kunsten en Wetenschappen
21 October–11 November 1945

Oude meesters in het Museum van Oudheden voor de Provincie en Stad Groningen: Keur van schilderijen uit het Rijksmuseum te Amsterdam en het Mauritshuis te 's-Gravenhage
Groningen, Groninger Museum
8 March–7 April 1946

Herwonnen Kunstbezit: Tentoonstelling van uit Duitschland teruggekeerde Nederlandsche kunstschatten
16 March–23 May 1946

[The bequest of Abraham Bredius to the Mauritshuis]
As of 13 March 1946 (no catalogue; see annual report 1946, p. 49)

Oud-Hollandsche meesters komen naar Friesland: Tentoonstelling van meesterwerken uit het Rijksmuseum en het Mauritshuis
Leeuwarden, Fries Museum
13 April–12 May 1946

Meesterwerken der Hollandse School uit de verzameling van Z.M. de Koning van Engeland ter gelegenheid van het 50-jarig regeringsjubileum van Koningin Wilhelmina
6 August–26 September 1948

[100 Paintings from the Mauritshuis]
The Hague, Gemeentemuseum
8 November 1950–1 March 1951 (no catalogue; see annual report 1950, p. 71)

Vermeer thuis: Het Koninklijk Kabinet [van Schilderijen] "Het Mauritshuis" in het Museum "Het Prinsenhof" te Delft
Delft, Stedelijk Museum Het Prinsenhof
18 November 1950–April 1951

Maurits de Braziliaan
7 April–17 May 1953

[A selection of 15th- and 16th-century paintings from the Mauritshuis]
c. 7 April–17 May 1953
Delft, Stedelijk Museum Het Prinsenhof (see annual report 1953, p. 117)

75 jaar Vereniging Rembrandt
12–19 October 1958 (no catalogue; see annual report 1958, p. 142)

Jan Steen
20 December 1958–1 March 1959

In het licht van Vermeer: Vijf eeuwen schilderkunst
25 June–5 September 1966 (*Dans la lumière de Vermeer: Cinq siècles de peinture*, Musée du Louvre, Orangerie des Tuileries, Paris, 24 September–28 November 1966)

150 jaar Koninklijk Kabinet van Schilderijen, Koninklijke Bibliotheek, Koninklijk Penningkabinet: Herdenkingstentoonstelling in het Mauritshuis
5 November 1966–14 January 1967

Goya
4 July–13 September 1970 (Musée du Louvre, Orangerie des Tuileries, Paris, 25 September–7 December 1970)

1945–1970: Vijfentwintig jaar aanwinsten Mauritshuis
19–28 October 1970

Schok der Herkenning: Het Engelse landschap der Romantiek en zijn Hollandse Inspiratie
24 November 1970–7 January 1971 (*"Shock of Recognition": The landscape of English Romanticism and the Dutch seventeenth-century school*, The Tate Gallery, London, 23 January–28 February 1971)

[Documentary presentation on the occasion of the completion of the restoration of Paulus Potter's 'Bull']
1972 (no catalogue; see annual report 1972, p. 217)

Gerard ter Borch Zwolle 1617 Deventer 1681
9 March–28 April 1974 (Landesmuseum, Münster, 12 May–23 June 1974)

[Documentary presentation on the influence of Rembrandt's 'Anatomy lesson of Dr Nicolaes Tulp']
1977 (see Duparc 1977 and annual report 1977, p. 192)

Zo wijd de wereld strekt: Tentoonstelling naar aanleiding van de 300ste sterfdag van Johan Maurits van Nassau-Siegen op 20 December 1979
21 December 1979–1 March 1980

Jacob van Ruisdael
1 October 1981–3 January 1982 (Fogg Art Museum, Harvard University, Cambridge, Massachusetts, 18 January–11 April 1982)

Terugzien in bewondering
19 February–9 March 1982

Mauritshuis: Dutch Painting of the Golden Age. Royal Picture Gallery The Hague
Travelling exhibition: National Gallery of Art, Washington, Kimbell Art Museum, Fort Worth, The Art Institute of Chicago, Chicago, Los Angeles County Museum of Art, Los Angeles, Art Gallery of Ontario, Toronto, The Metropolitan Museum of Art, New York
20 April 1982–10 April 1984

Dutch Painting of the Golden Age from the Royal Picture Gallery Mauritshuis
Travelling exhibition: The National Museum of Western Art, Tokyo, Nagoya City Museum, Nagoya, Hokkaido Migishi Kotaro Museum of Art, Sapporo
24 April–2 September 1984

"Holland im Engadin": Dutch Painting of the Golden Age from the Royal Picture Gallery Mauritshuis and the Galleries of Hans M. Cramer and John Hoogsteder The Hague Netherlands
Chesa Planta, Zuoz
6 February–2 March 1986

De Rembrandt à Vermeer: Les peintres hollandais au Mauritshuis de La Haye
Galeries nationales du Grand Palais, Paris
19 February–30 June 1986

Aanwinsten van het Mauritshuis 1981–1987
On the occasion of the re-opening on 4 June 1987 (with brochure)

Betwiste schilderijen van koning-stadhouder Willem III
12 November 1988–29 January 1989

[Presentation of Ger van Elk's 'Portrait of Queen Beatrix']
27 April–28 May 1989 (see annual report 1989, p. 22)

[Presentation focussing on Anthonie van Leeuwenhoek (1632–1723)]
14 June–16 July 1989 (see annual report 1989, p. 23)

"Een keuze": Een kleine en persoonlijke keuze van de gastconservator mr. drs. L.C. Brinkman uit de diverse aanwinsten die gedurende de laatste zeven jaar voor de rijkscollectie zijn verworven
4–26 November 1989 (with brochure)

Hollandse meesters uit Amerika
28 September 1990–13 January 1991 (*Great Dutch Paintings from America*, The Fine Arts Museums of San Francisco, San Francisco, 16 February–5 May 1991)

Portretten in miniatuur: Portretminiaturen uit de stadhouderlijke en koninklijke verzamelingen
6 June–18 August 1991 (Paleis Het Loo Nationaal Museum, Apeldoorn, 7 September–3 November 1991; Palace Huis ten Bosch Museum, Nagasaki, 1 October–30 November 1992)

Bredius, Rembrandt en het Mauritshuis!!!: Een eigenzinnig directeur verzamelt
30 November 1991–8 March 1992

Mauritshuis in bloei: Boeketten uit de Gouden Eeuw
16 April–2 August 1992

De aanwinst, presentatie ter gelegenheid van de aankoop van Jacob van Campens 'Dubbelportret van Constantijn Huygens en Suzanna van Baerle'
2 June–October 1992 (with brochure)

Nieuwe gezichten in het Mauritshuis: Venus en Adonis herenigd, presentatie ter gelegenheid van de schenking van Caesar van Everdingens 'Trompe-l'oeil met Venusbuste'
16 October–15 November 1992 (with brochure)

Princes and Paintings: Treasures from the Mauritshuis
Palace Huis ten Bosch Museum, Nagasaki
4 December 1992–31 August 1993

Een dansfestijn doorgrond: Technisch en kunsthistorisch onderzoek naar een Vlaams schilderij
11 December 1992–14 March 1993

Cornelis Troost en het theater: Tonelen van de 18de eeuw
26 March–11 July 1993

Twee jaar aanwinsten voor het Mauritshuis
21 August–17 October 1993 (with issue of *Mauritshuis in focus*)

Liefde, list en lijden: Historiestukken in het Mauritshuis
6 November 1993–13 March 1994

Jan van Goyen in het Mauritshuis
29 March–23 May 1994 (no cat.)

Vermeer in het licht (I), documentaire tentoonstelling bij de openbare restauratie van Vermeers 'Gezicht op Delft' en 'Meisje met de parel'
10 May–25 September 1994 (with brochure)

Vermeer in het licht (II), verslag van de restauratie van Vermeers 'Gezicht op Delft' en 'Meisje met de parel'
4 October–4 December 1994 (with brochure)

't Land van Paulus Potter
8 November 1994–12 March 1995

De aanwinst, presentatie ter gelegenheid van de aankoop van Meindert Hobbema's 'Boslandschap met boerenhoeven'
18 February–28 May 1995 (with brochure)

Uit de schatkamer van de verzamelaar: Hollandse zeventiende-eeuwse meesters uit Nederlands particulier bezit
10 October 1995–21 January 1996

Johannes Vermeer
1 March–9 June 1996 (National Gallery of Art, Washington, 12 November 1995–11 February 1996)

Kunst op vleugels: Rond een herenigd drieluik van Gerard David
1 March–22 June 1997

De aanwinst, presentatie van de recent verworven 'Aanbidding der herders' door Jan de Bray
28 March–1 June 1997 (with issue of *Mauritshuis in focus*)

Diversity and Specialisation: Seventeenth-Century Dutch Masters from the Mauritshuis
Travelling exhibition: Tochigi Prefectural Museum of Fine Arts, Tochigi, Sakura Museum of Art, Sakura, The Museum of Modern Art, Gunma, Palace Huis ten Bosch Museum, Nagasaki
2 November 1997–24 May 1998

Vorstelijk verzameld: De kunstcollectie van Frederik Hendrik en Amalia
6 December 1997–29 March 1998

Gerard ter Borch en de Vrede van Munster
3 July–11 October 1998

Rembrandt onder het mes: De anatomische les van Dr Nicolaes Tulp ontleed
3 October 1998–10 January 1999

Kunst op koper: Twee eeuwen meesterwerken op koperplaat
25 June–22 August 1999 (*Copper as Canvas: Two Centuries of Masterpiece Painting on Copper 1575–1775*, Phoenix Art Museum, Phoenix, Arizona, 19 December 1998–28 February 1999; The Nelson-Atkins Museum of Art, Kansas City, Missouri, 28 March–14 June 1999)

De aanwinst, presentatie van Rembrandts recent verworven 'Portret van een oude man'
3–12 September 1999 (with issue of *Mauritshuis in focus*)

Rembrandt zelf
25 September 1999–9 January 2000 (*Rembrandt by himself*, The National Gallery, London, 9 June–25 September 1999)

Scenes of everyday life: Dutch genre paintings from the Mauritshuis
Ashmolean Museum, Oxford
9 November 1999–8 January 2000

Ontmoetingen in het Mauritshuis: Zomerpresentatie rond de mooiste portretten van het Mauritshuis, aangevuld

met bruiklenen uit het Rijksmuseum
15 April–10 September 2000 (with issue of *Mauritshuis in focus*)

Treasures from the Mauritshuis
Huis ten Bosch Art Museum, Nagasaki
15 April 2000–15 April 2001

Gerrit Dou 1613–1675
9 December 2000–25 February 2001 (National Gallery of Art, Washington, 16 April–6 August 2000; Dulwich Picture Gallery, London, 6 September–19 November 2000)

Te mooi voor de handel: Uit de privé-collectie van Edward en Sally Speelman
1 May–22 July 2001 (*The Golden Age of Dutch and Flemish Painting: The Edward and Sally Speelman Collection*, The Museum of Fine Arts, Houston, 25 March–June 2000)

Winters van weleer: Sneeuw en ijs in het Mauritshuis
24 November 2001–3 March 2002

Een kwestie van kiezen: Hollandse 17de-eeuwse schilderijen uit de Collectie Frits Lugt
28 March–30 June 2002

De schenking van Willem baron van Dedem aan het Mauritshuis
9 September–3 November 2002 (with issue of *Mauritshuis in focus*)

Restauratie van 'Het puttertje'
8 April–12 May 2003 (with issue of *Mauritshuis in focus*)

Hans Holbein de Jonge 1497/98–1543
16 August–16 November 2003

The Age of Rembrandt: 17th Century Dutch Painting
Seoul, National Museum of Art
16 August–16 November 2003

In Brazilië met Albert Eckhout (c.1610–1666)
27 March–27 June 2004

Carel Fabritius 1622–1654: De jonge meester
24 September 2004–9 January 2005 (Staatliches Museum, Schwerin, 28 January–16 May 2005)

The Mauritshuis Project: An Introduction to Dutch 17th Century Painting
Portland, Oregon, Portland Art Museum
23 October 2004–29 January 2006 (with brochure)

Galerij Prins Willem V

Jan Davidsz. de Heem (1606–1683/84): Allegorisch portret van Prins Willem III
October 1983–April 1984 (with brochure; see also the annual report of the ICN of 1983, p. 294)

Koninklijk zilver in de stadhouderlijke galerij: Hoogtepunten uit de verzamelingen van het Huis Oranje-Nassau
26 October 2002–19 January 2003 (Paleis Het Loo Nationaal Museum, 25 January–5 May 2004)

Note
For catalogues and other publications accompanying these exhibitions and presentations, see pp. 410–419. For attendance figures, please consult the annual reports (and for figures until 1937: *Statistiek der musea 1937*, The Hague 1938).

Essential literature on the museum building and its original interior

1652

P. Post, *Huys van S:Ex. Graef J[oh]an Maurits van Nassau: Bij den selven gebouwt in 's Gravenhaege ten oosten van het hof van Holland: Aldus getekent ende met sijne voornaemste leden uytgebeeldt door P. Post, Architect van de Doorluchtighe Princen van Orange in 1652*, Manuscript, 1652 (The Hague, Koninklijke Bibliotheek, inv. no. 128 A 34)

1660

[A. de Wicquefort], *Verhael in Forme Van Journael, van de Reys Ende 't Vertoeven Van den Seer Doorluchtige ende Machtige Prins Carel de II Koning van Groot Britannien, &c. Welcke Hy in Hollandt gedaen heeft, zedert den 25 Mey, tot den 2 Junij 1660*, The Hague 1660, pp. 91–94 (with a print of the Great Hall on the first floor, now the Potter Room; see the reproduction on page 400)

[A. de Wicquefort], *Relation en Forme de Journal du Voyage et Sejour, Que Le Serenissime et Tres-Puissant Prince Charles II Roy de la Grand' Bretagne, &c. A fait en Hollande, depuis le 25. May, jusques au 2 Juin 1660*, The Hague 1660, pp. 78–80

W. Lower, *A Relation [...] of the Voiage and Residence which [...] Charles II [...] hath made in Holland*, The Hague 1660

1679

[List of paintings in the Mauritshuis], Manuscript, probably 1679 (The Hague, Royal Archives)

1681

J. de Hennin, ['Het Huis van zal. Prins Maurits van Nassauw, en al de rariteiten op 't zelve'], *De Zinrijke Gedachten Toegepast op de Vijf Sinnen, Van 's Menschen Verstand [...]*, Amsterdam 1681, pp. 110–121

1687

[Inventory of the Mauritshuis], Manuscript, 1687 (The Hague, National Archives)

1704

G. de Lamberty, *Mémoires, negotiations, traitez*, vol. 3, The Hague 1704, p. 445

1715

Les Ouvrages d'Architecture de Pierre Post, Leiden 1715

1880

[D. Veegens], 'Het Mauritshuis en het huis van Huygens', *Mededeelingen van de Vereeniging ter beoefening der geschiedenis van 's Gravenhage: Nieuwe uitgaaf: Tweede deel*, The Hague 1880, pp. 4–73

1911–1917

J.A. Worp, *De briefwisseling van Constantijn Huygens*, 6 vols, Den Haag 1911–1917, s.v.

1915

W. Martin, 'Het Mauritshuis en zijn Stichter (Slot.)', *Eigen Haard* 41 (1915), pp. 142–144

1923

C. Barlaeus, edited by S.P. L'Honoré-Naber, *Caspar Barlaeus: Nederlandsch Brazilië onder het bewind van Johan Maurits Grave van Nassau 1637–1644: Historisch-Geographisch-Ethnografisch: Naar de Latijnsche uitgave van 1647 voor het eerst in het Nederlandsch bewerkt*, The Hague 1923 (ed. princ. Amsterdam 1647), p. 398

1973

J. de Sousa-Leão, *Frans Post 1612–1680*, Amsterdam 1973, pp. 49–51

1979

J.J. Terwen, 'The Buildings of Johan Maurits van Nassau', in E. van den Boogaart (ed.), *Johan Maurits van Nassau-Siegen 1604–1679: A Humanist Prince in Europe and Brazil: Essays on the occasion of the tercentenary of his death*, The Hague 1979, pp. 54–87 (with references)

T.H. Lunsingh Scheurleer, 'The Mauritshuis as "Domus Cosmographica" I', in *ibid.*, pp. 142–190 (with references)

R.J. van Pelt, 'The Mauritshuis as "Domus Cosmographica" II', in *ibid.*, pp. 190–196

J.J. Terwen, 'Johann Moritz und die Architektur', in G. de Werd (ed.), *Soweit der Erdkreis reicht: Johann Moritz von Nassau-Siegen 1604–1679*, Kleef (Städtisches Museum Haus Koekkoek) 1979, pp. 127–131

1979–1980

E. van den Boogaart, F.J. Duparc (eds.), *Zo wijd de wereld strekt: Tentoonstelling naar aanleiding van de 300ste sterfdag van Johan Maurits van Nassau-Siegen op 20 december 1979*, The Hague (Mauritshuis) 1979–1980, pp. 239–241, appendix 2

1980

J.J. Terwen, 'De tuinen van het Mauritshuis', *Nederlands Kunsthistorisch Jaarboek* 31 (1980), pp. 104–121

1985

L. Vis, edited by E.J. Nusselder, *Bouwhistorische documentatie en waardebepaling: Mauritshuis 's-Gravenhage*, 2 vols, Manuscript, The Hague 1985 (with references)

1988

C. Schellekens, *Rombout Verhulst, Jan Blommendael en Pieter Adriaensz 't Hooft: Een verslag over het leven van deze kunstenaars en hun werk dat zich in of aan het Mauritshuis bevindt*, Manuscript, The Hague-Amsterdam 1988, pp. 19–23 (on the sculpture in the facades)

1986

J.R. Magendans, J.A. Waasdorp, *Putten uit het verleden: Opgravingen in Loosduinen, Kazernestraat en Mauritshuis* (*VOM-reeks*, no. 1), The Hague 1986, pp. 44–50

1987

E. de Regt, *Mauritshuis: De geschiedenis van een Haags stadspaleis*, The Hague 1987 (with references)

E.J. Nusselder, 'Het Mauritshuis: Bouwgeschiedenis van een Haags stadspaleis', *Spiegel Historiael* 22 (1987), no. 6, pp. 291–297, 311

1989

P.J.P. Whitehead, M. Boeseman, *A portrait of Dutch 17th century Brazil: Animals, plants and people by the artists of Johan Maurits of Nassau*, Amsterdam-Oxford-New York 1989, pp. 95–96

1993

J.J. Terwen, K.A. Ottenheym, *Pieter Post (1608–1669): Architect*, Zutphen 1993, pp. 21–23, 243, 244–245 (with references)

M. Simons, 'Johan Maurits van Nassau-Siegen', in E. Bergvelt *et al.* (eds.), *Verzamelen: Van rariteitenkabinet tot kunstmuseum*, Heerlen 1993, pp. 117, 120–121

1995

K. Ottenheym in *Jacob van Campen: Het klassieke ideaal in de Gouden Eeuw*, Amsterdam (Koninklijk Paleis) 1995, pp. 165–167

1997

H. Douna, 'Mauritshuis restoration project completed', *Mauritshuis in focus* 10 (1997), no. 2, pp. 16–21

1998

K. van Strien, *Touring the Low Countries: Accounts of British Travellers*, Amsterdam 1998, pp. 188 (1663), 192 (1697), 198 (1707)

2004

Q. Buvelot in *Albert Eckhout: A Dutch Artist in Brazil*, The Hague (Mauritshuis) 2004, pp. 34–35 and 137–141, appendices 4–5

Selected literature on former directors of the Mauritshuis

JOHAN STEENGRACHT VAN OOSTKAPELLE (1782–1846)
Nieuw Nederlandsch Biografisch Woordenboek, vol. 7, Leiden 1927, col. 1175; [W.F. del Campo Hartman], 'Steengracht', *Nederland's Adelsboek* 45 (1952), p. 12; A.B. de Vries in Lunsingh Scheurleer *et al.* 1967, pp. 53–59; Duparc 1975, p. 56; T. Laurentius, *Oude prenten: Een handleiding voor verzamelaars*, Lochem-Ghent 1987, figs. pp. 64–65; B. Broos in J. Turner (ed.), *The Dictionary of Art*, London-New York 1996, vol. 29, pp. 591–592; Bergvelt 1998, s.v.

JEAN ZACHARIA MAZEL (1792–1884)
Algemene Konst- en Letterbode (1837), p. 243; *Algemene Konst- en Letterbode* (1841), p. 194; A.B. de Vries in Lunsingh Scheurleer *et al.* 1967, pp. 59–65; Duparc 1975, pp. 56, 116; *Nederland's Patriciaat* 71 (1987), pp. 293–294; Bergvelt 1998, s.v.

JAN KAREL DE JONGE (1828–1880)
M.C. and C[arel] V[osmaer], 'Jhr. Mr. Johan Karel Jacob de Jonge', *De Nederlandsche Spectator*, 17 April 1880, no. 10, pp. 128–129; P.J. Veth, 'Jhr. Mr. J.K.J. de Jonge', *Eigen Haard* (1880), no. 14, pp. 148–151; *Nieuw Nederlandsch Biografisch Woordenboek*, vol. 4, Leiden 1918, cols. 814–816; *Nederlands Adelsboek* 41 (1943–1948), pp. 104–105; A.B. de Vries in Lunsingh Scheurleer *et al.* 1967, pp. 65–70; Duparc 1975, pp. 117–119; R. van Leeuwen, 'Jan Karel Jacob de Jonge, herschepper van het Mauritshuis', *Nieuwsbrief Mauritshuis* 5 (1992), no. 1, pp. 12–14; Bergvelt 1998, p. 218

SIMON VAN DEN BERG (1812–1891)
A.B. de Vries in Lunsingh Scheurleer *et al.* 1967, pp. 70–72; Duparc 1975, p. 119

ABRAHAM BREDIUS (1855–1946)
W. Martin, 'De werkzaamheid van Dr. A. Bredius aan het Mauritshuis', *Bulletin Nederlandschen Oudheidkundigen Bond* 2 (1909), pp. 109–116; S. Margadant *et al.*, *Dr. Abraham Bredius 1855–1925: Album hem aangeboden op 18 april 1925*, Amsterdam 1925; W. Martin, 'Abraham Bredius 1855–1946: In memoriam', *Maandblad voor Beeldende Kunsten* 22 (1946), pp. 71–74; W. Martin, 'Abraham Bredius (Amsterdam, 18 April 1855–Monaco, 13 Maart 1946)', *Jaarboek Maatschappij voor Nederlandse Letterkunde 1946–1947*, Leiden 1948, pp. 29–41; A.B. de Vries in Lunsingh Scheurleer *et al.* 1967, pp. 72–77; Duparc 1975, pp. 116, 120–123, 165–166, 169, 211–212, 274; R.E.O. Ekkart in J. Charité (ed.), *Biografisch Woordenboek van Nederland*, vol. 1, The Hague 1979, pp. 89–90; L. Barnouw-de Ranitz in A. Blankert, *Museum Bredius: Catalogus van de schilderijen en tekeningen*, Zwolle-The Hague 1991, pp. 12–27; M. de Boer, J. Leistra, B. Broos, *Bredius, Rembrandt en het Mauritshuis!!!: Een eigenzinnig directeur verzamelt*, The Hague-Zwolle 1991; M. de Boer, E. Buijsen, B. Broos, *Bredius, Rembrandt and the Mauritshuis!!!: A tenacious director collects: A guidebook to all the paintings Bredius acquired for or bequathed to the Mauritshuis*, The Hague 1991; Bergvelt 1998, s.v.; R.E.O. Ekkart in Hecht *et al.* 1998, pp. 11, 13–15

WILHELM MARTIN (1876–1954)
J.G. van Gelder, 'Prof. Dr. W. Martin: Ter gelegenheid van zijn zeventigsten verjaardag', *Maandblad voor Beeldende Kunsten* 22 (1946), pp. 75–77; A.B. de Vries in Lunsingh Scheurleer *et al.* 1967, pp. 77–83; Duparc 1975, pp. 166–170, 210–213, 274, 278; R.E.O. Ekkart in J. Charité (ed.), *Biografisch Woordenboek van Nederland*, vol. 2, The Hague 1985, pp. 378–380; E. Tholen, 'Het Museum van Fraaije Kunsten voor de Academische Jongelingschap der Leidsche Hoogeschool', *Het Leidse prentenkabinet: De geschiedenis van de verzamelingen* (*Leids Kunsthistorisch Jaarboek*, vol. 9), Leiden 1994, pp. 77–87; R.E.O. Ekkart in Hecht *et al.* 1998, pp. 21–22; A. Hoogenboom in *ibid.*, pp. 25–43

JAN GERRIT VAN GELDER (1903–1980)
A.B. de Vries in Lunsingh Scheurleer *et al.* 1967, p. 83; Duparc 1975, pp. 212–213, 278; R.E.O. Ekkart in J. Charité (ed.), *Biografisch Woordenboek van Nederland*, vol. 3, The Hague 1989, pp. 187–188; J. Bruyn, E. de Jongh (eds.), *In Memoriam J.G. van Gelder 1903–1980*, Utrecht 1982; C. Stolwijk, *"Die wetenschap noemen Gij en ik kunstgeschiedenis…": Denken over kunstgeschiedenis in Nederland: J.G. van Gelder (1903–1980)*, Steenwijk 1991; C. Stolwijk in Hecht *et al.* 1998, pp. 127–143

ARY BOB DE VRIES (1905–1983)
Lunsingh Scheurleer *et al.* 1967, pp. 84–89; Duparc 1975, pp. 271–277, 278–279, 280; H.R. Hoetink, 'Obituary: Ary Bob de Vries (1905–1983)', *The Burlington Magazine* 126 (1984), p. 782

STURLA GUDLAUGSSON (1913–1971)
A.B. de Vries, 'Obituary: S.J. Gudlaugsson', *The Burlington Magazine* 113 (1971), pp. 742–743; 'In Memoriam S.J. Gudlaugsson', *Oud Holland* 86 (1971), pp. 1–2; J.A. Emmens, 'In Memoriam Dr. Sturla Gudlaugsson', *Simiolus* 4 (1971), p. 123; H. Gerson in *Kunstchronik* 24 (1971), pp. 274–276; C. Müller Hofstede, 'Dr. Sturla J. Gudlaugsson †', *Weltkunst* 41 (1971), no. 7, p. 350; H. Gerson, 'Sturla Jonasson Gudlaugsson: Skagen (Denemarken) 16 juni 1913–Rotterdam 3 maart 1971', *Jaarboek van de Maatschappij der Nederlandse Letterkunde te Leiden 1971–1972*, Leiden 1973, pp. 150–164; I. Bergström, 'In memoriam: Sturla J. Gudlaugsson 1913–1971', *Konsthistorisk Tidskrift* 42 (1975), p. 67; Duparc 1975, pp. 277, 278, 279

HANS HOETINK (b. 1929)
B. Broos, R. van Leeuwen, E. Buijsen, P. van der Ploeg, *Twee decennia Mauritshuis: Ter herinnering aan Hans R. Hoetink, Directeur 1972–1991*, The Hague 1991

Note
For portraits of these directors, see pp. 46–47.

Key to abbreviated literature and exhibitions

A

ADAMS 1984
H. Adams, 'If not Rembrandt, Then His Cousin?', *The Art Bulletin* 66 (1984), pp. 427–441

ADAMS 1985
A. Jensen Adams, *The paintings of Thomas de Keyser (1596/7–1667): A study of portraiture in seventeenth-century Amsterdam* (diss.), 4 vols, Ann Arbor, Michigan 1985

ADLER 1980
W. Adler, *Jan Wildens: Der Landschaftsmitarbeiter des Rubens*, Fridingen 1980

AHM 1975–1979
A. Blankert, *Amsterdams Historisch Museum: Schilderijen daterend van voor 1800: Voorlopige catalogus*, Amsterdam 1975–1979

AIKEMA/MIJNLIEFF 1993
B. Aikema, E. Mijnlieff, 'Giovanni Antonio Pellegrini 1716–1718: A Venetian painter in the Low Countries', *Nederland-Italië: Relaties in de beeldende kunst van de Nederlanden en Italië 1400–1750 / Artistic relations between the Low Countries and Italy 1400–1750* (*Nederlands Kunsthistorisch Jaarboek*, vol. 44), Zwolle 1993, pp. 215–242

AIKEMA *et al.* 1997
B. Aikema, E. Mijnlieff, B. Treffers, *Italian Paintings from the Seventeenth and Eighteenth Centuries in Dutch Public Collections*, Florence 1997

ALLGEMEINES KÜNSTLER-LEXIKON
Saur Allgemeines Künstler-Lexikon: Die bildenden Künstler aller Zeiten und Völker, vol. 1– , Munich-Leipzig 1992–

AMBERG-THE HAGUE 2003–2004
P. Wolf *et al.*, *Der Winterkönig Friedrich V.: Der letzte Kurfürst aus der Oberen Pfalz, Amberg, Heidelberg, Prag, Den Haag*, Amberg (Stadtmuseum), The Hague (Haags Historisch Museum) 2003–2004

AMSTERDAM 1976
E. de Jongh *et al.*, *Tot leringh en vermaak: Betekenissen van Hollandse genrevoorstellingen uit de zeventiende eeuw*, Amsterdam (Rijksmuseum) 1976

AMSTERDAM 1984
P.J.J. van Thiel, *Prijs de lijst: De Hollandse schilderijlijst in de zeventiende eeuw*, Amsterdam (Rijksmuseum) 1984 (reprinted in English, in a revised edition: *Framing in the Golden Age: Picture and frame in 17th-century Holland*, Zwolle 1995)

AMSTERDAM 1986
J.P. Filedt Kok, W. Halsema-Kubes, W.T. Kloek (eds.), *Kunst voor de beeldenstorm: Noordnederlandse kunst 1525–1580*, Amsterdam (Rijksmuseum) 1986

AMSTERDAM 1988
R. Bastiaanse, H. Bots, *Glorieuze Revolutie: De wereld van Willem en Mary*, Amsterdam (Nieuwe Kerk) 1988

AMSTERDAM 1989–1990
P. Hecht, *De Hollandse fijnschilders: Van Gerard Dou tot Adriaen van der Werff*, Amsterdam (Rijksmuseum) 1989–1990

AMSTERDAM 1991–1992
A. Tümpel, P. Schatborn, *Pieter Lastman: Leermeester van Rembrandt / The Man who Taught Rembrandt*, Amsterdam (Museum Het Rembrandthuis) 1991–1992

AMSTERDAM 1992a
R.E. Jellema, M. Plomp, *Episcopius: Jan de Bisschop (1628–1671), advocaat en tekenaar / lawyer and draughtsman*, Amsterdam (Museum Het Rembrandthuis) 1992

AMSTERDAM 1992b
E. Bergvelt, R. Kistemaker (eds.), *De wereld binnen handbereik: Nederlandse kunst- en rariteitenverzamelingen, 1585–1735*, Amsterdam (Amsterdams Historisch Museum) 1992

AMSTERDAM 1993–1994
G. Luijten, A. van Suchtelen *et al.*, *Dawn of the Golden Age: Northern Netherlandish Art 1580–1620*, Amsterdam (Rijksmuseum) 1993–1994

AMSTERDAM 1994
M. van Rooijen-Buchwaldt, E.-J. Goossens, E. de Jong, W. Diedenhofen, *De fonteijn van Pallas: Een geschenk van Amsterdam aan Johan Maurits*, Amsterdam (Koninklijk Paleis) 1994

AMSTERDAM 1995
K. Ottenheym, Q. Buvelot *et al.*, *Jacob van Campen: Het klassieke ideaal in de Gouden Eeuw*, Amsterdam (Koninklijk Paleis) 1995 (with English summaries)

AMSTERDAM 1997a
E. de Jongh, G. Luijten, *Spiegel van Alledag: Nederlandse genreprenten 1550–1700*, Amsterdam (Rijksmuseum, Rijksprentenkabinet) 1997 (also in English edition)

AMSTERDAM 1997b
J. Peeters, P. Sutton, E.-J. Goossens *et al.*, *Het Paleis in de schilderkunst van de Gouden Eeuw*, Amsterdam (Koninklijk Paleis) 1997

AMSTERDAM 2000a
J. Kiers, F. Tissink, *De glorie van de Gouden Eeuw: Schilderijen, beeldhouwkunst en kunstnijverheid*, Amsterdam (Rijksmuseum) 2000 (also in English edition)

AMSTERDAM 2000b
J. Boonstra, G. van den Hout (eds.), *In de wolken: Jacob de Wit als plafondschilder*, Amsterdam (Bijbels Museum) 2000

AMSTERDAM 2000–2001
K. Zandvliet *et al.*, *Maurits: Prins van Oranje*, Amsterdam (Rijksmuseum) 2000–2001

AMSTERDAM 2001
P. Schatborn, *Tekenen van warmte: 17de-eeuwse Nederlandse tekenaars in Italië*, Amsterdam (Rijksmuseum, Rijksprentenkabinet) 2001 (also in English edition)

AMSTERDAM 2001–2002
R. Baarsen *et al.*, *Rococo in Nederland*, Amsterdam (Rijksmuseum) 2001–2002

AMSTERDAM 2002–2003a
N. Middelkoop (ed.), *Kopstukken: Amsterdammers geportretteerd 1600–1800*, Amsterdam (Amsterdams Historisch Museum) 2002–2003

AMSTERDAM 2002–2003b
J. Vrieze, V. Boele (eds.), *De rijkdom van Stroganoff: Het verhaal van een Russische familie*, Amsterdam (De Nieuwe Kerk) 2002–2003

AMSTERDAM 2003
C. Stolwijk *et al.*, *De keuze van Vincent: Van Goghs Musée Imaginaire*, Amsterdam (Van Gogh Museum) 2003

AMSTERDAM 2004
G. de Beer, E.-J. Goossens, B. van de Roemer, *Backhuysen aan het roer!: Zeeschilder 1630–1708 / Backhuysen at the Helm!: Marine Painter 1630–1708*, Amsterdam (Koninklijk Paleis) 2004

AMSTERDAM-DEN BOSCH 1982
S. Segal, *Een bloemrijk verleden: Overzicht van de Noord- en Zuidnederlandse bloemschilderkunst 1600–heden*, Amsterdam (P. de Boer Gallery), Den Bosch (Noordbrabants Museum) 1982

AMSTERDAM-BOSTON-PHILADELPHIA 1987–1988
P.C. Sutton *et al.*, *Masters of 17th-Century Dutch Landscape Painting*, Amsterdam (Rijksmuseum), Boston (Museum of Fine Arts), Philadelphia (Philadelphia Museum of Art) 1987–1988

AMSTERDAM-BRAUNSCHWEIG 1983
S. Segal, *A fruitful past*, Amsterdam (P. de Boer Gallery), Braunschweig (Herzog Anton Ulrich-Museum) 1983

AMSTERDAM-CLEVELAND 1999–2000
A. Chong, W. Kloek *et al.*, *Het Nederlandse Stilleven 1550–1720*, Amsterdam (Rijksmuseum), Cleveland (Cleveland Museum of Art) 1999–2000

AMSTERDAM-EMDEN 1985
B. Broos, R. Vorstman, W.L. van de Watering, *Ludolf Bakhuizen (1631–1708), schryfmeester — teyckenaer — schilder*, Amsterdam (Nederlands Scheepvaartmuseum), Emden (Ostfriesisches Landesmuseum) 1985

AMSTERDAM-NEW YORK 2003
F. Scholten *et al.*, *Willem van Tetrode, Sculptor (c.1525–1580)*, Amsterdam (Rijksmuseum), New York (The Frick Collection) 2003

AMSTERDAM-NEW YORK-TOLEDO 2003–2004
H. Leeflang, G. Luijten *et al.*, *Hendrick Goltzius (1558–1617): Drawings, prints and paintings*, Amsterdam (Rijksmuseum), New York (The Metropolitan Museum of Art), Toledo (Toledo Museum of Art) 2003–2004

AMSTERDAM-SAN FRANCISCO-HARTFORD 2002
G. Jansen, P. Sutton *et al.*, D. Bull (ed.), *Michael Sweerts (1624–1664)*, Amsterdam (Rijksmuseum), San Francisco (Fine Arts Museums of San Francisco), Hartford (Wadsworth Atheneum) 2002

ANCONA 1997
M. Gregori, P. Zampetti (eds.), *Antonio Francesco Peruzzini*, Ancona (Mole Vanvittelliana) 1997

ANGULO-IÑIGUEZ 1981
D. Angulo-Iñiguez, *Murillo: Su vida, su arte, su obra*, 3 vols, Madrid 1981

ANTWERP 1991
M. Klinge, *David Teniers de Jonge: Schilderijen · Tekeningen*, Antwerp (Koninklijk Museum voor Schone Kunsten) 1991

ANTWERP 1993
R.-A. d'Hulst, N. de Poorter, M. Vandeven, *Jacob Jordaens, Deel 1: Schilderijen en Wandtapijten*, Antwerp (Koninklijk

Museum voor Schone Kunsten) 1993

ANTWERP 2004
K.L. Belkin, F. Healy, J.M. Muller, *Een huis vol kunst: Rubens als verzamelaar*, Antwerp (Rubenshuis) 2004

ANTWERP-AMSTERDAM 1999–2000
C. Depauw, G. Luijten *et al.*, *Antoon van Dyck en de prentkunst*, Antwerp (Museum Plantin-Moretus), Amsterdam (Rijksmuseum) 1999–2000

ANTWERP-ARNHEM 1999–2000
K. van der Stighelen, M. Westen *et al.*, *Elck zijn waerom: Vrouwelijke kunstenaars in België en Nederland 1500–1950*, Antwerp (Koninklijk Museum voor Schone Kunsten), Arnhem (Museum voor Moderne Kunst) 1999–2000

ANTWERP-LONDON 1999
C. Brown, H. Vlieghe, *Anthony van Dyck 1599–1641*, Antwerp (Koninklijk Museum voor Schone Kunsten), London (Royal Academy of Arts) 1999

APELDOORN 2002
W. Erkelens, M. Frankenhuis, R. Zanderink (eds.), *Vorstelijk Vee: Vier eeuwen Nederlandse veerassen*, Apeldoorn (Paleis Het Loo Nationaal Museum) 2002

ARNASON 1975
H.H. Arnason, *The sculptures of Houdon*, London 1975

VAN ASPEREN DE BOER/DIJKSTRA/VAN SCHOUTE 1992
J.R.J. van Asperen de Boer, J. Dijkstra, R. van Schoute, with the assistance of C.M.A. Dalderup and J.P. Filedt Kok, *Underdrawing in paintings of the Rogier van der Weyden and Master of Flémalle groups* (*Nederlands Kunsthistorisch Jaarboek*, vol. 41), Zwolle 1992

ATHENS-DORDRECHT 2000–2001
P. Schoon, S. Paarlberg (eds.), *Griekse goden en helden in de tijd van Rubens en Rembrandt*, Athens (Ethniki Pinakothiki), Dordrecht (Dordrechts Museum) 2000–2001

ATLANTA 1985
F.J. Duparc, *Masterpieces of the Dutch Golden Age*, Atlanta (High Museum of Art) 1985

AUCKLAND 1982
E. de Jongh *et al.*, *Still life in the Age of Rembrandt*, Auckland (Art Galleries of Auckland, Wellington and Christchurch) 1982

AUERBACH 1961
E. Auerbach, *Nicholas Hilliard*, London 1961

B

B See BARTSCH 1803–1821

BAARSEN 1998
R. Baarsen, 'High rococo in Holland: William IV and Agostino Carlini', *The Burlington Magazine* 140 (1998), pp. 172–183

BACCI 1976
M. Bacci, *L'opera completa di Piero di Cosimo*, Milan 1976

BACHMANN 1982
F. Bachmann, *Aert van der Neer 1603/4–1677*, Bremen 1982

BAD HOMBURG-WUPPERTAL 1995
I. Ember, M. Chiarini (eds.), *Rembrandt, Rubens, Van Dyck...: Italiensehnsucht nordischer Barockmaler: Meisterwerke aus dem Museum der bildenden Künste Budapest*, Bad Homburg v.d. Höhe (Sinclair-Haus), Wuppertal (Von der Heydt-Museum) 1995

BAER 1990
R. Baer, *The Paintings of Gerrit Dou (1613–1675)* (diss.), New York 1990

BAKKER 1983
N. Bakker, 'De Dodo, symbool van een verloren paradijs', *Tableau* 6 (1983), no. 1, pp. 48–53

BANDMANN 1960
G. Bandmann, *Melancholie und Musik: Ikonographische Studien*, Cologne-Opladen 1960

BARTSCH 1803–1821
A. Bartsch, *Le peintre graveur*, 21 vols, Vienna 1803–1821

BASEL 1960
G. Schmidt, H. Reinhardt, E. Treu *et al.*, *Die Malerfamilie Holbein in Basel*, Basel (Kunstmuseum) 1960

BASEL 1974
D. Koepplin, T. Falk, *Lukas Cranach: Gemälde, Zeichnungen, Druckgrafik*, Basel (Kunstmuseum) 1974

BASEL 1987
P. ten Doesschate-Chu *et al.*, *Im Lichte Hollands: Holländische Malerei des 17. Jahrhunderts aus den Sammlungen des Fürsten von Liechtenstein und aus Schweizer Besitz*, Basel (Kunstmuseum) 1987

BASTET *et al.* 1989
F.L. Bastet *et al.*, *De verzameling van mr. Carel Vosmaer (1826–1888)*, Amsterdam 1989

BAUCH 1926
K. Bauch, *Jakob Adriaensz Backer: Ein Rembrandtschüler aus Friesland*, Berlin 1926

BAUER 2001
A.N. Bauer, *Jan Mijtens (1613/1614–1670): Leben und Werk eines Haager Portraitmalers* (diss. Freie Universität), Berlin 2001

BAUMGART 1944
F. Baumgart, 'Zusammenhänge der niederländischen mit der italienischen Malerei in der zweiten Hälfte des 16. Jahrhunderts', *Marburger Jahrbuch* 13 (1944), pp. 187–250

BECK 1972–1973
H.-U. Beck, *Jan van Goyen 1596–1656: Ein Oeuvreverzeichnis*, 2 vols, Amsterdam 1972–1973

BECK 1987
H.-U. Beck, *Jan van Goyen 1596–1656: Ergänzungsband*, Doornspijk 1987

BECK 1991
H.-U. Beck, *Künstler um Jan van Goyen: Ein Oeuvreverzeichnis*, Doornspijk 1991

DE BEER 2002
G. de Beer, *Ludolf Backhuysen (1630–1708): Sein Leben und Werk*, Zwolle 2002

BEHERMAN 1988
T. Beherman, *Godfried Schalcken*, Paris 1988

BEIJERMAN-SCHOLS *et al.* 2000
J. Beijerman-Schols *et al.*, *Geschiedenis in beeld*, Zwolle-Amsterdam-Dordrecht-Rotterdam 2000

BERKHOF 1988
J.A. Berkhof, 'Krakende harmonie: De plafondschildering Icarus Atlanticus van Ger Lataster in het Mauritshuis', *Beelding* (April 1988), pp. 12–13

BEUMER 1999
M. Beumer, 'Philippus Baldaeus en Gerrit Mosopotam: Een buitengewoon portret', *Bulletin van het Rijksmuseum* 47 (1999), pp. 144–173

BELLUNO 1993
D. Succi, A. Delneri, *Marco Ricci e il paesaggio veneto del Settecento*, Belluno (Palazzo Crepadona) 1993

BERARDI 1998
M. Berardi, *Science into art: Rachel Ruysch's early development as a still-life painter*, Pittsburgh 1998

BERENSON 1932
B. Berenson, *Italian pictures of the Renaissance: Florentine school*, Oxford 1932

BERENSON 1957
B. Berenson, *Italian pictures of the Renaissance: Venetian school*, London-New York 1957

VAN BERENSTEYN 1933
E.A. van Berensteyn, *Iconographie van Prins Willem I van Oranje*, Haarlem 1933

BERGAMO 1979
M. Gregori, *Giovan Battista Moroni (1520–1578)*, Bergamo (Palazzo della Ragione) 1979

BERGAMO 1981
A. Veca, *Vanitas: Il simbolismo del tempo*, Bergamo (Galleria Lorenzelli) 1981

BERGSTRÖM 1956
I. Bergström, *Dutch still-life painting in the seventeenth century*, London 1956

BERGSTRÖM 1977
I. Bergström, with C. Grimm, *Natura in prosa*, Milan 1977

BERGVELT 1998
E. Bergvelt, *Pantheon der Gouden Eeuw: Van Nationale Konst-Gallerij tot Rijksmuseum van Schilderijen (1798–1896)*, Zwolle 1998

BERLIN 1996
Dreihundert Jahre Akademie der Künste / Hochschule der Künste: „Die Kunst hat nie ein Mensch allein besessen", Berlin (Akademie der Künste / Hochschule der Künste) 1996

BERLIN-AMSTERDAM-LONDON 1991–1992
C. Brown, J. Kelch, P.J.J. van Thiel (eds.), *Rembrandt: The Master & His Workshop*, 2 vols, Berlin (Altes Museum), Amsterdam (Rijksmuseum), London (National Gallery) 1991–1992

BERNT 1969–1970
W. Bernt, *Die Niederländische Maler des 17. Jahrhunderts*, 3 vols, Munich 1969–1970

BIESBOER 1983
P. Biesboer, *Schilderijen voor het stadhuis Haarlem*, Haarlem 1983

BIGLER PLAYTER 1972
C. Bigler Playter, *Willem Duyster and Pieter Codde: The "Duystere Werelt" of Dutch Genre Painting c.1625–1635* (diss.), Harvard 1972

BIKKER 2001
J. Bikker, *Willem Drost (1633–1658): A Rembrandt pupil in Amsterdam, Rome and Venice* (diss.), Utrecht 2001

BIKKER *et al.* 2003
J. Bikker, J.P. Filedt Kok, M. van der Laar, W. de Ridder, 'Drie portretten van Antwerpse burgers geschilderd door Jacob Jordaens', *Bulletin van het Rijksmuseum* 51 (2003), pp. 234–273

BILLE 1961
C. Bille, *De tempel der Kunst of het kabinet van den Heer Braamcamp*, 2 vols, Amsterdam 1961

BILZEN-RIJKHOVEN 1992–1993
Ridders en Priesters: acht eeuwen Duitse orde in Noordwest-Europa, Bilzen-Rijkhoven (Landcommanderij Alden Biessen) 1992–1993

BLADE 1976
T.T. Blade, *The paintings of Dirck van Delen* (diss. 1976), Ann Arbor, Michigan 1984

BLANKERT 1967
A. Blankert, *Heraclitus en Democritus in het bijzonder in de Nederlandse kunst van de 17de eeuw*, s.l. 1967

BLANKERT 1978
A. Blankert, *Nederlandse 17e eeuwse Italianiserende landschapschilders / Dutch 17th Century Italianate Landscape Painters*, Soest 1978

BLANKERT 1982
A. Blankert, *Ferdinand Bol: Rembrandt's pupil*, Doornspijk 1982

BLANKERT 1995
A. Blankert, 'Rembrandt and his Followers: Notes on Connoisseurship — its Potential and Pitfalls', in G. Cavalli-Björkman (ed.), *Rembrandt and his Pupils: Papers given at a Symposium in Nationalmuseum Stockholm, 2–3 October 1992*, Stockholm 1993, pp. 77–97 (reprinted in BLANKERT 2004, pp. 239–250)

BLANKERT 2004
A. Blankert, *Selected Writings On Dutch Painting: Rembrandt, Van Beke, Vermeer and Others*, Zwolle 2004

BLANKERT/MONTIAS/AILLAUD 1992
A. Blankert, J.M. Montias, G. Aillaud, *Vermeer*, Amsterdam 1992 (English edition New York 1992)

BLEYERVELD 1991
Y. Bleyerveld, 'Een portret onder een "Bewening"', *Nieuwsbrief Mauritshuis* 4 (1991), no. 1, pp. 6–7

BLOCH 1946
V. Bloch, '"Monsú Bernardo" in het Mauritshuis', *Maandblad voor Beeldende Kunsten* 22 (1946), pp. 77–82

BLOCH 1969
V. Bloch, *Michael Sweerts*, The Hague 1969

BOCK/GAEHTGENS 1987
H. Bock, T.W. Gaehtgens (eds.), *Holländische Genremalerei im 17. Jahrhundert: Symposium Berlin 1984*, Berlin 1987

DE BOER *et al.* 1993
M. de Boer, B. Broos, E. Buijsen, R. van Leeuwen, P. van der Ploeg, 'Summary Catalogue of the Picture Gallery of Prince Willem V', *Mauritshuis in focus* 6 (1993), no. 3, pp. 22–38

BOERSMA 2000–2001
A. Boersma, 'Dou's Painting Technique: An Examination of Two Paintings', in WASHINGTON-LONDON-THE HAGUE 2000–2001, pp. 54–63

BOISCLAIR 1986
M.-N. Boisclair, *Gaspard Dughet: Sa vie et son œuvre (1615–1675)*, Paris 1986

BOL 1955
L.J. Bol, 'Een Middelburgse Brueghel-groep', *Oud Holland* 70 (1955), pp. 1–20, 96–109, 138–154

BOL 1956
L.J. Bol, 'Een Middelburgse Breughel-groep, V. Christoffel van den Berghe: Bloemen en landschap: Recuperatie voor een schilder die zijn oeuvre verloor', *Oud Holland* 71 (1956), pp. 183–195

BOL 1958
L.J. Bol, 'Een Middelburgse Brueghel-groep, VIII: Adriaen Pietersz. van de Venne, schilder en teyckenaer', *Oud Holland* 73 (1958), pp. 128–147

BOL 1960
L.J. Bol, *The Bosschaert dynasty: Painters of flowers and fruit*, Leigh-on-Sea 1960

BOL 1969
L.J. Bol, *Holländische Maler des 17. Jahrhunderts nahe den grossen Meistern*, Braunschweig 1969

BOL 1973
L.J. Bol, *Die holländische Marinemaler des 17. Jahrhunderts*, Braunschweig 1973

BOL 1977
L.J. Bol, *Adriaen Coorte: A Unique Late Seventeenth Century Dutch Still-Life Painter*, Assen-Amsterdam 1977

BOL 1981–1982
L.J. Bol, 'Goede onbekenden: Karel Slabbaert', *Tableau* 4 (1981–1982), pp. 582–588

BOL 1982
L.J. Bol, *Goede onbekenden: Hedendaagse herkenning en waardering van verscholen, voorbijgezien en onderschat talent*, Mijdrecht 1982

BOL 1983
L.J. Bol, 'Adriaen Pietersz. van de Venne, schilder en teyckenaer', *Tableau* 6 (1983), no. 1, pp. 54–63

BOLOGNA 1958
F. Bologna, *Francesco Solimena*, Naples 1958

BOLTEN *et al.* 1981
J. Bolten *et al.*, *Rembrandt and the incredulity of Thomas*, Leiden 1981

DEN BOSCH 1992
C. de Mooij, *Vastenavond — Carnaval: Feesten van de omgekeerde wereld*, Den Bosch (Noordbrabants Museum) 1992

DEN BOSCH 2001
P. Huys Janssen *et al.*, *Panorama op de wereld: Het landschap van Bosch tot Rubens*, Den Bosch (Noordbrabants Museum) 2001

DEN BOSCH 2003–2004
A. de Koomen *et al.*, *Monsters en fabeldieren: 2500 jaar geschiedenis van randgevallen*, Den Bosch (Noordbrabants Museum) 2003–2004

DEN BOSCH-HAARLEM 1996
E. de Jong, M. Dominicus-van Soest, *Aardse Paradijzen: De tuin in de Nederlandse kunst I, 15de-18de eeuw*, Den Bosch (Noordbrabants Museum), Haarlem (Frans Hals Museum) 1996

DEN BOSCH-HEINO-HAARLEM 1984
Herinneringen aan Italië: Kunst en toerisme in de 18de eeuw, Den Bosch (Noordbrabants Museum), Heino (Kasteel Het Nijenhuis), Haarlem (Frans Hals Museum) 1984

DEN BOSCH-LOUVAIN 2002–2003
Y. Bruijnen, P. Huys Janssen, *De Vier Jaargetijden in de kunst van de Nederlanden 1500–1750*, Den Bosch (Noordbrabants Museum), Louvain (Stedelijk Museum Vander Kelen-Mertens) 2002–2003

BOSCHLOO/VAN DER SMAN 1993
A.W.A. Boschloo, G.J.J. van der Sman (eds.), *Italian Paintings from the Sixteenth Century in Dutch Public Collections*, Florence 1993

BOSCHMA 1978
B. Boschma, *Willem Bartel van der Kooi (1768–1836) en het tekenonderwijs in Friesland*, Leeuwarden 1978

DE BOSQUE 1975
A. de Bosque, *Quinten Metsys*, Brussels 1975

BOSSHARD-VAN BRÜGGEN 1974
E. & V. Bosshard-Van Brüggen, 'Konservierung einer Tüchleinmalerei', *Maltechnik Restauro* 80 (1974), no. 1, pp. 16–20

BOSTON 2000–2001
A. Chong (ed.), *Rembrandt creates Rembrandt: Art and ambition in Leiden, 1629–1631*, Boston (Isabella Stewart Gardner Museum) 2000–2001

BOSTON-TOLEDO 1993–1994
P. Sutton *et al.*, *The Age of Rubens*, Boston (Museum of Fine Arts), Toledo (Toledo Museum of Art) 1993–1994

BRAUN 1966
H. Braun, *Gerard und Willem van Honthorst* (diss.), Göttingen 1966

BRAUN 1980
K. Braun, *Alle tot nu toe bekende schilderijen van Jan Steen*, Rotterdam 1980

BRAUNSCHWEIG 1979
J. Bialostocki, S. Jacob, R.E.O. Ekkart, *Jan Lievens: Ein Maler im Schatten Rembrandts*, Braunschweig (Herzog Anton Ulrich-Museum) 1979

BRAUNSCHWEIG 1993–1994
G. Biegel (ed.), *Geschichte des Alters in ihren Zeugnissen von der Antike bis zur Gegenwart*, Braunschweig (Braunschweigerisches Landesmuseum) 1993–1994

BRAUNSCHWEIG 2000
N. Büttner (ed.), *Der Krieg als Person: Herzog Christian d.J. von Braunschweig-Lüneborg im Bildnis von Paulus Moreelse*, Braunschweig (Herzog Anton Ulrich-Museum) 2000

BRAUNSCHWEIG 2004
N. Büttner, U. Heinen *et al.*, *Peter Paul Rubens: Barocke Leidenschaften*, Braunschweig (Herzog Anton Ulrich-Museum) 2004

BREDA 1952
Nassau-Oranje tentoonstelling, Breda (Huis van Brecht) 1952

BREDIUS 1902
A. Bredius, 'Pieter Jansz. Quast', *Oud Holland* 20 (1902), pp. 65–82

BREDIUS 1916
A. Bredius, 'Een Calraet-tentoonstelling', *Oude Kunst* 2 (1916), pp. 104–109

BREDIUS 1920
[A.] B[redius], 'Drie brieven van Rembrandt in het Mauritshuis', *Oude Kunst* 5 (1920), no. 4, pp. 101–104

BREDIUS 1921
A. Bredius, 'Claes Hals', *The Burlington Magazine* 38 (1921), pp. 138–139

BREDIUS/GERSON 1969
A. Bredius, revised by H. Gerson, *Rembrandt: The Complete Edition of the Paintings*, London 1969

BREJON DE LAVERGNÉE 1984
A. Brejon de Lavergnée, 'Nouvelles Toiles d'Andrea de Leone: Essai de Catalogue', in *Scritti di Storia dell'Arte in onore di Federico Zeri*, 2 vols, Milan 1984, vol. 2, pp. 656–680

BREMMER 1917
H.P. Bremmer, '[No title]', *Beeldende Kunst* 4 (1917), pp. 80–81

BRENNINKMEYER-DE ROOIJ/HARTKAMP 1988
B. Brenninkmeyer-de Rooij, A. Hartkamp, 'Oranje's erfgoed in het Mauritshuis', *Oud Holland* 102 (1988), pp. 181–235

BRIGANTI 1962
G. Briganti, *Pietro da Cortona o della pittura barocca*, Florence 1962

VAN DEN BRINK 1997
P.B.R. van den Brink, *Ondertekening en andere technische aspecten van de Antwerpse maniëristen 1500–1525* (diss.), Groningen 1997

BROCHHAGEN 1958
E. Brochhagen, *Karel Dujardin: Ein Beitrag zum Italianismus in Holland im 17. Jahrhundert* (diss.), Cologne 1958

BROOS 1989a
B. Broos, 'Een nieuwe aanwinst: Gerbrand van den Eeckhout, *Isaak en Rebecca*, 1665', *Mauritshuis Cahier* (1989), no. 1

BROOS 1989b
B. Broos, 'Kijken en zien', *Nieuwsbrief Mauritshuis* 2 (1989), no. 4, pp. 4–5

BROOS 1990a
B. Broos, 'Een schilderij nader bekeken: Rembrandts vader en moeder', *Nieuwsbrief Mauritshuis* 3 (1990), nos. 3–4, pp. 14–16

BROOS 1990b
B. Broos, 'Een schilderij nader bekeken: Venus poogt Adonis van de jacht te weerhouden uit het atelier van Peter Paul Rubens', *Nieuwsbrief Mauritshuis* 3 (1990), no. 1, p. 10

BROOS 1991a
B. Broos, 'Hippocrates bezoekt Democritus door Pynas, Lastman, Moeyaert en Berchem', *Kroniek van het Rembrandthuis* (1991), no. 2, pp. 16–23

BROOS 1991b
B. Broos, 'Een schilderij nader bekeken: Rembrandt (?) Saul en David', *Nieuwsbrief Mauritshuis* 4 (1991), no. 4, pp. 7–8

BROOS 1992
B. Broos, *Een portret van Huygens en zijn 'Sterre' voor het Mauritshuis*, brochure, The Hague 1992

BROOS 1993a
B. Broos, 'Landschap met jachtnimfen (en Diana?)', *Bulletin Vereniging Rembrandt* 3 (1993), no. 4, pp. 23–24

BROOS 1993b
B. Broos, 'A Painting in Focus: Bartholomeus Breenbergh, *Landscape with Nymphs (and Diana?)* (1647)', *Mauritshuis in focus* 6 (1993), no. 2, pp. 13–17

BROOS 1994
B. Broos, 'A Painting in Focus: A "Self-portrait" of Paulus Potter by Bartholomeus van der Helst', *Mauritshuis in focus* 7 (1994), no. 3, pp. 8–14

BROOS 1995a
B. Broos, 'Adriaen Coorte: *Still life with strawberries* (1705)', *Mauritshuis in focus* 8 (1995), no. 1, pp. 12–14

BROOS 1995b
B. Broos, 'A Painting in Focus: *Portrait of Michiel de Ruyter (1607–1676)*, Ferdinand Bol (1618–1680) and Willem van de Velde the Younger (1633–1707)', *Mauritshuis in focus* 8 (1995), no. 2, pp. 8–14

BROOS 1995c
B. Broos, 'Jan van Beuningen: A gentleman of standing in the art world', *Mauritshuis in focus* 8 (1995), no. 2, pp. 20–26

BROOS 1995d
B. Broos, 'Vermeer's *View of Delft* in Bloemendaal', *Mauritshuis in focus* 8 (1995), no. 3, pp. 8–15

BROOS *et al.* 1996
B. Broos, with D. de Clercq, Y. Kuiper, C. Vermeeren, 'Het *Gezicht op Delft* en het Stinstra-mysterie', *Oud Holland* 110 (1996), pp. 35–46

BROOS/VAN LEEUWEN 1992
B. Broos, R. van Leeuwen, 'Een schilderij nader bekeken: Daniël Seghers & Thomas Willeboirts Bosschaert, Bloemencartouche met Mariabeeld', *Nieuwsbrief Mauritshuis* 5 (1992), no. 1, pp. 15–16

BROOS/WADUM 1992
B.P.J. Broos, J. Wadum, 'Het "Dochters schilderijtje" van Adriaen van der Werff', *Delineavit et Sculpsit* (1992), no. 9, pp. 11–16

BROOS/WADUM 1993
B. Broos, J. Wadum, 'Four Panels From One Tree', *Mauritshuis in focus* 6 (1993), no. 1, pp. 13–16

BROULHIET 1938
G. Broulhiet, *Meindert Hobbema*, Paris 1938

BROWN 1981
C. Brown, *Carel Fabritius: Complete Edition with a catalogue raisonné*, Oxford 1981

BROWN 1982
C. Brown, *Van Dyck*, Oxford 1982

BRUGES 1994
D. De Vos, D. Marechal, W. Le Loup, *Hans Memling: Catalogus*, Bruges (Groeningemuseum) 1994

BRUGES 1998
Van Hans Memling tot Pieter Pourbus, Bruges (Memlingmuseum) 1998

BRUGES 2002
De eeuw van Van Eyck: De Vlaamse Primitieven en het Zuiden 1430–1530, Bruges (Groeningemuseum) 2002

BRUNIN 1968
H. Brunin, 'De Erasmusportretten van en naar Holbein de Jonge', *Bulletin Musées Royaux des Beaux-Arts de Belgique* 17 (1968), pp. 145–160

BRUNNER-BULST 2004
M. Brunner-Bulst, *Pieter Claesz. der Hauptmeister des Haarlemer Stillebens im 17. Jahrhundert: Kritischer Œuvrekatalog*, Lingen 2004

BRUSATI 1995
C. Brusati, *Artifice and Illusion: The Art and Writing of Samuel van Hoogstraten*, Chicago-London 1995

BRUSSELS 1971
Rembrandt en zijn tijd, Brussels (Paleis voor Schone Kunsten) 1971

BRUSSELS 1984
T.G. Kotte *et al.*, *Willem de Zwijger 1533–1584*, Brussels (Stedelijk Museum Het Broodhuis) 1984

BRUSSELS 1998–1999
L. Duerloo, W. Thomas (eds.), *Albrecht & Isabella 1598–1621*, Brussels (Musées Royaux des Beaux-Arts) 1998–1999

BRUSSELS-NIEDERÖSTERREICH 1991
J. Van der Stock, *Stad in Vlaanderen: Cultuur en maatschappij 1477–1787*, Brussel (Galerij van Het Gemeentekrediet), Niederösterreich (Schloss Schallaburg) 1991

BRUYN 1987
J. Bruyn, 'Mittelalterliche "doctrina exemplaris" und Allegorie als Komponente des sog. Genrebildes', in BOCK/GAEHTGENS 1987, pp. 33–59

DE BRUYN 1988
J.-P. de Bruyn, *Erasmus II Quellinus (1607–1678): De schilderijen met catalogue raisonné*, Freren 1988

BRUYN 1999
J. Bruyn, 'Een portret van Pieter Aertsen en de Amsterdamse portretschilderkunst 1550–1600 met een postscriptum over Huybrecht Beuckelaer (alias Hubbert/Hubbard)', *Oud Holland* 113 (1999), pp. 107–136

BRUYN 2003
J. Bruyn, 'Hubert (Huybrecht) Beuckelaer, an Antwerp portrait painter, and his English patron, the Earl of Leicester', in J. Roding (ed.), *Dutch and Flemish artists in Britain 1550–1800* (*Leids Kunsthistorisch Jaarboek*, vol. 13), Leiden 2003, pp. 85–112

BUCHAN 1981
M. Braman Buchan, *The Paintings of Pieter Aertsen* (diss. New York 1975), Ann Arbor, Michigan 1981

BUENDÍA/GUTIÉRREZ PASTOR 1986
J.R. Buendía, I. Gutiérrez Pastor, *Vida y obra del pintor Mateo Cerezo (1637–1666)*, Burgos 1986

BUIJSEN 1993a
E. Buijsen, 'Een bloemstilleven van Jan Davidsz. De Heem', *Antiek* 28 (1993), no. 4, p. 173

BUIJSEN 1993b
E. Buijsen, 'A Painting in Focus: Cornelis Troost, The Dispute between the Doctors Raasbollius and Urinaal', *Mauritshuis in focus* 6 (1993), no. 1, pp. 8–12

BUIJSEN 1994a
E. Buijsen, 'A Painting in Focus, An Acquisition: *River View with a church and Farm*, Jan van Goyen (Leiden 1596–1656 The Hague)', *Mauritshuis in focus* 7 (1994), no. 1, pp. 7–12

BUIJSEN 1994b
E. Buijsen, 'Rivierlandschap van Van Goyen geschonken aan het Mauritshuis', *Antiek* 28 (1994), no. 10, pp. 472–475

BUIJSEN 2000
E. Buijsen, 'Rembrandt's *Self-Portrait with Gorget*: An ongoing debate', *Oud Holland* 114 (2000), pp. 155–163

BUIJSEN *et al.* 1998
E. Buijsen *et al.*, *Haagse Schilders in de Gouden Eeuw: Het Hoogsteder Lexicon van alle schilders werkzaam in Den Haag 1600–1700*, The Hague-Zwolle 1998

BUIJSEN/VAN DER PLOEG 1993
E. Buijsen, P. van der Ploeg, 'Acquisitions for the Mauritshuis over the Past Two Years', *Mauritshuis in focus* 6 (1993), no. 2, pp. 18–33

BUMA 1994
J.H. Buma, *François Ryckhals 1609–1647: Een schilderende magiër uit Middelburg, 'Ryck in als'*, Goes 1994

BURGEMEISTER/SURH 2002
W. Burgemeister, D. Surh, *Salomon Lilian: Old Masters, 2002*, Amsterdam-Zwolle 2002

BURGER-WEGENER 1976
C. Burger-Wegener, *Johannes Lingelbach 1622–1674* (diss.), Munich 1976

BURKE 1976
J.D. Burke, *Jan Both: Paintings, drawings and prints*, New York 1976

BUTÔT/BOL/KEYES 1981
F.C. Butôt, L.J. Bol, G.S. Keyes, *Netherlandish Paintings and Drawings from the Collection of F.C. Butôt by little-known and rare Masters of the Seventeenth Century*, London 1981

BUVELOT 1995a
Q. Buvelot, 'Jacob van Campen als schilder en tekenaar', in AMSTERDAM 1995, pp. 53–119

BUVELOT 1995b
Q. Buvelot, 'Ontwerpen voor geschilderde decoratieprogramma's', in AMSTERDAM 1995, pp. 120–153

BUVELOT 1995c
Q. Buvelot, 'A painting in focus, An acquisition: *The violin player*, Gerard van Honthorst (1590– Utrecht–1656)', *Mauritshuis in focus* 8 (1995), no. 3, pp. 16–20

BUVELOT 1996
Q. Buvelot, 'A painting in focus, An old acquaintance: *The liberation of St Peter*, Hendrick ter Brugghen (The Hague? 1588–1629 Utrecht)', *Mauritshuis in focus* 9 (1996), pp. 12–18

BUVELOT 1998
Q. Buvelot, 'Two arcadian landscapes by Jan van Huysum', *Mauritshuis in focus* 11 (1998), no. 1, pp. 18–25

BUVELOT 2002a
Q. Buvelot, 'Catalogue Baron van Dedem gift', *Mauritshuis in focus* 15 (2002), no. 2, pp. 16–30

BUVELOT 2002b
Q. Buvelot, 'A mountain landscape with a waterfall by Roelant Roghman', *Mauritshuis in focus* 15 (2002), no. 3, pp. 8–14

BUVELOT 2004
Q. Buvelot, 'On Des Tombe, donor of Vermeer's "Girl with a pearl earring"', *Mauritshuis in focus* 17 (2004), no. 1, pp. 22–30

BUVELOT *et al.* 1998
Q. Buvelot, M. Hilaire, O. Zeder, *Tableaux flamands et hollandais du Musée Fabre de Montpellier*, Paris-Montpellier-Zwolle 1998

BUVELOT/WADUM 1999
Q. Buvelot, J. Wadum, 'Rembrandt's early self portrait unmasked', *Mauritshuis in focus* 12 (1999), no. 3, pp. 32–42

C

CAEN 1990
A. Tapié, *Les Vanités dans la peinture au XVIIe siècle: Méditations sur la richesse, le dénuement et la rédemption*, Caen (Musée des Beaux-Arts) 1990

DE CALLATAY 1971
E. de Callatay, 'Attributions à Pierre van Mol', *Revue Belge d'Archéologie et d'Histoire de l'Art* 40 (1971), pp. 95–104

CANOVA 1964
G. Canova, *Paris Bordone*, Venice 1964

CARROLL 1987
J.L. Carroll, *The Paintings of Jacob Cornelisz. Van Oostsanen (1472?–1533)* (diss.), Ann Arbor, Michigan 1987

CHAPMAN 1990
H.P. Chapman, *Rembrandt's Self-Portraits: A Study in Seventeenth-Century Identity*, Princeton, New Jersey 1990

CHÂTELET 1980
A. Châtelet, *Early Dutch painting: Painting in the Northern Netherlands in the fifteenth century*, Amsterdam 1980

CHIARINI 1977
M. Chiarini, 'Il catalogo completo dei dipinti del Rijksmuseum', *Paragone* 28 (1977), pp. 89–98

CHONG 1992a
A.D. Chong, *Aelbert Cuyp and the meanings of landscape* (diss.), New York 1992

CHONG 1992b
A. Chong, *Johannes Vermeer: Gezicht op Delft*, Bloemendaal 1992

CHRISTIE/WADUM 1992
N. Christie, J. Wadum, 'De grond der zinnen', *Nieuwsbrief Mauritshuis* 5 (1992), no. 1, pp. 9–11

CLEVES 1979
G. de Werd (ed.), *Soweit der Erdkreis reicht: Johann Moritz von Nassau-Siegen 1604–1679*, Cleves (Städtisches Museum Haus Kockkock) 1979

DE CLIPPEL 2003
K. de Klippel, 'Adriaen Brouwer, portrait painter: New identifications and an iconographic novelty', *Simiolus* 30 (2003), pp. 196–216

COLLINS 1953
L.C. Collins, *Hercules Seghers*, Chicago 1953

COLLINS BAKER 1912
C.H. Collins Baker, *Lely and the Stuart portrait painters: A study of English portraiture before and after Van Dyck*, 2 vols, London 1912

COLOGNE 1955
Barthel Bruyn 1493–1555: Gesamtverzeichnis seiner Bildnisse und Altarwerke. Gedächtnisausstellung aus Anlass seines vierhundertsten Todesjahres, Cologne (Wallraf-Richartz-Museum) 1955

COLOGNE 1982–1983
Die Heiligen drei Könige: Darstellung und Verehrung, Cologne (Wallraf-Richartz-Museum in the Joseph-Haubrich-Kunsthalle) 1982–1983

COLOGNE-ANTWERP-VIENNA 1992–1993
F. Baudouin *et al.*, *Van Bruegel tot Rubens: De Antwerpse schilderschool 1550–1650*, Cologne (Wallraf-Richartz-Museum), Antwerp (Koninklijk Museum voor Schone Kunsten), Vienna (Kunsthistorisches Museum) 1992–1993

COLOGNE-UTRECHT 1985–1986
E. Mai (ed.), *Roelant Savery in seiner Zeit*, Cologne (Wallraf-Richartz-Museum), Utrecht (Centraal Museum) 1985–1986

COLOGNE-UTRECHT 1991–1992
D.A. Levine, W. Mai (eds.), *I Bamboccianti: Niederländische Malerrebellen im Rom des Barock*, Cologne (Wallraf-Richartz-Museum), Utrecht (Centraal Museum) 1991–1992

COPENHAGEN 1999
O. Koester *et al.*, *Illusions: Gijsbrechts, Royal Master of Deception*, Copenhagen (Statens Museum for Kunst) 1999

COPENHAGEN-AMSTERDAM 2001
L. Bøgh Rønberg *et al.*, *Twee Gouden Eeuwen: Schilderkunst uit Nederland en Denemarken*, Copenhagen (Statens Museum for Kunst), Amsterdam (Rijksmuseum) 2001

CORPUS
J. Bruyn, B. Haak, S.H. Levie, P.J.J. van Thiel, E. van de Wetering, *A Corpus of Rembrandt Paintings*, vols 1– , Amsterdam, Foundation Rembrandt Research Project 1982–

COSTARAS 1994
N. Costaras, 'A Contrast in Styles: *The Descent into Limbo* by Jan Brueghel the Elder and Hans Rottenhammer', *Mauritshuis in focus* 7 (1994), no. 1, pp. 18–22

COUVREUR 1967
W. Couvreur, 'Daniël Seghers' inventaris van door hem geschilderde bloemstukken', *Gentse Bijdragen* 20 (1967), pp. 87–158

CUGINI 1939
D. Cugini, *Moroni Pittore*, Bergamo 1939

CUST/MARTIN 1906–1907
L. Cust, K. Martin, 'The portraits of Mary Queen of Scots', *The Burlington Magazine* 19 (1906–1907), pp. 38–47

D

DAVIDSON 1980
J.P. Davidson, *David Teniers the Younger*, London 1980

DAVIES 1978
A.I. Davies, *Allart van Everdingen*, New York-London 1978

DAVIES 1992
A.I. Davies, *Jan van Kessel (1641–1680)*, Doornspijk 1992

DAVIES 2001
A. Davies, with the collaboration of F.J. Duparc, *Allart van Everdingen 1621–1675: First Painter of Scandinavian Landscape*, Doornspijk 2001

DEFOER *et al.* 2003
H.L.M. Defoer *et al.*, *Goddelijk geschilderd: Honderd meesterwerken van Museum Catharijneconvent*, Utrecht-Zwolle 2003

DEKKING *et al.* 1987
N. Dekking *et al.*, *Tischbein: Een reizend portrettist in Nederland*, Utrecht 1987

DELBANCO 1927–1928
G. Delbanco, *Der Maler Abraham Bloemaert (1564–1651)* (diss. 1927), Strasbourg 1928

DELFT 1948
Vrede van Münster 1648–1948, Delft (Stedelijk Museum Het Prinsenhof) 1948

DELFT 1966
L. de Vries, *Twintig miniaturen uit Koninklijken Rijksbezit*, Delft (Stedelijk Museum Het Prinsenhof) 1966

DELFT 1984
Prins Willem van Oranje 1533–1584, Delft (Stedelijk Museum Het Prinsenhof) 1984

DELFT 1996
M. Kersten, D. Lokin, M. Plomp, *Delftse Meesters: Tijdgenoten van Vermeer. Een andere kijk op perspectief, licht en ruimte*, Delft (Stedelijk Museum Het Prinsenhof) 1996

DELFT 1998
M. van Maarseveen, J. Hilkhuijsen, J. Dane, *Beelden van een strijd: Oorlog en kunst vóór de Vrede van Munster, 1621–1648*, Delft (Stedelijk Museum Het Prinsenhof) 1998

DELFT-ANTWERP 1964–1965
De schilder en zijn wereld: Van Jan van Eyck tot Van Gogh en Ensor, Delft (Stedelijk Museum Het Prinsenhof), Antwerp (Koninklijk Museum voor Schone Kunsten) 1964–1965

DEN BOSCH
See: DEN BOSCH

DESSAU 2003
W. Savelsberg *et al.*, *Oranienbaum — Huis van Oranje: Wiederentdeckung eines anhaltischen Fürstenschlosses. Oranische Bildnisse aus fünf Jahrhunderte*, Dessau (Schloss Oranienbaum) 2003

DIJKSTRA *et al.* 2002
J. Dijkstra, P.P.W.M. Dirkse, A.E.A.M. Smits, *De schilderijen van Museum Catharijneconvent*, Utrecht-Zwolle 2002

DIJON-PARIS-ROTTERDAM 1992–1993
P. Rosenberg, G. Jansen, J. Giltaij, *Franse schilderkunst uit Nederlands bezit, 1600–1800*, Dijon (Musée des Beaux-Arts), Paris (Institut Néerlandais), Rotterdam (Museum Boijmans Van Beuningen) 1992–1993

VAN DISSEL 1980
A.J. van Dissel, 'Marten Jozef Geeraerts (1707–1791)', *Nederlands Kunsthistorisch Jaarboek* 31 (1980), pp. 387–400

D/LS 1974–1976
See: DROSSAERS/LUNSINGH SCHEURLEER 1974–1976

DOBRZYCKA 1966
A. Dobrzycka, *Jan van Goyen*, Poznan 1966

DOGAER 1971
G. Dogaer, 'De inventaris der schilderijen van Diego Duarte', *Jaarboek van het Koninklijk Museum voor Schone Kunsten Antwerpen* (1971), pp. 195–221

DOMELA NIEUWENHUIS 2001
E.N. Domela Nieuwenhuis Nyegaard, *Paulus Moreelse (1571–1638)* (diss. Leiden), 2 vols, s.l. 2001

DORDRECHT 1977–1978
Aelbert Cuyp en zijn familie: Schilders te Dordrecht, Dordrecht (Dordrechts Museum) 1977–1978

DORDRECHT 1992–1993
P. Marijnissen *et al.* (eds.), *De Zichtbaere Werelt: Schilderkunst uit de Gouden Eeuw in Hollands oudste stad*, Dordrecht (Dordrechts Museum) 1992–1993

DORDRECHT-COLOGNE 1998–1999
Arent de Gelder (1645–1727): Rembrandts laatste leerling, Dordrecht (Dordrechts Museum), Cologne (Wallraf-Richartz-Museum) 1998–1999

DORDRECHT-ENSCHEDE 2000
C. Dumas (ed.), *In helder licht: Abraham en Jacob van Strij, Hollandse meesters van landschap en interieur omstreeks 1800*, Dordrecht (Dordrechts Museum), Enschede (Rijksmuseum Twenthe) 2000

DORDRECHT-LEEUWARDEN 1988–1989
B. Boschma, J.M. de Groot *et al.*, *Meesterlijk vee: Nederlandse veeschilders 1600–1900*, Dordrecht (Dordrechts Museum), Leeuwarden (Fries Museum) 1988–1989

DORIVAL 1976
B. Dorival, *Philippe de Champaigne, 1602–1674*, Paris 1976

DROSSAERS 1932
S.W.A. Drossaers, 'Inventaris van de meubelen van het stadhouderlijk kwartier met het speelhuis en van het Huis in het Noordeinde te 's-Gravenhage', *Oud Holland* 47 (1932), pp. 193–236, 241–276

DROSSAERS/LUNSINGH SCHEURLEER 1974–1976
S.W.A. Drossaers, T.H. Lunsingh Scheurleer, *Inventarissen van de inboedels in de verblijven van de Oranjes en daarmede gelijk te stellen stukken 1567–1795*, 3 vols, The Hague 1974–1976

DUBLIN-GREENWICH 2003–2004
P. Sutton *et al.*, *Love letters: Dutch genre paintings in the Age of Vermeer*, Dublin (National Gallery of Ireland), Greenwich, Connecticut (Bruce Museum of Art and Science) 2003–2004

DÜLBERG 1990
A. Dülberg, *Privatporträts: Geschichte und Ikonologie einer Gattung im 15. und 16. Jahrhundert*, Berlin 1990

DÜSSELDORF 1971
Europäische Barockplastik am Niederrhein, Düsseldorf (Kunstmuseum) 1971

DUFAIS 1998
N. Dufais, 'Aert Schouman after Joris van der Haagen: A copy in watercolour', *Mauritshuis in focus* 11 (1998), no. 1, pp. 29–34

DUMAS 1991
C. Dumas, assisted by J. van der Meer Mohr, *Haagse stadsgezichten 1550–1800: Topografische schilderijen van het Haags Historisch Museum*, The Hague-Zwolle 1991

DUPARC 1975
F.J. Duparc [Senior], *Een eeuw strijd voor Nederlands Cultureel Erfgoed*, The Hague 1975

DUPARC 1977
F.J. Duparc, '"Deze allerberoemdste schilderij": De anatomische les van Rembrandt', *Kunstschrift Openbaar Kunstbezit* 21 (1977), pp. 129–134

DUPARC 1978
F.J. Duparc, 'De collectie van Stadhouder Willem V: Enkele aanvullingen', *Antiek* 13 (1978), pp. 282–284

DUPARC 1980
F.J. Duparc, 'Een teruggevonden schilderij van N. Berchem en J.B. Weenix', *Oud Holland* 94 (1980), pp. 37–42

DUPARC 1993
F. Duparc, 'Unknown Masterpiece by De Heem for the Mauritshuis', *Mauritshuis in focus* 6 (1993), no. 3, pp. 5–8

DUPARC 1994
F. Duparc, 'A Painting in Focus, An Acquisition: *The Old Lace-Maker*, Nicolaes Maes (Dordrecht 1634–1693 Amsterdam)', *Mauritshuis in focus* 7 (1994), no. 2, pp. 10–14

DUPARC 1995a
F. Duparc, 'A Painting in Focus, An Acquisition: *Landscape with hunters*, Pieter van Laer (Haarlem 1599–after 1642)', *Mauritshuis in focus* 8 (1995), no. 1, pp. 6–11

DUPARC 1995b
F. Duparc, 'A Recently Rediscovered Painting by Pieter van Laer', in *Shop Talk: Studies in Honour of Seymour Slive*, Cambridge, Massachusetts 1995, pp. 68–70

DUPARC 1996
F. Duparc, 'Masterpiece by Koninck on temporary loan to the Mauritshuis', *Mauritshuis in focus* 9 (1996), no. 3, pp. 19–22

E

VAN ECK 1993
X. van Eck, 'Een parel aan de kroon: Het bloemstilleven van De Heem in de collectie van het Mauritshuis', *Bulletin Vereniging Rembrandt* 3 (1993), no. 4, pp. 13–20

EDINBURGH 1992
J. Lloyd Williams, *Dutch art and Scotland: A Reflection of Taste*, Edinburgh (National Gallery of Scotland) 1992

EDINBURGH-LONDON 2001
J. Lloyd Williams *et al.*, *Rembrandt's women*, Edinburgh (National Gallery of Scotland), London (Royal Academy of Arts) 2001

EDWARDS 1954
R. Edwards, *Early conversation pictures from the Middle Ages to about 1730: A study in origins*, London [1954]

VAN EEGHEN 1963
I.H. van Eeghen, 'Huygh Pietersz Voskuyl of twee eeuwen in de Nes', *Amstelodamum* 50 (1963), pp. 123–129

EFFERT 2003
R. Effert, *Volkenkundig verzamelen: Het Koninklijk Kabinet van Zeldzaamheden en het Rijks Etnographisch Museum 1816–1883* (diss. Leiden University), Leiden 2003

EIDELBERG/ROWLANDS 1994
M. Eidelberg, E.W. Rowlands, 'The Dispersal of the Last Duke of Mantua's Paintings', *Gazette des Beaux-Arts* 123 (1994), pp. 207–294

EISELE 2000
K. Eisele, *Jan Wijnants (1631/32–1684): Ein Niederländischer Maler der Ideallandschaft im Goldenen Jahrhundert, Mit umfassenden Oeuvre-katalog*, Stuttgart 2000

EKKART 1977
R.E.O. Ekkart, *Franeker professorenportretten: Iconografie van de professoren aan de Academie en het Rijksathenaeum te Franeker*, Franeker 1977

EKKART 1979
R.E.O. Ekkart, *Johannes Cornelisz. Verspronck*, Haarlem 1979

ELZENGA 2003
E. Elzenga, 'Een troon bij de haard: Argumenten voor een lengteopstelling in de Ridderzaal', in J.R. ter Molen (ed.), *Een vorstelijk archivaris: Opstellen voor Bernard Woelderink*, Zwolle 2003, pp. 117–123

ENSCHEDE 1980
Z. Kolks, M. Niermeyer, *Oost-Nederland model: Landschappen, stads- en dorpsgezichten 17de- en*

19de eeuw, Enschede (Rijksmuseum Twenthe) 1980

ENSCHEDE 1987–1988
Z. Kolks, *Van schaamte ontbloot: Het naakt in de Nederlandse kunst ca. 1500–heden*, Enschede (Rijksmuseum Twenthe) 1987–1988

ENSCHEDE 1996
W. Frijhoff, F. Grijzenhout, M. Knuijt, *Een groot gedruis en eene onbesuisde vrolykheit: Feesten in de 18de eeuw*, Enschede (Rijksmuseum Twenthe) 1996

ERTZ 1979
K. Ertz, *Jan Brueghel der Ältere (1568–1625): Die Gemälde mit kritischem Œuvrekatalog*, Cologne 1979

ERTZ 1984
K. Ertz, *Jan Brueghel der Jüngere (1601–1678): Die Gemälde mit kritischem Œuvrekatalog*, Freren 1984

ESSEN-VIENNA 2003–2004
A. Wied *et al.*, *Die Flämische Landschaft 1520–1700*, Essen (Kulturstiftung Ruhr, Villa Hügel), Vienna (Kunsthistorisches Museum) 2003–2004

ESSEN-VIENNA-ANTWERP 1997–1998
K. Ertz, C. Nitze-Ertz (eds.), *Breughel — Brueghel: Pieter Breughel der Jüngere — Jan Brueghel der Ältere. Flämische Malerei um 1600: Tradition und Fortschritt*, Essen (Kulturstiftung Ruhr, Villa Hügel), Vienna (Kunsthistorisches Museum), Antwerp (Koninklijk Museum voor Schone Kunsten) 1997–1998

EVERS 1912
G.A. Evers, 'De menagerieën op het Loo', *Gelre* 15 (1912), pp. 533–540

EVERS 1914
G.A. Evers, 'De menagerie van prins Willem V op het Loo', *Gelre* 17 (1914), pp. 201–213

EX/SCHOLTEN 2001
N. Ex, F. Scholten, *De prins en De Keyser: Restauratie en geschiedenis van het grafmonument voor Willem van Oranje*, Bussum 2001

F

FALKENBURG/FILEDT KOK/LEEFLANG 1993
R. Falkenburg, J.P. Filedt Kok, H. Leeflang (eds.), *Goltzius-Studies: Hendrick Goltzius (1558–1617)* (*Nederlands Kunsthistorisch Jaarboek*, vols 42–43), Zwolle 1993

FERRARI/SCAVIZZI 1992
O. Ferrari, G. Scavizzi, *Luca Giordano: L'opera completa*, 2 vols, Naples 1992

FILIPCZAK 1987
Z.Z. Filipczak, *Picturing art in Antwerp*, Princeton, New Jersey 1987

FINSTEN 1981
J. Finsten, *Isaac Oliver: Art at the Courts of Elizabeth I and James I* (diss.), 2 vols, New York-London 1981

FISCHER 1975
P. Fischer, *Music in paintings of the Low Countries in the 16th and 17th centuries*, Amsterdam 1975

FOCK 1983
C.W. Fock, 'Willem van Mieris en zijn mecenas Pieter de la Court van der Voort', *Leids Kunsthistorisch Jaarboek* 2 (1983), pp. 261–281

FOCK *et al.* 2001
C.W. Fock *et al.*, *Het Nederlandse interieur in beeld 1600–1900*, Zwolle 2001

FORLANI TEMPESTI/CAPRETTI 1996
A. Forlani Tempesti, E. Capretti, *Piero di Cosimo: Catalogo completo*, Florence 1996

FOSKETT 1974
D. Foskett, *Samuel Cooper 1609–1672*, London 1974

FOUCART 2001
J. Foucart, '*Fleurs et coquillages* de Balthazar van der Ast (1593/94–1657): Défense et illustration de la peinture de fleurs hollandaise au Louvre', *La Revue du Louvre* 51 (2001), no. 3, pp. 15–18

FRANCHINI GUELFI 1991
F. Franchini Guelfi, *Alessandro Magnasco: Con un saggio sulla tecnica e sui materiali pittorici di Paolo Bensi*, Soncino 1991

FRANCKEN 1878
D. Francken, *Adriaen van de Venne*, Amsterdam 1878

FRANITS 1997
W. Franits (ed.), *Looking at Seventeenth-Century Dutch Art: Realism Reconsidered*, Cambridge 1997

FRANKE 1995
K. Franke, 'John Bettes', in ALLGEMEINES KÜNSTLER-LEXIKON, vol. 10, Munich-Leipzig 1995, p. 152

FRANKFURT AM MAIN 1993–1994
S. Schultze *et al.*, *Leselust: Niederländische Gemälde des Goldenen Zeitalters von Rembrandt bis Vermeer*, Frankfurt am Main (Schirn Kunsthalle) 1993–1994

FRANKFURT AM MAIN 2003
J. Giltaij, *Rembrandt, Rembrandt*, Frankfurt am Main (Städelsches Kunstinstitut) 2003

FRANSEN 1997
H. Fransen, *Michaelis Collection, The Old Town House, Cape Town: Catalogue of the Collection of Paintings and Drawings*, Zwolle 1997

FRANZ 1969
H. Franz, *Niederländische Landschaftsmalerei im Zeitalter des Manierismus*, 2 vols, Graz 1969

FREEDBERG 1984
D. Freedberg, *Rubens: The Life of Christ after the Passion* (*Corpus Rubenianum Ludwig Burchard*, vol. 4), New York 1984

FREISE 1911
K. Freise, *Pieter Lastman: Sein Leben und seine Kunst*, Leipzig 1911

FREMANTLE 1974
K. Fremantle, 'The Identity of Johan Moreelse, Painter', *The Burlington Magazine* 116 (1974), pp. 619–620

FRIEDLÄNDER 1937
M.J. Friedländer, 'Ein vlämischer Portraitmaler in England', *Gentsche Bijdragen tot de Kunstgeschiedenis* 4 (1937), pp. 5–18

FRIEDLÄNDER 1967–1976
M.J. Friedländer, *Early Netherlandish painting*, 14 vols, Leiden-Brussels 1967–1976 (revised edition; ed. princ. Berlin 1924–1937)

FRIEDLÄNDER 1975
M.J. Friedländer, *Antonis Mor and his Contemporaries*, Leiden-Brussels 1975

FRIEDLÄNDER/ROSENBERG 1978
M.J. Friedländer, J. Rosenberg, *The paintings of Lucas Cranach*, Amsterdam 1978

FRITZ 1967
R. Fritz, *Sammlung Becker, I: Gemälde alter Meister*, Dortmund 1967

FUCHS 1973
R.H. Fuchs, 'Over het landschap: Een verslag naar aanleiding van Jacob van Ruisdael, "*Het Korenveld*"', *Tijdschrift voor geschiedenis* 86 (1973), pp. 281–292

G

GAEHTGENS 1987a
B. Gaehtgens, *Adriaen van der Werff 1659–1722*, Munich 1987

GAEHTGENS 1987b
B. Gaehtgens, 'Imitare und Aemulare im Werk Adriaen van der Werffs', in BOCK/GAEHTGENS 1987, pp. 91–116

GANZ 1950
P. Ganz, *Hans Holbein*, Basel 1950

GASTON-DREYFUS/INGERSOLL-SMOUSE 1923
P. Gaston-Dreyfus, F. Ingersoll-Smouse, *Catalogue raisonné de l'œuvre peint et dessiné de Nicolas-Bernard Lépicié*, Paris 1923

GAYA NUÑO 1958
J.A. Gaya Nuño, *La pintura Española fuera de España*, Madrid 1958

GAYA NUÑO 1978
J.A. Gaya Nuño, *L'Opera completa di Bartolomé Esteban Murillo*, Milan 1978

GEIGER 1949
B. Geiger, *Saggio di un catalogo delle pitture di Alessandro Magnasco*, Venice 1949

DE GELDER 1921
J.J. de Gelder, *Bartholomeus van der Helst*, Rotterdam 1921

VAN GELDER 1947
H.E. van Gelder, 'Moro's "Goudsmid"', *Nederlands Kunsthistorisch Jaarboek* 1 (1947), pp. 47–59

VAN GELDER 1948–1949
J.G. van Gelder, 'De schilders van de Oranjezaal', *Nederlands Kunsthistorisch Jaarboek* 2 (1948–1949), pp. 118–164

VAN GELDER 1953
J.G. van Gelder, 'Hercules Seghers: Addenda', *Oud Holland* 68 (1953), pp. 149–151

VAN GELDER 1957
H.E. van Gelder, *Ikonografie van Constantijn Huygens en de zijnen*, The Hague 1957

VAN GELDER 1960
H.E. van Gelder, 'Twee Braziliaanse schildpadden door Albert Eckhout', *Oud Holland* 75 (1960), pp. 5–29

VAN GELDER-SCHRIJVER 1930
N.F. van Gelder-Schrijver, 'De Meester van Alkmaar: Eene bijdrage tot de kennis van de Haarlemsche Schilderschool', *Oud Holland* 47 (1930), pp. 97–121

GEMAR-KOELTZSCH 1995
E. Gemar-Koeltzsch, *Luca Bild-Lexikon: Holländische Stillebenmaler im 17. Jahrhundert*, 3 vols, Lingen 1995

GENAILLE 1954
R. Genaille, 'L'oeuvre de Pieter Aertsen', *Gazette des Beaux-Arts* 44 (1954), pp. 267–288

GENAILLE 1977
R. Genaille, 'Pieter Aertsen, précurseur de l'art Rubénien', *Jaarboek van het Koninklijk Museum voor Schone Kunsten Antwerpen* (1977), pp. 7–96

GENOA 1949
Mostra del Magnasco, Genoa (Palazzo Bianco) 1949

GENOA 1956
Luca Cambiaso e la sua fortuna, Genoa (Palazzo

dell' Accademia) 1956

GERSON 1940
H. Gerson, 'Leven en werken van den paardenschilder Pieter Verbeeck', *Genealogie van het geslacht Van Beresteyn II, Appendix III*, The Hague 1940, pp. 179–209

GERSON 1968
H. Gerson, *Rembrandt paintings*, Amsterdam 1968

GERSON 1980
H. Gerson, *Philips Koninck: Ein Beitrag zur Erforschung der holländischen Malerei des XVII. Jahrhunderts*, Berlin 1980 (ed. princ. 1936)

GERSON 1983
H. Gerson, *Ausbreitung und Nachwirkung der holländischen Malerei des 17. Jahrhunderts*, Amsterdam 1983 (ed. princ. 1942)

GIBSON 2000
W.S. Gibson, *Pleasant Places: The Rustic Landscape from Bruegel to Ruisdael*, Berkeley-Los Angeles-London 2000

GILTAIJ 1996
J. Giltaij, *Ruffo en Rembrandt: Over een Siciliaanse verzamelaar in de zeventiende eeuw die drie schilderijen bij Rembrandt bestelde*, Rotterdam 1996

GILTAIJ 2000
J. Giltaij, 'Scientific examination of the underdrawing of seventeenth-century architectural painters', in J.R.J. van Asperen de Boer, L.M. Helmus (eds.), *The Paintings of Pieter Jansz. Saenredam (1597–1665): Conservation and Technique*, Utrecht 2000, pp. 32–55

GINNINGS 1970
R.J. Ginnings, *The art of Jan Baptist Weenix and Jan Weenix* (diss.), Delaware 1970

GLÜCK 1928
G. Glück, 'Schicksale einer Komposition Leonardo's', *Pantheon* 2 (1928), pp. 502–507

GLÜCK 1931
G. Glück, *Van Dyck: Des Meisters Gemälde in 571 Abbildungen* (*Klassiker der Kunst*, vol. 13), Stuttgart-Berlin 1931

GODDARD 1984
S. Goddard, *The Master of Frankfurt and his Shop*, Brussels 1984

VAN GOOL 1750–1751
J. van Gool, *De nieuwe schouburg der Nederlantsche Kunstschilders en schilderessen*, 2 vols, The Hague 1750–1751

GOOSSENS 1954
K. Goossens, *David Vinckboons*, Antwerp-The Hague 1954

GORISSEN 1962
F. Gorissen, *B.C. Koekkoek*, Düsseldorf 1962

GRANT 1954
M.H. Grant, *Jan van Huysum 1682–1749, including a catalogue raisonné of the artist's fruit & flower paintings*, Leigh-on-Sea 1954

GRANT 1956
M.H. Grant, *Rachel Ruysch 1664–1750*, Leigh-on-Sea 1956

GREINDL 1944
E. Greindl, *Corneille de Vos*, Strasbourg 1944

GREINDL 1956
E. Greindl, *Les peintres flamands de nature morte au XVIIe siècle*, Brussels 1956

GREINDL 1983
E. Greindl, *Les peintres flamands de nature morte au XVIIe siècle*, revised edition, Brussels 1983 (ed. princ. 1956)

VAN GREVESTEIN *et al.* 1998
A. van Grevestein *et al.*, *Lataster: Schilderijen 1939–1996*, Ghent 1998

GRIJZENHOUT 1993
F. Grijzenhout, *Cornelis Troost: NELRI*, Bloemendaal 1993

GRIMM 1989
C. Grimm, *Frans Hals: Das Gesamtwerk*, Stuttgart-Zürich 1989

GRISEBACH 1974
L. Grisebach, *Willem Kalf*, Berlin 1974

GRONINGEN 1980
Het verraad: David geeft de brief aan Uria, een schilderij van Pieter Lastman uit 1619, Groningen (Groninger Museum) 1980

GRONINGEN-MAASTRICHT 1989
R. Vos, H. van Os (eds.), *Aan de oorsprong van de schilderkunst: Vroege Italiaanse schilderijen in Nederlands bezit / The Birth of Panel Painting: Early Italian Paintings in Dutch Collections*, Groningen (Groninger Museum), Maastricht (Bonnefantenmuseum) 1989

GROSSHANS 1980
R. Grosshans, *Maerten van Heemskerck: Die Gemälde*, Berlin 1980

VAN GRUTING 1995–1996
R.R.A. van Gruting, 'Gravin Maria Elisabeth II van den Bergh: Achtergronden van een portret uit 1628', *Virtus: Bulletin van de Werkgroep Adelsgeschiedenis* 3 (1995–1996), no. 2, pp. 49–70

GUDLAUGSSON 1943
S. Gudlaugsson, 'Jacob Jordaens of Heinrich Dittmers?', *Oud Holland* 60 (1943), pp. 143–147

GUDLAUGSSON 1954
S. Gudlaugsson, 'Aanvullingen omtrent Pieter Post's werkzaamheid als schilder', *Oud Holland* 69 (1954), pp. 59–71

GUDLAUGSSON 1959–1960
S. Gudlaugsson, *Katalog der Gemälde Gerard ter Borch sowie biographisches Material*, 2 vols, The Hague 1959–1960

H

VAN DER HAAGEN 1932
J.K. van der Haagen, *De schilders Van der Haagen en hun werk*, Voorburg 1932

HAAK 1969
B. Haak, *Rembrandt*, Amsterdam 1969

HAAK 1984
B. Haak, *Hollandse schilders in de Gouden Eeuw*, Amsterdam 1984

HAARLEM 1972
Wybrand Hendriks, Haarlem (Teylers Museum) 1972

HAARLEM 1986
E. de Jongh, *Portretten van echt en trouw: Huwelijk en gezin in de Nederlandse kunst van de zeventiende eeuw*, Haarlem (Frans Hals Museum) 1986

HAARLEM 1989
F. Grijzenhout, C. van Tuyll van Serooskerken (eds.), *Edele eenvoud: Neo-classicisme in Nederland 1765–1800*, Haarlem (Frans Hals Museum / Teylers Museum) 1989

HAARLEM 1998
B.C. Sliggers (ed.), *Naar het lijk: Het Nederlandse doodsportret 1500–heden*, Haarlem (Teylers Museum) 1998

HAARLEM-ANTWERP 2000–2001
J.B. Bedaux, R. Ekkart (eds.), *Kinderen op hun mooist: Het kinderportret in de Nederlanden 1500–1700*, Haarlem (Frans Hals Museum), Antwerp (Koninklijk Museum voor Schone Kunsten) 2000–2001

HAARLEM-HAMBURG 2003–2004
P. Biesboer, M. Sitt (eds.), *Satire en vermaak: Schilderkunst in de 17e eeuw. Het genrestuk van Frans Hals en zijn tijdgenoten 1610–1670*, Haarlem (Frans Hals Museum), Hamburg (Hamburger Kunsthalle) 2003–2004

HAARLEM-PARIS 2001–2002
M. van Berge-Gerbaud *et al.*, *Hartstochtelijk Verzameld: Beroemde tekeningen in 18de-eeuwse Hollandse collecties*, Haarlem (Teylers Museum), Paris (Fondation Custodia) 2001–2002

HAARLEM-WORCESTER 1993
J.A. Welu, P. Biesboer *et al.*, *Judith Leyster: Schilderes in een mannenwereld / A Dutch Master and Her World*, Haarlem (Frans Hals Museum), Worcester (Worcester Art Museum) 1993

HAARLEM-ZÜRICH-WASHINGTON 2004–2005
P. Biesboer *et al.*, *Pieter Claesz 1596/97–1660*, Haarlem (Frans Hals Museum), Zürich (Kunsthaus), Washington (National Gallery of Art) 2004–2005

HÄRTING 1983
W.A. Härting, *Studien zur Kabinettbildmalerei des Frans Francken II. 1581–1642: Ein repräsentativer Werkkatalog*, Hildesheim-Zürich-New York 1983

HÄRTING 1989
U. Härting, *Frans Francken der Jüngere (1581–1642): Die Gemälde mit kritischem Oeuvrekatalog*, Freren 1989

HÄRTING/BORMS 1989
U. Härting, K. Borms, *Abraham Govaerts: Der Waldmaler (1589–1626)*, Schoten 2003

THE HAGUE 1948
Zeven eeuwen Den Haag, The Hague (Gemeentemuseum) 1948

THE HAGUE 1958–1959
A. van Duinkerken, P.N.H. Domela Nieuwenhuis, *Jan Steen*, The Hague (Mauritshuis) 1958–1959

THE HAGUE 1966
H.E. van Gelder, C. Reedijk, A.B. de Vries, *150 jaar Koninklijk Kabinet van Schilderijen, Koninklijke Bibliotheek, Koninklijk Penningkabinet: Herdenkingstentoonstelling in het Mauritshuis*, The Hague 1966

THE HAGUE 1979–1980
E. van den Boogaert, F. Duparc *et al.*, *Zo wijd de wereld strekt*, The Hague (Mauritshuis) 1979–1980

THE HAGUE 1982
H.R. Hoetink, W.L. van de Watering, *Terugzien in bewondering / A Collector's Choice*, The Hague (Mauritshuis) 1982

THE HAGUE 1988–1989
B. Brenninkmeyer-de Rooij *et al.*, *Paintings from England: William III and the Royal Collections*, The Hague (Mauritshuis) 1988–1989

THE HAGUE 1991
M. Tiethoff, with

K. Schaffers, *Portretten in miniatuur: Portretminiaturen uit de stadhouderlijke en koninklijke verzamelingen*, The Hague (Mauritshuis) 1991

THE HAGUE 1991–1992
M. de Boer, J. Leistra, B. Broos, *Bredius, Rembrandt en het Mauritshuis!!!: Een eigenzinnig directeur verzamelt*, The Hague (Mauritshuis) 1991–1992

THE HAGUE 1992a
B. Brenninkmeyer-de Rooij *et al.*, *Mauritshuis in bloei: Boeketten uit de Gouden Eeuw / The Mauritshuis in Bloom: Bouquets from the Golden Age*, The Hague (Mauritshuis) 1992

THE HAGUE 1992b
P. Huys Janssen, W. Sumowski, *Rembrandt's Academy*, The Hague (Hoogsteder & Hoogsteder Gallery) 1992

THE HAGUE 1992–1993
F. de Graaf, J. Wadum, *Een dansfestijn doorgrond: Technisch en kunsthistorisch onderzoek naar een Vlaams schilderij*, The Hague (Mauritshuis) 1992–1993

THE HAGUE 1993
E. Buijsen, J.W. Niemeijer, *Cornelis Troost en het theater: Tonelen van de 18de eeuw / Cornelis Troost and the theatre of his time: Plays of the 18th century*, The Hague (Mauritshuis) 1993

THE HAGUE 1994–1995
A. Walsh, E. Buijsen, B. Broos, edited by Q. Buvelot, *Paulus Potter: Paintings, drawings and etchings*, The Hague (Mauritshuis) 1994–1995

THE HAGUE 1995–1996
B. Broos, Q. Buvelot *et al.*, *The Amateur's Cabinet: Seventeenth-Century Dutch Masterpieces from Dutch Private Collections*, The Hague (Mauritshuis) 1995–1996

THE HAGUE 1997
A. van Suchtelen, Y. Bruijnen, E. Buijsen, *Art on Wings: Celebrating the Reunification of a Triptych by Gerard David*, The Hague (Mauritshuis) 1997

THE HAGUE 1997–1998a
P. van der Ploeg, C. Vermeeren *et al.*, *Princely Patrons: The Collection of Frederick Henry and Amalia of Solms in The Hague*, The Hague (Mauritshuis) 1997–1998

THE HAGUE 1997–1998b
M. Keblusek, J. Zijlmans (eds.), *Princely Display: The Court of Frederik Hendrik of Orange and Amalia van Solms*, The Hague (Haags Historisch Museum) 1997–1998

THE HAGUE 1998
A. McNeil Kettering, edited by A. van Suchtelen, *Gerard ter Borch and the Treaty of Münster*, The Hague (Mauritshuis) 1998

THE HAGUE 1998–1999
N. Middelkoop *et al.*, *Rembrandt under the Scalpel: The Anatomy Lesson of Dr Nicolaes Tulp Dissected*, The Hague (Mauritshuis) 1998–1999

THE HAGUE 2001–2002
A. van Suchtelen *et al.*, *Holland Frozen in Time: The Dutch Winter Landscape in the Golden Age*, The Hague (Mauritshuis) 2001–2002

THE HAGUE 2002
Q. Buvelot, H. Buijs, with E. Reitsma, *A Choice Collection: Seventeenth-Century Dutch Paintings from the Frits Lugt Collection*, The Hague (Mauritshuis) 2002

THE HAGUE 2003
S. Buck, J. Sander, A. van Suchtelen, Q. Buvelot, P. van der Ploeg, *Hans Holbein the Younger 1497/98–1543*, The Hague (Mauritshuis) 2003

THE HAGUE 2004
Q. Buvelot *et al.*, *Albert Eckhout: A Dutch artist in Brazil*, The Hague (Mauritshuis) 2004

THE HAGUE-SCHWERIN 2004–2005
F.J. Duparc, G. Seelig, A. van Suchtelen, *Carel Fabritius 1622–1654*, The Hague (Mauritshuis), Schwerin (Staatliches Museum) 2004–2005

THE HAGUE-CAMBRIDGE 1981–1982
S. Slive, *Jacob van Ruisdael*, The Hague (Mauritshuis), Cambridge, Mass. (Fogg Art Museum, Harvard University) 1981–1982

THE HAGUE-LONDON 1970–1971
A.G.H. Bachrach, L. Thijssen, D. van Karnebeek-van Roijen, *"Shock of Recognition": The landscape of English Romanticism and the Dutch seventeenth-century school*, The Hague (Mauritshuis), London (The Tate Gallery) 1970–1971

THE HAGUE-MÜNSTER 1974
G. Langemeyer *et al.*, *Gerard ter Borch: Zwolle 1617, Deventer 1681*, The Hague (Mauritshuis), Münster (Landesmuseum für Kunst und Kulturgeschichte) 1974

THE HAGUE-SAN FRANCISCO 1990–1991
B. Broos *et al.*, *Great Dutch Paintings from America*, The Hague (Mauritshuis), San Francisco (The Fine Arts Museums of San Francisco) 1990–1991

HAIRS 1985
M.-L. Hairs, *Les peintres flamands de fleurs au XVIIe siècle*, third edition, 2 vols, Paris-Brussels 1985

HAMBURG 1984
Luther und die Folgen für die Kunst, Hamburg (Hamburger Kunsthalle) 1984

HAMBURG 1995–1996
H.R. Leppien, K. Müller *et al.*, *Im Blickfeld: Holländische Kirchenbilder*, Hamburg (Hamburger Kunsthalle) 1995–1996

HAMBURG-HAARLEM 2002
M. Sitt, P. Biesboer (eds.), *Jacob van Ruisdael: Die Revolution der Landschaft*, Hamburg (Hamburger Kunsthalle), Haarlem (Frans Hals Museum) 2002

HAND 1978
J.O. Hand, *Joos van Cleve: The Early and Mature Paintings* (diss.), 2 vols, Princeton, New Jersey 1978

HARWOOD 1988
L.B. Harwood, *Adam Pynacker (c. 1620–1673)*, Doornspijk 1988

HAVERKAMP BEGEMANN 1968
E. Haverkamp Begemann, *Hercules Seghers*, Amsterdam 1968

HAVERKAMP BEGEMANN 1973
E. Haverkamp Begemann, *Hercules Seghers: The Complete Etchings*, Amsterdam 1973

HdG 1907–1928
See: HOFSTEDE DE GROOT 1907–1928

HECHT 1981
E. Hecht, 'The Infants Christ and St. John Embracing: Notes on a Composition by Joos van Cleve', *Apollo* 113 (1981), pp. 222–229

HECHT 1997
P. Hecht, 'Dutch Seventeenth-Century Genre Painting: A Reassessment of some Current Hypotheses', in FRANITS 1997, pp. 88–97

HECHT *et al.* 1998
P. Hecht *et al.* (eds.), *Kunstgeschiedenis in Nederland*, Amsterdam 1998

HECKSCHER 1958
W. Heckscher, *Rembrandt's 'Anatomy of Dr. Nicolaes Tulp': An iconographical study*, New York 1958

HEIMBÜRGER 1988
M. Heimbürger, *Bernardo Keilhau detto Monsú Bernardo*, Rome 1988

HELD 1965
J. Held, 'Notes on Jacob Jordaens', *Oud Holland* 80 (1965), pp. 112–122

HELD 1980
J. Held, *The oil sketches of P.P. Rubens: A critical catalogue*, 2 vols, Princeton, New Jersey 1980

HELD 1991
J.S. Held, 'Constantijn Huygens and Susanna van Baerle: A Hitherto Unknown Portrait', *The Art Bulletin* 73 (1991), pp. 633–668 (see also 'Postscript' with corrections in *The Art Bulletin* 74 (1992), p. 173)

HELMUS 1999
L.M. Helmus, *Schilderkunst tot 1850* (*De verzamelingen van het Centraal Museum te Utrecht*, vol. 5), 2 vols, Utrecht 1999

HENDRIKS/VAN GREVESTEIN/GROEN 1993
E. Hendriks, A. van Grevestein, K. Groen, 'The Painting Technique of Four Paintings by Hendrick Goltzius and the Introduction of Coloured Ground', in FALKENBURG/FILEDT KOK/LEEFLANG 1993, pp. 481–497

HEPPNER 1937
A. Heppner, 'Pieter Quast en P.C. Hooft: Schilderijen naar een "vertooning" en een tooneelscène', *Maandblad voor Beeldende Kunst* 14 (1937), pp. 370–376

HERZOG 1969
S.J. Herzog, *Jan Gossaert, called Mabuse (ca. 1478–1532): A Study of his Chronology with a Catalogue of his Work* (diss. 1968), Ann Arbor, Michigan 1969

HILLEBRAND 1996
W.B. Hillebrand, *Spaanse schilderkunst in Nederlands bezit* (unpublished Master's thesis), Nijmegen 1996

HINTERDING/HORSCH 1989
E. Hinterding, F. Horsch, '"A small but choice collection": The art gallery of King Willem II of the Netherlands (1792–1849)', *Simiolus* 19 (1989), pp. 4–122 (also published seperately, Zwolle 1989)

HIRSCHMANN 1916
O. Hirschmann, *Hendrick Goltzius als Maler 1600–1617*, The Hague 1916

HÖHNE 1960
E. Höhne, *Adriaen Brouwer*, Leipzig 1960

HOETINK 1962
H.R. Hoetink, 'Jan Baptist Xavery (1697–1742): Prins Willem IV', *Openbaar Kunstbezit* 6 (1962), pp. 22a–b

HOFRICHTER 1975/1982
F. Fox Hofrichter, 'Judith

Leyster's *Proposition* — Between Virtue and Vice', *The Feminist Art Journal* 4 (1975), no. 3, pp. 22–26 (reprinted in N. Broude, M.D. Garrad (eds.), *Feminism and Art History: Questioning the Litany*, New York 1982, pp. 173–182)

HOFRICHTER 1989
F. Fox Hofrichter, *Judith Leyster: A Woman Painter in Holland's Golden Age*, Doornspijk 1989

HOFSTEDE DE GROOT 1892
C. Hofstede de Groot, 'Schilderijenverzamelingen van het Geslacht Slingelandt', *Oud Holland* 10 (1892), pp. 229–237

HOFSTEDE DE GROOT 1907–1928
C. Hofstede de Groot, *Beschreibendes und kritisches Verzeichnis der Werke der hervorragendsten holländischen Maler des XVII. Jahrhunderts*, 10 vols, Esslingen-Paris 1907–1928

HOLLSTEIN
F.W.H. Hollstein, *Dutch and Flemish Etchings, Engravings and Woodcuts, ca. 1450–1700*, vols 1– , Amsterdam 1949–

HONNENS DE LICHTENBERG 1991
H. Honnens de Lichtenberg, *Johan Gregor van der Schardt: Bildhauer bei Kaiser Maximilian II., am dänischen Hof und bei Tycho Brahe*, Copenhagen 1991

HOOGEWERFF 1912
G.J. Hoogewerff, *Nederlandsche schilders in Italië in de XVIe eeuw*, Utrecht 1912

HOOGEWERFF 1936–1947
G.J. Hoogewerff, *De Noord-Nederlandse Schilderkunst*, 4 vols, The Hague 1936–1947

HOUSTON-THE HAGUE 2000–2001
A.K. Wheelock, C. Brown, *The Golden Age of Dutch and Flemish Painting: The Edward and Sally Speelman Collection*, Houston (Museum of Fine Arts), The Hague (Mauritshuis) 2000–2001

D'HULST 1961
R.-A. d'Hulst, 'Jakob Jordaens: Apollo beurtelings in strijd met Marsyas en Pan', *Bulletin Musées Royaux des Beaux-Arts* 10 (1961), pp. 28–36

D'HULST 1968
R.-A. d'Hulst, *Olieverfschetsen van Rubens uit Nederlands en Belgisch openbaar bezit*, s.l. 1968

D'HULST 1982
R.A. d'Hulst, *Jacob Jordaens*, Antwerp 1982

HUYS JANSSEN 1990
P. Huys Janssen, *Schilders in Utrecht 1600–1700*, Utrecht 1990

HUYS JANSSEN 2002
P. Huys Janssen, *Caesar van Everdingen 1616/17–1678: Monograph and Catalogue Raisonné*, Doornspijk 2002

I

INDIANAPOLIS-SAN DIEGO 1958
The young Rembrandt and his time: A loan exhibition of Dutch painting of the first four decades of the seventeenth century, Indianapolis (The John Herron Art Museum), San Diego (The Fine Arts Gallery) 1958

INGAMELLS 1992
J. Ingamells, *The Wallace Collection: Catalogue of Pictures, vol. IV: Dutch and Flemish*, London 1992

INGERSOLL-SMOUSE 1926
F. Ingersoll-Smouse, *Joseph Vernet I*, Paris 1926

J

JACOBS/RÜTTEN 1998
S. Jacobs, T. Rütten, '*Democritus ridens* — ein weinender Philosoph?: Zur Tradition des *Democritus melancholicus* in der Bildenden Kunst', *Wolfenbütteler Beiträge* 11 (1998)

JAMES 1998
S.E. James, '*Lady Margaret Douglas* and *Sir Thomas Seymour* by Holbein: Two miniatures re-identified', *Apollo* 147 (1998), pp. 15–20

JANECK 1968
A. Janeck, *Untersuchung über den holländischen Maler Pieter van Laer, genannt Bamboccio*, Würzburg 1968

JANTZEN 1979
H. Jantzen, *Das Niederländische Architekturbild*, enlarged and improved edition, Braunschweig 1979 (ed. princ. Leipzig 1910)

JEDDING 1955
H. Jedding, *Der Tiermaler Johann Heinrich Roos*, Strasbourg 1955

JEDDING 1998
H. Jedding, *Johann Heinrich Roos: Werke einer Pfälzer Tiermalerfamilie in den Galerien Europas*, Mainz 1998

DE JONGE 1938
C.H. de Jonge, *Paulus Moreelse: Portret- en genreschilder te Utrecht 1571–1638*, Assen 1938

DE JONGH 1967
E. de Jongh, *Zinne- en minnebeelden in de schilderkunst van de zeventiende eeuw*, s.l. 1967

DE JONGH 1975–1976
E. de Jongh, 'Pearls of Virtue and Pearls of Vice', *Simiolus* 8 (1975–1976), pp. 69–97

DE JONGH 1981–1982
E. de Jongh, 'Bol vincit amorem', *Simiolus* 12 (1981–1982), pp. 147–161

DE JONGH 1997
E. de Jongh, 'Realism and Seeming Realism in Seventeenth-Century Dutch Painting', in FRANITS 1997, pp. 21–56

JONKER 1996
M. Jonker, 'A painting in focus, An acquisition: *Flower still life with shells*, Balthasar van der Ast (Middelburg 1593/4–Delft 1657)', *Mauritshuis in focus* 9 (1996), no. 3, pp. 14–18

JUDSON/EKKART 1999
J.R. Judson, R.E.O. Ekkart, *Gerrit van Honthorst 1592–1656*, Doornspijk 1999

K

KARLSRUHE 1999
M.R. Michel *et al.*, *Jean Siméon Chardin 1699–1779: Werk, Herkunft, Wirkung*, Karlsruhe (Staatliche Kunsthalle) 1999

KASSEL-AMSTERDAM 2001–2002
E. van de Wetering *et al.*, *The mystery of the young Rembrandt*, Kassel (Gemäldegalerie Alte Meister), Amsterdam (Museum Het Rembrandthuis) 2001–2002

KEERS 1994
F. Keers, 'Bibliografische aantekeningen bij Ben Broos, *Liefde, list en lijden: Historiestukken in het Mauritshuis*', *Oud Holland* 108 (1994), pp. 137–140

KETTERING 1983
A. McNeil Kettering, *The Dutch Arcadia: Pastoral art and its audience in the Golden Age*, Montclair, New Jersey 1983

KEYES 1975
G.S. Keyes, *Cornelis Vroom: Marine and landscape artist* (diss.), 2 vols, Alphen aan den Rijn 1975

KEYES 1978
G.S. Keyes, 'Landscape Drawings by Alexander Keirincx and Abraham Govaerts', *Master Drawings* 16 (1978), pp. 293–302

KEYES 1984
G. Keyes, *Esaias van de Velde 1587–1630*, Doornspijk 1984

KILIAN 1993
J.M. Kilian, *The Paintings of Karel du Jardin (1626–1675)* (diss.), New York 1993

DE KINKELDER 2000
M. de Kinkelder, '*View of Beverwijk from the Wijkermeer* by Salomon van Ruysdael', *Mauritshuis in focus* 13 (2000), no. 1, pp. 12–20

KLESSMANN 1983
R. Klessmann, *Die holländischen Gemälde: Herzog Anton Ulrich-Museum Braunschweig*, Braunschweig 1983

KLINGER/HÖTTLER 1998
D.M. Klinger, A. Höttler, *Holbein: Die Malerbrüder Ambrosius und Hans d.J., Werkverzeichnis: Gemälde und Miniaturen*, Nuremberg 1998

KLOEK 1990
W. Kloek, with J.W. Niemeijer, *De kasteeltekeningen van Roelant Roghman*, vol. 2, Alphen aan den Rijn 1990

VAN DER KLOOSTER 1959
L.J. van der Klooster, 'Een portret van Hans Hogendorp?', *De Nederlandsche Leeuw* 76 (1959), cols. 183–185

VAN DER KLOOSTER 1970
L.J. van der Klooster, 'Jan Baptist Xavery (1697–1742): Documentatie over enkele van zijn werken', *Nederlands Kunsthistorisch Jaarboek* 21 (1970), pp. 99–138

KNOX 1995
G. Knox, *Antonio Pellegrini 1675–1741*, Oxford 1995

KNUTTEL 1962
G. Knuttel, *Adriaen Brouwer: The master and his work*, The Hague 1962

KOCH 1968
R.A. Koch, *Joachim Patenir*, Princeton, New Jersey 1968

KOLFIN 1998
E. Kolfin, 'A dancing company with a masquerade by Pieter Codde', *Mauritshuis in focus* 11 (1998), no. 3, pp. 10–17

KOLFIN/POTTASCH 2003
E. Kolfin, C. Pottasch, 'Pendanten van twee meesters: Twee Italiaanse landschapjes uit de collectie De Rainer (Mauritshuis, Den Haag)', *Cr: Interdisciplinair tijdschrift voor conservering en restauratie* 4 (2003), pp. 39–45

KOLFIN/POTTASCH/HOPPE 2002
E. Kolfin, C. Pottasch, R. Hoppe, 'The metamorphosis of Diana: Changing perceptions of the young Vermeer's painting technique', *ArtMatters: Netherlands Technical*

Studies in Art 1 (2002), pp. 90–103

KORTHALS ALTES 2000–2001
E. Korthals Altes, 'The eighteenth-century gentleman dealer Willem Lormier and the international dispersal of seventeenth-century Dutch paintings', *Simiolus* 28 (2000–2001), pp. 251–311

KORTHALS ALTES 2003
E. Korthals Altes, 'Philip van Dijk, een achttiende-eeuwse Haagse schilder-kunsthandelaar met een lokale en internationale clientèle', *Oud Holland* 116 (2003), pp. 34–56

KRAEMER-NOBLE 1973
M. Kraemer-Noble, *Abraham Mignon 1640–1679*, Leigh-on-Sea 1973

KREFELD-ORANIENBURG-APELDOORN 1999–2000
Onder den Oranje boom: Niederländische Kunst und Kultur im 17. und 18. Jahrhundert an deutschen Fürstenhöfen, 2 vols, Krefeld (Kaiser-Wilhelm-Museum), Oranienburg (Schloss Oranienburg), Apeldoorn (Paleis Het Loo Nationaal Museum) 1999–2000

KREMPEL 2000
L. Krempel, *Studien zu den datierten Gemälden des Nicolaes Maes (1634–1693)*, Petersburg 2000

VAN KRETSCHMAR 1970
F.G.L.O. van Kretschmar, 'Nog een weinig bekend portrettist: Gerrit Alberts, "Pourtraitschilder te Nijmegen"', *Nederlands Kunsthistorisch Jaarboek* 21 (1970), pp. 69–98

KUBLER/SORIA 1959
G. Kubler, M. Soria, *Art and architecture in Spain and Portugal and their American dominions 1500–1800*, Harmondsworth 1959

TER KUILE 1976
O. ter Kuile, *Adriaen Hanneman, een Haags portretschilder*, Alphen aan den Rijn 1976

KULTZEN 1954
R. Kultzen, *Michael Sweerts 1624–1664* (diss.), Hamburg 1954

KULTZEN 1996
R. Kultzen, *Michael Sweerts*, Ghent 1996

KURETSKY 1979
S. Donahue Kuretsky, *The paintings of Jacob Ochtervelt (1634–1682)*, Oxford 1979

L

LAAN 2003
C. Laan, *Drank & Drinkgerei: Een archeologisch en cultuurhistorisch onderzoek naar de alledaagse drinkcultuur van de 18de-eeuwse Hollanders*, Amsterdam 2003

LANG 1999
A. Lang, '*The Game Larder* by Frans Snyders (Antwerp 1597–1657) at Charlecote and its depiction in The Hague', *The National Trust Views* (Winter 1999), no. 31, pp. 32–33

LAKENHAL 1983
M.L. Wurfbain *et al.*, *Stedelijk Museum De Lakenhal: Catalogus van de schilderijen en tekeningen*, Leiden 1983

LANGENSTEIN 1997
E. Langenstein, *Spurensuche — Bilder der Alten Pinakothek in neuem Licht: Eine Ausstellung der Bayerischen Staatsgemäldesammlungen*, Munich 1997

LARSEN 1962
E. Larsen, *Frans Post*, Amsterdam-Rio de Janeiro 1962

LARSEN 1988
E. Larsen, *The Paintings of Anthony van Dyck*, 2 vols, Freren 1988

LASIUS 1992
A. Lasius, *Quiringh van Brekelenkam*, Doornspijk 1992

LAURENTIUS/NIEMEIJER/PLOOS VAN AMSTEL 1980
T. Laurentius, J.W. Niemeijer, G. Ploos van Amstel, *Cornelis Ploos van Amstel 1726–1798: Kunstverzamelaar en prentuitgever*, Assen 1980

LEEUWARDEN 2001
Jacobus Sibrandi Mancadan: De Friese landschapschilder uit de Gouden Eeuw, Leeuwarden (Fries Museum) 2001 (no catalogue)

LEEUWARDEN-DEN BOSCH-ASSEN 1979–1980
C. Dumas, *In het zadel: Het Nederlandse ruiterportret van 1550 tot 1900*, Leeuwarden (Fries Museum), Den Bosch (Noordbrabants Museum), Assen (Provinciaal Museum van Drenthe) 1979–1980

VAN LEEUWEN 1990
R. van Leeuwen, 'De schoonmaakwoede van Mazel', *Nieuwsbrief Mauritshuis* 3 (1990), nos. 3–4, pp. 12–13

VAN LEEUWEN 1992–1993
R. van Leeuwen, 'Venus en Adonis herenigd', *Tableau* 15 (1992–1993), no. 2, pp. 94–101

VAN LEEUWEN 1993
R. van Leeuwen, 'Provenance: House of Orange', *Mauritshuis in focus* 6 (1993), no. 1, pp. 21–26

LEIDEN 1966
Gabriel Metsu, Leiden (Stedelijk Museum De Lakenhal) 1966

LEIDEN 1970
IJdelheid der ijdelheden: Hollandse vanitas-voorstellingen uit de zeventiende eeuw, Leiden (Stedelijk Museum De Lakenhal) 1970

LEIDEN 1980
Een verzameling schilderijen uit de 17de, 18de en 19de eeuw, Leiden (Stedelijk Museum De Lakenhal) 1980

LEIDEN 1988
E.J. Sluijter *et al.*, *Leidse fijnschilders: Van Gerrit Dou tot Frans van Mieris de Jonge, 1630–1760*, Leiden (Stedelijk Museum De Lakenhal) 1988

LEIDEN 1996–1997
C. Vogelaar *et al.*, *Jan van Goyen*, Leiden (Stedelijk Museum De Lakenhal) 1996–1997

LEMGO-ANTWERP 2002
H. Borggrefe *et al.*, *Tussen stadspaleizen en luchtkastelen: Hans Vredeman de Vries en de Renaissance*, Lemgo (Weserrenaissance-Museum Schloss Brake), Antwerp (Koninklijk Museum voor Schone Kunsten) 2002

LEMMENS/KLOEK 1990
G. Lemmens, W.T. Kloek (eds.), *Pieter Aertsen* (*Nederlands Kunsthistorisch Jaarboek*, vol. 40), Maarssen 1990

VAN LENNEP 1966
J. van Lennep, 'L'Alchimiste: Origine et développement d'un thème de la peinture du dix-septième siècle', *Revue Belge d'Archéologie et d'Histoire de l'Art* 35 (1966), nos. 3–4, pp. 149–168

LEVY-VAN HALM/SCHLÜTER 1993
K. Levy-van Halm, L.F. Schlüter, 'Schildertechniek: Middel en doel? De 'Mercurius' en 'Minerva' van Hendrick Goltzius', in FALKENBURG/FILEDT KOK/LEEFLANG 1993, pp. 499–508

LIEDTKE 1982
W. Liedtke, *Architectural painting in Delft*, Doornspijk 1982

LIEDTKE 1989
W. Liedtke, *The Royal Horse and Rider: Painting, sculpture, and horsemanship 1500–1800*, New York 1989

LIEDTKE 1991
W. Liedtke, 'Pepys and the pictorial arts: "Great plenty of good pictures"', *Apollo* 133 (1991), pp. 227–237

LILIENFELD 1914
K. Lilienfeld, *Arent de Gelder: Sein Leben und seine Kunst*, The Hague 1914

LILLE 2004
A. Brejon de Lavergnée *et al.*, *Rubens*, Lille (Palais des Beaux-Arts) 2004

LINDEMAN 1929
C.M.A.A. Lindeman, *Joachim Anthonisz. Wtewael*, Utrecht 1929

LISKEN-PRUSS 2002
M. Lisken-Pruss, *Studien zum Œuvre des Gonzales Coques (1614/18–1684)* (diss. University of Bonn), Bonn 2002

LÖCHER 1962
K. Löcher, *Jakob Seisenegger: Hofmaler Kaiser Ferdinands I.*, Munich-Berlin 1962

LÖW 2002
A. Löw, *Bartholomäus Bruyn: Die Sammlung im Städtischen Museum Wesel*, Wesel 2002

LOEWINSON-LESSING/NICOULINE 1965
V. Loewinson-Lessing, N. Nicouline, *Les primitifs flamands: Le musée de l'Ermitage, Leningrad*, Brussels 1965

LONDON 1947
G. Reynolds, *Nicolas Hilliard and Isaac Oliver*, London (Victoria and Albert Museum) 1947

LONDON 1967–1968
France in the eighteenth century, London (Royal Academy of Arts) 1967–1968

LONDON 1974
D. Foskett, *Samuel Cooper and his contemporaries*, London (National Portrait Gallery) 1974

LONDON 1977
J. Rowlands, *Rubens: Drawings and Sketches*, London (British Museum) 1977

LONDON 1983
R. Strong, *Artists of the Tudor court: The portrait miniature rediscovered*, London (Victoria and Albert Museum) 1983

LONDON 1986
C. Brown, *Dutch landscape: The early years, Haarlem and Amsterdam 1590–1650*, London (National Gallery) 1986

LONDON 1995–1996
K. Hearn (ed.), *Dynasties: Painting in Tudor and Jacobean England 1530–1630*, London (Tate Gallery) 1995–1996

LONDON 1996
P. Taylor, *Dutch Flower Painting 1600–1750*, London (Dulwich Picture Gallery) 1996

LONDON 1996–1997
C. Brown, *Making and Meaning: Rubens' Landscapes*, London (National Gallery) 1996–1997

LONDON 2001
B.L. Brown (ed.), *The Genius of Rome 1592–1623*, London (Royal Academy of Arts) 2001

LONDON 2002
L.B. Harwood, with contributions by C. Brown and A.C. Steland, *Inspired by Italy: Dutch landscape painting 1600–1700*, London (Dulwich Picture Gallery) 2002

LONDON-THE HAGUE 1999–2000
C. White, Q. Buvelot (eds.), *Rembrandt by Himself*, London (National Gallery), The Hague (Mauritshuis) 1999–2000

LONDON-NEW HAVEN 2001–2002
C. MacLeod, J.M. Alexander *et al.*, *Painted Ladies: Women at the Court of Charles II*, London (National Portrait Gallery), New Haven (Yale Center for British Art) 2001–2002

LONDON-PARIS-CAMBRIDGE 2002–2003
W.W. Robinson, with an essay by M. Royalton-Kisch, *Bruegel to Rembrandt: Dutch and Flemish Drawings from the Maida and George Abrams Collection*, London (British Museum), Paris (Institut Néerlandais), Cambridge, Massachusetts (Fogg Art Museum) 2002–2003

LONG 1929
B.S. Long, *British miniatures*, London 1929

LOS ANGELES 1976–1977
Women artists: 1550–1950, Los Angeles (Los Angeles County Museum of Art) 1976–1977

LOS ANGELES 2002
L.M. Helmus *et al.*, *Pieter Saenredam, the Utrecht work: Paintings and drawings by the 17th-century master of perspective*, Los Angeles (The J. Paul Getty Museum) 2002

LOUGHMAN/MONTIAS 2000
J. Loughman, J.M. Montias, *Public and Private Spaces: Works of Art in Seventeenth-Century Dutch Houses*, Zwolle 2000

LOUVAIN 1975
Dirk Bouts en zijn tijd, Louvain (Sint-Pieterskerk) 1975

LOUVAIN 1998
M. Smeyers, K. Smeyers, *Dirk Bouts (ca. 1410–1475), een Vlaams primitief te Leuven*, Louvain (Sint-Pieterskerk and Predikherenkerk) 1998

LOWENTHAL 1986
A.W. Lowenthal, *Joachim Wtewael and Dutch Mannerism*, Doornspijk 1986

LOWENTHAL 1995
A.W. Lowenthal, *Joachim Wtewael: Mars and Venus surprised by Vulcan*, Malibu, California 1995

LUBBERHUIZEN-VAN GELDER 1947
A.M. Lubberhuizen-van Gelder, 'Japonsche Rocken', *Oud Holland* 62 (1947), pp. 137–152

LUGT 1936
F. Lugt, 'Italiaansche kunstwerken in Nederlandsche verzamelingen van vroeger tijden', *Oud Holland* 53 (1936), pp. 97–134

LUGT 1938–1987
F. Lugt, *Répertoire des catalogues de ventes publiques intéressant l'art ou la curiosité*, 4 vols, The Hague-Paris 1938–1987

LUNSINGH SCHEURLEER 1971–1972
D.F. Lunsingh Scheurleer, 'Een chinese celadonschaal: Wan Li en Overgangsporselein op zeventiende-eeuwse stillevens', *Antiek* 6 (1971–1972), no. 1, pp. 35–42

LUNSINGH SCHEURLEER 1979
T.H. Lunsingh Scheurleer, 'The Mauritshuis as "Domus Cosmographica" I', in E. van den Boogaart (ed.), *Johan Maurits van Nassau-Siegen 1604–1679: A Humanist Prince in Europe and Brazil. Essays on the occasion of the tercentenary of his death*, The Hague 1979, pp. 142–190

LUNSINGH SCHEURLEER *et al.* 1967
T.H. Lunsingh Scheurleer, A.B. de Vries, L. Brummel, H.E. van Gelder, *150 jaar Koninklijk Kabinet van Schilderijen Koninklijke Bibliotheek Koninklijk Penningkabinet*, The Hague 1967

VAN LUTTERVELT 1957
R. van Luttervelt, 'Herinneringen aan Michiel Adriaenszoon de Ruyter in het Rijksmuseum', *Bulletin van het Rijksmuseum* 5 (1957), pp. 28–70

VAN LUTTERVELT 1960
R. van Luttervelt, 'Herinneringen aan Johan en Cornelis de Witt in het Rijksmuseum', *Bulletin van het Rijksmuseum* 8 (1960), pp. 27–63

M

MAASTRICHT 2003
D.H. van Wegen, *Kunst uit de Kaap: Hollandse en Vlaamse meesterwerken uit de Michaelis Collectie te Kaapstad*, Maastricht (Bonnenfantenmuseum) 2003

MACLAREN 1960
N. MacLaren, *National Gallery Catalogues: The Dutch School*, London 1960

MADRID 1994–1995
P.C. Sutton *et al.*, *The Golden Age of Dutch Landscape Painting*, Madrid (Museo Thyssen-Bornemisza) 1994–1995

MADRID 2003
A. Vergara, with M. Westermann, *Vermeer y el interior holandés*, Madrid (Museo Nacional del Prado) 2003

MADRID 2004
C. Eisler *et al.*, *Gerard David y el paisaje flamenco*, Madrid (Museo Thyssen-Bornemisza) 2004

MADRID-LONDON 1982–1983
D. Angulo-Iñiguez *et al.*, *Bartolomé Murillo 1617–1672*, Madrid (Museo Nacional del Prado), London (Royal Academy of Arts) 1982–1983

MAETERLINCK 1906–1907
L. Maeterlinck, 'Un "petit maître" flamand inconnu de XVe siècle', *Les arts anciens de Flandre* 2 (1906–1907), pp. 48–52

MAGNANI 1995
L. Magnani, *Luca Cambiaso da Genova all' Escorial*, Genoa 1995

MANKE 1963
I. Manke, *Emanuel de Witte*, Amsterdam 1963

MANUTH/RÜGER 2004
V. Manuth, A. Rüger (eds.), *Collected Opinions: Essays on Netherlandish Art in Honour of Alfred Bader*, London 2004

VAN DER MARK 2003
B. van der Mark, 'Een slapend kindje van Quellinus', *Bulletin van het Rijksmuseum* 51 (2003), pp. 146–155

MARLIER 1934
G. Marlier, *Antonis Mor van Dashorst (Antonio Moro)*, Brussels 1934

MARLIER 1957
G. Marlier, *Ambrosius Benson et la peinture au temps de Charles Quint*, Damme 1957

MARTIN 1901
W. Martin, *Het leven en de werken van Gerrit Dou beschouwd in verband met het schildersleven van zijn tijd*, Leiden 1901

MARTIN 1908
W. Martin, 'Een schilderij van Willem van Haecht in het Mauritshuis', *Bulletin Nederlandschen Oudheidkundigen Bond* (second series) 1 (1908), pp. 33–39

MARTIN 1912
W. Martin, 'Aanwinsten van het Mauritshuis', *Bulletin Nederlandschen Oudheidkundigen Bond* (second series) 5 (1912), pp. 214–218

MARTIN 1918
W. Martin, 'Aanwinsten van het Mauritshuis', *Bulletin Nederlandschen Oudheidkundigen Bond* 11 (1918), pp. 214–217

MARTIN 1934
W. Martin, 'De aap van 1777', *Jaarboek Die Haghe* (1934), pp. 152–155

MARTIN 1935–1936
W. Martin, *De Hollandsche schilderkunst in de zeventiende eeuw*, 2 vols, Amsterdam 1935–1936

TE MARVELDE 1997
M. te Marvelde, 'Two wings by Von Kulmbach (cat. nos. 10a–b)', *Mauritshuis in focus* 10 (1997), no. 1, pp. 24–26

TE MARVELDE/VAN DEN BERG 1998
M. te Marvelde, K.J. van den Berg, 'An unusual pastiglia-like technique in the eighteenth-century', *Painting Technique-History, Materials and Studio Practice: Summaries of the Posters at the Dublin Congress, 7–11 September 1998*

MAURITSHUIS 1935
W. Martin, H. Schneider, *Musée Royal de Tableaux Mauritshuis à La Haye: Catalogue Raisonné des Tableaux et Sculptures: Troisième édition*, The Hague 1935

MAURITSHUIS 1968
M.M. Tóth-Ubbens *et al.*, *Schilderijen en beeldhouwwerken 15e en 16e eeuw [Koninklijk Kabinet van Schilderijen Mauritshuis]: Catalogus I*, The Hague 1968

MAURITSHUIS 1970
S.J. Gudlaugsson, *1945 . 1970: Vijfentwintig jaar aanwinsten Mauritshuis*, The Hague 1970

MAURITSHUIS 1978
A.B. de Vries, M. Tóth-Ubbens, W. Froentjes, *Rembrandt in the Mauritshuis*, The Hague 1978

MAURITSHUIS 1980
F.J. Duparc, *Mauritshuis: Hollandse schilderkunst: Landschappen 17de eeuw*, The Hague 1980

MAURITSHUIS 1987
B. Broos, *Meesterwerken in het Mauritshuis*, The Hague 1987

MAURITSHUIS 1991
B. Broos, R. van Leeuwen, E. Buijsen, P. van der Ploeg, *Twee decennia Mauritshuis:*

Ter herinnering aan Hans R. Hoetink, Directeur 1972–1991, The Hague 1991

MAURITSHUIS 1993
B. Broos, *Intimacies & Intrigues: History painting in the Mauritshuis*, The Hague-Ghent 1993

MAURITSHUIS 2000
Q. Buvelot (ed.), *Royal Cabinet of Paintings Mauritshuis: Guide*, The Hague 2000

MAZEL 1909
M. Mazel, 'Van een aap in 1777', *Jaarboek Die Haghe* (1909), pp. 361–380

MEIJER 2000
F.G. Meijer, [Review of VROOM 1999], *Oud Holland* 114 (2000), pp. 223–236

MEIJER 2003
F.G. Meijer, *The Collection of Dutch and Flemish Still-Life Paintings Bequeathed by Daisy Linda Ward: The Ashmolean Museum Oxford*, Zwolle 2003

MEIJER 2004
M.C. Meijer, 'The Century of the Orangutan', *New Perspectives on the Eighteenth Century* (2004), pp. 62–78

MELBOURNE-CANBERRA 1997–1998
A. Blankert *et al.*, *Rembrandt: A Genius and His Impact*, Melbourne (National Gallery of Victoria), Canberra (National Gallery of Victoria) 1997–1998

MEULEMEESTER 1984
J.L. Meulemeester, *Jacob van Oost de Oudere en het zeventiende-eeuwse Brugge*, Bruges 1984

DE MEYERE 1978
J.A.L. de Meyere, 'Utrechtse schilderkunst in de tweede helft van de 16de eeuw', *Jaarboek Oud-Utrecht* (1978), pp. 106–191

MIEDEMA 1994–1999
H. Miedema (ed.), *Karel van Mander: The Lives of the Illustrious Netherlandish and German Painters*, 6 vols, Doornspijk 1994–1999

VAN MIEGROET 1989
H.J. van Miegroet, *Gerard David*, Antwerp 1989

MILAN 1996
M. Bona Castellotti *et al.*, *Alessandro Magnasco 1667–1749*, Milan (Palazzo Reale) 1996

MILLER 1971
D. Miller, 'Some Unpublished Drawings by Marcantonio Franceschini and a Proposed Chronology', *Master Drawings* 9 (1971), pp. 119–138

MINNEAPOLIS-TOLEDO-LOS ANGELES 1990–1991
G.S. Keyes, *Mirror of Empire: Dutch Marine Art of the Seventeenth Century*, Minneapolis (Minneapolis Institute of Arts), Toledo (Toledo Museum of Art), Los Angeles (Los Angeles County Museum of Art) 1990–1991

MINNEAPOLIS-TOLEDO-PHILADELPHIA 1971–1972
E.R. Mandle, *Dutch masterpieces from the eighteenth century: Paintings & drawings 1700–1800*, Minneapolis (Minneapolis Institute of Arts), Toledo (Toledo Museum of Art), Philadelphia (Philadelphia Museum of Art) 1971–1972

DE MIRIMONDE 1970
A.P. de Mirimonde, 'Musique et symbolisme chez Jan-Davidszoon de Heem, Cornelis-Janszoon de Heem et Jan II Janszoon de Heem', *Jaarboek van het Koninklijk Museum voor Schone Kunsten Antwerpen* (1970), pp. 241–295

MOES 1897–1905
E.W. Moes, *Iconographia Batava*, 2 vols, Amsterdam 1897–1905

MOES/VAN BIEMA 1909
E.W. Moes, E. van Biema, *De Nationale Konst-Gallery en het Koninklijk Museum: Bijdrage tot de geschiedenis van het Rijksmuseum*, Amsterdam 1909

MOLENAAR 1998
Y. Molenaar, *Bloemen Constig geschikt*, Zwolle 1998

VON MOLTKE 1938–1939
J.W. von Moltke, 'Jan de Bray', *Marburger Jahrbuch für Kunstgeschichte* 11–12 (1938–1939), pp. 421–523

VON MOLTKE 1965
J.W. von Moltke, *Govert Flinck 1615–1660*, Amsterdam 1965

VON MOLTKE 1994
J.W. von Moltke *et al.*, *Arent de Gelder: Dordrecht 1645–1727*, Doornspijk 1994

MONTIAS 1989
J.M. Montias, *Vermeer and His Milieu: A Web of Social History*, Princeton, New Jersey 1989

MONTIAS 2002
J.M. Montias, *Art at Auction in 17th Century Amsterdam*, Amsterdam 2002

MONTREAL 1990
F.J. Duparc, L.L. Graif, *Italian Recollections: Dutch Painters of the Golden Age*, Montreal (Montreal Museum of Fine Arts) 1990

MONTREAL-TORONTO 1969
Rembrandt and his pupils, Montreal (Montreal Museum of Fine Arts), Toronto (Art Gallery of Ontario) 1969

MOXEY 1977
K.P.F. Moxey, *P. Aertsen, J. Beuckelaer, and the rise of secular painting in the context of the Reformation*, New York-London 1977

MÜLLENMEISTER 1988
K.J. Müllenmeister, *Roelant Savery (Kortrijk 1576–1639 Utrecht), Hofmaler Kaiser Rudolf II. in Prag: Die Gemälde mit kritischem Oeuvrekatalog*, Freren 1988

MÜLLER HOFSTEDE 1983
J. Müller Hofstede, 'Höfische und bürgerliche Damenporträts: Anmerkungen zu Rubens' Antwerpener Bildnismalerei 1609–1620', *Pantheon* 41 (1983), pp. 308–321

MÜNSTER 1994
C. Tümpel (ed.), *Im Lichte Rembrandts: Das Alte Testament in Goldenen Zeitalter der niederländischen Kunst*, Münster (Westfälisches Landesmuseum für Kunst und Kulturgeschichte) 1994

MÜNSTER 1996
A. Lorentz, *Die Maler tom Ring*, 2 vols, Münster (Westfälisches Landesmuseum für Kunst und Kulturgeschichte) 1996

MÜNSTER 1998–1999
1648: Krieg und Frieden in Europa, Münster (Westfälisches Landesmuseum für Kunst und Kulturgeschichte) 1998–1999 (English edition: *1648: War and Peace in Europe*)

MÜNSTER-BADEN-BADEN 1979–1980
Stilleben in Europa, Münster (Westfälisches Landesmuseum für Kunst und Kulturgeschichte), Baden Baden (Staatliche Kunsthalle) 1979–1980

MULDER-RADETZKY 2003
R. Mulder-Radetzky, 'Een poging tot reconstructie van de verzameling portretten van de Friese stadhouder Willem Frederik', in J.R. ter Molen (ed.), *Een vorstelijk archivaris: Opstellen voor Bernard Woelderink*, Zwolle 2003, pp. 237–243

MULLER 1989
J.M. Muller, *Rubens: The Artist as Collector*, Princeton, New Jersey 1989 (see also ANTWERP 2004)

MULLER 1998
S.D. Muller, *"Enlightened by Peace, Amsterdam Inspires the Arts": A Painted Allegory by Domenicus van Wijnen (1661–ca.1700)*, Utah 1998

MUNICH 2001
R. Baumstark *et al.*, *Venus: Bilder einer Göttin*, Munich (Alte Pinakothek) 2001

MUNICH-COLOGNE 2002
E. Mai, K. Wettengl, *Wettstreit der Künste: Malerei und Skulptur von Dürer bis Daumier*, Cologne (Wallraf-Richartz-Museum) 2002

MURDOCH 1981
J. Murdoch, *The English miniature*, New Haven 1981

MUTI/DE SARNO PRIGNANO 1994
L. Muti, D. de Sarno Prignano, *Alessandro Magnasco*, Faenza 1994

MUTI/DE SARNO PRIGNANO 1996
L. Muti, D. de Sarno Prignano, *Antonio Francesco Peruzzini*, Faenza-Monfalcone 1996

N

NAGASAKI 1992–1993
B. Broos *et al.*, *Princes and Paintings: Treasures from the Mauritshuis*, Nagasaki (Palace Huis ten Bosch Museum) 1992–1993

NATIONAL GALLERY 2001
The National Gallery: Supplement to the Complete Illustrated Catalogue. New acquisitions and long term loans 1995–2000, London 2001

NAUMANN 1981
O. Naumann, *Frans van Mieris the Elder*, 2 vols, Doornspijk 1981

NEHLSEN-MARTEN 2003
B. Nehlsen-Marten, *Dirck Hals 1591–1656: Œuvre und Entwicklung eines Haarlemer Genremalers*, Weimar 2003

NÉMETH 1996
I. Németh, 'De portretten van Jacob Trip en Margaretha de Geer door Nicolaes Maes in Boedapest', *Oud Holland* 110 (1996), pp. 79–84

NEUMEISTER 2003
M. Neumeister, *Das Nachtstück mit Kunstlicht in der niederländischen Malerei und Graphik des 16. und 17. Jahrhunderts: Ikonographische und koloristische Aspekte*, Petersberg 2003

NEURDENBURG 1930
E. Neurdenburg, *Hendrick de Keyser: Beeldhouwer en bouwmeester van Amsterdam*, Amsterdam 1930

NEURDENBURG 1948
E. Neurdenburg, *De zeventiende eeuwsche beeldhouwkunst in de Noordelijke Nederlanden*, Amsterdam 1948

NEW YORK 1979
William & Mary and their house, New York (The Pierpont Morgan Library) 1979

NEW YORK 1991
M.G. Roethlisberger, *Bartholomeus Breenbergh*, New York (Richard L. Feigen & Company) 1991
NEW YORK 1998–1999
M. Ainsworth *et al.*, *From Van Eyck to Breugel: Early Netherlandish Painting in The Metropolitan Museum of Art*, New York (The Metropolitan Museum of Art) 1998–1999
NEW YORK-LONDON 2001
W.A. Liedtke, M.C. Plomp, A. Rüger *et al.*, *Vermeer and the Delft School*, New York (The Metropolitan Museum of Art), London (National Gallery) 2001
NEW YORK-MAASTRICHT 1982
M. Klinge, *Adriaen Brouwer, David Teniers the Younger*, New York and Maastricht (Noortman & Brod Galleries) 1982
NICOLSON 1958
B. Nicolson, *Hendrick Terbrugghen*, London 1958
NICOLSON 1979
B. Nicolson, *The International Caravaggesque Movement*, Oxford 1979
NIEMEIJER 1962
J.W. Niemeijer, 'De portretten van Ploos van Amstel', *Nederlands Kunsthistorisch Jaarboek* 13 (1962), pp.181–215
NIEMEIJER 1973
J.W. Niemeijer, *Cornelis Troost 1696–1750*, Assen 1973
NIJMEGEN 1994
L. Kamerbeek, F. van der Schoor, *De gebeeldhouwde kop*, Nijmegen (Nijmeegs Museum Commanderie van Sint-Jan) 1994
NOBLE 1997
P. Noble, 'Conservation and restoration for *Art on wings*: The authenticity of the frames of the Solomon Triptych (cat.no.7)', *Mauritshuis in focus* 10 (1997), no.1, pp.27–30
NOBLE/POTTASCH 1997
P. Noble, C. Pottasch, 'A painting in focus, An acquisition: *Portrait of a woman* by Pieter Pietersz', *Mauritshuis in focus* 10 (1997), no.2, pp.8–15
NOORDERVLIET 1999
N. Noordervliet, *'Op de zeef van de tijd': Een geschiedenis van Nederland*, Amsterdam-Zwolle 1999
VAN NOTTEN 1907
H. van Notten, *Rombout Verhulst, beeldhouwer 1624–1698: Een overzicht zijner werken*, The Hague 1907
NUREMBERG 1983
Martin Luther und die Reformation in Deutschland, Nuremberg (Germanisches Nationalmuseum) 1983

O

OLDENBOURG 1911
R. Oldenbourg, *Thomas de Keysers Tätigkeit als Maler: Ein Beitrag zur Geschichte des Holländischen Porträts*, Leipzig 1911
OLDENBOURG 1921
R. Oldenbourg, *P.P. Rubens: Des Meisters Gemälde im 538 Abbildungen* (*Klassiker der Kunst*, vol.5), Berlin-Leipzig 1921
OLSON 1994/1996
G.S. Olson, *Giovanni Antonio Pellegrini and the Origins of Venetian Rococo Painting* (diss. University of Chicago 1994), Ann Arbor, Michigan 1996
VAN OS 1978
H.W. van Os *et al.*, *The early Venetian paintings in Holland*, Maarssen 1978
VAN OS 1979
H.W. van Os, 'De gebreken van de beeldtaal: De middeleeuwse schilderkunst', *Openbaar Kunstbezit* 23 (1979), pp.130–136
OSAKA 2000
A.K. Wheelock *et al.*, *The Public and the Private in the Age of Vermeer*, Osaka (Municipal Museum of Art) 2000
OSAKA-TOKYO-SYDNEY 1990
S. Segal, *Flowers and Nature: Netherlandish Flower Painting of Four Centuries*, Osaka (Nabio Museum of Art), Tokyo (Tokyo Station Gallery), Sydney (Art Gallery of New South Wales) 1990
VON DER OSTEN 1961
G. von der Osten, 'Zur Barockskulptur im südlichen Niedersachsen', *Niederdeutsche Beiträge zur Kunstgeschichte* 1 (1961), pp.239–258
VON DER OSTEN/VEY 1969
G. von der Osten, H. Vey, *Painting and sculpture in Germany and the Netherlands 1500–1600*, Harmondsworth 1969
OTTAWA 1968–1969
Jacob Jordaens, Ottawa (National Gallery of Canada) 1968–1969
OUWERKERK 2002
A. Ouwerkerk, 'Met kunst geïllustreerd: De kunstreproductie in de eerste helft van de negentiende eeuw in Nederland', in N. Bartelings *et al.*, *Beelden in veelvoud: De vermenigvuldiging van het beeld in prentkunst en fotografie* (*Leids Kunsthistorisch Jaarboek*, vol.12), Leiden 2002, pp.275–293
OXFORD 1999–2000
C. Brown, *Scenes of everyday life: Dutch genre paintings from the Mauritshuis*, Oxford (Ashmolean Museum) 1999–2000
OZINGA 1969
M.D. Ozinga, 'Jan Baptist Xavery als decoratief-architectonisch ontwerper', in H. Miedema *et al.* (eds.), *Miscellanea I.Q. van Regteren Altena*, Amsterdam 1969, pp.166–173

P

PADUA 1998–1999
A. Bettagno *et al.*, *Il maestro veneto del Rococò alle corti d'Europa*, Padua (Pallazzo della Ragione) 1998–1999
PARIS 1937
Descartes, Paris (Bibliothèque Nationale) 1937
PARIS 1970–1971
Le siècle de Rembrandt: Tableaux hollandais des collections publiques françaises, Paris (Musée du Petit Palais) 1970–1971
PARIS 1972–1973
Coligny, protestants et catholiques en France au XVIe siècle, Paris (Hotel de Rohan) 1972–1973
PARIS 1986
B. Broos *et al.*, *De Rembrandt à Vermeer: Les peintres hollandais au Mauritshuis de La Haye*, Paris (Galeries nationales du Grand Palais) 1986
PELTZER 1916
R.A. Peltzer, 'Hans Rottenhammer', *Jahrbuch der kunsthistorischen Sammlungen des allerhöchsten Kaiserhauses in Wien* 33 (1916), pp.293–365
PETER-RAUPP 1980
H. Peter-Raupp, *Die Ikonographie des Oranjezaal*, Hildesheim 1980
ST PETERSBURG-AMSTERDAM 1996–1997
R. Kistemaker, N. Kopaneva, A. Overbeek (eds.), *Peter de Grote en Holland: Culturele en wetenschappelijke betrekkingen tussen Rusland en Nederland ten tijde van tsaar Peter de Grote*, St Petersburg (Hermitage), Amsterdam (Amsterdams Historisch Museum) 1996–1997
PETTERSON 1987
E. Petterson, *'Amans Amanti Medicus*: Die Ikonologie des Motivs *Der ärztliche Besuch'*, in BOCK/GAEHTGENS 1987, pp.193–224
PETTERSON 2000
E. Petterson, *Amans Amanti Medicus: Das Genremotiv Der ärztliche Besuch in seinem kulturhistorischen Kontext*, Berlin 2000
PHILADELPHIA-BERLIN-LONDON 1984
P.C. Sutton *et al.*, *Masters of seventeenth-century Dutch genre painting*, Philadelphia (Philadelphia Museum of Art), Berlin (Gemäldegalerie, Staatliche Museen zu Berlin), London (Royal Academy of Arts) 1984
PHILADELPHIA-HOUSTON 2000
E. Peters Bowron, J.J. Rishel, *Art in Rome in the Eighteenth Century*, Philadelphia (Philadelphia Museum of Art), Houston (Museum of Fine Arts) 2000
PHILIPPOT 1970
P. Philippot, *Pittura fiamminga e Rinascimento italiano*, Turin 1970
PHOENIX-KANSAS CITY-THE HAGUE 1998–1999
M.K. Komanecky *et al.*, *Copper as canvas: Two centuries of masterpiece paintings on copper, 1575–1775*, Phoenix (Phoenix Art Museum), Kansas City (The Nelson-Atkins Museum of Art), The Hague (Mauritshuis) 1998–1999
PIGNATTI 1976
T. Pignatti, *Veronese: L'opera completa*, 2 vols, Venice 1976
PIJL 1995
L. Pijl, 'Over de chronologie van de schilderijen van Hercules Seghers', *Bulletin van het Rijksmuseum* 43 (1995), pp.172–180
PIJL 1998
L. Pijl, 'Paintings by Paul Bril in collaboration with Rottenhammer, Elsheimer and Rubens', *The Burlington Magazine* 140 (1998), pp.660–667
PIJL 2002
L. Pijl, 'A rediscovered pendant of Perseus and Andromeda', *Mauritshuis in focus* 15 (2002), no.3, pp.21–26
PLEIBISZ 1911
I. Pleibisz, *Maerten van Heemskerck*, Leipzig 1911
PLIETZSCH 1960
E. Plietzsch, *Holländische und Flämische Maler des 17. Jahrhunderts*, Leipzig 1960
VAN DER PLOEG 1993
P. van der Ploeg, 'A Painting in Focus: Gonzales Coques (and others), *Interior with Picture Collection*', *Mauritshuis in focus* 6 (1993), no.3, pp.17–21
VAN DER PLOEG 1994
P. van der Ploeg, 'De oude kantwerkster: Nicolaes Maes 1634–1693',

Bulletin Vereniging Rembrandt 4 (1994), no. 3, pp. 13–17
VAN DER PLOEG 1995a
P. van der Ploeg, 'Meindert Hobbema (1638–1709), *Wooded landscape with cottages*', *Mauritshuis in focus* 8 (1995), no. 1, pp. 15–20
VAN DER PLOEG 1995b
P. van der Ploeg, *Meindert Hobbema, Boslandschap met boerenhoeven: Een monumentale aanwinst voor Nederland / Meindert Hobbema, Wooded landscape with cottages: A major acquisition for the Netherlands*, brochure, The Hague 1995
VAN DER PLOEG 1995c
P. van der Ploeg, 'Boslandschap met boerenhoeven', *Bulletin Vereniging Rembrandt* 5 (1995), no. 1, pp. 10–13
VAN DER PLOEG 1997
P. van der Ploeg, 'A second Stadholder in The Hague: The journals of William Frederick', *Mauritshuis in focus* 10 (1997), no. 3, pp. 18–24
VAN DER PLOEG 2000
P. van der Ploeg, 'Two portraits by Rubens', *Mauritshuis in focus* 13 (2000), no. 3, pp. 14–17
VAN DER PLOEG 2001a
P. van der Ploeg, 'Too good to trade: From the private collection of Edward and Sally Speelman', *Mauritshuis in focus* 14 (2001), no. 1, pp. 8–21
VAN DER PLOEG 2001b
P. van der Ploeg, 'An early Vermeer rediscovered', *Mauritshuis in focus* 14 (2001), no. 3, pp. 18–26
VAN DER PLOEG 2003
P. van der Ploeg, 'Two portraits by Rubens', *Mauritshuis in focus* 16 (2003), no. 3, pp. 12–23
VAN DER PLOEG *et al.* 2002
P. van der Ploeg, E. Runia, A. van Suchtelen, with contributions by Q. Buvelot *et al.*, *Dutch and Flemish Old Masters from the Kremer Collection*, [Vaduz] 2002
PLOOS VAN AMSTEL 1980
G. Ploos van Amstel, *Portret van een koopman en uitvinder: Cornelis Ploos van Amstel. Maatschappelijk, cultureel en familieleven van een achttiende-eeuwer*, Assen 1980
PONT 1958
D. Pont, *Barent Fabritius*, Utrecht 1958
DE POORTER/JANSEN/GILTAIJ 1990
N. de Poorter, G. Jansen, J. Giltaij, *Rubens en zijn tijd / Rubens and his age*, Rotterdam 1990
PORTRAITS IN THE MAURITSHUIS
B. Broos, A. van Suchtelen, with contributions by Q. Buvelot, G. Sluiter, P. Noble, P. van der Ploeg, H. Vlieghe and F. Duparc, with an introductory essay by R. Ekkart, *Portraits in the Mauritshuis, 1430–1790*, The Hague-Zwolle 2004
POTSDAM-SANSSOUCI 1994
Von Sanssouci nach Europa: Geschenke Friedrichs des Großen an europäische Höfe, Potsdam-Sanssouci (Stiftung Preussische Schlösser und Gärten Berlin-Brandenburg) 1994
POTTASCH 1994
C. Pottasch, 'Jan Provoost (ca 1465–1529): Triptych with Madonna and Child (central panel), John the Evangelist and Mary Magdalene (wings)', *Mauritshuis in focus* 7 (1994), no. 1, pp. 14–17
POTTASCH 1997
C. Pottasch, 'Conservation and restoration for *Art on wings:* A triptych by Provoost (cat. no. 3)', *Mauritshuis in focus* 10 (1997), no. 1, pp. 21–23
POTTASCH 2003a
C. Pottasch, 'Pale pastels and shimmering satin', *Mauritshuis in focus* 16 (2003), no. 1, pp. 22–30
POTTASCH 2003b
C. Pottasch, 'Pendanten van twee meesters: Restauratie van twee schilderijen op koper', *Cr: Interdisciplinair tijdschrift voor conservering en restauratie* 4 (2003), pp. 46–48
POTTASCH/HOPPE 2003
C. Pottasch, R. Hoppe, 'The Restoration of an Early Vermeer: Diana and her Companions Transformed. A Case Study about a Painting scarred by Time', *Zeitschrift für Kunstgeschichte und Konservierung* 17 (2003), no. 1, pp. 148–155
PRESTON 1937
L. Preston, *Sea and river painters of the Netherlands in the 17th century*, London 1937
PRIEM 1997
R. Priem, 'The "most excellent collection" of Lucretia Johanna van Winter: The years 1809–22', *Simiolus* 25 (1997), nos. 2–3, pp. 103–235
PRUD'HOMME VAN REINE 1996
R.B. Prud'homme van Reine, *Rechterhand van Nederland: Biografie van Michiel Adriaenszoon de Ruyter*, Amsterdam 1996
PRUD'HOMME VAN REINE *et al.* 1992
R.B. Prud'homme van Reine *et al.*, *Ter navolging: Maritieme kunst en curiosa uit de Kweekschool voor de Zeevaart*, Zutphen 1992
PUPPI 1966
L. Puppi, *Marcello Fogolino: Pittore e incisore*, Trento 1966
VAN PUYVELDE 1939
L. van Puyvelde, *Die Skizzen des P.P. Rubens*, Frankfurt am Main 1939
VAN PUYVELDE 1953
L. van Puyvelde, *Jordaens*, Paris-Brussels 1953

R

RALEIGH-COLUMBUS-MANCHESTER 2002–2003
D.P. Weller *et al.*, *Jan Miense Molenaer*, Raleigh (North Carolina Museum of Art), Columbus (Indianapolis Museum of Art), Manchester (The Currier Museum of Art) 2002–2003
DE RANITZ 1971
L.C. de Ranitz, 'Portret-miniaturen uit het Rijksmuseum', *Bulletin van het Rijksmuseum* 19 (1971), pp. 7–10
RAUPP 1984
H.-J. Raupp, *Untersuchungen zu Künstlerbildnis und Künstlerdarstellung in den Niederlanden im 17. Jahrhundert*, Hildesheim-Zürich-New York 1984
RÉAU 1964
L. Réau, *Houdon: Sa vie et son œuvre*, 2 vols, Paris 1964
VAN REGTEREN ALTENA 1926
I.Q. van Regteren Altena, 'Cornelis Symonsz. van der Schalke', *Oud Holland* 43 (1926), pp. 48–61
VAN REGTEREN ALTENA 1983
I.Q. van Regteren Altena, *Jacques de Gheyn: Three generations*, 3 vols, The Hague-Boston-London 1983
REISS 1975
S. Reiss, *Aelbert Cuyp*, London 1975
REMPT 1988
J. Rempt, 'Ger Lataster in the Mauritshuis', *Dutch Art and Architecture Today* (June 1988), no. 23, pp. 20–21
RENCKENS 1954
B.J.A. Renckens, 'Nicolaes Ficke en een Haarlems Monogrammist', *Oud Holland* 69 (1954), pp. 115–123
RENGER 1972
K. Renger, 'Joos van Winghe's "Nachtbancket met een mascarade" und verwandte Darstellungen', *Jahrbuch der Berliner Museen* 14 (1972), pp. 190–193
RENGER 1987
K. Renger, 'Adriaen Brouwer: Seine Auseinandersetzung mit der Tradition des 16. Jahrhunderts', in BOCK/GAEHTGENS 1987, pp. 253–282
REZNICEK 1954
E. Reznicek, 'Notities bij "de Konstkamer" van Gonzales Coques', *Bulletin van het Rijksmuseum* 2 (1954), pp. 43–46
REZNICEK 1977
E.K.J. Reznicek, 'Opmerkingen bij Rembrandt', *Oud Holland* 94 (1977), pp. 75–103
RICCI 1918
C. Ricci, *Rembrandt in Italia*, Milan 1918
VAN RIEMSDIJK 1892
B.W.F. van Riemsdijk, 'Schilderijenkabinetten in de XVIIIe eeuw', *Oud Holland* 10 (1892), pp. 219–228
RIJKSMUSEUM 1973
J. Leeuwenberg, W. Halsema-Kubes, *Beeldhouwkunst in het Rijksmuseum: Catalogus*, The Hague-Amsterdam 1973
RIJKSMUSEUM 1976
P.J.J. van Thiel *et al.*, *All the paintings of the Rijksmuseum in Amsterdam: A completely illustrated catalogue*, Amsterdam-Haarlem 1976
RIJKSMUSEUM 1992
P.J.J. van Thiel *et al.*, *All the paintings of the Rijksmuseum in Amsterdam: A completely illustrated catalogue. First supplement: 1976–91*, Amsterdam-The Hague 1992
RIJKSMUSEUM 2000
H. van Os, J.P. Filedt Kok, G. Luijten *et al.*, *Nederlandse kunst in het Rijksmuseum 1400–1600*, Zwolle-Amsterdam 2000
RIJKSMUSEUM 2001
J.P. Filedt Kok, R. Baarsen, B. Cornelis *et al.*, *Nederlandse kunst in het Rijksmuseum 1600–1700*, Zwolle-Amsterdam 2001
RM
See: RIJKSMUSEUM
ROBELS 1989
H. Robels, *Frans Snijders: Stilleben- und Tiermaler 1579–1657*, Munich 1989
ROBINSON 1974
F.W. Robinson, *Gabriel Metsu*, New York 1974
ROBINSON 1990
M.S. Robinson, *The paintings of the Willem van de Veldes*, 2 vols, London 1990
ROBINSON 1996
W.W. Robinson, *The Early Works of Nicolaes Maes*,

1653 to 1661 (diss.), Ann Arbor, Michigan 1996

RODNEY 2003
H. Rodney Nevitt, *Art and the Culture of Love in Seventeenth-Century Holland*, Cambridge 2003

ROETHLISBERGER 1981
M. Roethlisberger, *Bartholomeus Breenbergh: The paintings*, Berlin-New York 1981

ROETHLISBERGER/BOK 1993
M.G. Roethlisberger, M.J. Bok, *Abraham Bloemaert and his sons*, 2 vols, Doornspijk 1993

ROMANKO GIER 1990
R. Romanko Gier, *Adriaen van Ostade and Dutch rural landscape achievements* (diss.), Utah 1990

ROME 1983
La pastorale Olandese nel Seicento: L'inspirazione poetica della pittura nel secolo d'oro, Rome (Istituto Olandese) 1983

ROOSES 1886–1892
M. Rooses, *L'Œuvre de P.P. Rubens: Histoire et description de ses tableaux et dessins*, 5 vols, Antwerp 1886–1892

ROSCAM ABBING 1993
M. Roscam Abbing, *De schilder & schrijver Samuel van Hoogstraten 1627–1678: Eigentijdse bronnen & oeuvre van gesigneerde schilderijen*, Leiden 1993

ROSENBERG 1900
A. Rosenberg, *Adriaen und Isack van Ostade*, Bielefeld-Leipzig 1900

ROSENBERG 1928
J. Rosenberg, *Jacob van Ruisdael*, Berlin 1938

ROSENBERG 1983
P. Rosenberg, *L'Opera completa di Chardin*, Milan 1983

ROTTERDAM 1953
Olieverfschetsen van Rubens, Rotterdam (Museum Boijmans Van Beuningen) 1953

ROTTERDAM 1954
Hercules Seghers, Rotterdam (Museum Boijmans Van Beuningen) 1954

ROTTERDAM 1958
Michael Sweerts en zijn tijdgenoten, Rotterdam (Museum Boijmans Van Beuningen) 1958

ROTTERDAM 1973
Adriaen van der Werff: Kralingen 1659–1722 Rotterdam, Rotterdam (Historisch Museum) 1973

ROTTERDAM 1983
Brood: De geschiedenis van het brood en het broodgebruik in Nederland, Rotterdam (Museum Boijmans Van Beuningen) 1983

ROTTERDAM 1989–1990
B. Treffers, G.J. van der Sman, E. Mijnlieff, *Van Titiaan tot Tiepolo: Italiaanse schilderkunst in Nederlands bezit / From Titian to Tiepolo: Italian Painting in Dutch Collections*, Rotterdam (Museum Boijmans Van Beuningen) 1989–1990

ROTTERDAM 1991
J. Giltaij, G. Jansen, *Perspectiven: Saenredam en de architectuurschilders van de 17e eeuw*, Rotterdam (Museum Boijmans Van Beuningen) 1991

ROTTERDAM 1994–1995
N. Schadee, L. van der Zeeuw *et al.*, *Rotterdamse Meesters uit de Gouden Eeuw*, Rotterdam (Historisch Museum) 1994–1995

ROTTERDAM-BERLIN 1996–1997
J. Kelch, J. Giltaij, *Lof der Zeevaart*, Berlin (Gemäldegalerie, Staatliche Museen), Rotterdam (Museum Boijmans Van Beuningen) 1996–1997

ROTTERDAM-BRUGES 1965
S. Herzog, H.R. Hoetink, H. Pauwels, *Jan Gossaert genaamd Mabuse*, Rotterdam (Museum Boijmans Van Beuningen), Bruges (Groeninge Museum) 1965

ROTTERDAM-FRANKFURT AM MAIN 1999–2000
A. Blankert *et al.*, *Hollands Classicisme in de zeventiende-eeuwse schilderkunst*, Rotterdam (Museum Boijmans Van Beuningen), Frankfurt am Main (Städelsches Kunstinstitut) 1999–2000

ROTTERDAM-FRANKFURT AM MAIN 2004–2005
J. Giltaij *et al.*, *Zinnen en minnen: Schilders van het dagelijks leven in de zeventiende eeuw*, Rotterdam (Museum Boijmans Van Beuningen), Frankfurt am Main (Städelsches Kunstinstitut) 2004–2005

ROWLANDS 1985
J. Rowlands, *Holbein. The Paintings of Hans Holbein the Younger: Complete Edition*, Oxford 1985

ROY 1992
A. Roy, *Gérard de Lairesse 1640–1711*, Paris 1992

RUNIA/NOBLE/WADUM 2003
E. Runia, P. Noble, J. Wadum, 'Two nudes by Rembrandt restored and examined', *Mauritshuis in focus* 16 (2003), no. 1, pp. 8–19

RUSSELL 1975
M. Russell, *Jan van de Cappelle*, Leigh-on-Sea 1975

S

SALERNO 1977–1980
L. Salerno, *Pittori di Paesaggio del Seicento a Roma/Landscape Painters of the Seventeenth Century in Rome*, 3 vols, Rome 1977–1980

SALVINI/GROHN 1971
R. Salvini, W. Grohn, *Das gemalte Gesamtwerk von Hans Holbein der Jüngere*, Milan 1971

SAN FRANCISCO-BALTIMORE-LONDON 1997–1998
J. Spicer, L. Federle Orr *et al.*, *Masters of Light: Dutch Painters in Utrecht during the Golden Age*, San Francisco (The Fine Arts Museums of San Francisco), Baltimore (The Walters Art Gallery), London (National Gallery) 1997–1998

SAN FRANCISCO-TOLEDO-BOSTON 1966–1967
The Age of Rembrandt: An Exhibition of Dutch Paintings of the Seventeenth Century, San Francisco (California Palace of the Legion of Honor), Toledo (Toledo Museum of Art), Boston (Museum of Fine Arts) 1966–1967

SCALLEN 2004
C.B. Scallen, *Rembrandt: Reputation and the Practice of Connoisseurship*, Amsterdam 2004

SCHAAR 1958
E. Schaar, *Studien zu Nicolaes Berchem*, Cologne 1958

SCHAFFERS-BODENHAUSEN/TIETHOFF-SPLIETHOFF 1993
K. Schaffers-Bodenhausen, M. Tiethoff-Spliethoff, *The Portrait Miniatures in the Collections of the House of Orange-Nassau*, The Hague-Zwolle 1993

SCHELLER 1996
R.W. Scheller, 'Art of the state: Forms of government and their effect on the collecting of art 1550–1800', *Simiolus* 24 (1996), pp. 275–286

SCHIEDAM-GOUDA 1986–1987
J. Bokhoven (ed.), *Leven en werk van Christoffel Pierson (1631–1714): 'Den kloeken Rijmer en konstrijken Schilder'*, Schiedam (Stedelijk Museum), Gouda (Stedelijk Museum Het Catharina Gasthuis) 1986–1987

SCHLICHTENMAIER 1988
H. Schlichtenmaier, *Studien zum Werk Hans Rottenhammers des Älteren (1564–1625), Maler und Zeichner mit Werkkatalog* (diss.), Tübingen 1988

SCHLOSS 1982
C. Skeeles Schloss, *Travel, Trade and Temptation: The Dutch Italianate Harbor Scene, 1640–1680* (diss.), Ann Arbor, Michigan 1982

SCHLOSS 1983
C. Skeeles Schloss, 'The Early Italianate Genre Paintings by Jan Weenix (ca. 1642–1719)', *Oud Holland* 97 (1983), pp. 69–97

SCHMIDT-DÖRRENBERG 1969
J. Schmidt-Dörrenberg, *David and Saul: Variationen über ein Thema von Rembrandt*, Vienna 1969

SCHMITT 1993
S. Schmitt, *Diogenes: Studien zu seiner Ikonographie in der niederländischen Emblematik und Malerei des 16. und 17. Jahrhunderts*, Hildesheim-Zürich-New York 1993

SCHNACKENBURG 1981
B. Schnackenburg, *Adriaen van Ostade, Isack van Ostade: Zeichnungen und Aquarelle*, 2 vols, Hamburg 1981

VON SCHNEIDER 1925–1926
A. von Schneider, 'Jakob van Loo', *Zeitschrift für bildende Kunst* 59 (1925–1926), pp. 66–78

VON SCHNEIDER 1933
A. von Schneider, *Caravaggio und die Niederländer*, Marburg-Lahn 1933

SCHNEIDER/EKKART 1973
H. Schneider, R.E.O. Ekkart, *Jan Lievens: Sein Leben und seine Werke*, revised edition, Amsterdam 1973 (ed. princ. 1932)

SCHOLTEN 1991
F. Scholten, 'Prudentia en Minerva: Enige onbekende werken van de beeldhouwer Bartholomeus Eggers', *Antiek* 26 (1991), no. 4, pp. 185–192

SCHOLTEN 1994
F. Scholten, 'Het portret van Don Luis da Cunha door Jan Baptist Xavery (1737)', *Bulletin van het Rijksmuseum* 42 (1994), pp. 107–119

SCHOLTEN 1995
F. Scholten, *Gebeeldhouwde portretten / Portrait sculptures*, Amsterdam-Zwolle 1995

SCHOLTEN 1998a
F. Scholten, 'De kracht van zwijgzaamheid', *Kunstschrift* 42 (1998), no. 2, pp. 36–40

SCHOLTEN 1998b
F. Scholten, 'Uit één blok eikenhout', *Kunstschrift* 42 (1998), no. 3, p. 2

SCHOLTEN 1999
F. Scholten, *'Een ijvore*

Mars van Francis, de beeldsnijder Van Bossuit en de familie De la Court', *Bulletin van het Rijksmuseum* 47 (1999), pp. 26–43

SCHOLTEN 2000
F. Scholten, 'A terracotta portrait of Count Johan Maurits', *Mauritshuis in focus* 13 (2000), no. 1, pp. 22–32

SCHOLTEN 2001
F. Scholten, 'Johan Gregor van der Schardts zelfportret, circa 1573', *Bulletin van het Rijksmuseum* 49 (2001), pp. 310–325

SCHOLTEN 2003a
F. Scholten, *Sumptuous Memories: Studies in seventeenth-century Dutch tomb sculpture*, Zwolle 2003

SCHOLTEN 2003b
F. Scholten, 'Rombout Verhulsts ivoren Madonna met Christus', *Bulletin van het Rijksmuseum* 51 (2003), pp. 102–117

SCHRADER 1995
K. Schrader, *Der Bildnismaler Johann Georg Ziesenis (1716–1776): Leben und Werk mit kritischem Oeuvrekatalog*, Münster 1995

SCHULZ 1978
W. Schulz, *Cornelis Saftleven, 1607–1681: Leben und Werke. Mit einem kritischen Katalog der Gemälde und Zeichnungen*, Berlin-New York 1978

SCHULZ 1982
W. Schulz, *Herman Saftleven 1609–1685: Leben und Werke. Mit einem kritischen Katalog der Gemälde und Zeichnungen*, Berlin-New York 1982

SCHULZ 2002
W. Schulz, *Aert van der Neer*, Doornspijk 2002

SCHUPBACH 1978
W. Schupbach, 'A new look at *The cure of folly*', *Medical History* 22 (1978), no. 3

SCHUPBACH 1982
W. Schupbach, *The paradox of Rembrandt's 'Anatomy Lesson of Dr. Tulp'*, London 1982

SCHUURMAN 1947
K.E. Schuurman, *Carel Fabritius*, Amsterdam 1947

SCHWARTZ 1984
G. Schwartz, *Rembrandt: Zijn leven, zijn schilderijen*, Maarssen 1984 (also in English edition)

SCHWARTZ 1996
G. Schwartz, 'Love in the Kunstkamer: Additions to the work of Guillam van Haecht (1593–1637)', *Tableau* 18 (1996), no. 6, pp. 43–52

SCHWARTZ/BOK 1989
G. Schwartz, M.J. Bok, *Pieter Saenredam: De schilder in zijn tijd*, Maarssen-The Hague 1989 (English edition: 1990)

SCHWARZ 2004
B. Schwarz, *Hitlers Museum: Die Fotoalben Gemäldegalerie Linz: Dokumente zum "Führermuseum"*, Vienna-Cologne-Weimar 2004

SCRASE 1983
D. Scrase, *Flowers of Three Centuries: One Hundred Drawings & Watercolours from the Broughton Collection*, Washington 1983

SEOUL 2003
G. Sluiter, B. van der Mark, edited by Q. Buvelot, *The Age of Rembrandt: 17th Century Dutch Painting*, Seoul (National Museum of Art) 2003

SERVOLINI 1944
L. Servolini, *Jacopo de' Barbari*, Padua 1944

VAN SETERS 1947
W.H. van Seters, 'De maker van het borstbeeld van Mr. Pieter Lyonet in het Mauritshuis', *Oud Holland* 62 (1947), pp. 156–164

SIEGEN 1930
Reformationsausstellung, Siegen (Museum des Siegerlandes, Oberes Schloss) 1930

SILLEVIS-CHODZINSKA 1990
Z. Sillevis-Chodzinska, 'Restauratie van *Venus poogt Adonis van de jacht te weerhouden*', *Nieuwsbrief Mauritshuis* 3 (1990), no. 1, pp. 11–12

SILVER 1984
L. Silver, *The Paintings of Quinten Massys: With catalogue raisonné*, Oxford 1984

SKREINER 1963
W.A. Skreiner, *Studien zu den Eitelkeits- und Vergänglichkeitsdarstellungen in der abendländischen Malerei* (diss.), Graz 1963

SLIGGERS/WERTHEIM 1994
B.C. Sliggers, A.A. Wertheim (eds.), *Een vorstelijke dierentuin: De menagerie van Willem V / Le zoo du prince: La ménagerie du stathouder Guillaume V*, Haarlem-Paris-Zutphen 1994

SLIVE 1970–1974
S. Slive, *Frans Hals*, 3 vols, London 1970–1974

SLIVE 1995
S. Slive, *Dutch Painting 1600–1800*, New Haven-London 1995

SLIVE 2001
S. Slive, *Jacob van Ruisdael: A Complete Catalogue of his Paintings, Drawings and Etchings*, New Haven-London 2001

SLUIJTER 1975
E.J. Sluijter, 'Hendrik Willem Schweickhardt (1746–1797): Een Haagse schilder in de tweede helft van de achttiende eeuw', *Oud Holland* 89 (1975), pp. 142–212

SLUIJTER 1986
E.J. Sluijter, *De 'heydensche fabulen' in de noordnederlandse schilderkunst, circa 1590–1670* (diss.), The Hague 1986 (see SLUIJTER 2000a)

SLUIJTER 2000a
E.J. Sluijter, *De 'heydensche fabulen' in de schilderkunst van de Gouden Eeuw: Schilderijen met verhalende onderwerpen uit de klassieke mythologie in de Noordelijke Nederlanden circa 1590–1670*, Leiden 2000 (see above)

SLUIJTER 2000b
E.J. Sluijter, '*The Tronie of a Young Officer with a Gorget* in the Mauritshuis: A second version by Rembrandt himself?', *Oud Holland* 114 (2000), pp. 188–194

SLUIJTER-SEIJFFERT 1983–1984
N. Sluijter-Seijffert, 'De Nassause cavalcade: Een opmerkelijk doek in het Mauritshuis. Levende en overleden vorsten bijeen op één schilderij', *Tableau* 6 (1983–1984), no. 1, pp. 52–53

SLUIJTER-SEIJFFERT 1984
N. Sluijter-Seijffert, *Cornelis van Poelenburch (ca. 1593–1667)* (diss.), Enschede 1984

SMIT 2000
C.G.M. Smit, *Pieter Langendijk: Een wetenschappelijke proeve op het gebied van de Letteren* (diss. University of Nijmegen), Hilversum 2000

SMITH 1982
D.R. Smith, *Masks of Wedlock: Seventeenth-Century Dutch Marriage Portraiture*, Ann Arbor, Michigan 1982

SNOEP 1969
D.P. Snoep, 'Honselaersdijk: Restauraties op papier', *Oud Holland* 84 (1969), pp. 270–294

DE SOUSA-LEÃO 1973
J. de Sousa-Leão, *Frans Post*, Amsterdam 1973

SPETH-HOLTERHOFF 1957
S. Speth-Holterhoff, *Les peintres flamands de cabinets d'amateurs au XVIIe siècle*, Brussels 1957

SPRUIT 1995
C. Spruit, *Jan van Ravesteyn: De officiersportretten 1611–1624* (unpublished Master's thesis), Utrecht 1995

SPRUIT 1997
C. Spruit, 'New light on Jan van Ravesteyn's series of officers' portraits', *Mauritshuis in focus* 10 (1997), no. 2, pp. 22–30

STANTON-HIRST 1982
B.A. Stanton-Hirst, 'Pieter Quast and the Theatre', *Oud Holland* 96 (1982), pp. 213–237

STARING 1923
A. Staring, 'De loterijzaal door H. Pothoven 1779 (Nieuwe aanwinst voor het Mauritshuis)', *Jaarboek Die Haghe* (1923), pp. 98–103

STARING 1943
A. Staring, 'De vroege Engelsche portretminiaturisten en ons land', *Oudheidkundig Jaarboek* 12 (1943), pp. 85–98

STARING 1947
A. Staring, *Fransche kunstenaars en hun Hollandsche modellen in de 18de eeuw en in de aanvang der 19de eeuw*, The Hague 1947

STARING 1948
A. Staring, *Kunsthistorische verkenningen: Een bundel kunsthistorische opstellen*, The Hague 1948

STARING 1950–1951
A. Staring, 'De portretten van den koning-stadhouder', *Nederlands Kunsthistorisch Jaarboek* 3 (1950–1951), pp. 151–196

STARING 1958
A. Staring, *Jacob de Wit 1695–1754*, Amsterdam 1958

STARING 1978
A. Staring, *Johann Friedrich August Tischbein's Hollandse jaren*, Zutphen 1978

STECHOW 1948
W. Stechow, 'Jan Baptist Weenix', *Art Quarterly* 11 (1948), pp. 181–198

STECHOW 1966
W. Stechow, *Dutch Landscape Painting of the 17th Century*, London 1966

STECHOW 1972
W. Stechow, '"Lusus laetitaeque modus"', *Art Quarterly* 35 (1972), pp. 165–175

STECHOW 1975
W. Stechow, *Salomon van Ruysdael*, revised and extended edition, Berlin 1975 (ed. princ. 1938)

STEENSMA 1999
S. Steensma, *Otto Marseus van Schrieck: Leben und Werk*, Hildesheim-Zürich-New York 1999

STELAND-STIEF 1971
A.C. Steland-Stief, *Jan Asselijn, nach 1610 bis 1652*, Amsterdam 1971

STELAND-STIEF 1980
A.C. Steland-Stief, 'Zum zeichnerischen Werk des Jan Asselyn: Neue Funde und Forschungsperspektiven', *Oud Holland* 94 (1980), pp. 213–258

VAN DER STIGHELEN 1990–1991
K. van der Stighelen, '[Review of FILIPCZAK 1987]', *Simiolus* 20 (1990–1991), pp. 293–298

STOCKHOLM 1992
G. Cavalli-Björkman *et al.*, *Rembrandt och hans tid: Människan i Centrum / Rembrandt and his Age: Focus on Man*, Stockholm (Nationalmuseum) 1992

STOCKHOLM 2001–2002
G. Cavalli-Björkman *et al.*, *Face to Face: Portraits from Five Centuries*, Stockholm (Nationalmuseum) 2001–2002

STONE-FERRIER 2000
L. Stone-Ferrier, 'Metsu's Justice Protecting Widows and Orphans: Patron and Painter Relationships and Their Involvement in the Social and Economic Plight of Widows and Orphans in Leiden', in A.K. Wheelock, A. Seff (eds.), *The Public and Private in Dutch Culture of the Golden Age*, Newark-London 2000, pp. 227–265

VAN STRAATEN 1977
A. van Straaten, *Koud op het bot*, The Hague 1977

STRONG 1983
R. Strong, *The English Renaissance miniature*, London 1983

STUKENBROCK 1993
C. Stukenbrock, *Frans Hals: Fröhliche Kinder, Musikanten und Zecher. Eine Studie zu ausgewählten Motivgruppen und deren Rezeptionsgeschichte*, Frankfurt am Main-Berlin 1993

VAN SUCHTELEN 1997a
A. van Suchtelen, 'A painting in focus, An acquisition: *The adoration of the shepherds* by Jan de Bray', *Mauritshuis in focus* 10 (1997), no. 1, pp. 10–16

VAN SUCHTELEN 1997b
A. van Suchtelen, 'Twee portretten van Pieter Pietersz herenigd in het Mauritshuis', in P. van den Brink, L.M. Helmus (eds.), *Album Discipulorum J.R.J. van Asperen de Boer*, Zwolle 1997, pp. 203–210

VAN SUCHTELEN 2000
A. van Suchtelen, 'A diptych by Bartholomäus Bruyn', *Mauritshuis in focus* 13 (2000), no. 3, pp. 18–24

SUIDA-MANNING/SUIDA 1958
B. Suida-Manning, W. Suida, *Luca Cambiaso*, Milan 1958

SUMOWSKI 1983–1995
W. Sumowski, *Gemälde der Rembrandt-Schüler*, 6 vols, Landau/Pfalz 1983[–1995]

SUTTON 1980
P.C. Sutton, *Pieter de Hooch: Complete Edition*, Oxford-New York 1980

SUTTON 1992
P.C. Sutton, *Dutch & Flemish Seventeenth-Century Paintings: The Harold Samuel Collection*, Cambridge 1992

SUTTON 2002
P.C. Sutton, *Dutch & Flemish Paintings: The Collection of Willem Baron van Dedem*, London 2002

SWILLENS 1935
P.T.A. Swillens, *Pieter Janszoon Saenredam: Schilder van Haarlem 1597–1675*, Amsterdam 1935

T

TAMIS 2002
D. Tamis, '"In kompagnie geordonneert en geschildert": Een onderzoek naar de ontstaansgeschiedenis van het Aards Paradijs van Peter Paul Rubens en Jan Brueghel d.O.', *Oud Holland* 115 (2002), pp. 111–130

TAX/TAX-KOOLEN 1995
C.J.H.M. Tax, A.C.M. Tax-Koolen, 'De portretten en iconografie van Michael Ophovius', *Jaarboek Koninklijk Museum voor Schone Kunsten Antwerpen* (1995), pp. 85–134

TAYLOR 1995
P. Taylor, *Bloemstillevens in de Gouden Eeuw 1600–1720*, Zwolle 1995 (also in English edition)

THE HAGUE
See: THE HAGUE

VAN THIEL 1981
P.J.J. van Thiel, 'De inrichting van de Nationale Konst-Gallerij in het openingsjaar 1800', *Oud Holland* 95 (1981), pp. 170–227

VAN THIEL 1999
P.J.J. van Thiel, *Cornelis Cornelisz van Haarlem 1562–1638: A Monograph and Catalogue Raisonné*, Doornspijk 1999

THIÉRY 1953
Y. Thiéry, *Le paysage Flamand au XVIIe siècle*, Paris-Brussels 1953

THORNTON 1978
P. Thornton, *Seventeenth-Century Interior Decoration in England, France and Holland*, New Haven-London 1978

TIETHOFF-SPLIETHOFF 1979
M.E. Tiethoff-Spliethoff, 'Een ridder van de Olifantsorde: Johan Wolfert van Brederode en zijn familie', *Jaarboek van het Centraal Bureau voor Genealogie* 33 (1979), pp. 201–213

TISSINK/DE WIT 1987
F. Tissink, H.F. de Wit, *Gorcumse schilders in de Gouden Eeuw*, Gorinchem 1987

TOCHIGI-SAKURA-GUNMA-NAGASAKI 1997–1998
B. Broos *et al.*, *Diversity and Specialisation: Seventeenth-century Dutch Masters from the Mauritshuis*, Tochigi (Prefectural Museum of Fine Arts), Sakura (Sakura City Museum of Art), Gunma (Museum of Modern Art), Nagasaki (Huis ten Bosch Museum of Art) 1997–1998

TOKYO 2003
A. Kofuku (ed.), *Rembrandt and the Rembrandt School: The Bible, Mythology and Ancient History*, Tokyo (National Museum of Western Art) 2003

TOKYO-CHIBA-YAMAGUCHI 1992
Rembrandt: His Teachers and His Pupils, Tokyo (Bunkara Museum of Art), Chiba (Kawamura Memorial Museum of Art), Yamaguchi (Yamaguchi Prefectural Museum of Art) 1992

TOKYO-KASAMA-KUMAMOTO-LEIDEN 1992–1993
E. Buijsen *et al.*, *Between fantasy and reality: 17th Century Dutch Landscape Painting*, Tokyo (Station Gallery), Kasama (Nichido Museum of Art), Kumamoto (Prefectural Museum of Art), Leiden (Stedelijk Museum De Lakenhal) 1992–1993

TÓTH-UBBENS 1969
M.M. Tóth-Ubbens, 'Kijken naar een vogeltje', in H. Miedema *et al.* (eds.), *Miscellanea I.Q. van Regteren Altena*, Amsterdam 1969, pp. 155–159

TRAVERSI/WADUM 1999
L. Traversi, J. Wadum, 'Un tableau avec *Deux enfants s'embrassant* au Mauritshuis', in H. Verougstraete, R. van Schoute (eds.), *La peinture dans les Pays-Bas au 16e siècle: Pratiques d'atelier infrarouges et d'autres méthodes d'investigation*, Louvain 1999, pp. 99–109

TRIVAS 1941
N.S. Trivas, *The paintings of Frans Hals*, London 1941

TRIZNA 1976
J. Trizna, *Michel Sittow: Peintre revalais de l'école brugeoise (1468–1525/1526)*, Brussels 1976

TÜMPEL 1974
A. Tümpel, 'Claes Cornelisz. Moeyaert', *Oud Holland* 88 (1974), pp. 1–163, 245–290

TÜMPEL 1986
C. Tümpel, *Rembrandt*, Antwerp 1986

U

UTRECHT 1965
A. Blankert, *Nederlandse 17e eeuwse italianiserende landschapschilders*, Utrecht (Centraal Museum) 1965

UTRECHT 1988
P. Dirkse *et al.*, *Vermaakt aan de staat: Het legaat Thurkow-van Huffel*, Utrecht (Museum Catharijneconvent) 1988

UTRECHT 1991
P. Dirkse, *Jezuïeten in Nederland*, Utrecht (Museum Catharijneconvent) 1991

UTRECHT 1994
T.G. Kootte, *Rekkelijk of precies: Remonstranten en contraremonstranten ten tijde van Maurits en Oldenbarnevelt*, Utrecht (Museum Catharijneconvent) 1994

UTRECHT 2000–2001
L.M. Helmus *et al.*, *Pieter Saenredam, het Utrechtse werk: Schilderijen en tekeningen van de 17de-eeuwse grootmeester van het perspectief*, Utrecht (Centraal Museum) 2000–2001

UTRECHT 2001
A. Blankert, *Utrechts Gouden Eeuw: Caravaggisten en Italianisanten uit Nederlands bezit*, Utrecht (Centraal Museum) 2001

UTRECHT-BRAUNSCHWEIG 1986–1987
A. Blankert, L. Slatkes *et al.*, *Nieuw licht op de Gouden Eeuw: Hendrick ter Brugghen en tijdgenoten*, Utrecht (Centraal Museum), Braunschweig (Herzog Anton Ulrich-Museum) 1986–1987

UTRECHT-BRAUNSCHWEIG 1991
S. Segal, *Jan Davidsz de Heem en zijn kring*, Utrecht (Centraal Museum), Braunschweig (Herzog Anton Ulrich-Museum) 1991

UTRECHT-FRANKFURT AM MAIN 1993
P. van den Brink *et al.*, *Het gedroomde land: Pastorale schilderkunst in de Gouden Eeuw*, Utrecht (Centraal Museum), Frankfurt am Main (Schirn Kunsthalle) 1993

V

VACCARO 2002
M. Vaccaro, *Parmigianino: The Paintings*, Turin 2002

VALENTINER 1923
W.R. Valentiner, *Frans Hals: Des Meisters Gemälde*

(Klassiker der Kunst, vol. 28) Stuttgart-Leipzig 1923
VEERE/VLISSINGEN 1955
Vier eeuwen Markiezaat, Veere (Schotse Huizen), Vlissingen (Stedelijk Museum) 1955
VENICE 1959
A. Bettagno, *Disegni e dipinti di Giovanni Antonio Pellegrini 1675–1741*, Venice (Fondazione Giorgio Cini) 1959
VENICE 1999–2000
B. Aikema, B.L. Brown (eds.), *Renaissance Venice and the North: Crosscurrents in the time of Bellini, Dürer, and Titian*, Venice (Palazzo Grassi) 1999–2000
VENICE-FLORENCE 1985
B.W. Meijer, B. Aikema, *Disegni veneti di collezioni olandesi*, Venice (Fondazione Giorgio Cini), Florence (Istituto Universitario di Storia dell'Arte) 1985
VERBEEK/SCHOTMAN 1957
J. Verbeek, J.W. Schotman, *Hendrick ten Oever: Een vergeten Overijssels meester uit de zeventiende eeuw*, Zwolle 1957
VERONA 1999
D. Scaglietti Kelescian, *Alessandro Turchi detto l'Ordetto 1578–1649*, Verona (Museo di Castelvecchio) 1999
VERSAILLES-MUNICH-LONDON 2002–2003
X. Salmon, *Madame de Pompadour et les arts*, Versailles (Musée national des châteaux de Versailles et de Trianon), Munich (Kunsthalle der Hypo-Kulturstiftung), London (National Gallery) 2002–2003
VERSPEYCK MYNSSEN 1918
J.A.G. Versp[e]yck Mynssen, 'De marmeren busten van Falconet in het Mauritshuis', *Oude Kunst* 4 (1918), no. 3, pp. 78–79
VEY 1962
H. Vey, *Die Zeichnungen Anton van Dycks*, Brussels 1962
VIENNA-ESSEN 2002
W. Seipel (ed.), *Das Flämische Stilleben 1550–1680*, Vienna (Kunsthistorisches Museum), Essen (Kulturstiftung Ruhr) 2002
VLIEGENTHART 1981
A.W. Vliegenthart, *Bildersammlung der Fürsten zu Salm*, Anholt 1981
VLIEGHE 1983
H. Vlieghe, 'Some Remarks on the Identification of Sitters in Rubens' Portraits', *Papers presented at the International Rubens Symposium*, published in *The Ringling Museum of Art Journal* (1983), pp. 106–115
VLIEGHE 1987
H. Vlieghe, *Rubens Portraits of Identified Sitters in Antwerp* (*Corpus Rubenianum Ludwig Burchard*, vol. 19–2), Antwerp 1987
VLIEGHE 1998
H. Vlieghe, *Flemish Art and Architecture 1585–1700*, New Haven-London 1998
VAN VLIERDEN 1997
M. van Vlierden, 'Vier wenende vrouwen van een Brussels passieretabel', *Catharijnebrief* 15 (1997), no. 60
VAN VLIERDEN 1998
M. van Vlierden, 'Uit het-zelfde hout gesneden: Een bijzondere ontdekking', *Catharijnebrief* 16 (1998), no. 61
VAN VLIERDEN 2004
M. van Vlierden, with H.L.M. Defoer, H.M.E. Höppener-Bouvy, *Houten en steensculptuur van Museum Catharijneconvent ca. 1200–1600*, Zwolle-Utrecht 2004
VAN VLIET 1966
P. van Vliet, 'Spaanse schilderijen in het Rijksmuseum, afkomstig van schenkingen van Koning Willem I', *Bulletin van het Rijksmuseum* 14 (1966), pp. 131–149
DE VOS 1994
D. De Vos, *Hans Memling: Het volledige oeuvre*, Antwerp 1994
DE VOS 1999
D. De Vos, *Rogier van der Weyden: Het volledige oeuvre*, Antwerp 1999
DE VRIES 1953a
A.B. de Vries, 'Morgenstond en Avondstemming door Aert van der Neer', *Bulletin van het Rijksmuseum* 1 (1953), pp. 82–83
DE VRIES 1953b
A.B. de Vries, 'Een portret van Pieter Pietersz. uit 1597', *Bulletin van het Rijksmuseum* 1 (1953), pp. 79–81
DE VRIES 1960
A.B. de Vries, 'Karel du Jardin, De Jonge Herder', *Openbaar Kunstbezit* 4 (1960), pp. 29a–b
DE VRIES 1968
A.B. de Vries, *De verzameling Sidney van den Bergh*, Wassenaar 1968
DE VRIES 1969a
L. de Vries, 'Vorstelijke beeltenissen in miniaturen', *Spiegel Historiael* 4 (1969), pp. 165–168
DE VRIES 1969b
A.B. de Vries, 'P.A. de Suffren de Saint-Tropez, Jean Antoine Houdon (1741–1828)', *Openbaar Kunstbezit* 13 (1969), pp. 3a–b
DE VRIES 1975
J. de Vries, 'Gerard Houckgeest', *Hamburger Kunstsammlungen* 20 (1975), pp. 25–56
DE VRIES 1976
L. de Vries, *Jan Steen: De schilderende Uilenspiegel*, Weert 1976
DE VRIES 1977
L. de Vries, *Jan Steen, de kluchtschilder* (diss.), Groningen 1977
DE VRIES 1984
L. de Vries, *Jan van der Heyden*, Amsterdam 1984
DE VRIES 1998
L. de Vries, *Gerard de Lairesse: An Artist between Stage and Studio*, Amsterdam 1998
VROOM 1945
N.R.A. Vroom, *De schilders van het monochrome banketje*, Amsterdam 1945
VROOM 1980
N.R.A. Vroom, *A modest message as intimated by the painters of the 'monochrome banketje'*, 2 vols, Schiedam 1980
VROOM 1999
N.R.A. Vroom, *A modest message as intimated by the painters of the 'monochrome banketje'*, Nuremberg 1999

W

WADUM 1991
J. Wadum, 'Portretten in miniatuur minimaal belicht', *Nieuwsbrief Mauritshuis* 4 (1991), no. 2, pp. 6–7
WADUM 1995
J. Wadum, 'Hobbema examined', *Mauritshuis in focus* 8 (1995), no. 1, pp. 21–23
WADUM 1998
J. Wadum, 'The Antwerp Brand on Paintings on Panel', in E. Hermens (ed.), *Looking Through Paintings: The Study of Painting Techniques and Materials in Support of Art Historical Research* (*Leids Kunsthistorisch Jaarboek*, vol. 9), Baarn-London 1998, pp. 179–198
WADUM 2000
J. Wadum, 'Rembrandt under the Skin: The Mauritshuis *Portrait of Rembrandt with Gorget* in retrospect', *Oud Holland* 114 (2000), pp. 164–187
WADUM 2001
J. Wadum, 'The latest news from paradise', *Mauritshuis in focus* 14 (2001), no. 1, pp. 22–30
WADUM 2002
J. Wadum, 'Latest news from Paradise: A preliminary attempt to identify Rubens's studio practice, Part II', *ICOM Committee for Conservation: 13th Triennial Meeting Rio de Janeiro. Preprints*, vol. I (2002), pp. 473–478
WADUM 2003
J. Wadum, 'Rembrandts erster "hässlicher" Akt: "Andromeda" von ca. 1630 restauriert und untersucht', *Restauro: Zeitschrift für Kunsttechniken, Restaurierung und Museumsfragen* 109 (2003), pp. 496–502
WADUM 2004
J. Wadum, 'The goldfinch restored and scanned', *Mauritshuis in focus* 17 (2004), no. 2, pp. 24–30
WADUM/HERMENS 1994
J. Wadum, E. Hermens, 'Report of a Relining', *Mauritshuis in focus* 7 (1994), no. 1, pp. 23–26
WADUM/HOPPENBROUWERS/ STRUICK VAN DER LOEFF 1994
J. Wadum, R. Hoppenbrouwers, L. Struick van der Loeff, *Vermeer Illuminated: Conservation, Restoration and Research*, The Hague 1994
WAGNER 1924
J.D. Wagner, 'Brederode', *Maandblad van het Genealogisch-heraldisch Genootschap 'De Nederlandsche Leeuw'* 42 (1924), cols. 368–371
WAGNER 1971
H. Wagner, *Jan van der Heyden*, Amsterdam-Haarlem 1971
WALFORD 1991
E.J. Walford, *Jacob van Ruisdael and the Perception of Landscape*, New Haven-London 1991
WALLEN 1983
B. Wallen, *Jan van Hemessen: An Antwerp Painter Between Reform and Counter-Reform*, Ann Arbor, Michigan 1983
WALLERT 2002
A. Wallert, 'Questions and Answers: The Technical Examination of Polychrome Terra-Cotta Sculptures by Johan Georg van der Schardt', *ArtMatters: Netherlands Technical Studies in Art* 1 (2002), pp. 32–45
WANSINK 1990
C.J.A. Wansink, 'De decoratieve schilderkunst van Mattheus Terwesten, een Haagse meester uit de achttiende eeuw', *Oud Holland* 104 (1990), pp. 270–292
WANSINK 1991
I. Wansink, 'Een schoorsteenstuk van Mattheus Terwesten thuisgebracht', *Nieuws-*

brief Mauritshuis 4 (1991), pp. 11–12

WARDLE 2002
P. Wardle, *For Our Royal Person: Master of the Robes Bills of King-Stadholder William III*, Apeldoorn 2002

WASHINGTON 1990–1991
A.K. Wheelock, S.J. Barnes, J.S. Held, *Anthony van Dyck*, Washington (National Gallery of Art) 1990–1991

WASHINGTON 2002–2003
S. Ebert-Schifferer *et al.*, *Deceptions and Illusions: Five Centuries of Trompe l'Oeil Painting*, Washington (National Gallery of Art) 2002–2003

WASHINGTON 2003
A. Wheelock, *Small Wonders: Dutch Still Lifes by Adriaen Coorte*, Washington (National Gallery of Art) 2003

WASHINGTON-AMSTERDAM 1996–1997
H. Perry Chapman, W.T. Kloek, A.K. Wheelock, *Jan Steen: Painter and Storyteller*, Washington (National Gallery of Art), Amsterdam (Rijksmuseum) 1996–1997

WASHINGTON-DETROIT 2004–2005
A.K. Wheelock *et al.*, *Gerard ter Borch*, Washington (National Gallery of Art), Detroit (The Detroit Institute of Arts) 2004–2005 (a selection will also be shown in the Rijksmuseum, Amsterdam, 2005)

WASHINGTON-DETROIT-AMSTERDAM 1980–1981
A. Blankert *et al.*, *God en de goden: Verhalen uit de bijbelse en klassieke oudheid door Rembrandt en zijn tijdgenoten*, Washington (National Gallery of Art), Detroit (The Detroit Institute of Arts), Amsterdam (Rijksmuseum) 1980–1981

WASHINGTON ETC. 1982–1984
Mauritshuis: Dutch Paintings of the Golden Age, Washington (National Gallery of Art), Forth Worth (Kimbell Art Museum), Chicago (The Art Institute of Chicago), Los Angeles (Los Angeles County Museum of Art), Toronto (Art Gallery of Ontario), New York (The Metropolitan Museum of Art) 1982–1984

WASHINGTON-THE HAGUE 1995–1996
A. Wheelock, B. Broos *et al.*, *Johannes Vermeer*, Washington (National Gallery of Art), The Hague (Mauritshuis) 1995–1996

WASHINGTON-LONDON-HAARLEM 1989–1990
S. Slive *et al.*, *Frans Hals*, Washington (National Gallery of Art), London (Royal Academy of Arts), Haarlem (Frans Hals Museum) 1989–1990

WASHINGTON-LONDON-THE HAGUE 2000–2001
R. Baer *et al.*, *Gerrit Dou 1613–1675: Master Painter in the Age of Rembrandt*, Washington (National Gallery of Art), London (Dulwich Picture Gallery), The Hague (Mauritshuis) 2000–2001

WEISNER 1963
U. Weisner, *Moyses van Uyttenbroeck: Studien und kritischer Katalog seiner Gemälde und Zeichnungen* (diss.), 2 vols, Kiel 1963

WEISS 1913
E. Weiss, *Jan Gossaert: Sein Leben und seine Werke*, Parchim i.M. 1913

WELCKER/HENSBROEK-VAN DER POEL 1979
C.J. Welcker, revised and edited by D.J. Hensbroek-van der Poel, *Hendrick Avercamp (1585–1634) bijgenaamd "De Stomme van Campen" en Barent Avercamp (1612–1679): "Schilders tot Campen"*, Doornspijk 1979

WELLER 1992
D.P. Weller, *Jan Miense Molenaer (c.1609/10–1668): The life and art of a seventeenth-century Dutch painter* (diss.), Maryland 1992

WESCHER 1929
P. Wescher, 'Der Maler Pieter Pietersz. und sein Werk', *Oud Holland* 46 (1929), pp. 152–171

WESTERMANN 1999
M. Westermann, 'Adriaen van de Venne, Jan Steen, and the art of serious play', *De zeventiende eeuw* 15 (1999), no. 1, pp. 34–47

WESTHOFF-KRUMMACHER 1965
H. Westhoff-Krummacher, *Barthel Bruyn der Ältere als Bildnismaler*, Munich-Berlin 1965

WESTPHAL 1931
D. Westphal, *Bonifazio Veronese*, Munich [1931]

VAN WESTRHEENE 1867
T. van Westrheene, *Paulus Potter: Sa vie et ses oeuvres*, The Hague 1867

WETHEY 1975
H.E. Wethey, *The Paintings of Titian*, 3 vols, London 1975

WHEELOCK 1988
A. Wheelock, *Jan Vermeer*, New York 1988 (ed. princ. 1981)

WHEELOCK 1995
A. Wheelock, *Vermeer and the Art of Painting*, New Haven-London 1995

WHITEHEAD/BOESEMAN 1989
P.J.P. Whitehead, M. Boeseman, *A portrait of Dutch 17th century Brazil: Animals, plants and people by the artists of Johan Maurits of Nassau*, Amsterdam-Oxford-New York 1989

WIESEMAN 2002
M.E. Wieseman, *Caspar Netscher and Late Seventeenth-Century Dutch Painting*, Doornspijk 2002

WIESEMAN 2004
M.E. Wieseman, 'Paper Trails: Drawings in the Work of Caspar Netscher and his Studio', in MANUTH/RÜGER 2004, pp. 248–261

WIJNMAN 1959
H.F. Wijnman, *Uit de kring van Rembrandt en Vondel: Verzamelde studies over hun leven en omgeving*, Amsterdam 1959

WILDENSTEIN 1922
G. Wildenstein, *Le peintre Aved*, Paris 1922

WILDENSTEIN 1923
G. Wildenstein, *Louis Moreau*, Paris 1923

WILDENSTEIN 1963
G. Wildenstein, *Chardin*, Zürich 1976

WILENSKI 1960
R.H. Wilenski, *Flemish painters 1430–1830*, 2 vols, London 1960

VAN DER WILLIGEN/MEIJER 2003
A. van der Willigen, F.G. Meijer, *A dictionary of Dutch and Flemish still-life painters working in oils, 1525–1725*, Leiden 2003

WILLIS 1911
F. Willis, *Die Niederländische Marinemalerei*, Leipzig 1911

WINKLER 1959a
F. Winkler, *Hans von Kulmbach: Leben und Werk eines fränkischen Künstlers der Dürerzeit*, Kulmbach 1959

WINKLER 1959b
F. Winkler, 'Zur Kenntnis und Würdigung des Jan Mostaert', *Zeitschrift für Kunstwissenschaft* 13 (1959), pp. 177–214

WINTERNITZ 1958
E. Winternitz, 'The Inspired Musician: A Sixteenth-Century Musical Pastiche', *The Burlington Magazine* 100 (1958), pp. 48–55

WINTERNITZ 1967
E. Winternitz, *Musical Instruments and their Symbolism in Western Art*, London 1967

WISHNEVSKY 1967
R. Wishnevsky, *Studien zum 'Portrait historié' in den Niederlanden* (diss.), Munich 1967

WOLF 1989
J. Wolf, 'Ger Lataster', *Holland Herald* 24 (1988), no. 6, pp. 34–37

WOLFF 2004
M. Wolff, 'Hebrew Kings and Antwerp Mannerists', in MANUTH/RÜGER 2004, pp. 278–293

WUESTMAN 1998
G.E. Wuestman, *De Hollandse schilderschool in prent: Studies naar reproduktietechniek in de tweede helft van de zeventiende eeuw / Dutch art seen through prints: Studies in reproductive printmaking in the second half of the seventeenth century* (diss.), Utrecht 1998

Y

YAMAGUCHI-KUMAMOTO-TOKYO-ROTTERDAM 1994–1995
E. de Jongh *et al.*, *Faces of the Golden Age: Seventeenth-Century Dutch Portraits*, Yamaguchi (Prefectural Museum of Art), Kumamoto (Prefectural Museum of Art), Tokyo (Station Gallery), Rotterdam (Kunsthal) 1994–1995

Z

ZAMBONI 1968
S. Zamboni, *L. Mazzolino*, Milan 1968

ZEVENHUIZEN/DE BOER 1998
E. Zevenhuizen, P. de Boer, *Maerten van Heemskerck 1498–1574: 'Constigh vermaert schilder'*, Heemskerk-Amsterdam 1998

ZONDERVAN 1982
J.W. Zondervan, 'Het Panhuys-paneel van het Mauritshuis: Beeld van een snel vervlogen droom', *Jaarboek van het Centraal Bureau voor Genealogie* 36 (1982), pp. 74–116

ZWEITE 1980
A. Zweite, *Marten de Vos als Maler*, Berlin 1980

ZWOLLE 1997
J. Streng, L. van Dijk, *Zwolle in de Gouden Eeuw: Cultuur en schilderkunst*, Zwolle (Stedelijk Museum) 1997

Index of names

Including artists, collectors, dealers, as well as historical, biblical and mythological characters, and personifications. The appendices have not been indexed.

A

Aarentz, Herman • 72
Abigail • 268
Abraham • 338
Abrams, George • 124
Abrams, Maida • 124
Achilles • 178
Adam • 82, 84, 122
Addington, J. • 152
Adonis • 96, 118, 272, 320
Adrian, Saint • 346
Adrichem, Symon van • 356
Aelst, Anna van • 156
Aelst, Willem van • 50
Aeneas • 92
Aerssen, Cornelis van • 198
Aerssen, François van • 198
Aerssen Beyeren van Voshol, Willem Frederik Ernst, Baron van • 44, 198
Aertsen, Pieter • 50, 236
Aesculapius • 96
Agnes of Sayn-Wittgenstein • 160
Agnew's • 78, 132, 262
Albert of Habsburg, Archduke of Austria • 122
Albertine Agnes of Orange-Nassau, Princess • 18, 98, 130, 164, 208, 218, 364
Alberts, Gerrit • 50, 108
Albrechts, N. • 312
Aldenburg Bentinck and Waldeck-Limpurg, Willem, Count of • 94
Alewijn, D.M. • 192
Alexander, Sir Claude • 104
Alexander I, Czar • 152
Alexander the Great • 260, 400
Allegri, Antonio: see Correggio
Allori, Alessandro • 50
Almkerk, Willem Fabricius d' • 244
Alphaus • 178
Amalia Charlotte Wilhelmina Louise of Nassau-Weilburg, Princess • 304
Amalia Elisabeth, Countess of Hanau • 248
Amalia of Solms-Braunfels • 17, 18, 19, 20, 68, 78, 120, 158, 160, 208, 370
Amor • 86
Andersen, Alfred • 84
Andromeda • 36, 172, 174, 260
Angelica • 274
Angelis, De • 266
Angély, Elie • 236
Anna of Austria • 290
Anna of Egmond and Buren • 130
Anna of Saxony • 200
Anne, Queen • 20
Anne, Saint • 178, 316
Anne of Denmark • 370, 372, 376
Anne of Hannover • 20, 22, 54, 304, 306, 374, 378, 394
Anraadt, Pieter van • 39, 52
Anspach, Johannes • 52
Anthony, Saint • 346
Anthony of Padua, Saint • 122, 126
Antigone • 92
Apelles • 22, 136
Apollo • 232, 338
Apostool, Cornelis • 26
Appleby • 280
Arcade Gallery • 98, 148
Aretin, Carl von • 280
Argus • 88, 184
Ariadne • 180
Ariosto • 274
Aristotle • 260
Arisz, Adriaen (Aris Kint) • 258
Arlaud, Benjamin • 364
Armida • 204
Arney, D' • 230
Arp, Jan Willem van • 216
Artis, Richard • 190
Arundel, Thomas Howard, Earl of • 97
Ashburton, Lord • 230
Asscher and Welcker • 106, 280
Asselijn, Jan • 52
Asselijn, Thomas • 308
Ast, Balthasar van der • 39, 42, 52–54
Asta, F. • 344
Athena • 56
Atlas • 174
Audry, Alphonse • 262
August Wilhelm of Hohenzollern, Prince • 304, 390
Augusta Maria Carolina of Nassau-Weilburg, Princess • 304
Augustine • 334
Augustus III, King of Poland • 23, 122, 136
Aurora • 232
Aved, Jacques-André-Joseph • 54
Avercamp, Hendrick • 38, 54
Aynard, Edouard • 216

B

Baburen, Dirck van • 18
Bacchus • 96, 97, 180, 208, 274
Bache, Jules S. • 104
Bachstitz • 214, 332
Backer, Jacob Adriaensz • 34, 39, 54–56
Backhuysen: see Bakhuysen
Baen, Jan de • 14, 26, 56, 108
Baerle, Suzanna van • 13, 40, 88
Bakhuysen, Ludolf • 58
Bakker, G.J.T. • 58, 88
Bakker Korff, Alexander Hugo • 58
Balckeneynde, Adriana van • 148
Balen, Hendrik van • 17, 82, 268
Balen, Jan van • 358
Balsac, Lady Katherine de • 374
Balthasar Carlos, Infante • 194
Barbara, Saint • 232, 348
Barbari, Jacopo de' • 58
Baring, Thomas • 220
Baring, Thomas George, Earl of Northbrook • 220
Bary, Hendrick • 334
Bassen, Bartholomeus van • 60
Baumgärtner, Julius Alexander • 78
Beatrix, Queen • 400
Beauharnais, Josephine de • 152
Beavan, Henry • 104
Bebber, Elisabeth van • 138, 190, 222
Beck, Catharina • 170
Beck, Hans-Ulrich • 132
Beck, Jan • 168, 170
Beck, Margaretha • 170
Beck, Nicolaas • 170
Beck, Sara • 170
Becker, H. • 70
Beckford, W. • 220
Beek, Jacob Frederiksz van • 64
Beeldemaker, Adriaen • 276
Beest, Sybrand van • 60
Bega, Cornelis Pietersz • 60
Begeyn, Abraham • 60, 80
Bellevois, Jacob Adriaensz • 62
Bellinghausen, Elisabeth • 86
Benedict, C. • 170, 242
Benjamin • 106
Bennet, J.A. • 310
Benson, Ambrosius • 106
Bentinck • 250
Berchem, Nicolaes Pietersz • 22, 39, 62–64, 292
Berckheyde, Gerrit Adriaensz • 64, 192
Berckheyde, Job Adriaensz • 64
Berckman, Hendrick • 72
Berg, Simon van den • 28, 30, 46, 66
Bergen, Pieter van den • 178
Bergen van der Grijp, J. van • 74
Bergeon, J. • 210
Bergh, A.S. van den • 44, 130
Bergh, J.B. van den • 136
Bergh, L. van den • 44, 70
Bergh, Sidney van den • 52
Berghe, Christoffel van den • 66
Berlage, H.P. • 34
Bernini, Gian Lorenzo • 364
Berry, Duchesse de • 230
Berwick, Lord • 260
Beschey, Jan Frans • 78
Bettes, John • 380
Beuckelaer, Joachim • 66
Beukelaar, Maria • 296
Beuningen, Jan van • 82, 268
Beurdeley, M.A. • 212
Beverwijck, Johan van • 226
Beyeren, Abraham van • 39, 66–68
Beyerman, Samuel • 274
Bezborodko, Count • 386
Bicker van Swieten, Gerard • 62, 156, 170, 202
Bièvre-Duijndam, Mrs C.C.M. de • 45, 166
Bijlert, Jan van • 17
Bischof, J. • 214
Biset, Charles Emmanuel • 96
Bisschop, Jan • 168
Bisschop, Jan de • 58, 314
Bisschop, Pieter • 168
Bixby, William H. • 140
Blaauwsonnevelt van den Bergh, Joannes M.C. van • 356

Bles, David • 294
Bleyswyk, F. van • 228
Blijenburgh, C.W. van • 45, 236, 380
Bloch, Vitale • 45, 52, 116, 168, 172, 192, 280, 300, 342
Block, Gerard • 328
Bloemaert, Abraham • 18, 68–70
Blok • 220
Blom Coster, Timon Hendrik • 44, 64, 120, 142, 144, 210, 358
Blommendael, Jan • 386
Bloot, Pieter de • 296
Bloteling, Abraham • 218
Bloudoff, Count and Countess • 276
Blumenthal • 150
Bode, Wilhelm von • 30
Boeijermans, Theodor • 96, 97
Boel, Peeter • 96
Boer, P. de • 52, 116, 278, 284, 298
Boerhaave, Herman • 124
Bohemen, N. van • 52
Böhler, J. • 176
Boijmans • 266
Bois, Guillaume du • 30, 70
Boissière, Charles de • 260
Bojano, Comte de • 130
Bol, Ferdinand • 54, 56, 70–72
Bol, Hans • 72
Boleyn, Anne • 368
Bolomey, Benjamin • 22
Bonaparte, Lucien • 306
Bongard, Anna van den • 294
Bonn, Andreas • 220
Boom, Abraham Pietersz • 174
Borch, Gerard ter • 23, 26, 34, 35, 39, 40, 72–74, 298
Bordone, Paris • 76
Boreel, E. • 314
Boreel, W.M.F. • 314
Bos, S.B. • 60
Bos de Harlingen • 326
Bosch, Hieronymus • 17
Bosch, Joannes de • 390
Bosch, W.A. van den • 45, 64
Bosschaert the Elder, Ambrosius • 32, 76
Both, Jan • 17, 76, 116
Boucher, François • 306
Bourbon, Charlotte de • 248
Bourdon, Sébastien • 186
Bourke, Count Edmund • 90, 166, 232, 316, 352
Bout, Adriaan • 20, 144, 256, 286, 294, 342
Bouts, Aelbert (Albrecht) • 76
Bouts, Dirk • 26, 76
Braamcamp, Gerret • 22, 122, 174, 276, 328, 330
Braams • 322
Braams, G.H.G. • 284
Brakenburgh, Richard • 76
Bramer, Leonaert • 15
Brandt, Mortimer • 236
Brant, Clara • 270
Brant, Isabella • 270
Brants, Jan Jacob • 298
Bray, Jan de • 76–77
Bray, Salomon de • 78
Bredael, Peeter van • 96
Bredel, Charles • 204
Bredenhoff, François van • 128
Brederode, Johan Wolfert van • 208, 254
Brederode, Reinout van • 254
Brederode, Wolfert van • 208
Bredius, Abraham • 30, 32, 34, 36, 39, 40, 44, 46, 68, 80, 86, 90, 106, 130, 156, 214, 216, 258, 260, 262, 264, 266, 278, 292, 296, 318, 322, 326, 356, 390
Breenbergh, Bartholomeus • 42, 78–80, 238
Brekelenkam, Quiringh van • 80
Bremen, Nicolaas van • 296
Breugel-du Peyrou, J. van • 326
Bril, Paulus • 17, 268
Brind, Charles • 152
Brod, Alfred • 45, 52, 78, 190, 204, 240
Bronzino, Agnolo • 50
Brosterhuijsen, Johannes • 15
Brounckhurst, Arnold van • 380
Brouwer, Adriaen • 30, 80
Brueghel the Elder, Jan • 17, 18, 22, 80–84, 130, 268
Brueghel the Younger, Jan • 82, 84
Bruggen, Louis van der • 364
Brugghen, Hendrick ter • 84
Bruijn, J.C. de • 274
Brutus • 246
Bruyn, George • 60
Bruyn, Jan de • 306, 312
Bruyn, Jan Jacob de • 308
Bruyn the Elder, Bartholomäus • 84–86
Buchanan, William • 168
Buckingham, George Grenville, first Marquess of • 348
Buijs, Jacobus • 372
Bukowski • 92
Bullens, Catharina • 186
Bunel II, François • 86
Burgh, Albert Coenraedsz • 174
Burn, G.A. • 94
Burton, Constable • 204
Bury, Friedrich • 86
Bus de Gisignies, Bernard du • 136, 228, 318, 336
Busch • 236
Busch, Otto • 116
Butôt, F.C. • 188
Buttery, A.H. • 346
Buys, Cornelis • 346
Buysero, Dirk • 312
Bylandt-van Hogendorp van Hofwegen, Catharina Frederica Augustine Alexandrina, Countess van • 44, 170

C

Cacus • 128
Caffieri, Jean-Jacques • 396
Caliari, Paolo: see Veronese, Paolo
Calkoen, Abraham, Baron • 242
Calkoen, Petronella • 242
Calkoen, Pieter • 186
Call, Jan van • 10
Calliope • 338
Calonne, M. de • 270
Calraet, Abraham van • 86
Camberlyn, Chevalier Joseph-Guillaume-Jean • 118
Cambiaso, Luca • 86–88
Campaspe • 22, 136
Campen, Jacob van • 11, 12, 13, 15, 18, 40, 88, 142
Candace, Queen of • 268
Cappelle, Jan van de • 30, 34, 88
Carignan, Prince De • 340
Carlevarijs, Luca • 230
Carolina Louise Frederika of Nassau-Weilburg, Princess • 304
Carolina Wilhelmina, Princess of Orange • 304, 374
Carracci, Annibale • 90
Cassirer • 280
Cassirer, Paul • 100, 152, 170, 236, 288, 348
Castiglioni, Camillo • 128
Cate, H.E. ten • 32, 45, 88, 192
Cate-van Wulfften Palthe, Mr and Mrs Ten • 162
Catharina Belgica • 248
Catherine, Saint • 122, 348
Catherine of Braganza, Queen • 366, 368
Cauda, Count von • 176
Cavendish, Elisabeth • 374
Cavens, Count • 118, 288
Caylus, François-Joseph, Duc de • 280
Ceres • 274
Cerezo, Mateo • 90
Ceulen, Cornelis Jonson van: see Jonson van Ceulen, Cornelis
Cevat, D. • 266
Champaigne, Philippe de • 90
Chaplin • 204
Chardin, Jean-Baptiste-Siméon • 36, 90
Chariclea • 68
Charles I, King • 17, 25, 142, 154, 156, 162, 324, 366, 368, 370, 372, 376, 378
Charles II, King • 12, 18, 20, 110, 154, 186, 366, 368, 378, 400
Charles V, Emperor • 97, 130, 306
Charles VI, Emperor • 314
Charles the Bold • 97
Charlotte Marguerite of Montmorency, Princess • 122
Châtillon: see Coligny
Cheseman, Robert • 154
Chester Beatty, Sir A. • 266
Chesterfield, Catherine, Countess of • 366
Choiseul, Etienne François, Duc de • 74, 168
Choiseul, Louis-César-Renaud de, Duc de Praslin • 238
Chouvalov, A.P. Count • 386
Christ (see also: Madonna) • 17, 26, 66, 76, 84, 90, 92, 96, 97, 100, 114, 248, 316, 334, 348, 350, 352
Christopher, Saint • 348
Christus, Petrus • 346
Cignani, Carlo • 122
Cimon • 96
Claessen, Michiel • 274
Claesz, Pieter • 38, 42, 90–92
Clemens, Jacques • 182
Cleopatra • 97

Cleophas • 178
Clercq, A. de • 278
Clercq, Matthijs de • 45, 278
Cleve, Joos van • 92
Clifden, Henry Welbore Ellis Agar, 2nd Viscount • 154
Clingnet, P.F. • 80
Clio • 338
Clowes, H.A. • 190
Clusius, Carolus • 390
Coats, W.A. • 280
Cochian, Lady • 278
Codde, Pieter • 94
Coehoorn, Menno, Baron Van • 80
Coligny, François de • 350
Coligny, Gaspard de • 250, 350
Coligny, Louise de • 17, 160, 198, 350
Coligny, Odet de • 350
Collier, Edwaert • 94
Colnaghi's • 88, 104, 136, 228, 270
Colterman I, Johan • 128
Colterman II, Johan • 128
Coninck de Mercken • 228
Constantine, Emperor • 270
Conti, Comte de • 168
Conway, Anne • 162
Cooghen, Leendert van der • 94
Cook, Sir Francis • 192, 270
Cook, Herbert • 192, 270
Cooper, Alexander • 364–366
Cooper, Samuel • 366–368
Coorte, Adriaen • 42, 94
Coques, Gonzales • 18, 20, 96
Coray-Stoop, H. • 288
Cornelisz van Haarlem, Cornelis • 17, 98, 146
Cornelisz van Oostsanen, Jacob • 98
Correggio • 98–100
Cortona, Pietro da • 316
Cosimo, Piero di • 20, 100
Cossiers, Jan • 96
Costa, Benjamin da • 22, 284, 294, 340
Cottreau, L. • 150
Cottreau, Marcel • 150
Court, Petronella de la • 72, 178
Court van der Voort, Pieter de la • 22, 78, 82, 164, 204, 330, 332
Courtois, Jacques • 350
Couwenhoven, Allaert van • 212
Cowdray, Lord • 262
Cramer, H. • 70, 84, 186, 240
Cramer, Hendrik Willem • 120, 328
Cranach the Elder, Lucas • 100–102
Cranach the Younger, Lucas • 102
Crawford and Balcarres, Earl of • 32, 162
Cremer, J.H. • 226, 282
Cremer, T.T. • 220
Cremer van den Bergh, J.L. • 44, 272
Crewe, Earl of • 104
Crews, Charles • 88, 292
Croes, Willem • 32
Croese, Henry • 152, 216
Croiset, G.T.B. • 396
Croix, Pieter Frederik de la • 102, 354
Cromwell, Lord • 58
Croy-d'Espine, Princess L. de • 44, 276
Cunliffe Brooks, Sir William • 124
Cuylenborch, Abraham van • 102
Cuyp, Aelbert • 23, 102–104
Cybele • 82
Czernin, Count • 52

D

Dahl, Werner • 184
Darby, William • 154
Darius • 400
Davelaer, Cornelis van • 174
David • 32, 182, 262, 268
David, Gerard • 104–106
Davies, F.T. • 270
Davison, Alexander • 204
Dedem, Willem, Baron van • 42, 44, 92, 172, 240, 280, 284
Delafield, William • 152
Delen, Dirck van • 60, 96
Delestre, J.B. • 184
Delff, Willem Jacobsz • 152, 198
Delfos, Abraham • 80
Delilah • 114, 126
Demidoff, Anatole • 230
Democritus • 208, 212
Descourtis, Charles Melchior • 304
Deterding, Sir Henri W.A. • 34, 35, 44, 74, 88, 104, 204, 298, 348
Deutz, Agneta • 74
Deutz, Isabella Agneta • 286
Deyman, Maria • 116
Diana • 32, 78, 102, 320
Diaz Estévez • 280
Dibbits, J.E. • 354
Dibbits-Kaas, A.J.S. • 44, 354
Dido • 92
Didot de Saint-Marc • 262
Diemen, Van • 174, 242
Diemen, Françoisia van • 284
Dierquens, Catharina • 188, 190
Dierquens, Johannes • 138, 190, 222
Dierquens, Nicolaas • 332
Dierquens, Pieter • 136, 138, 224
Dijck, Abraham van • 106
Dijk, Miss G.J.L. van • 44, 312
Dijk, Philip van • 50, 106–108
Dimon, L. • 126
Diogenes • 116
Dirksen • 156, 320
Dishoeck, Ewout van • 58, 298
Dissius, Abraham • 320, 322
Dissius, Jacob • 320, 322
Dittlinger, M.F. • 210
Dittmers, Heinrich • 108
Dixon, Nicholas • 368
Does, Simon van der • 108
Doetsch, Henry • 296
Dokkum, P.J.D. van • 44, 240
Dolci, Carlo • 350
Doll, Diethelm • 172, 190
Dominic, Saint • 126
Donaldson, George • 260, 348
Doorn, Van • 286
Doorne, Mr P.J.G. van • 45
Doort, Charles van der • 370
Dorens, Weduwe G. • 86
Dou, Gerrit • 20, 21, 32, 108–110, 204, 258, 264, 322
Doublet, Philips • 142
Douglas, Archibald • 368
Douglas, Lady Margaret, Countess of Lennox • 368, 382
Douglas, R.L. • 260
Douwes • 52, 280, 380
Dowdeswell & Dowdeswell • 80, 214
Drabbe, Floris • 316
Dreesmann, A.C.R. • 45, 262
Droochsloot, Joost Cornelisz • 110
Droste, Coenraat, Baron • 110, 168, 202
Drucker, Holger • 186
Duarte, Diego • 268
Dudley, Earl of • 204
Dughet, Gaspard • 110
Duin-Priester, Mrs S.F. • 45, 132
Duits • 52, 204
Duits, Jan de • 96
Duits, W.E. • 44, 94
Duparc, Frederik J. • 40
Duquesnoy, François • 204, 364
Duquesnoy, Jérôme • 364
Durand-Ruel • 262
Dürer, Albrecht • 334
Dusart, Cornelis • 110
Duval, Marc • 350
Duveen • 104, 278
Duvenvoorde, Lysbeth van • 36, 356
Duyn, Geertruida Quirina van der, Countess of Albemarle • 122
Duyster, Willem Cornelisz • 112
Duyveland, Adriana van • 348
Dyck, Anthony van • 18, 20, 23, 26, 97, 112–114, 290, 330, 364, 366, 370
Dyk, C. van • 228
Dyl, D. van • 312

E

Eckhout, Albert • 15, 16, 114
Ede van de Pals, Herman Pieter van • 44, 334
Edward, Prince of Wales • 154
Edward VI, King of England • 380
Eeckhout, Gerbrand van den • 40, 114–116, 176
Eersel, Van • 358
Eggers, Bartholomeus • 386
Ehrenberg, Wilhelm von • 96
Eleonore of Bourbon-Condé, Princess • 122
Elink, Anna • 276
Elisabeth of Austria • 288
Elisabeth Christine of Braunschweig-Wolfenbüttel • 390
Elizabeth, Princess of the Palatinate • 17, 364
Elizabeth I, Queen • 368
Elizabeth of France, Princess • 194
Elizabeth Stuart • 372
Elsheimer, Adam • 180, 182
Emont, Adriaen van • 116
Engelberts, Meinouda • 206
Enthoven • 284
Epstein • 138
Erard, Sébastien • 262
Erasmus, Desiderius • 156

Erato • 338
Ernestine Yolande, Princess de Ligne • 114, 248, 252
Es, G.L.M. van • 168
Escalante, Juan Antonio de Frias y • 116
Espinasse de Langeac, A.L.C.H.T. de l' • 304
Este • 262
Eternity • 180
Ettlinger-Rathenau, E. • 260
Eugenius of Savoy • 164
Euterpe • 338
Eve • 82, 84, 122
Everdingen, Allart van • 116
Everdingen, Caesar van • 40, 116–118
Eyck, Van • 210, 216, 336
Eyck, Jan van • 26
Eywerven, Marie-Anne van • 96

F
Fabritius, Barent • 106
Fabritius, Carel • 30, 31, 118, 264, 266
Faith • 32
Falconet, Etienne-Maurice • 386–388
Falconet-Collot, Marie-Anne • 22, 388, 396
Farinato, Paolo • 118
Febure, Alexis-Joseph • 130, 262
Feigen, Richard L. • 78
Feitama, Jacob • 148, 150
Feitama, Maria • 150
Felicianus, Saint • 324
Fenwick, Alan G. • 148
Féral, Eugène • 212
Ferdinand, Archduke • 20
Ferdinand, Cardinal-Infant of Spain • 97
Ferdinand I, Emperor • 288
Ferdinand of Austria • 288
Fesch, Joseph, Cardinal • 306
Feti, Domenico • 118
Figdor, Albert • 236
Fijt, Jan • 118–120
Filips Lodewijk, Count of Hanau-Münzenberg • 248
Fischel, Oskar • 39
Fischer, August • 30
Fizeaux, Jean-Etienne • 114, 154
Flinck, Govert • 56, 120
Flinck, Nicolaes Anthonis • 212
Flines, Philips de • 314
Flora • 166, 374
Floris of Egmond • 130
Fogolino, Marcello • 122
Fontaine, Sir Andrew • 194
Fontaine, Jean • 242
Fontaine, Joan • 242
Forchoudt • 274
Forestier d'Orges van Waalwijk, Pauline de • 44, 222
Foster, Richard • 104, 140
Foucquet, Pieter • 296
Fourment, Clara • 270
Fourment, Daniel • 270
Fourment, Hélène • 270, 272
Franceschini, Marcantonio • 122
Francis, Saint • 122
Francis I of Austria • 196
Francken III, Frans • 218
Francken the Younger, Frans • 20, 112, 122
Francottay, Monsieur le Chevalier • 64
Franssen, C.J.H. • 266
Franz, F. von • 214
Fraula, Count • 80, 110, 150, 202
Frederik III, King of Denmark • 15, 16
Frederik of Nassau • 18, 208
Frederik Hendrik, Stadholder • 12, 17, 18, 19, 20, 68, 78, 120, 158, 160, 162, 164, 172, 198, 200, 208, 218, 224, 248, 256, 282, 288, 318, 350, 392
Frederik Willem of Nassau-Weilburg, Prince • 304
Frederika Louise Wilhelmina, Princess of Prussia • 44, 86, 304
Frederika Sophia Wilhelmina of Nassau-Dietz • 378
Frederika Sophia Wilhelmina, Princess of Prussia • 304, 344, 378, 382, 388
Frediano, Saint • 100
Fremantle, Sir Francis Edward • 262
Friederike of Hesse-Darmstadt • 304, 390
Friedländer-Fuld, Baroness de Goldschmidt-Rothschild, Marie-Anne • 140
Friedrich I of Prussia, King • 20
Friedrich V of the Palatinate (Winter King) • 17, 200, 364, 372, 376
Friedrich August, Elector of Saxony • 184
Friedrich Wilhelm I, Elector of Brandenburg • 15, 16, 18, 160
Friedrich Wilhelm II, King • 304, 390
Friedsam, Michael • 32
Fruwirth, K. • 236

G
Gabriel, Archangel • 146
Gabron, Guilliam • 82
Gaillard de Gagny • 62
Galerie Internationale • 80, 144
Garey, Eliza • 320
Gascoyne Bulwer, Edward • 214
Gascoyne Bulwer, William • 214
Gauchez, Léon • 128, 270
Gautrey, Amédée • 130
Geedts, Joseph • 334
Geer, Margaretha de • 188
Geeraerts, Martinus Josephus • 122–124
Geest, Cornelis van der • 136
Geesteranus, Arnoldus • 334
Gelder, Van • 246
Gelder, Arent de • 40, 124
Gelder, H.E. van • 34
Gelder, Jan Gerrit van • 36, 45, 47, 400
Gelder, M.F. van • 192
Gelder, W. van • 160
Geldorp the Elder, Gortzius • 124–126
Gelijs, P.H. • 164
Gendt, Willem Joseph, Baron van • 392
Georg Wilhelm of Hohenzollern, Elector of Brandenburg • 160
George, Philippe • 262
George II, King • 20, 306
George III, King • 23
Geus van den Heuvel, B. de • 284
Gevers, Abraham • 62
Gevers, Hugo • 332
Gheyn the Younger, Jacob (Jacques) de • 17, 126
Giamberti: see San Gallo
Gibour • 212
Gibson, Richard • 368
Gideon, Sampson • 262
Gijsels, Peeter • 96
Gildemeester, H. • 144
Giordano, Luca • 126
Giorgione • 148
Giovanelli • 118
Girardet, H. • 52, 342
Glory • 180
God • 314
Goedhart, J.E. • 132, 296
Goethals, Joris • 236
Goldberg, Johannes • 198
Goldschmidt, Adolf • 170
Goldschmidt, Emil • 320
Goldsmid, Neville • 52, 60, 66, 112, 156, 10, 244, 290, 320, 322, 328
Golovkine, Count • 386
Goltz, Fransise de • 126–128
Goltzius, Hendrick • 18, 128
Gonzaga, Valenti • 324
Gool, Councillor • 392
Göpel, E. • 132
Gordon, George, second Marquess of Huntley • 366
Goring, George, Lord • 97
Göring, Hermann • 100, 176, 282, 302, 348, 350
Görlitz, F. • 288
Gossaert, Jan • 26, 36, 128–130, 348
Gosschalk, J.H. • 342
Gottschewski • 284
Goubau, Anton • 96
Goudstikker, Jacques • 44, 58, 76, 86, 88, 106, 114, 118, 128, 132, 136, 142, 150, 168, 176, 182, 192, 228, 282, 292, 298, 302, 338, 352
Govaerts, Abraham • 82, 130
Govaerts, Jacobus • 90
Goya, Francisco José de • 38
Goyen, Grietje van • 296
Goyen, Jan van • 18, 30, 36, 130–134
Graeff, Cornelis de • 74
Graham, Reggie • 190
Granges, David des • 364
Gray, Edward • 168
Graziani, Francesco • 350
Green, Richard • 78, 284
Grenville: see Buckingham
Gretor, W. • 130
Grisart-van Hogendorp van Hofwegen, Margaretha Johanna • 44, 174
Grondt, Helena • 302
Groot, Jan de • 244
Groot Jamin, J.G. de • 44, 244
Grosvenor, Lady Mary • 154
Grosvenor, Robert, 2nd Earl of • 154
Gruyter, W. • 296, 312
Gucht, Maximiliaan van der • 15
Gudlaugsson, Sturla • 39, 47

Guijot, P.C.G. • 152
Gumprecht, Wilhelm • 140
Gutmann, F. • 136
Gutmann, F.B. • 136

H
Haag, Tethart Philip Christian • 23, 134
Haagen, J.K. van der • 322
Haagen, Joris van der • 134, 400
Haagen, M.J.F.W. van der • 44, 178
Haan, Elisabeth de • 148, 150
Haarlem, Cornelis Cornelisz van: see Cornelisz van Haarlem, Cornelis
Haberstock, Karl • 130, 136
Haboldt, Bob • 160
Hackaert, Jan • 39, 136
Haecht, Hans van • 122
Haecht, Willem van • 22, 112, 136, 194
Haeften, Johnny van • 82
Haensbergen, Johan van • 136–138, 224
Haga, Cornelis • 354
Hairen, Lambert van • 64
Hallsborough Gallery • 178
Hals, Claes • 138
Hals, Dirck • 138–140
Hals, Frans • 18, 23, 28, 30, 32, 37, 38, 140–142
Hals, Harmen • 142
Hammius, Maria • 326
Hanemans, Aletta (see also: Loo) • 28, 140
Hanneman, Adriaen • 26, 88, 142–144, 218, 368, 378
Hardman, William • 88
Harrach • 264
Harrison • 262
Harssevoort, Adriaen • 152
Hartsoeker, Theodoor • 62
Hasselaar, Pieter • 174
Hasselt, Samuel van • 274
Hauser, L. • 160
Hauser, Professor • 32
Hecke, Ferdinandus van • 270
Hecke, Jan van • 96
Hecke, Peter van • 270
Heda, Gerrit Willemsz • 144
Heda, Willem Claesz • 144
Hedberg, Oscar • 92
Heeckeren van Brandsenburg, François Henri Corneille, Baron van • 214
Heeckeren van Brandsenburg-Van Foreest van Heemse, Christine Louise van • 214
Heek, J.H. van • 44, 346
Heem, Cornelis de • 144
Heem, Dirck de • 328
Heem, Jan Davidsz de • 25, 42, 43, 144–146
Heemskerck, Coenraad van • 316
Heemskerck, Maerten van • 94, 98, 146
Heemskerck van Beest • 94
Heerschop, Hendrick • 146
Hees, Andries • 218
Hees, Jan • 218
Hees, Thomas • 218
Heijligers, Antoon François • 146
Heilbuth, Paul Herman • 140
Heinrich, T.A. • 148
Heinrich (Henry) of Mecklenburg • 58
Heldring, J.C.H. • 58, 114
Helen • 222
Helst, Bartholomeus van der • 26, 148
Helst, Louis van der • 148
Hemessen, Jan Sanders van • 148
Hemsterhuis, Frans • 23
Henderson, Robert • 252
Hendrik, Prince • 306
Hendrik Casimir II • 164
Hendriks, Wybrand • 148–150
Hennin • 296
Henri IV of France • 17, 370
Henrietta, Duchess of Orléans • 366
Henrietta Maria, Queen • 17, 142, 162, 366, 368, 370, 372
Henriette Catharina, Princess • 18, 60, 150, 158, 206
Henriette Marie, Princess of the Palatinate • 364
Henry the Placid (or Peaceable) • 58
Henry VII, King • 368, 382
Henry VIII, King • 154, 368, 380
Henry Frederick, Prince • 376
Heraclitus • 212
Hercules • 128
Héris • 176
Hermaphroditus • 342
Hero • 97
Heise • 208, 238
Hertaing, Daniel de • 252, 254
Herwijck, Steven van • 23, 212
Heseltine, P.J. • 296
Heshuysen, Herman J. • 356
Heteren, Adriaan Leonard van • 80, 170, 238, 282
Heteren Gevers, Adriaan Leonard van • 80, 170, 238, 282
Heusch, F. • 220
Heusch, Willem de • 150
Heusden, Adriana Johanna van • 354
Heybroek, J.W. • 312
Heyden, Jan van der • 22, 38, 150–152, 224
Heywood-Lonsdale, A.P. • 152
Hibbert, George • 104
Hijmersma, H.J. • 12, 400
Hillegaert, Pauwels van • 152
Hilliard, Lawrence • 370
Hilliard, Nicholas • 368–370
Hippocrates • 208
Hirschmann • 174
Hitler, Adolf • 58, 86, 94, 118, 120, 132, 152, 168, 182, 184, 192, 204, 212, 220, 230, 260, 278, 298, 320
Hobbema, Meindert • 23, 26, 32, 34, 38, 39, 42, 152–154
Hoeken, Michiel van • 62
Hoetink, Hans R. • 39, 40, 47, 182
Hoeufft, Agneta Catherina • 108
Hoeufft, Diederick • 286, 356
Hoeven, Willem van der • 308
Hofer, W.A. • 176
Hofstede de Groot, Cornelis • 30, 32, 34, 44, 164, 260, 274, 326
Hogarth, William • 306, 308, 310
Hogendorp, Hans van • 174
Hogendorp van Hofwegen, van: see under Grisart and Van Bylandt
Holbein the Elder, Hans • 156
Holbein the Younger, Hans • 20, 40, 92, 154–156
Holbein, Sigmund • 350
Hollender, M.J. • 54, 76, 148
Hollitscher, Carl von • 128
Holofernes • 106
Homer • 36, 97, 258, 260
Hondecoeter, Gijsbert Gillisz d' • 156
Hondecoeter, Melchior d' • 156–158
Honert, Miss M.C. van den • 45, 298
Honigh, Johan • 354
Honthorst, Gerrit van • 17, 18, 19, 25, 42, 158–162, 364, 370
Honthorst, Willem van • 160
Hooch, Pieter de • 162
Hoofman, M. • 312
Hoofman van Diepenbroek, J. • 312
Hooft, Elizabeth • 60
Hooft, Pieter Cornelis • 246
Hooftman, Anna • 242
Hoog, Herman Cornelis • 56
Hoog, Willem • 44, 56
Hoogenbergh, I. • 294
Hoogendijk, Cornelis • 86, 102, 246, 300
Hoogendijk, D.A. • 104, 204, 264
Hoogsteder, J. • 45, 88, 114, 148, 314
Hoogstraten, Samuel van • 162
Hope • 270
Hope, Jan • 168
Hope, John • 64
Hopman, Nicolaas • 28
Hopman, Willem A. • 32
Hora Siccama, Jacob Hendrik • 44, 218
Hora Siccama, Wiardus • 44, 218
Horn, C. ten • 132
Hornes, Willem Adriaan, Count of • 252
Hoskins, John • 370–372
Houbraken, Jacob • 198
Houckgeest, Gerard • 22, 162–164, 390
Houdon, Jean-Antoine • 22, 388
Houten, Dr Van • 32
Houthakker • 284
Houthakker, B. • 58
Hove, Cornelis ten • 188, 190, 222
Hove, Michiel ten • 190, 222
Howard, Frances • 374
Howard, Lord Thomas • 368
Howard, Thomas, Earl of Suffolk • 374
Howe, Earl of • 104
Howgate, W. • 264
Huchtenburgh, Jan van • 64, 164
Huls, Samuel van • 136, 238, 328, 340
Hulswit, Jan • 116
Hultmark, David • 92
Humphry, Ozias • 164–166
Hurter, Johann Friedrich • 372
Huntley: see Gordon
Huybrechts, P.C. • 54
Huygens, Christiaen • 142
Huygens, Constantijn • 10, 12, 13, 15, 17, 18, 19, 26, 40, 88, 142, 160, 288
Huygens, Constantijn II • 142
Huygens, Lodewijk • 142

Huygens, Philips • 142
Huysum, Jan van • 166, 216
Hyde of Clarendon, Anne • 368

I
Ibbetson, Sir Henry • 204
Icarus Atlanticus • 182
Ietswaart, David • 312
IJzerloo, M.J. • 298
Ingram, Bruce • 240
Io • 88, 184
Iphigenia • 96
Irene, Saint • 256
Iriarte, Ignacio de • 166
Irving, J.T. • 132
Isaac • 40, 114
Isabella of Habsburg, Archduchess of Austria • 20, 122
Isabella Charlotte, Princess • 160
Isenbrant, Adriaen • 106
Israel, Menasseh ben • 120

J
Jacob • 244
Jacobson • 266, 284
Jaffé, Alfons • 188
Jaffé, Mrs H. • 188
James I, King • 352, 370, 372, 374, 376, 380, 382
James II, King • 100, 110, 154, 368
James V, King • 380
James the Greater, Saint • 178
James the Lesser, Saint • 178
Jan III (VIII), Count of Nassau-Siegen • 114, 248, 252
Jan the Elder of Orange • 14, 56
Janssen, August • 136, 168, 298
Janssen, P.W. • 298
Janssen, Vrerijk • 174
Jansz van Haarlem, Jacob • 216
Jardin, Karel du • 22, 38, 168
Jerome, Saint • 106
Joachim • 178
Jode the Younger, Pieter de • 112, 114
Johan Maurits, Count of Nassau-Siegen • 11, 12, 14, 15, 16, 17, 38, 39, 40, 56, 114, 240, 248, 252, 386, 390
Johan Willem Friso, Stadholder • 20, 54, 68, 84, 154, 324, 342
Johann Albrecht of Solms • 160
Johann Georg of Anhalt-Dessau • 18
Johann Wilhelm of Pfalz-Neuburg • 204
John IV, King of Portugal • 366
John the Baptist, Saint • 86, 90, 92, 98, 122, 248
John the Evangelist, Saint • 72, 122, 166, 178, 246, 268
Jonge, De • 120
Jonge, A.H.W. de • 230
Jonge, Jan Karel de • 28, 46
Jonge-de Kock, dowager J.K.H. de • 146, 230
Jonson van Ceulen, Cornelis • 168–170
Jordaens, Jacob • 18, 170
Joseph • 90, 214, 248, 316, 348
Joseph the Righteous • 178
Juchen, Maerten van • 72
Judah • 124
Jude, Saint • 178
Judith • 106
Julius II, Pope • 100

K
Kaiser • 208
Kaiser, F. • 354
Kalf, Willem • 42, 170–172
Kann, Rodolphe • 278
Kappel, Marcus • 132, 260
Karel Frederik Willem of Nassau-Weilburg, Prince • 304
Karl Christian of Nassau-Weilburg • 304, 374
Katz, B. • 45, 270
Katz, D. • 45, 62, 94, 132, 162, 176, 192, 278, 282, 298
Katz, N. • 45, 270
Kay, A. • 132
Keil, Bernhard • 172
Keirincx, Alexander • 172
Kellen, David van der • 30, 110, 268, 316, 330
Kessel, Jan van • 276
Kessel the Elder, Jan van • 96
Kessler, Dominicus Anthonius Josephus • 44, 124
Kessler-Stoop, E.M.L. • 288
Ketelaar, Huybert • 276, 338
Keverberg van Kessel, C.L.G.J. Baron • 334
Key, Adriaen Thomasz • 172
Keynooghe, Jan • 172–174
Keyser, Hendrick de • 388–390
Keyser, Thomas de • 22, 174–176, 266
Kien van Citters, W.A. • 334
Kindt, Dirk • 176
Kingston, J. • 52
Kinschot, Caspar van • 74
Kinschot, Johan Anthony van • 82, 162
Kipshaven, Isaac van • 176
Kleinberger, F. • 44, 106, 120, 124, 218, 220, 260, 278
Kleykamp • 230
Klok, Pieter de • 136, 314
Kneller, Godfrey (Gottfried) • 284, 364
Knight • 270
Knighton: see Wellesley Knighton
Knoedler • 168, 260
Knyvett, Lady Catherine • 374
Kobell, Jan Baptist • 26
Kobler, Peter • 196
Koekkoek, Barend Cornelis • 56, 176
Koetser, David • 114
Koetser, L. • 104
Königswärter, Baron • 298
Koninck, Philips • 176
Koninck, Salomon • 176
Kops, Willem Philip • 320
Koster, H.D. de • 240
Koster, H.J. de • 45, 124
Koster-van Rijckevorsel, Mr and Mrs De • 45, 266
Kramm, Christiaan • 182
Kraus, J. • 284
Krauth, Johan Balthasar • 68
Kretschmar, Hendrick van • 204, 212
Kruseman, Cornelis • 26
Kruyselbergen, Mr • 162
Kuijper, J. de • 320
Kulmbach, Hans Suess von • 176–178, 350

L
Laban • 244
Laer, Pieter van • 42, 62, 178
Lafontaine, Pierre • 238
Lagrenée, Louis-Jean-François • 178
Lairesse, Gerard de • 178–180
Lambrechtsen van Ritthem, C. • 334
Lambrechtsen van Ritthem, Constant L.M. • 44, 354
Lancelle, Peter Laurenz • 72
Landschot, Van • 290
Lang, Theodor • 220
Langendijk, Pieter • 310, 312
Langetti, Giovanni Battista • 180, 344
Lantsheer, W.N. • 44, 236
Lanz, G.B. • 298
Laocoön • 97
Lapeyrière • 76, 168
Lapp, Jan Willemsz • 180–182
Largillière, Nicolas de • 182
Larsen, Hans Ludwig • 132, 264
Larsen, S. • 45
Lastman, Pieter • 182
Lataster, Ger • 182
Lauri, Filippo • 184
Laverge, J.L. • 278
Lazarus • 182, 192
Leah • 244
Lebrun, Jean-Baptiste-Pierre • 104, 262
Leda • 97
Leemans, Coenraad • 354
Leeuw, Steven de • 174
Leeuwen, Van • 68
Leeuwen Boomkamp, Van • 120
Leeuwenhart van den Bosch, Richard • 260
Leger, J. • 266
Lehrs, Max • 32
Lelie, J.A.A. de • 296
Lely, Sir Peter • 212, 338
Lennep-Deutz van Assendelft, dowager van • 74
Leonard, Saint • 106
Leonardo da Vinci • 92, 156
Leopold, Emperor • 74
Lépicié, Nicolas-Bernard • 184
Lespinette family • 30, 194
Lesser • 262
Leu de Wilhem, Maurits Le • 222
Levy, A. • 204
Levy, Percy • 92
Leyden, Diederik, Baron van • 60
Leyden, Hermina Jacoba, Baroness van • 62, 76, 150, 166, 296
Leyden, Lucas van • 346, 348
Leyden van Vlaardingen, Diederik van • 338
Leyen, Antoine van • 96
Leyster, Judith • 184
Lichnowsky, Prince • 100, 170
Liechtenstein, Fürsten von • 62
Lievens, Jan • 17, 184
Ligne-Amblise, Lamoral de • 248
Lilian, Salomon • 178
Lill, Van • 64

Limburg Stirum, Hendrik, Count van • 44, 124
Lin, S.E. • 298
Linden, B.H. van der • 45, 144
Linden, Jan Antonides van der • 300, 302
Linden van Slingelandt, Johan van der • 104, 220
Lingelbach, David • 306
Lingelbach, Johannes • 20, 154, 184–186, 216, 336
Lione, Andrea de • 186
Liphart family, Von • 290
Liphart, Ernest, Baron von • 290
Lippi, Filippino • 100
Lippmann, Friedrich • 182, 350
Lippmann von Lissingen, L. • 60, 130, 300
Lisse, Dirck van der • 18, 42, 186–188
Locquet, Pieter • 298
Lodewijk Hendrick of Nassau-Dillenburg • 358
Loeff, H.D. • 276, 314
Logteren, Ignatius van • 390
Loo, Aletta van • 140
Loo, Jacob van • 188
Loo, Nicolaes Jansz van • 140
Loon, Van • 320
Lormier, Willem • 22, 62, 64, 80, 164, 186, 202, 220, 292, 294, 316, 328, 340
Loudon, J. • 45, 140
Loudon, John H. • 42, 45, 54
Louis XIII, King • 270
Louis XIV, King • 16, 240
Louis François de Bourbon, Prince de Conti • 238
Louis Napoleon, King • 14, 25, 80, 170, 238, 282
Louisa Christina of Solms-Braunfels • 208
Louise Henriette of Nassau, Princess • 18, 20, 25, 160
Lucretia • 84
Ludick, Lodewijk van • 262
Ludwig I of Bavaria, King • 204
Ludwig Heinrich of Simmern, Count Palatine • 18, 158, 208
Lugt, Frits • 50, 120, 280, 296
Lugt-Klever, Mr and Mrs • 45, 50
Luise Amalie of Braunschweig-Wolfenbüttel • 304, 390
Luppi-Olivazzi, Countess P. • 214
Lust, Abraham de • 146
Luther, Martin • 102
Luttichuys, Isaac • 188
Lutz, J.W. • 84
Luzern, A.G. • 62
Lycomedes • 178
Lynden van Pallandt, Count and Countess C.J. van • 32, 44, 332
Lyonet, Pierre (Pieter) • 396

M

Mackay family • 256
Madonna • 36, 86, 98, 122, 126, 128, 194, 216, 248, 346
Maecenas • 324
Maes family • 14
Maes, Dirk • 190
Maes, Gerrit • 12
Maes, Nicolaes • 42, 188–190, 320
Magdalene • 358
Magnasco, Alessandro • 190–192, 234
Magnus II, Duke of Mecklenburg • 58
Maitland, William Fuller • 128
Malmedé • 116
Man, Cornelis de • 192
Mancadan, Jacob Sibrandi • 192
Mander III, Karel van • 358
Mannheimer, Fritz • 38, 152, 184, 204, 212, 220, 230, 320, 386
Mantua, Dukes of • 180, 344
Mar and Kellie, Earl of • 278
Marck, Johan van der • 64, 72, 178, 238, 306, 312
Maria of Orange-Nassau, Princess • 18, 158, 208
Maria Theresa, Empress • 196
Marie Louise of Hessen-Cassel • 20, 54
Marigny, Marquis de • 230
Marin • 104, 216
Maris, Jacob • 356
Markgraf, Georg • 15
Marlborough, Duke of • 14
Mars • 342
Marseus van Schrieck, Otto • 192
Martin, Wilhelm • 32, 34, 36, 40, 46, 164, 242, 292, 346
Martinet • 118
Mary (see also: Madonna) • 88, 90, 100, 146, 194, 246, 248, 270, 282, 288, 316, 348, 350, 396
Mary of Guise • 380
Mary Cleophas • 176, 178
Mary Magdalene • 90, 122, 124, 246, 352
Mary Salome • 178
Mary Stuart, Queen of Scots • 352, 370, 380, 382
Mary I Stuart • 58, 142, 162, 364
Mary II Stuart • 18, 58, 248, 368, 394
Massé, Marie-Anne • 154
Massys, Quinten • 194
Master of Alkmaar • 346
Master of Frankfurt • 348
Master of the Brandon portrait • 346
Master of the female half-lengths • 346–348
Master of the Solomon triptych • 348
Matham, Theodor • 208
Matthes, C.W. • 44, 284
Matthew, Saint • 39, 64
Matthys, Geertruid • 72
Maurer, Jacob • 206
Maurits, Prince • 17, 114, 160, 200, 202, 224, 250
Maximilian of Austria • 290
Mayer, O. • 348
Mazel family • 45, 240
Mazel, Jean Zacharia • 26, 28, 46, 238, 240
Mazo, Juan Bautista Martinez del • 194
Mazzola, Girolamo: see Parmigianino
Mazzolino, Lodovico • 194
Medici family, de' • 97, 100
Medici, Maria de' • 174, 370
Meetkerken, Adolf van • 250
Mège, M.C. • 58
Meijers, Jaques • 238
Meissner, Bruno • 238
Melanchton, Philipp • 102
Melchizedek • 338
Melpomene • 338
Melun-Espinay, Marie de • 248
Memling, Hans • 26, 30, 194, 334
Menars, Marquis de • 230
Mentzel, Cristian • 15
Menzies, Colonel • 366
Mercury • 88, 128, 184, 208, 238
Mertens • 50
Mesdag, Hendrik Willem • 36, 44, 188
Mestral de St Saphorin, Armand de • 260
Metella, Caecilia • 52
Metsu, Gabriel • 23, 196, 354
Meurs Pruyssenaar, Roelof • 274
Meytens the Younger, Martin • 196
Michaelis • 118
Michelangelo • 26
Miedl, Alois • 120
Mierevelt, Michiel Jansz van • 198–202, 252
Mieris the Elder, Frans van • 38, 202–204
Mieris, Willem van • 20, 204
Mignon, Abraham • 206
Mijn, George van der • 206–208
Mijtens, Isaac • 298
Mijtens, Jan • 22, 25, 208
Millais, John Everett • 300
Minerva • 128, 180, 264
Mniszech, Count L. • 120
Moeyaert, Nicolaes • 208–210
Mol, Pieter van • 226
Molenaer, Jan Miense • 210
Moltke, Adam Gottlob, Count • 84, 186
Monchen, Joseph • 72
Moni, Louis de • 210–212
Monnot, Martin-Claude • 390
Monogrammist RF • 380
Monsu Bernardo: see Keil, Bernhard
Montribloud, De • 260
Mor van Dashorst, Anthonis • 23, 212
Moreau the Elder, Louis-Gabriel • 212
Moreelse, Johannes • 212
Moreelse, Paulus • 17, 18, 214
Morel, Jean Baptiste • 214
Moroni, Giovanni Battista • 214
Morton, Countess of • 264
Moses • 328
Mostaert, Gillis • 86
Mostaert, Jan • 214–216
Moucheron, Frederik de • 216
Moyne, Jean-Baptiste Le • 396
Muilman, Hendrik • 64, 76
Mulier the Elder, Pieter • 216
Muller, Frederik • 136, 140, 230, 346
Muller, Gerrit • 216, 232, 274
Muller, Jan • 202
Munnicks van Cleeff, Gerard • 260
Münzenberger • 184
Murillo, Bartolomé Esteban • 216
Mussard, Robert • 372–374
Musscher, Michiel van • 216–218

N

Nagell tot Ampsen, A.W. van • 136
Nahuijs • 242
Napoleon • 42
Nardus, L. • 44, 68, 212, 238, 278, 346, 356
Nason, Pieter • 218
Naumann, Otto • 78
Neeffs the Younger, Peter • 22, 218
Neeld, Audley W. • 260
Neeld, Sir John • 260

Neeld, Sir Joseph • 260
Neer, Aert van der • 30, 218–220
Neer, Eglon van der • 220
Netscher family • 224
Netscher, Caspar • 56, 138, 190, 220–224
Netscher, Constantijn • 138, 222, 224
Netscher, Pieter Marinus • 44, 224
Netten, E.C. • 66
Neufville, De, brothers • 276
Neufville, Leendert Pieter de • 174
Neufville, Pieter Leendert de • 22, 62, 164, 168, 174, 316, 318
Neufville, Robert de • 166
Neufville Brants, J.S. de • 306, 308
Newhouse • 68
Newport, Mountjoy Blunt, Earl of • 97
Nickele, Jan van • 224
Nienhuys, J. • 45, 74
Nienhuys, J.W. • 280
Nienhuys-Versteegh, Mrs A.M. • 45, 280
Nieuhoff, N. • 126
Nieulandt, Adriaen van • 224
Nieuwenhuizen Segaar, G.J. • 132
Nieuwenhuys, C.J. • 168, 306
Nijstad, A. • 94
Nijstad, H. • 45
Nijstad, S. • 45, 68, 70, 72, 92, 132, 136, 158, 170, 172, 236, 266, 330, 332
Noé • 336
Nole, Andreas Colijns de • 112, 114
Noort, Pieter van • 226
Noortman, Robert • 45, 56, 64, 146, 152, 172, 238, 240, 282, 390
Norris, Christopher • 52
Northwick, Lord • 190, 220

O

Ochtervelt, Jacob • 226
Odinot, Eugène • 240
Oedipus • 92
Oetgens van Waveren, Anthonie • 174
Oever, Hendrick ten • 226
Oldenbarneveldt, Johan van • 202
Olis, Jan • 226
Olivazzi family • 214
Olivazzi, Vercellino • 214
Oliver, Isaac • 374, 376
Oliver, Peter • 364, 370, 376
Olycan, Jacob Pietersz • 28, 140
Omphalius, Jacobus • 86
Onnes van Nijenrode • 88
Oost II, Jacob van • 226
Oostdijk, Susanna Pietersdr • 334
Oosterdijk, Justus • 186
Oosterwyck, Maria van • 28, 228
Oosthuyse van Rijsenburg-de Jongh, Van • 312
Oostrum, Gerard van • 162
Oostsanen: see Cornelisz van Oostsanen
Ophovius, Michael (Michiel van Ophoven) • 272
Oppenheim, Albert, Baron von • 140, 262
Opperdoes Alewijn, P. • 54
Opstal the Younger, Kaspar van • 96
Orlando • 274
Orpheus • 282
Ortiz-Patiño, J. • 45
Os, George Jacobus van • 26
Ostade, Adriaen van • 23, 110, 228
Ostade, Isack van • 228–230
Oultremont, Countess d' • 260
Overstone, Lord • 162
Ovid • 174

P

Pabst van Bingerden, Rudolph Willem Jacob, Baron van • 44, 84
Pacx, Hendrick Ambrosius • 152
Paech, W. • 284
Paffenrode, Willem van • 308
Pagniet, Baroness De • 74
Palamedesz, Anthonie • 60, 230, 354
Pallandt, Van • 332
Pallandt van Eerde, Baron R.T. van • 44, 116, 330, 348
Pallavicini-Grimaldi, A. • 346
Palmer Morewood, C.R. • 114
Palmer-Morewood, William • 114
Pals, G. van der • 226
Pan • 170
Panhuys family • 328, 330
Panhuys, Margarita • 330
Panhuys, Peeter • 330
Panhuys, Pieter van • 26, 44, 328
Panini, Giovanni Paolo • 230
Pannwitz, Catharina von • 348, 350
Pannwitz, Walter von • 348, 350
Pape, Abraham de • 230–232
Paris • 96, 346
Parisi, Raphael • 240
Parmigianino • 232
Paul, John Dean • 104
Paul I, Czar • 174
Paul, Saint • 100
Paul of Thebes, Saint • 352
Peene, Michiel van • 196
Peeters, Jan • 96
Peleus • 68, 98
Pellegrini, Giovanni Antonio • 8, 14, 232–234, 400
Perls, H. • 176
Perseus • 172, 174
Persijn family • 148
Persijn, Reinier van • 236
Peruzzini, Antonio Francesco • 234
Peter, Saint • 84, 166
Peters-Wetzlar, Mrs M.O. • 45
Peyrou-de Villepontoux, du: see Villepontoux, Anna Maria de
Pfungst, Henry • 322
Phaeton • 268
Phaff, 'Le Chevalier' • 378
Philip II, King of Spain • 97, 172
Philip IV, King of Spain • 97, 194
Philippe, Duc d'Orléans • 366
Philippe, Pierre • 12, 358, 400
Philip(s) Willem of Orange, Prince • 122, 200
Philips, Anton F. • 44, 78, 138, 242
Philips, Eduard J. • 44, 56, 190
Philips-de Jong, Mrs • 44, 138, 242
Pieneman, Jan Willem • 25, 26
Piero di Cosimo: see Cosimo, Piero di
Pierson, Christoffel • 236
Pietersz, Pieter • 236
Pignoni, Simone • 236
Pijnacker, Adam • 238
Pinder, Wilhelm • 39
Piso, Willem • 15
Pitati, Bonifazio de': see Veronese, Bonifazio
Plietzsch, E. • 74
Ploos van Amstel, Cornelis • 206, 208, 228, 294, 372, 400
Pluym, Karel van der • 262
Poel, Egbert van der • 238
Poelenburch, Cornelis van • 17, 18, 20, 136, 172, 238
Poisson, Raymond • 308
Poll, C.F. van de • 314
Polyhymnia • 338
Pompadour, Madame de • 386
Poort van Oostkapelle, Johan Gualtherus van der • 228
Poorter, Bastiaan de • 238–240
Poorter, Willem de • 258
Porcellis, Jan • 240
Porgès, Jules • 220
Porus • 400
Post, Frans • 240
Post, Johan • 224
Post, Pieter • 11, 12, 16, 40, 42, 240–242
Pot, Hendrick • 25, 242
Pot van Groeneveld, Gerrit van der • 76, 108, 186, 276
Pothoven, Hendrik • 242–244
Potter, Paulus • 20, 23, 26, 40, 148, 244
Potter, Pieter Symonsz • 244
Poullain • 332
Poussin, Nicolas • 364
Prado, Eduardo • 240
Prado, Paul Plinio • 240
Preisler, Johann Martin • 84
Primus, Saint • 324
Proli, Charles de • 260
Provoost, Jan • 246
Pynas, Jan Symonsz • 246

Q

Quarles van Ufford, L.J. • 312
Quast, Pieter Jansz • 246
Quellinus, Artus • 56
Quellinus, Erasmus • 96
Quist, P.A. • 54

R

Rachel • 244
Radix Sainte-Foix • 230
Raesfelt, Bernardina Margriet van • 292, 294
Raesfelt, Johan van • 294
Raesfelt, Wennemar van • 294
Ragueneau, Abraham • 246
Rainer, Victor de • 26, 50, 88, 92, 98, 100, 110, 118, 126, 156, 180, 182, 194, 248, 274, 282, 288, 292, 306, 350, 352
Rakoczy, Sigismund • 364
Randon de Boisset, P.-L. • 230, 332, 386
Raphael • 26, 248
Rasponi, F. • 338

Rathenau, Ernest G. • 260
Raven, C. • 52
Ravesteyn, Jan Anthonisz van • 17, 126, 128, 248–256
Ravesteyn, Nicolaes van • 256
Rebecca • 40, 114
Rechteren Limpurg, Van • 332
Reghellini Schio, Martial • 26, 76, 90, 118, 122, 126, 168, 180, 184, 186, 232, 234, 236, 248, 256–266, 268, 298, 324, 344, 350, 358
Regnier, Nicolas • 256
Reijn, Theo van • 390
Reinhardt • 302
Rembrandt • 17, 18, 20, 23, 26, 28, 29, 30, 32, 34, 36, 38, 39, 40, 41, 42, 120, 256, 260, 262, 264, 266, 300, 356
Renesse, Constant van • 106
Reni, Guido • 84
Renieri, Nicolò: see Regnier, Nicolas
Repelaer van Driel, Ocker • 102
Reyger, Jacob de • 266
Reynolds, Sir Joshua • 88
Rhodius, A.N.F. • 170
Rhodius, F.R.H. • 170
Ricci, Marco • 234
Ricci, Sebastiano • 234
Ridder, A. de • 220
Ridder, C.C.J. de • 312
Rijckevorsel van Rijsenburg-Dommer van Poldersveld, Baroness L.V.S. van • 44, 358
Rijn, Adriaen van • 262
Rijn, Harmen Gerritsz van • 262
Rijn, Rembrandt van: see Rembrandt
Rijn, Titus van • 32
Rinaldo • 204
Riquet, Victor de, Duke of Caraman • 262
Robinson, Sir John • 262
Robinson, John Charles • 192, 270
Robit • 230, 332
Roegholt, M.N. • 54
Roelofs, B.G. • 112
Roelofs Thijssen, M.J. • 298
Roels, Johanna Charlotte Hendrika • 44, 214
Roghman, Roelant • 266
Rohan-Chabot, Duc de • 386
Rolinxwerth, Johann von • 84
Roman, Anna Maria • 138, 224
Romeyn, Willem • 80
Rooij, Mrs Beatrijs de • 45
Roos, C.F. • 226
Roos, Johann Heinrich • 266
Roovere, Pieter de • 102, 104
Roque, De la • 264
Rose-Molewater, Cornelia Adriana • 34, 44, 54, 58, 176
Rosenberg, S. and R. • 220, 320
Rosenberg & Stiebel • 216, 270
Rosenhagen, Johannes • 268
Rosnagel, Johannes • 268
Rosselli, Matteo • 268
Rössler, Ludwig • 132
Rothan, G. • 326
Rothmann, F. • 78
Rothschild, Alfred de • 220, 230, 320
Rothschild, Edmond de • 270
Rotschild, Louis de • 216
Rothschild, Victor de • 220, 320
Rottenhammer, Hans • 82, 84, 268
Rottermond, H. • 74
Rottiers, Bernard Eugène • 90, 126, 226
Röver, Valerius • 152
Röver-van der Dussen, Cornelia • 152
Roxard de la Salle, H. • 326
Royer-Kerst • 242
Rubens, Peter Paul • 18, 20, 22, 25, 26, 38, 42, 82, 97, 112, 130, 136, 270–274, 338, 340
Ruffo, Don Antonio • 258, 260
Ruggero • 274
Ruijven, Pieter Claesz van • 320
Ruisdael, Jacob van • 18, 23, 39, 40, 274–276
Ruthart, Carl Borromäus Andreas • 276
Ruysch, Rachel • 276–278
Ruysdael, Salomon van • 36, 42, 132, 278–280
Ruyter, Engel de • 70
Ruyter, Michiel Adriaensz de • 56, 70, 392
Ruzicka, L. • 50
Ryckhals, François • 280

S

Saenredam, Pieter • 23, 38, 280
Saftleven, Cornelis • 280–282
Saftleven, Herman • 18, 282
Salmacis • 342
Salm-Salm, Fürst zu • 32, 358
Salomas • 178
Salome • 98
Salvi, Giovanni Battista: see Sassoferrato
Samson • 114, 126
San Gallo, Francesco da (Giamberti) • 100
San Gallo, Giuliano da • 100
Santi, Raphaello: see Raphael
Santvoort, Pieter van • 282
Sassoferrato • 282
Saul • 32, 262
Savery the Elder, Jacob • 282
Savery, Roelant • 17, 42, 282–284
Schaeffer, Hans • 116, 140
Schalcke, Cornelis Symonsz van der • 284
Schalcken, Godfried • 20, 284–286, 356
Schall, Jos • 296
Schardt, Johan Gregor van der • 390
Scharff • 94
Scheffer, Ary • 26
Schellinger, Cornelis Cornelisz • 236
Scheltema, J. • 354
Schepeler, Von • 116
Schepp, Johann Heinrich • 392
Schinkel, A.D. • 354
Schlichte Bergen, J. • 114
Schloss, M. • 302
Schmelzing, Nicolaas • 252
Schmid, Elisabeth • 156
Schmidt, Robert • 39
Schmidt, Wilhelm • 182
Schneider, H. • 34
Schoeff, Johannes Pietersz • 358
Schönborn, Baron • 220
Schonck, Philip • 23
Schouman, Aert • 134, 168, 198, 294, 400
Schrieck, Otto Marseus van: see Marseus van Schrieck, Otto
Schröder, Miss A.A.W. • 45
Schuyl, Florentius • 202
Schuylenburch, Johan van • 294, 302, 332
Schwarz, F. • 132
Schwarzenraben • 188
Schweickhardt, Hendrik Willem • 22, 286
Sebastian, Saint • 236, 256
Secrétan, E. • 130, 212
Sedelmeyer, Carl • 130
Sedelmeyer, Charles • 70, 130, 262, 278
Seghers, Daniel • 18, 288
Seghers, Hercules • 38, 288
Seisenegger, Jacob • 288–290
Sellar, David • 278
Semenoff • 338
Seymour, Jane • 154, 380
Sheffield, T. • 218
Sideroff • 266
Sievers, L. • 288
Simeon • 20, 40, 124, 256, 352
Simon, James • 130
Simon, Saint • 178
Simons, Quentin: see Symons, Quintin
Simonsz, Willem, Lord of Stavenisse and Cromstrijen • 348
Singendonck, Maria Johanna • 44, 50, 108, 138, 188, 222, 224, 256, 286, 356
Singendonck, Mathias Lambertus • 50, 108
Sisyphus • 180, 344
Sittow, Michel • 36, 290
Six • 34, 74, 198, 298
Six, Willem • 170
Slabbaert, Karel • 290
Slatter, Eugene • 280
Slingelandt, Govert van • 22, 23, 62, 72, 106, 112, 156, 168, 196, 202, 212, 220, 228, 244, 258, 264, 268, 272, 286, 290, 294, 302, 316, 318, 340, 342
Slingelandt, H. van • 228
Smeth van Alphen, Pieter de • 80, 216, 314
Smies, J. • 312
Smissaert family • 150
Smissaert, Frans A.E.L. • 150
Smissaert, Marinus A.P. • 150
Smith, G. • 296
Smith, John • 162
Smith, S.T. • 258
Snakenburg, Theodoor van • 310
Sneijers, P.J. • 258
Snellen van Vollenhoven, S.C. • 312
Snijders, Frans • 136, 290–292, 330
Snijers, Jean A. • 216
Snouck van Loosen, M.M. • 54
Snoy, C. de • 224
Solimena, Francesco • 292
Solirène • 168
Solomon • 312, 348
Son, Pierre van • 356
Sonmans, Margaretha • 206
Soolmaker, Jan Frans • 292
Sophie of Sakse-Weimar-Eisenach, Grand Duchess • 44, 306
Soutman, Pieter • 292

Speelman, Anthony • 92
Speelman, Edward • 42, 45, 94, 104, 132, 154, 224, 270, 330
Speelman, Mrs Edward • 42, 45, 94
Spencer, 5th Earl • 172
Spencer, 8th Earl • 172
Spencer-Churchill, E.G. • 114
Spierinckx, Pieter • 96
Spinny, Guillaume de • 22
Spinola, Ambrogio, Marquis de los Balbases • 122
Spoelberch, Vicomtesse de • 270
Staring, A. • 116
Staring-de Mol van Otterloo, Mrs J.H.M. • 40, 45, 116
Stavenisse family • 348
Steen, Jan • 18, 22, 23, 26, 34, 36, 38, 39, 292–298
Steengracht van Duivenvoorde, Hendrik Adolf • 34, 168
Steengracht van Oostkapelle, Johan • 25, 26, 39, 46, 54, 64, 74, 136, 228, 296
Steenwijck the Younger, Hendrick van • 20, 22, 298
Stein, Adolphe • 98
Steinkopf, Edward • 204
Steinmeyer, H. • 302
Stengelin, A. • 44, 324
Sternberg, Christine von • 84
Stevens, Peeter • 112
Steyn family • 116
Steyn, Augustijn • 116
Steyn, Pieter • 116
Steyn-Schellinger, Cornelia • 116, 260
Stier van Aertselaer, Henricus-Josephus, Baron • 272
Stinstra • 320
Stinstra, S. • 226
Stolk, David • 23
Stoop, Dirck • 298–300
Storck, Abraham • 298
Straten Ponthoz, August, Count van der • 44, 152
Stuart, Arabella • 374
Stuart, Charles • 368, 374
Stuart, Esmee I • 374
Stuart, Frances Teresa • 366
Stuart, Henry • 352, 370, 382
Stuart, Ludovic • 374
Stuart, Matthew • 368, 382
Stubbé-Butôt, Mrs M.A. • 45, 124, 188
Stuers, A. de • 346
Stuers, Victor de • 28, 30, 32, 44, 102, 140, 354
Stutterd, Nancy • 314
Suffren, Pierre-André de • 388
Susanna • 258
Suyderhoeff, Jonas • 174
Svenonius, B. • 44, 146
Swanevelt, Herman van • 300
Sweerts, Michael • 300
Swoll, Herman van • 62, 64
Sykes, Christopher • 156
Symons, Quintin • 112
Sypesteyn family, Van • 140
Sypesteyn, Evert van • 286

T

Tak, J. • 310
Talbot, Alatheia • 97
Tamar • 124
Tarquinius, King • 246
Tegenbosch, Lambert • 400
Teissier, Jean George • 60
Teixeira de Mattos, D.F. • 138
Teixeira de Mattos, E.V.E. • 45, 138
Teixeira de Mattos, Henri • 356
Teixeira de Mattos, Margaretha A. • 356
Tempel, Abraham van den • 300–302
Teniers, Anna • 302
Teniers the Younger, David • 23, 30, 112, 302
Teniers III, David • 302
Terpsichore • 338
Tersteeg • 356
Terwesten, Mattheus • 302
Terwesten, Pieter • 23
Tesse, P. • 282
Tetrode, Willem van • 97
Thach, Nathaniel • 378
Thalia • 338
Theagenes • 68
Theroude, Steven • 268
Thetis • 68, 98
Thomas • 94
Thoré, Etienne-Joseph-Théophile (William Bürger) • 118
Thott, Count Otto • 56
Thurkow, C.T.F. • 52, 80, 278
Thurkow-van Huffel, Louise • 44, 52, 80, 278
Thyssen-Bornemisza, Hans Heinrich, Baron • 43, 44, 146, 154, 336, 386
Tiberghien, P.F. • 72, 304
Tierens, Seger • 220
Tietje, Hans • 100
Tilborgh, Gillis van • 304
Timmers, Maria • 222
Timmers, Paulus • 222
Tintoretto • 350, 352
Tischbein, Anton Wilhelm • 304
Tischbein, Johann Friedrich August • 22, 304–306
Titian • 20, 97, 272, 306
Tityus • 180
Tol, Pieter van • 114
Tolozan, Claude • 230
Tombe, Arnoldus Andries des • 32, 33, 44, 66, 68, 76, 120, 134, 282, 286, 316, 322, 328, 346, 356
Tonneman, Jeronimus • 306, 312, 316
Toorenburgh, Gerrit • 306
Toorenvliet, Jacob • 12, 160, 400
Tóth-Ubbens, Magdi • 39
Tournier, Gérard • 64
Toutin, Henri • 378
Traill, W.S. • 116
Trip, Jacob • 188
Trip, Louis, Junior • 72
Troost, Cornelis • 40, 208, 306–314
Troost, Elisabeth • 206, 208
Troost, Sara • 306
Truth • 180
Tudor, Margaret • 368
Tulp, Nicolaes • 26, 28, 29, 32, 258
Turchi, Alessandro • 314
Twent, Hendrik • 80, 312

U

Uden, Lucas van • 358
Ulft, Jacob van der • 314
Urania • 338
Uriah • 182
Urrutia, Ramon F. • 104
Utenhoven, Anthonis van • 254
Utrecht, Adriaen van • 290
Utterson, Edward Vernon • 190
Uyttenboogaert, Johannes • 202
Uyttenbroeck, Moses van: see Wtenbrouck, Moyses van

V

Vaccaro, Domenico Antonio • 314
Valckenier, Simon • 176
Valckenier, Wouter • 60
Valkenburg, D.L.M. van • 24
Valkenburg, Dirk • 332
Vanni, Raffaello • 316
Vasari, Giorgio • 100
Vegelin van Claerbergen, V.L. • 338
Velázquez, Castor • 90
Velázquez, Diego • 97, 194
Velde, Adriaen van de • 22, 134, 152, 316, 400
Velde, Esaias van de • 60, 316
Velde, F. van de • 312
Velde III, Jan van de • 316
Velde the Younger, Willem van de • 22, 70, 318
Veltman, E.A. • 220
Ven, H.B. van der • 45, 78
Vence, Comte de • 168
Venne, Adriaen van de • 152, 318
Venus • 40, 96, 116, 148, 272, 274, 306, 342, 352
Venus Master • 156
Verbeecq, Pieter • 320
Vere, Horatio • 254
Verheije van Citters, Jacob • 348
Verhulst, Rombout • 392–394
Verkade, E.G. • 296
Verkolje, Jan • 320
Verkolje, Johan • 276
Verkolje, Nicolaas • 284
Verloren van Themaat, P. • 316
Vermeer, Johannes • 18, 23, 26, 27, 28, 32, 33, 38, 40, 320–322
Vermeer van Haarlem, Jan • 322
Vermeulen, Jan • 322
Vernet, Claude-Joseph • 22, 324
Veronese, Bonifazio (de' Pitati) • 324, 350
Veronese, Paolo • 324
Veronica, Saint • 360
Verschuere, Baron van • 298
Verschuring, Hendrik • 312, 324
Verspronck, Johannes • 326
Verstolk van Soelen, Jean Gisbert • 220
Verstralen, Anthonie • 326
Veth, Jan • 32
Vierssen, Hillegonda van • 354
Vigné de Vigny, Pierre • 238
Villepontoux, André de • 326

Villepontoux, Anna Maria de • 326
Villiers, George • 376
Vincent, Ysbrand • 308
Vinck van Wesel, J.F. de • 272
Vinckboons, David • 152, 326
Virieu, F.W. de • 44, 354
Virieu, François de • 354
Vis, E. • 45, 152
Visscher II, Claes • 198
Visscher, Cornelis • 62, 178
Visscher, Cornelis de • 198
Visscher-Boelger, A. • 296
Vlieger, Simon de • 30, 326
Vliet, Hendrik van • 326–328
Vliet, Jan Gillisz van • 260
Vogel, G. • 296
Vogelaer, Karel van • 328
Vogelsang, Willem • 36
Vois, Arie de • 328
Voltaire • 386
Volz, A.W. • 36, 45, 290
Vonck, Elias • 328
Vondel, Joost van den • 312
Vorsterman the Elder, Lucas • 114
Vos, Cornelis de • 360
Vos, Maerten de • 26, 328–330, 360
Vos, Paul de • 330
Voskuyl, Huygh Pietersz • 330
Vosmaer, Arnout • 23, 392
Vosmaer, Carel • 356
Vosmaer-Hudig, Mrs M.D. • 45, 392
Vrancx, Sebastiaen • 136
Vredeman de Vries, Paul • 122
Vredericx, Andries • 176
Vredericx (Fredericksz), Loef • 174, 176
Vredericx, Machtelt • 176
Vriendt, Michiel • 82, 272, 358
Vries, De • 216
Vries, Ary Bob de • 36, 38, 39, 40, 47, 242
Vries, Catharina de • 156
Vries, Joan de • 156, 176
Vries, M.F. de • 298
Vries, Roelof Jansz van • 330
Vugt, Hendrik van der • 220
Vulcan • 274, 342

W

Wael Rogiers, Catherina Nicolaesdr de • 170
Wake, Anna • 112
Wake, Lionel • 112
Walker • 152, 264, 348
Walker, Thomas B. • 124
Wallace • 230
Waller, F.G. • 32
Walraven, Isaac • 178
Wannaar • 292
Wantage, Lord and Lady • 162
Ward, R.M. • 132
Ward, T. Humphrey • 44, 136, 216, 258, 318
Warhol, Andy • 400
Waspick, De • 336
Waspick, C. de • 318
Wassenaer, Jacoba Maria van • 294
Wassenaer Obdam, Johan Hendrik, Count of • 204, 268
Webb, John • 270
Weel, Van • 104
Weenix, Jan • 22, 330–332
Weenix, Jan Baptist • 39, 64, 332
Weill, David • 184, 212
Weisbach, Werner • 39
Welcker: see Asscher and Welcker
Wellesley, Henry Richard • 318
Wellesley Knighton, Sir William • 262
Wellington, Duke of • 25
Wells of Redleaf, William • 162
Werf, H. van der • 314
Werff, Adriaen van der • 20, 106, 332–334
Werff, Maria van der • 332
Wertheimer • 104, 168, 220, 260, 396
Westerbaen the Elder, Jan • 334
Westminster, Duke of • 32
Westminster, Hugh, 2nd Duke of • 154
Westminster, Hugh, 3rd Marquess of • 154
Wetzlar, Mr and Mrs H.A. • 45, 118
Weyden, Rogier van der • 26, 334–336, 396
Widener, J.E. • 168
Widener, Peter A.B. • 168
Wiegersma, J.H. • 400
Wierman, J.P. • 168
Wijck, Thomas • 336
Wijnants, Jan • 336
Wijnantz, Augustus • 336
Wijntgis, Melchior • 342
Wilberforce, R.G. • 88
Wild, C.F.L. de • 32
Wildens, Jan • 330
Wilhelm VIII of Hessen, Prince • 152
Wilhelmina, Queen • 38
Wilhelmina Louise of Nassau Weilburg, Princess • 304
Wilhelmine Christine von Brandenburg • 306
Willaerts, Adam • 336
Willeboirts Bosschaert, Thomas • 18, 288
Willem I, King • 14, 25, 26, 29, 44, 50, 56, 76, 86, 88, 90, 92, 98, 100, 110, 118, 122, 126, 156, 166, 168, 180, 182, 184, 186, 190, 194, 216, 226, 232, 234, 236, 248, 256, 258, 268, 272, 274, 282, 288, 292, 298, 304, 316, 324, 334, 344, 350, 352, 358, 386, 388, 396
Willem I of Orange • 14, 17, 56, 122, 160, 162, 164, 172, 198, 200, 212, 236, 248, 350, 354, 388
Willem II, King • 26, 306
Willem II, Stadholder • 17, 18, 58, 68, 142, 160, 162, 186, 318, 364, 366, 394
Willem III, King • 334
Willem (William) III, King-Stadholder • 18, 20, 23, 25, 58, 68, 82, 84, 100, 110, 142, 154, 158, 180, 182, 246, 248, 284, 288, 314, 324, 336, 338, 364, 368, 386, 394
Willem IV, Stadholder • 20, 22, 23, 54, 106, 110, 144, 182, 196, 238, 244, 256, 286, 298, 300, 302, 304, 306, 314, 332, 374, 378, 394
Willem V, Stadholder • 22, 23, 25, 26, 50, 54, 58, 60, 62, 68, 72, 82, 84, 96, 98, 100, 106, 110, 112, 116, 122, 130, 134, 136, 144, 150, 154, 156, 158, 162, 164, 168, 174, 176, 178, 182, 184, 186, 196, 202, 204, 206, 212, 218, 220, 228, 238, 244, 246, 248, 256, 258, 264, 266, 268, 272, 282, 284, 286, 290, 292, 294, 298, 300, 302, 304, 314, 316, 318, 324, 328, 330, 332, 336, 340, 342, 344, 350, 354, 372, 374, 378, 386, 388, 392
Willem Frederik, Stadholder • 18, 164, 218, 364, 368
Willem Hyacinth, Prince of Nassau-Siegen • 182
Willemsen, Jacobus • 290
Willett, Henry • 44, 390
William the Silent: see Willem I of Orange
Willigen, Adriaan van der • 112, 236, 318
Winkler, G. • 78
Winter, Pieter van • 230, 298
Winter King: see Friedrich V
Wirz, Hermann • 296
Wissing, Willem • 336–338
Wit, Jacob de • 34, 96, 124, 338
Witsen, Jonas • 186
Witt, Cornelis de • 40, 56, 356
Witt, Jacob de • 356
Witt, Johan de • 56, 108, 224, 356
Witt, Maria de • 286, 356
Witte, Emanuel de • 30, 338
Witte, Françoise de • 354
Witte, Sara de • 196
Witte van Citters, De • 66, 76
Witte van Citters, Jacob de • 44, 348
Wittelsbach, Elisabeth Charlotte • 160
Wolf, De • 244
Wolfvoet, Victor • 338–340
Woudhuysen, Mr and Mrs A. • 45
Wouwerman, Philips • 20, 22, 340–342
Wreesman, Werner • 60
Wtenbrouck, Moyses van • 342
Wtewael, Joachim • 342–344
Wttewaal van Stoetwegen • 332
Wulc, Stanley S. • 190
Wyndham, George Francis • 78

X

Xavery, Jan Baptist • 22, 394

Y

Ykens, Jan (Johannes) • 96
Yver, Pieter • 22

Z

Zanchi, Antonio • 180, 344
Zebedee • 178
Zeus • 62
Ziesenis, Johann Georg • 344
Zincke, Christian Friedrich • 378
Zorn, Anders • 262
Zoutman, Johan Arnold • 102, 354
Zuccarelli, Francesco • 344
Zuijlestein, Hendrik van • 208
Zuylen van Nijevelt, dowager A.M.B. • 74
Zuytbrouck, Neeltgen Willemsdr van • 266

Credits

COMPILATION
Quentin Buvelot, with contributions by Carola Vermeeren

EDITING, PICTURE RESEARCH AND APPENDICES
Quentin Buvelot

ENGLISH LANGUAGE EDITING
Rachel Esner, Amsterdam

DESIGN
DeLeeuwOntwerper(s), The Hague

PRODUCTION
Quentin Buvelot & Dorine Duyster

PRINTING
Waanders Printers, Zwolle

PUBLISHING
Waanders Publishers, Zwolle

ISBN 90 400 8958 2 (hardback)
NUGI 921, 911

For more information on Waanders, see www.waanders.nl
For more information on the Mauritshuis, see www.mauritshuis.nl

COVER ILLUSTRATION
Jacob van Campen, *Double portrait of Constantijn Huygens (1596–1687) and Suzanna van Baerle (1599–1637)*, *c.*1635. Inv. no. 1089.